PRINCIPLES OF
CHEMICAL ENGINEERING

McGRAW-HILL CHEMICAL ENGINEERING SERIES

THE SERIES

BADGER AND BAKER—*Inorganic Chemical Technology*

BADGER AND McCABE—*Elements of Chemical Engineering*

CLARKE—*Manual for Process Engineering Calculations*

DAVIS—*Chemical Engineering Nomographs*

DODGE—*Chemical Engineering Thermodynamics*

EDWARDS, FRARY, AND JEFFRIES—*The Aluminum Industry (in Two Volumes): Aluminum and Its Production; Aluminum Products and Their Fabrication*

GRISWOLD—*Fuels, Combustion, and Furnaces*

GROGGINS—*Unit Processes in Organic Synthesis*

HUNTINGTON—*Natural Gas and Natural Gasoline*

KIRKBRIDE—*Chemical Engineering Fundamentals*

LEWIS AND RADASCH—*Industrial Stoichiometry*

MANTELL—*Adsorption*

MANTELL—*Industrial Electrochemistry*

NELSON—*Petroleum Refinery Engineering*

PERRY (EDITOR)—*Chemical Engineers' Handbook*

PIERCE—*Chemical Engineering for Production Supervision*

RHODES, F. H.—*Technical Report Writing*

RHODES, T. J.—*Industrial Instruments for Measurement and Control*

ROBINSON AND GILLILAND—*Elements of Fractional Distillation*

SCHMIDT AND MARLIES—*Principles of High-polymer Theory and Practice*

SHERWOOD—*Absorption and Extraction*

SHERWOOD AND REED—*Applied Mathematics in Chemical Engineering*

SHREVE—*The Chemical Process Industries*

SMITH—*Introduction to Chemical Engineering Thermodynamics*

TYLER—*Chemical Engineering Economics*

VILBRANDT—*Chemical Engineering Plant Design*

WALKER, LEWIS, McADAMS, AND GILLILAND—*Principles of Chemical Engineering*

WILSON AND WELLS—*Coal, Coke, and Coal Chemicals*

WINDING AND HASCHE—*Plastics, Theory and Practice*

CHEMICAL ENGINEERING SERIES

PRINCIPLES OF CHEMICAL ENGINEERING

BY

WILLIAM H. WALKER

WARREN K. LEWIS

WILLIAM H. McADAMS

AND

EDWIN R. GILLILAND

Associate Director, Laboratory for Nuclear Science and Engineering,
Massachusetts Institute of Technology

THIRD EDITION
REVISED AND REWRITTEN
SEVENTEENTH IMPRESSION

McGRAW-HILL BOOK COMPANY, Inc.

NEW YORK AND LONDON

1937

THE MAPLE PRESS COMPANY, YORK, PA.

PREFACE TO THE THIRD EDITION

The death of Dr. William H. Walker makes it necessary for an edition of this book to appear without his collaboration and guidance. The book was originally the product of his initiative, and its whole development was molded by his influence and direction. Every effort will be made to maintain it in the tradition which he established.

The last decade has been characterized by the introduction in chemical industry of a large number of new processes and by important modification and refinement of old ones. Fortunately, this has been parallelled by extensive developments in insight into the underlying mechanisms of the fundamental operations of chemical engineering, in expansion of the data available for the formulation of quantitative relationships, and in the technique of using these basic tools in the solution of practical problems. It cannot be denied that these changes have made the practice of the art of chemical engineering far more complex. In consequence, there is more necessity than ever for the utmost clarity in presentation of fundamental concepts, for increased emphasis upon the dependability of those concepts as guiding threads through the mazes of complicated operations and processes, and for the development of trustworthy and usable correlations and of satisfactory techniques in the solution of practical problems. The major purpose of revision is to meet this situation.

Because the four most important fundamental relationships underlying all phases of chemical engineering are material and energy balances and the laws of reaction equilibrium and of reaction rate, the most extensive changes are in the chapters on Flow of Fluids and Flow of Heat, and in those involving diffusional processes, in which these principles come most directly into play. In all these cases, the theoretical development of the subject has been clarified, and emphasis laid upon detailed derivation of equations incorporated in the text. Thus, in Flow of Heat there is careful discussion of the mechanisms of con-

v

vection and of their relation to the important correlations developed in recent years. The problem of mean temperature difference has been expanded and the treatment of radiation enlarged. A section on dimensional analysis has been added and the utility of consistent units emphasized.

The chapters on Crushing and Grinding, Sedimentation, and Evaporation are revised and brought up to date. The discussion of Filtration is rewritten in an attempt to present for this important but controversial subject the soundest engineering analysis attainable in the light of present knowledge. The chapters on Absorption and Extraction, Distillation, and Air Conditioning have been modified in the light of the discussion of diffusion already referred to. The treatment of psychrometry is new and includes humidity charts based on recent data. The chapter on Drying not only presents the important new data and developments of recent years, but attempts to make them more useful in the solution of practical problems.

The illustrative problems have been revised, and a new, enlarged list of unsolved problems is appended.

Circumstances have unfortunately prevented the cooperation of Dr. Lewis in this revision, except to a minor degree in Chapters III and IV. As throughout the history of this book, the debt to many friends for assistance and advice is very extensive, and to them we wish to express our gratitude.

WILLIAM H. McADAMS,
EDWIN R. GILLILAND.

CAMBRIDGE, MASS.,
September, 1937.

PREFACE TO THE FIRST EDITION

Just as the arts of tanning and dyeing were practiced long before the scientific principles upon which they depend were known, so also the practice of Chemical Engineering preceded any analysis or exposition of the principles upon which such practice is based. The unit operations of chemical engineering have in some instances been developed to such an extent in individual industries that the operation is looked upon as a special one adapted to these conditions alone, and is, therefore, not frequently used by other industries. All important unit operations have much in common, and if the underlying principles upon which the rational design and operation of basic types of engineering equipment depend are understood, their successful adaptation to manufacturing processes becomes a matter of good management rather than of good fortune.

In this book we have attempted to recall to the reader's mind those principles of science upon which chemical engineering operations are based, and then to develop methods for applying these principles to the solution of such problems as present themselves in chemical engineering practice. We have selected for treatment basic operations common to all chemical industries, rather than details of specific processes, and so far as is now possible, the treatment is mathematically quantitative as well as qualitatively descriptive. We venture to hope that the book will stimulate engineers to *design* apparatus adapted for any particular purpose, rather than just to *build* it and then to rely on large scale experimentation with expensive changes in construction to effect efficient operation.

This book may be divided roughly into five parts.

First, the principles of stoichiometry are reviewed, special emphasis being laid upon the utility of the pound mol as a unit for calculation, and the relative ease with which the units of one system may be transformed into those of another system. Experience has taught us that practicing engineers as well as students fail to realize the vast amount of useful data there is available,

vii

largely in chemical literature, and hence in the metric system. There is a lack, also, of an effort to select properly those data to be recorded in laboratory experimentation and factory operation, in order that any definite information may be obtained. Frequently also data are used inadequately, and much desired information overlooked because of faulty interpretation. Therefore we have introduced illustrative problems and their solution throughout the book, in which we believe the reader may find helpful suggestions relative to the plan of an experimental run, the data to choose, and the method of solution and interpretation to adopt. These problems should not be looked upon as nuts for students to crack, but as an integral part of the text vitally illustrative of the subject matter considered.

Second, because of their fundamental importance the phenomena accompanying the flow of heat and the flow of fluids, together with the laws governing these operations, are considered in detail. An interchange of heat is a necessary step in almost every chemical reaction and must be provided for adequately to insure continuous operation. So far as possible we have illustrated the use of the more complex equations with problems stated and solved.

Third, fuels and their efficient combustion are treated at considerable length in order to render clear the important relationships here involved. More economical use of fuel will be demanded in the future.

Fourth, processes of crushing and grinding, mechanical methods for separating materials, together with filtration in its many different forms, are given a descriptive treatment with a mathematical analysis when such seems advantageous.

Fifth, those processes depending upon vaporization are treated from the common standpoint of vapor pressure equilibria. With drying in its many phases we consider also humidification, dehumidification and water cooling. Evaporation and distillation are placed in separate chapters.

The greater part of the text has for some time been in use as students' notes at the Massachusetts Institute of Technology, and at times has been drawn upon freely by both staff and students in their published papers.

It may seem to the reader that brevity is sometimes sacrificed by repetition of ideas, and that the detailed derivation of mathematical equations is unnecessarily separated from the descriptive matter to which they relate.   Experience in teaching this subject has proven the desirability of this method of treatment.

This book is the outgrowth of extensive engineering practice in the course of which we have profited by many ideas offered in the way of suggestions, criticism or advice.   We have assayed these ideas in the crucible of experience, and have endeavored to incorporate those found to be of value.   These contributions have come from so many sources that detailed acknowledgment here is impossible, but for this very real help we are deeply grateful to our many friends.

WILLIAM H. WALKER,
WARREN K. LEWIS,
WILLIAM H. McADAMS.

CAMBRIDGE, MASS.,
February, 1923.

CONTENTS

xi

PRINCIPLES OF CHEMICAL ENGINEERING

CHAPTER I

ELEMENTS OF INDUSTRIAL STOICHIOMETRY

Introduction.—Science makes it possible to predict the future through the ability to reason from known facts and conditions, or to make a mathematical calculation based upon established data, and thus to reach a rational conclusion in advance of the actual realization of the phenomenon. However, the ability to state mathematically the relationship between any two or more factors frequently calls for a knowledge of methods of analysis which is not possessed by the average college student or young man in the works. Likewise, the English-speaking chemical engineer is accustomed to find his scientific data given in metric units and to carry on his laboratory calculations in grams, centimeters and liters. Since the calculations arising in the quantitative application of scientific data and methods in the field of applied chemistry are often in themselves very complicated and involved, frequently the confusion occasioned by the necessity for converting conceptions and data formulated heretofore in the metric system into corresponding English terms is sufficient to deter the technical man from making the attempt.

It is the purpose of this chapter to recall to the reader the principles upon which such computations are based, and to point out certain methods of calculation by which experimental data may be more readily interpreted in terms of factory conditions and made available for the solution of everyday problems, so that the confusion occasioned by handling data in two systems may be minimized or eliminated.

LAWS USED IN INDUSTRIAL STOICHIOMETRY

Chemical Engineering calculations involve three simple basic generalizations of universal usefulness. These are the Law of the

Conservation of Elements, the Law of the Conservation of Energy, and the Stoichiometric Relationships* as to combining weights expressed in chemical formulas and equations. The importance of these three laws arises from the fact that they are quantitatively applicable under all conditions, and at least the first and third of them are used, sometimes implicitly, in the course of every chemical calculation. Faraday's Law of Electrolysis is also quantitatively applicable under all conditions, but is employed only in the solution of a special type of problem.

Other laws or principles, such as the Laws of Mass Action, of Reaction Rate, of the Vapor Pressure Relations of Solutions, and similar generalizations of Physical Chemistry, are of only limited applicability, in the present state of our knowledge, owing to the wide deviations from and nonconformity to these laws in some cases, and must be employed quantitatively with intelligent caution.

Use of English Units

Whatever the advantages of the metric system of units, most readers of this book will be compelled to employ English units in much of their work. Such units will therefore be freely used, and it is hoped to show that the disadvantages of carrying out calculations in the English system and the difficulties of conversion of calculations from one system to the other are often greatly overestimated.

The Molal Unit and Its Utility

Chemical reactions occur between atoms, either alone or when combined into molecules, and these quantities furnish very convenient units with which to calculate the results of such reactions. Thus the equation

$$C + O_2 = CO_2$$
$$12 \quad 32 \quad \quad 44$$

states that one atom of carbon unites with one molecule of oxygen and produces one molecule of carbon dioxide. It also states that 12 parts by weight, be they grams, ounces or tons, of carbon, combine with 32 parts by weight of the same unit of oxygen to

* For a statement of these relationships the reader is referred to any of the standard works on inorganic chemistry.

furnish 44 parts by weight of CO_2. It is convenient, therefore, to combine these two ideas and speak of a *gram atom* of carbon or a *pound atom* of carbon, meaning the quantity of carbon in any convenient unit of weight which is represented by the symbol C, and to realize that it will combine with a gram molecule, or a pound molecule or any unit selected, of oxygen. One can then speak of a gram molecule or a pound molecule of any material and mean thereby the number of grams or pounds which is represented by the relative weight of the reacting unit, be it atom or molecule.

But gases are generally measured by volume and analyses are given in volume per cent, while solids are usually measured by weight and analyses expressed in per cent by weight. In practice, therefore, the above equation involves materials usually reported in two different ways. It is convenient, then, to be able to use a common basis. This is found in the pound molecule, or, as contracted, the *pound mol.*

If 20 cu. ft. of O_2 at 1 atmosphere is mixed with 80 cu. ft. of N_2 at the same pressure, the volume of the mixture at 1 atmosphere will be 100 cu. ft. and the mixture is said to contain 20 per cent O_2 and 80 per cent N_2 by volume. According to the accepted hypothesis of Avogadro, equal volumes of all perfect gases contain the same number of molecules. Hence this gas contains 20 per cent O_2 and 80 per cent N_2 on the basis of the *number of molecules present;* that is, of every 100 molecules in the gas, 20 of them are O_2 and 80 are N_2. Furthermore, Avogadro's hypothesis implies that the pressure exerted by any ideal gas at a given temperature is proportional to the number of molecules of that gas per unit volume, while Dalton's law states that, in mixtures of gases, the pressure of each individual component is independent of the presence of the others and the partial pressures of the components are additive, the total pressures being the sum of all the partial pressures. Consequently, for mixtures of gases obeying these two gas laws, the pressure of each component, expressed as a percentage of the total pressure, is numerically equal to the mol per cent of that component in the mixture and also to its volume per cent.

Since equal volumes of all perfect gases contain the same number of molecules, it is evident that a certain volume may be chosen, such that under standard conditions of temperature and pressure (0°C. and 760 mm.) it will contain just the number of molecules necessary to weigh the number of pounds or grams expressed by its molecular weight. This volume is found experimentally to be 22.4 liters for the gram mol, equivalent to 359 cu. ft. for the pound mol, and is called the *molal volume*. Unless otherwise noted, throughout this book the *pound* mol and *pound* atom are used, which may be abbreviated to mol and atom, respectively.

The molecular weight of a perfect gas is defined as the weight in pounds of 359 cu. ft. of the gas, measured under standard conditions (S. C.)* of temperature and pressure. In this sense the average molecular weight of a mixture of gases can be spoken of as well as that of a single gas. Thus air which is moisture-free has the following average analysis:†

	Per Cent by Volume
Oxygen	20.95
Nitrogen	78.08
Carbon dioxide	0.03
Argon, etc	0.94

The average molecular weight of air or any other gas mixture may be calculated by adding together the weights of each component in one molal volume of the mixture as follows:

Component	Mols in 1 mol air	Molecular weight	Pounds in 1 molal volume air
O_2	0.2095	32.00	6.70
N_2	0.7808	28.02	21.88
CO_2	0.0003	44.00	0.01
A	0.0094	40.	0.38

Total weight of 1 mol of air is.......................... 28.97 lb., which for all practical purposes is 29.0.

In most chemical processes the nitrogen is inert, and is analytically determined by difference, the argon and the traces of other noble gases being included with it. The composition of dry air is

* Throughout the book the abbreviation "S. C." is used to designate "standard conditions."

† F. A. PANETH, *Sci. J. Roy. Coll. Sci.*, **6**, 120 (1936).

frequently taken, for the purpose of stoichiometric calculations, as 21 per cent O_2, and 79 per cent N_2. The only variable which must be determined experimentally in each case is the moisture content.

Gas Laws.—Since gases are seldom if ever measured at standard conditions, it becomes necessary to know how to find the molal volume at different temperatures and pressures. This can, of course, be done by the use of the perfect gas equation in the form, $PV = nRT$, where n is the number of gram mols of the gas in question, while R is a single constant applicable to all perfect gases, the numerical value of which depends only on the particular units of pressure, volume and temperature (P, V, T) employed.

Obviously similar relationships must obtain in English units. For all perfect gases this equation may be written $PV = 1543nT$, the quantities being given in English Engineering units, where P is the total absolute pressure in pounds per square foot, V is the total volume in cubic feet, T is in degrees Rankine,* while n is the number of pound mols of the gas involved in the calculation.

Instead of solving this equation for the volume, it is often simpler, as will appear in later calculations, to find the volume by multiplying the volume of the gas at standard conditions by a ratio. If one writes the equation for the gas under any conditions of temperature and pressure as $PV = 1543nT$, and under standard conditions as $P_0V_0 = 1543nT_0$, dividing the first equation by the second and solving for V gives

$$V = V_0 \times \frac{P_0}{P} \times \frac{T}{T_0}.$$

Since the correction factors applied to V_0 in order to get V, P_0/P and T/T_0 are ratios, and therefore contain no units, they may be expressed in any absolute units of temperature or pressure, so long as the units are the same in any one ratio.

Instead of memorizing this equation it is well to remember only that the volume measured must be multiplied by an absolute temperature ratio and an absolute pressure ratio, and to rely on common sense to determine whether these ratios should be greater or less than unity, according to whether the gas is passing from a lower to a higher temperature or from a greater to a smaller pressure, or vice versa.

* Equals degrees Fahrenheit absolute, *i.e.*, deg. F. +460.

This relationship will be made clearer by the following examples:

The volume of ½ mol of any perfect gas at 60°F. and 780 mm. pressure is determined by the equation:

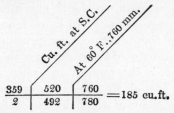

$$\frac{359}{2} \left| \frac{520}{492} \right| \frac{760}{780} = 185 \text{ cu.ft.}$$

The volume of 25 lb. of a natural gas containing 85 per cent CH_4 and 15 per cent C_2H_6 at 20°C. and 1 lb. gauge pressure is found as follows:

First, determine the apparent or average molecular weight of the gas.

Since the volume percentage composition based upon 100 units is at the same time the molal percentage relationship,

$$0.85 \times 16.07 = 13.65 \text{ lb. of methane}$$
$$0.15 \times 30.11 = \ 4.52 \text{ lb. of ethane}$$

$$\overline{}$$

$$18.17 \text{ lb. of mixture}$$

Thus 18.17 is the average molecular weight of this gas mixture. One lb. gauge pressure is equivalent to 15.7 lb. absolute pressure since 1 standard atmosphere equals 14.7 lb./sq. in. Then the volume is

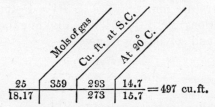

$$\frac{25}{18.17} \left| 359 \right| \frac{293}{273} \left| \frac{14.7}{15.7} \right. = 497 \text{ cu.ft.}$$

How many pounds of carbon dioxide are in 1000 cu. ft. of dry flue gas containing 15 per cent CO_2 at 500°F., the barometer being 29.2 in. of mercury? (Normal barometer in inches of mercury is 29.92 or 29.9 for most calculations.)

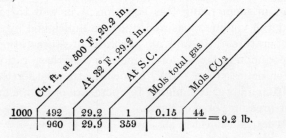

$$1000 \left| \frac{492}{960} \right| \frac{29.2}{29.9} \left| \frac{1}{359} \right| 0.15 \left| 44 \right. = 9.2 \text{ lb.}$$

The gas laws in this form are subject only to those limitations with which all are familiar. They cannot be applied without proper modification to gases, the molecules of which associate or dissociate, or to any gases at high pressures, especially if near their saturation temperatures.* However, the errors involved in applying these laws to the so-called permanent gases up to 15 or 20 atmospheres at or above ordinary temperatures, or even to saturated vapors up to 1 or perhaps 2 atmospheres, are negligible for most engineering purposes (not over 2 or 3 per cent). Consequently none of the many refinements of the perfect gas equation are necessary in many industrial calculations.

Heat Units.—In the metric system heat quantities are measured in gram calories, and in the English in B.t.u. (British thermal units). Because even in English plants the centigrade scale is so extensively used, the pound-centigrade unit,† (P.c.u.) the heat required to raise 1 lb. of water 1°C., has certain advantages in thermal calculations. One P.c.u. is obviously 1.8 B.t.u. or 454 gm. cal. The basic quantities in determining the energy effects in chemical systems are the heats of reaction. In the chemical literature heats of reaction are frequently reported as gram calories per gram mol (or kilogram calories per gram mol). Thus the statement that the heat of combustion of C, in the form of coke, to CO_2 is accompanied by a positive heat of reaction of 97,000 cal. means that the combustion of 1 gm. atom of carbon (12 gm.) to form 1 gm. mol of CO_2 (44 gm.) liberates enough heat to raise 97,000 gm. of water 1°C. Obviously, then, if 1 lb. atom of carbon (12 lb.) were burned, forming 1 lb. mol of CO_2 (44 lb.), the heat evolved would suffice to heat 97,000 lb. of water 1°C., *i.e.*, would amount to 97,000 P.c.u. In other words, heats of reaction in gram calories per gram mol are numerically identical with heats of reaction in P.c.u. per pound mol. This means that, if a chemical calculation is carried through, expressing the quantities of the reacting substances in gram mols or gram atoms and the heat effects in gram calories, the same numerical figures apply unchanged to the reaction if the quantities taken were pound mols or atoms and the heat effects were P.c.u. By the use of this method, the basic data as to heats of reaction can be

* Correction factors for the gas laws are given by W. K. Lewis, *Ind. Eng. Chem.*, **28**, 257–262 (1936).

† Also called the *centigrade heat unit* (C.h.u.), or the *pound calorie* (lb. cal.).

taken from metric tables and used directly and conveniently in calculations in English units.

If it is preferred to know the heats of reaction in B.t.u., these quantities expressed in gram calories per gram mol or atom are converted to B.t.u. per pound mol or atom by multiplying by 1.8.

The gas constant R in the gas equation $PV = nRT$ is an energy term, which it is frequently convenient to express in heat units, as, for example, in estimating the heat equivalent of the external work corresponding to the evolution of a gas against the pressure of the atmosphere. The value of R in heat units per mol per degree is 1.985 in both metric and English units, though the heat quantity obtained by multiplying R by nT is in gram calories in the metric system, while in the English system it is in B.t.u. if the Fahrenheit temperature scale is used or in P.c.u. if the centigrade is employed.

Molal Heat Capacities. *Gases.*—A further advantage of the use of the mol as unit in calculations lies in the fact that many of the physical properties of substances have relatively simple molal relationships. Thus, while the *specific heats* at constant pressure C_p of the permanent diatomic gases vary widely (from about 0.2 to over 3.0), their *molal heat capacities*, MC_p, *i.e.*, the heat required to raise 1 mol of these gases 1° in temperature, are approximately equal, varying only about 5 per cent among themselves at room temperature. The molal heat capacity at constant pressure is substantially 5.0 for all monatomic gases over wide ranges of temperature. The molal heat capacities of SO_2 and CO_2 are nearly identical one with the other, and the same is true of the halogens, etc.*

In stoichiometry, heat capacities are most frequently needed to calculate the quantity of heat required to heat (or to cool) a material through a temperature range. When the value of heat capacity for a gas, for instance, is known as a function of temperature, it is necessary to calculate this heat quantity by integration over the temperature range involved, $Q = \int_{T_1}^{T_2} MC_p \, dT$. This is clearly a laborious procedure. The

* These quantities have until recently been determined principally by calorimetric measurements, the results of such measurements being commonly stated in the form of equations giving molal heat capacities as functions of absolute temperature on the centigrade scale. The results of a

time required for such calculation is however greatly shortened if the *average* value of heat capacity over the temperature range is known, for then the relation is simply $Q = (MC_p)_{av.}(T_2 - T_1)$. Average values of this sort can be calculated once and for all by integration of equations for the point values of MC_p, followed by division of the integral by the value of the temperature range over which the integral is taken, or by other suitable calculations.

Accurate average values of MC_p, for the more common gases, between 60°F. and the temperatures used as abscissas are plotted in Fig. 1.* Taking carbon dioxide as an example to

---

careful survey of existing data in 1929 are given as follows by Eastman, *Bur. Mines Tech. Paper* 445, (1929):

Molal Heat Capacities of Gases at Constant Pressure ($T =$ Deg. K $=$ Deg. C. $+273$)	Temperature Range, Deg. K.
Hydrogen:	
$MC_p = 6.85 + 0.00028T + 0.00000022T^2$	300–2500
Nitrogen, oxygen, carbon monoxide:	
$MC_p = 6.76 + 0.000606T + 0.00000013T^2$	300–2500
Carbon dioxide and sulfur dioxide:	
$MC_p - 7.70 + 0.0053T - 0.00000083T^2$	300–2500
Water vapor:	
$MC_p = 8.22 + 0.00015T + 0.00000134T^2$	300–2500
Hydrogen sulfide:	
$MC_p = 7.20 + 0.0036T$	300– 600
Ammonia:	
$MC_p = 6.70 + 0.0063T$	300– 800
Methane:	
$MC_p = 5.90 + 0.0096T$	150– 400
Chlorine, sulfur vapor (S_2):	
$MC_p = 8.58 + 0.0003T$	300–2500

While these data are believed to be intrinsically less accurate than are those of Fig. 1, especially at high temperatures, they are given here to facilitate occasional special computations in which the convenience of data expressed algebraically may outweigh precision as a desideratum.

* These curves represent recent data obtained by spectrographic measurements, results of which are believed to be far more precise than are those obtained by the calorimetric method, especially at high temperatures.

Point values of specific heat, it may be noted, are obtainable from these curves by equating $MC_p \, dt$ to $d[(MC_p)_{av.}(t-60)]$, from which it follows that at any temperature $MC_p = (MC_p)_{av.} + (t-60)d(MC_p)_{av.}/dt$.

Figure 1 is based on the paper by LEWIS and VON ELBE, *J. Amer. Chem. Soc.*, **55**, 507 (1933), and a personal communication from H. C. HOTTEL,

illustrate the use of these curves, the heat required to raise 1 lb. mol of this gas from 60 to 2000°F. at atmospheric pressure is equal to the average molal heat capacity between these temperatures (which from Fig. 1 is 12.06) times the temperature

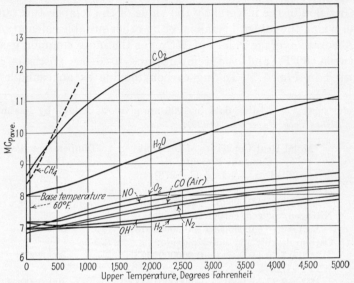

FIG. 1.—Average molal heat capacities of gases for the temperature interval from 60°F. to temperature shown by the abscissa.

rise (2000−60), giving 23,400 B.t.u. Similarly, the heat required to raise 1 mol from 60 to 1000° is 10.88(1000−60) = 10,230. By difference, the heat required to raise 1 mol from 1000 to 2000° is 23,400−10,230 = 13,170 B.t.u.

It requires more heat to raise the temperature of a gas at constant pressure than at constant volume, because of the addi-

1936. The original data on which the curves are based are from the following sources:

    CH₄: EUCKEN and LÜDE, *Z. physik. Chem.*, **B5**, 436 (1929).

     H₂: DAVIS and JOHNSTON, *J. Amer. Chem. Soc.*, **56**, 1045 (1934).

     O₂: LEWIS and VON ELBE, *J. Amer. Chem. Soc.*, **55**, 507 (1933).

N₂, CO: JOHNSTON and DAVIS, *J. Amer. Chem. Soc.*, **56**, 271 (1934).

    NO: JOHNSTON and CHAPMAN, *J. Amer. Chem. Soc.*, **55**, 155 (1933).

    OH: JOHNSTON and DAWSON, *J. Amer. Chem. Soc.*, **55**, 2744 (1933).

    CO₂: KASSEL, *J. Amer. Chem. Soc.*, **56**, 1838 (1934).

H₂O: GORDON, *J. Chem. Physics*, **2**, 65, 549 (1934).

tional energy required to create the larger volume. But, for all gases obeying the gas laws, the difference in the molal heat capacity of a gas under the two conditions is equal to R.

Liquids.—While no definite relationship is available for correlating the heat-capacity data for liquids, it is interesting to note that the molal heat capacities (and likewise the specific heats) increase with rise in temperature, as shown in Fig. 2.*

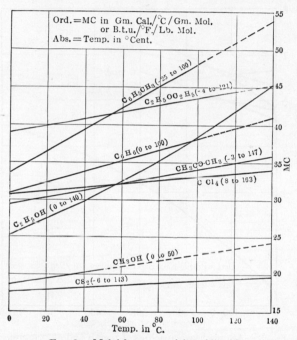

Fig. 2.—Molal heat capacities of liquids.

Solids. For solids, the law of Dulong and Petit and the law of Kopp are sometimes useful in estimating heat capacities of substances. The former states that atomic heat capacity of all solid elementary substances is a constant and the average value is 6.2 at room temperature, although some elements, notably carbon, boron and silicon, deviate widely from this. Furthermore, these heat capacities vary with the temperature, in most cases increasing as temperature rises, as shown in Fig. 3.* Kopp's law states that the formal heat capacity (*i.e.*, the heat

* Data taken from the literature.

capacity of a formula weight of the substance) is an additive function of the atomic heat capacities of the constituent atoms. The following are the atomic heat capacities at room temperature of the elements *in solid compounds:* C = 1.8; H = 2.3; B = 2.7; Si = 3.8; O = 4.0; F = 5.0; P = 5.4; S = 5.4; all other elements 6.2. For example, the formal heat capacity of pure limestone ($CaCO_3$) would be $6.2 + 1.8 + 3 \times 4 = 20.0$ as against an observed value of

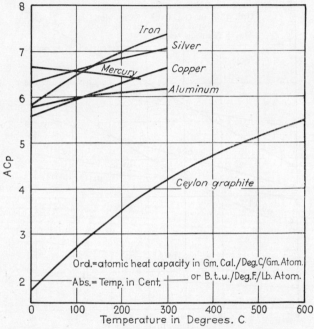

Fig. 3.—Atomic heat capacities of metals and of graphite.

20.2. The specific heat would then be 0.20. These values are, of course, empirical constants and deviations of 10 per cent from the results calculated and those observed are not uncommon.

Molal Heat of Vaporization.—Another heat quantity often required is the molal latent heat of vaporization Mr of liquids. Where exact data are wanting, this quantity can be estimated conveniently through a variation of the rule of Hildebrand, which states that for many liquids the ratio Mr/T is a unique function of the molal concentration of the saturated vapor. In practice, one is usually handicapped by not having data on vapor densities. However, where vapor pressure is low, vapors follow the gas laws, at least approximately, and hence the molal concentration of vapor is proportional to P/T. Consequently one would anticipate that at low pressures Mr/T should be a function of P/T only. At high pressures, where the gas laws break down, it is to be expected that deviations from this relationship will occur, but, as shown by the plot of Mr/T vs. P/T for various liquids in Fig. 4, these deviations are not excessive. It will be

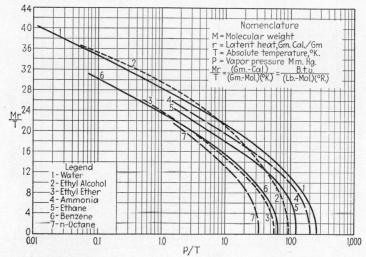

Fig. 4.—Hildebrand chart for estimating latent heats of vaporization.

noted that the curves for such highly associated liquids as water and a typical alcohol lie considerably higher than do those for the more normal liquids. In general, the data for these latter nonassociating liquids lie quite close together at low pressures, but fan out as they approach the critical point, where the latent heat of vaporization equals zero. Curves for hydrocarbons can be drawn in on the figure with reasonable accuracy by reference to the data given for three of these compounds.* Latent heats of vaporization of petroleum fractions† may be approxi-

* These may all be expected to lie close to the benzene curve when P/T is less than 1 or 2. The values of P/T at which they should intercept the axis of abscissas (the critical point) can be estimated from the relations that for paraffins $(P/T)_{\mathrm{crit.}}$ equals very nearly $3800/M$, while for most cyclic hydrocarbons this ratio lies between $4500/M$ and $5300/M$.

† For other methods of estimating this quantity, see the articles by Watson, *Ind. Eng. Chem.*, **23**, 360 (1931), and by Watson and Nelson, *Ind. Eng. Chem.*, **25**, 880 (1933).

mated with accuracy sufficient for many purposes by assuming that these fractions follow the same curves in Fig. 4 as do the pure hydrocarbons of equal molecular weight* and of similar chemical type.

Examination of Fig. 4 shows that, for each of the normal liquids on which data are given, the value of Mr/T at the atmos-

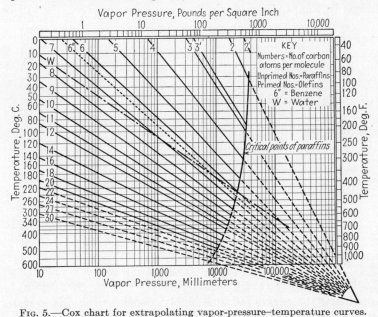

Fɪɢ. 5.—Cox chart for extrapolating vapor-pressure–temperature curves.

pheric boiling point is very close to 21, when expressed in the consistent units here used. *Trouton's rule*, in fact, states that for all normal liquids this ratio has approximately the same value at atmospheric pressure. The rule is surprisingly accurate when applied to nonpolar liquids,† and holds very roughly

* The average molecular weight of the fraction may be taken with sufficient precision as corresponding to that of the normal aliphatic hydrocarbon boiling at a temperature equal to the average boiling point of the hydrocarbon mixture under consideration. The relation between the molecular weight M of any normal paraffin hydrocarbon and its atmospheric boiling point t, expressed in degrees centigrade, is given approximately by the equation

$$\log_{10} M = 2.51 \log_{10} (t + 393) - 4.7523.$$

† According to Kɪsᴛʏᴀᴋᴏᴡsᴋʏ, *Z. physik. Chem.*, **107**, 65 (1923), a more precise rule is one stating that at the atmospheric boiling point of nonpolar

when applied even to the most abnormal ones, *e.g.*, water and the more common alcohols (for which Mr/T at the atmospheric boiling point is about 26), and the lower fatty acids (in which case the value of this ratio lies in the neighborhood of 15).

Vapor Pressure of Liquids.—In many cases it is necessary to interpolate or extrapolate the curve of vapor pressure *vs.* temperature. The method proposed by Cox* is quite helpful. A straight line is drawn at a convenient angle on coordinate paper. The vapor pressures of water are then plotted on a logarithmic scale, allowing the corresponding temperatures to determine the temperature scale, as shown on Fig. 5 by the dotted line for "Water." Using these coordinates, data for various paraffin hydrocarbons are plotted, giving substantially straight lines. Since the latter intersect at a common point, one experimental point is sufficient for the estimation of the vapor-pressure curve of any normal paraffin hydrocarbon.

GENERAL DISCUSSION OF STOICHIOMETRIC PROBLEMS IN APPLIED CHEMISTRY

Types of Operation.—The operations or processes of applied chemistry can be classified under three heads: intermittent, continuous and a combination of these two, or semicontinuous. Illustrations of an intermittent process are the burning of brick and pottery in the older type of kiln, in which, after firing, the whole is allowed to cool for discharging and refilling; the production of coke in beehive ovens; the pot process for the production of nitric acid from Chili saltpeter and sulfuric acid; the recovery of oil from seeds in hydraulic presses; and the like. Typical of continuous processes are the chamber production of sulfuric acid from sulfur, the extraction of light oils and ammonia from illuminating gas by solution in suitable solvents, the operation of continuous stills and distillation columns for the separation of volatile solvents, etc. Continuity of operation offers such obvious and marked advantages that it is used wherever practicable; but in many cases continuity can only be approximated,

---

liquids $Mr/T = 8.75 + 4.571 \log_{10} T$, where T must be expressed in degrees Kelvin in the logarithmic term.

* E. R. Cox, *Ind. Eng. Chem.*, **15**, 592 (1923); see also CALINGAERT and DAVIS, *Ind. Eng. Chem.*, **17**, 1287 (1925).

giving rise to semicontinuous operations, as in the intermittent firing and cleaning of a hand-fired boiler, the operation of a "ring" furnace, the manipulation of the leaching tanks in the extraction of black ash or tanbark, the charging of a blast furnace and the like. Where the character of the operation is essentially intermittent, continuity is often approached by the combination of a number of units operating simultaneously but in different stages, as in the coking of coal in by-product ovens and the recovery of waste heat in regenerative chambers of refractory checker work (*e.g.*, blast-furnace stoves). While this last class can be treated as semicontinuous if the whole process, made up of the combination of all the unit operations, is under consideration, it must be classified as intermittent when one is dealing with the individual unit operation.

Those chemical reactions in which a single substance is transformed into another single substance are comparatively rare. On one or both sides of the reaction equation there usually appears more than one substance. Most chemical operations can therefore be conceived as made up of diverging, converging or crossing and intermingling streams of flow. *Diverging streams* are illustrated by the electrolysis of a salt solution to form caustic, chlorine and hydrogen; by the electrolysis of water (containing caustic) to produce hydrogen and oxygen; by the separation of mixtures of volatile liquids by distillation (alcohol and water, benzol and toluol, etc.); by the destruction distillation of wood, coal and the like. In each case one stream or substance enters the process, to leave by several streams *diverging* from it. Illustrations of *converging streams* are found in the production of vulcanized rubber by the compounding and curing of raw rubber with sulfur and other admixed materials; in the combustion of gaseous fuels, etc. Here two or more substances enter the process to combine or *converge* into one substance and thus leave by a single stream. The combustion of coal with air to form flue gases and ash, the reduction and liquefaction of iron in the blast furnace and the roasting of sulfide ores with air to form metallic oxides and eliminate the sulfur are typical of *crossing streams;* in these cases, several streams enter into an operation, undergo chemical combination and transformation or, in other words, *cross* and leave by several entirely different streams.

Balance of Material Involved in an Operation.—In the quantitative calculation of problems in applied chemistry it is advisable to start with the following equation:

Total input = total output + accumulation, or
Total input + depletion = total output,

accumulation and *depletion* referring to increase or decrease of material in the system itself. This equality may be applied to a single unit operation, or to a whole process made up by the combination of any number of unit operations. It may be applied separately to each element entering into the operation or process, for which data are available; when so applied to a number of elements, the equation for each element is not equivalent to, but is independent of, the others, provided the data for that element were independently obtained. It may be applied to the energy relations of the systems, and in this form gives another independent equation. It may be applied to the input and output of matter as a whole, but this last is obviously not an independent expression, being merely the sum of the equations for the various elements. The use of this principle is observed in nearly every problem.

In these equalities the only awkward factors are the terms *accumulation* and *depletion* in the system itself. These can, of course, be determined, but usually with some difficulty. They can, however, almost always be eliminated by proper choice of data and method of calculation. In the great majority of cases in industrial practice intermittent operations are repeated in cycles which recur a relatively large if not an almost indefinite number of times, and both continuous and semicontinuous operations function steadily over long periods. The possibility of accumulation or storage of materials or energy in a system or apparatus is necessarily limited, and it is usually possible to control the amounts in process without much difficulty. If, now, the above equalities are applied over a period of time such that the maximum possible fluctuations of amounts in process are known, from the nature of the operation and apparatus, to be negligible in comparison with the input and output for the time period chosen, then the terms for accumulation or depletion may be dropped, giving total input = total output. This is perhaps more conveniently written

Total input = useful output + losses, or, more simply,
Input = output + losses.

These equations are used for two main purposes; first, in testing existing apparatus and operations, to determine the actual performance and to provide tests of the self-consistency of the data taken; second, in designing new apparatus and in planning new operations for future installation and service. This chapter deals primarily with the first of these functions, *i.e.*, with the methods used to secure data and information that will give insight into the present or past operation of an apparatus, but the methods employed can be generally used in the design of new equipment, as will be developed later.

Efficiency.—The present performance of an apparatus is determined not only by its capacity but by its efficiency, and, since there can be different kinds of efficiencies, accurate definition of the term is essential. Thus there can be at least two heat efficiencies, defined as the heat utilized by an apparatus divided by its heat input, or as the heat utilized divided by that theoretically capable of utilization. There is also the chemical efficiency, which may be applied to each chemical element in the process. An example of the chemical efficiency of a process is given in the crystallization of a salt; in the impure salt used, there is 1000 lb. of the pure substance; in the output there is 600 lb.; and there is left 380 lb. of recoverable salt in the wash water and mother liquor. As efficiency is generally defined as output/input, that of this process would seem at first to be $^{600}/_{1000} \times 100 = 60$ per cent, yet, since a large amount of the apparent losses are entirely recoverable and would in practice be recovered, it is hardly fair to charge the process with such a low efficiency. Therefore the chemical efficiency should be defined as output/net input, where net input means that amount of material which would have to be put into the process in order to get the *same* output. In order to obtain an output of 600 lb. in the succeeding cycles, it will be necessary to add crude salt containing only 620 lb. of pure substance. The efficiency is then $^{600}/_{620} \times 100 = 96.8$ per cent.

Test Period.—The choice of what may be termed the *test period*, *i.e.*, the length of time during which data as to input and output must be taken in order to render negligible any accumulations or depletions in the system itself, must depend on the condi-

each stream. Since, however, an independent expression can be set up involving equality of input and output of each element, for each such equation formulated it is allowable to omit from the above one measurement, either of quantity or of composition. As already indicated, the measurements to be omitted should be so chosen that those measurements which are actually taken will be accurate and easy to make. Because analytical determinations are usually easier than large-scale measurements of quantity, the former are generally employed to evaluate the latter. However, it is always necessary to make at least one direct measurement of quantity in order to determine the capacity of any system.

In making calculations of this sort care must always be observed to avoid the possibility of gross error in the result due to insufficient accuracy in the measurements made. For example, a quantity, obtained by subtracting two other quantities nearly equal, may itself be very inaccurate, if relatively small errors in the two latter happen to be of opposite sign. The data to be taken experimentally should be chosen with this point in mind.

Sampling.—In securing analytical data in connection with industrial processes the necessity for proper methods of sampling cannot be overemphasized. It is useless to waste time in the laboratory carrying out an analysis if the sample is not truly representative of the stream from which it was taken. Indeed, worse than this, analytical results on nonrepresentative samples may lead to false conclusions.

To be representative a sample should be collected (as nearly as may be) continuously during the test period. Where possible, the amount of sample withdrawn should be proportional to the volume of the stream at each point of time. The sample should be withdrawn not at one point in the stream but at a number of points well distributed over its cross section, except in those cases where the stream is known to be uniform (*e.g.*, a gas that has traveled some distance or around a number of obstructions). These conditions imply the collection of large samples and these must be subdivided before analysis. It is not difficult to get complete mixing of a large sample of gas or homogeneous liquid and the removal of the ultimate sample for analysis involves no difficulty.

The sampling of solid materials is an entirely different problem. Because of the tendency of the large lumps of the solid to separate

tions of each individual case, and can usually be estimated easily
In intermittent operations, the test period should be at least on
complete cycle, and in those cases in which a certain amount c
material is left in process from cycle to cycle, as in soap boiling
must be more than a single cycle. Where practicable it is alway
desirable to cover a number of cycles to eliminate individua
variability. In continuous processes the test period can be th
shorter the more uniform the operation and the less the materia
in process. Semicontinuous operations and processes should, i
possible, be followed over a time period sufficiently long tha
they may be considered as practically continuous. Thus a boile
test must extend over a period of about 36 hr., in order to
eliminate errors due to variations in the amount of fuel in the
firebox at the beginning and end of the test. If test periods of
adequate length cannot be provided, correction must be made for
variations of amounts in process.

Choice of Data to Be Secured and Used.—If a test actually
includes the measurements of every item of input and output,
then the use of the given equalities (page 17) serves as a check
upon the accuracy of the measurements. Usually, however,
these relationships are employed to lessen the amount of data
to be collected and the number of measurements to be made,
without sacrifice of any information obtainable from the test.
Measurements are restricted to those made easily and with
precision, other quantities, which could be directly determined
only with difficulty, being calculated. For example, without the
installation of very special equipment, it would be difficult to
measure the air consumption and the volume of the flue gases in
a boiler test, while it is easy to measure the coal actually burned
and the water evaporated. The first two quantities are therefore
calculated by use of the above equalities from the other data
collected. In testing practice it is unwise to restrict the measurements taken to the minimum necessary for the calculations
required. All data that can be secured with reasonable effort
should be recorded, because any excess may be used to furnish
desirable checks on the accuracy of the other observations.

In order to get a complete determination of the balance of the
elements in any operation, the amount and composition of each
stream entering and leaving the system must be measured. This
requires the determination of the quantity and of the analysis of

from the fine material, the sample must be crushed before sub-division (quartering). Even thus a satisfactory analytical sample can be obtained only by successive subdivisions with most thorough mixing before each successive quartering. The largest individual particle in the mass must be extremely small compared with the sample before quartering is undertaken. It is frequently difficult to reduce the whole original sample of a powder, and to meet this requirement in such case the subdivision must be reground as the sample gets progressively smaller. Mechanical samplers are on the market and are desirable because they reduce the human element in collecting the sample.

General Methods of Calculation.—There are certain practical suggestions and methods which, while theoretically adding nothing to the preceding generalizations, are nonetheless worth mentioning. These are in the nature of stratagems in computation, which, in many special cases, simplify not only calculations but sometimes experimental work as well.

It frequently happens that some one element taking part in a chemical operation enters solely by one stream and leaves solely by another. This is true, for example, of the sodium in the electrolysis of salt, of the nitrogen in a blast furnace and for all practical purposes of the nitrogen in the combustion of coal. It is obvious that, if the quantity of one of these streams is known, the amount of the other can be obtained directly from analysis of the two for this one element. Furthermore, if the analyses of the two streams are complete, the quantities of all other elements present in each of them can at once be calculated. This idea is utilized by the illustrative problem on pages 26 to 27.

Where an element enters and leaves mainly by a single stream, the same method is advantageously employed, merely correcting for divergencies. Thus, in the furnace combustion of coal, the carbon enters mainly in the solid fuel, the amount of which is measured and the carbon content determined by analysis. The carbon leaves mainly in the flue gas, that small portion remaining in the ash as unburned combustible being determined and correction being made for it. This gives immediately the amount of the flue gas. Since the nitrogen of the flue gas comes mainly from the air (the nitrogen of the fuel is usually negligible in comparison), one can immediately calculate the quantity of air used for combustion. It will be noted that the carbon and the nitrogen are used to determine the ratios of the amounts of corresponding ingoing and outgoing streams.   The use of single elements or components for such a purpose is often possible, and offers marked simplification in calculation.

The stoichiometric relations known to exist from the nature of the reactions taking place in a given case often greatly simplify the problem, and make possible important quantitative deductions.   Thus the analysis of a flue gas from the combustion of coal shows certain amounts of CO_2, CO, O_2 and N_2.   Since practically all the N_2 came from the air, one can directly obtain the amount of O_2 that came with it.   The total O_2 shown by the flue-gas analysis, including both free and combined, is always *less than that entering in the air*.   From our knowledge of the chemical composition of coal, we know that almost the whole of this deficit must have been used up in the combustion of hydrogen in the fuel. This difference between oxygen corresponding to the nitrogen and oxygen appearing in the analysis* must, therefore, correspond to and be a measure of the *combustible* hydrogen in the coal.   The analysis of the flue gas is in this case in a very real sense equivalent to an analysis of the fuel itself (see illustrative problem on pages 26 to 27).   While such definite reaction relationships are of the greatest value where they exist, there are many cases where the number of possible side reactions is so great and the extent to which they take place so uncertain that the stoichiometric relationships implied in the chemical equations lose much of their utility.   This is very likely to be the case in organic reactions, but even in inorganic problems it is imperative to formulate and in the calculations to provide for all side reactions that can appreciably affect the result.   These limitations must not, however, make one fail to use these relationships where really applicable.

As in stoichiometric calculations in analytical chemistry, it is unnecessary that the chemical equations employed correspond to

---

* It must be kept in mind that a gas analysis in which the gases are kept saturated with water vapor whenever measurements are made (as is almost universally done) automatically eliminates the water vapor from the results, and gives directly the composition of the water-free gases.   The reason for this is that, although the volume of the gases is increased by the presence of the water vapor, the increase is at all times the same fraction of the total gas volume.   It is as though the analysis were carried out at a pressure lower than that actually used by an amount equal to the constant vapor pressure of the water (see also page 205).

the exact mechanism of reaction. Any combination of the actual reaction steps, even though eliminating intermediate but conpensatory stages, can be used; *e.g.*, reactions in aqueous solutions need not be written in ionic form in the calculation of quantities of precipitates, volumes of solutions and the like.

Basis of Calculation.—It is comparatively seldom that a complete balance of input and output is made in connection with an industrial operation or process, but much more frequently interpretation of partial results is desired. Usually these results are the analyses of different streams. Such analyses are almost never directly comparable, as will appear in a complete balance of input and output, and direct comparison may lead to gross error. This is because analyses are usually reported in per cent of the stream in question, and it is obvious that analysis alone cannot show the relation between the *amount* of that stream and that of any other.

An illustration will make this point clear. A drier is delivering 1 ton per hr. of a product containing 20 per cent of water. The wet charge entering the apparatus for drying carries 60 per cent of water. How many pounds of water are evaporated per hour? The first impulse may be to say that the water decreases from 60 to 20 per cent *i.e.*, by 40 per cent. But the first two figures have no direct relation to each other, because they do not refer to a common basis. The weight of material entering, of which water is 60 per cent, is greater than the 2000 lb. of material leaving. It is believed that difficulties of this sort are best avoided by reducing the analytical results to a common basis in order that direct comparison may be made. Where, as in the case cited, there is a common component which both enters and leaves by a single stream, and there is no accumulation or depletion of that component during the process, the amount of that component passing through the operation in a given time must be the same in both analyses, and hence may serve as a constant basis of comparison. This unidirectional component is, in this case, the dry material itself. If, therefore, the analytical results are expressed as ratio of water to dry material, *i.e.*, 0.25 in the dried product and 1.50 in the wet, the difference, 1.25, truly represents the water evaporated per pound of dry material. Since the dry material is 80 per cent of the product or 1600 lb. per hr., the evaporation is 1.25 times this, or 2000 lb. per hr.

The concept of the preceding paragraph may be expressed by the following rule: Where there are unidirectional elements or components in an operation, express compositions (*i.e.*, analyses) as ratios to these elements.

It must be admitted that the method just outlined, in cases where the flow of all components is complicated, becomes very involved. However, it is so frequently applicable, and where applicable is so direct, that it is advisable to form the habit of using it.

To be sure, this same problem may be solved without recalculation of the analytical data to a new basis. Call y the weight of wet material entering the drier. Equate input of dry material to output.

$$0.40y = 0.80 \ (2000)$$
whence $\qquad y = 4000.$
$$\text{Evaporation} = \text{loss in wt.} = 4000 - 2000 = 2000 \text{ lb.}$$

The basis of such a calculation involves the concept not only of quantity but also of time. For example, in the preceding calculation the time basis was 1 hr. The time basis of calculation may be the duration of a test, or any convenient unit. Frequently the time basis may be implicit, and its actual value unknown, *e.g.*, the time necessary to produce a certain quantity of product or to consume a certain amount of raw material.

Not infrequently one must, at the start of the computation at least, employ two or more bases, but effort should always be directed to reducing them to a common basis. Indeed, when an analysis is reported in per cent, it represents the arbitrary choice as a basis of 100 parts of the particular substance or stream analyzed, and inferentially the acceptance as a time basis of the period required for the development or passage of 100 parts of that particular stream.

When one is dealing with crossing streams, it often occurs that some element or component passes from one stream to the other, either completely or in part; such an element can be made the basis of computation for determining the ratio between the two streams. For example, in the blast furnace a stream of solids, the composition and amount of which are known from the records ordinarily kept of the furnace, flows down through the furnace and out as two separate streams of slag and pig iron. Up through the furnace flows a stream of air, leaving as tunnel-head gas. The ratio of air to tunnel-head gas is determined by the nitrogen, the common component. The ratio of charge to pig is similarly determined by the iron. The ratio of these two streams to each other can be determined by either carbon or oxygen, both of which pass from the charge to the gas stream. If carbon is used, allowance must be made for carbon left in the pig, as found by analysis; if oxygen is employed, that entering in the air and that in the unreduced part of the charge must be taken into account.

It is advisable to write at the head of the computation the basis employed and to indicate clearly change to a new basis, transformation from one basis to another and the ratios by which such transformations are effected. Tabulation of figures is a great help towards brevity and clearness.

Missing Data.—Finally, it must be pointed out that the calculations of applied chemistry often require the making of assumptions and approximations. In industrial work it is frequently impracticable, on account of inconvenience, expense or interference with plant operation, to make all the measurements necessary for a complete determination of the quantities that it is desired to evaluate. In such cases it is advisable not to give up, but to make wisely such simplifying assumptions as are justified by the conditions, and on these, utilizing data already available and such as can readily be obtained, to base a quantitative estimate, always keeping in mind the limitations in accuracy imposed by the assumptions made.

General Procedure in Solving Problems.—In the solution of problems the following steps will be found helpful:

1. Sketch a diagrammatic flow sheet of the process.
2. Write the chemical equations involved.
3. Indicate the basis (or bases) of calculation.
4. Tabulate the data, and the intermediate steps in calculation. In simple cases the formal writing out of the first two may be omitted.

The application and utility of certain of the general principles outlined above are illustrated by the following problem. Additional illustrative problems are given on pages 206, 219 and 235.

Illustration 1.—A boiler furnace burns fuel oil with dry air at 40°F. and at a barometric pressure of 30.1 in. of mercury.   The average Orsat analysis of the flue gas is 12.9 per cent CO_2, 3.8 per cent O_2 and 83.3 per cent N_2, and the temperature of the flue gases at the base of the stack is 560°F.   Assuming[*] the oil to contain only carbon and hydrogen, calculate: (*a*) per cent of excess air,[†] (*b*) the weight per cent of carbon in the oil, (*c*) cu. ft. of air/lb. of oil, (*d*) cu. ft. of flue gas entering the stack/lb. of oil, and (*e*) the partial pressure of water vapor in the stack gases.

Solution.   *a.* Since the analysis of this particular fuel oil is unknown, the oil cannot conveniently be made the basis of calculation.   The analysis of the flue gas is known and can therefore be made the basis.   Consider 100 lb. mols of the flue gas as analyzed, *i.e.*, on the *dry basis.*[‡]   For the purpose of calculation the distribution of the individual elements may be taken as shown in the following tabular form:

Gas	Mols	Atoms C	Mols O_2	Mols N_2
CO_2.............	12.9	12.9	12.9	
O_2...............	3.8	....	3.8	
N_2...............	83.3	....	....	83.3
Totals.........	100.0	12.9	16.7	83.3

Neglecting the small amount of nitrogen in the oil, all the N_2 in the flue gas must have come from the air; hence, the air used is $83.3/0.79 = 105.4$ mols.   (Thus, a "nitrogen balance" is employed to determine the air used.)

Since the dry air contains 21 mol per cent O_2, the O_2 entering the furnace amounts to $(0.21)(105.4) = 22.2$ mols.   Since there is no unburned combustible, the unnecessary O_2 is 3.8 mols.

The per cent of excess air is then

$$\frac{\text{Unnecessary}}{\text{Total} - \text{unnecessary}} = \frac{(3.8)(100)}{(22.2 - 3.8)} = 20.6 \text{ per cent.}$$

[*] This assumption has been made to simplify the calculations.   The oil actually contains a small percentage of nitrogen, sulfur, ash, etc., but it can be shown that the above assumption introduces little error.   This is because the volume of the nitrogen coming from the oil is so small relative to that of the nitrogen from the air used.   Similarly, the nitrogen in coal, coke and wood may be neglected without serious error.   In the case of the combustion of producer gas, the nitrogen cannot be neglected without introducing a considerable error.

[†] "Per cent excess air" refers to the air used in excess of that theoretically needed for complete combustion, compared with that theoretically needed for perfect combustion.   If one deals with O_2 coming from the air, excess air may be interpreted in terms of "O_2" instead of "air," and this is convenient.

[‡] See p. 22.

The total O_2 in the dry flue gas is 16.7 mols; hence the difference, $22.2-16.7$, or 5.5 mols of O_2 has disappeared to form 11.0 mols of water vapor, thus burning 11.0 mols of hydrogen.

b. Since the weight of the oil equals the weight of the carbon $(12.9)(12)$ plus the weight of the hydrogen $(11.0)(2.02)$, the per cent of carbon by weight in the oil is readily calculated:

$$\frac{(12.9)(12)(100)}{(12.9)(12)+(11.0)(2.02)} = \frac{(154.5)(100)}{154.5+22.2} = 87.4 \text{ per cent.}$$

This figure is not required in further calculations, but it serves as a rough check on the accuracy of the flue-gas analyses, since it should compare well with that usually found in fuel oils, as it does in this case. In passing, it should be noted that the atomic ratio of hydrogen to carbon found, $(2)(11.0)/12.9 = 1.70$, corresponds to the formula $(CH_{1.70})_n$ for the oil.

c. Since the weight of oil is 176.7 lb. and the dry air on the basis is 105.4 mols, the air used per lb. of oil may be readily calculated:

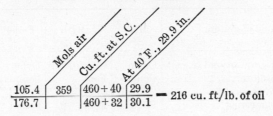

$$\frac{105.4}{176.7} \left| 359 \right| \frac{460+40}{460+32} \left| \frac{29.9}{30.1} \right. = 216 \text{ cu. ft/lb. of oil}$$

d. The mols of flue gas entering the stack will contain the 100 mols of dry gases (CO_2, O_2 and N_2) plus the 11.0 mols of water vapor, a total of 111.0 mols of wet flue gas. The volume of stack gases per lb. of oil is calculated as follows:

$$\frac{111.0}{176.7} \left| 359 \right| \frac{460+560}{460+32} \left| \frac{29.9}{30.1} \right. = 464 \text{ cu. ft./lb. of oil}$$

e. The partial pressure of the water vapor in the stack gases is readily calculated, remembering Dalton's law:

$$p = 30.1\frac{11.0}{111.0} = 2.98 \text{ in. of mercury.}$$

SYSTEMS OF PHYSICAL UNITS

It is well to remind the reader that the fundamental properties and conditions of matter bear interrelationships on the basis of which they can be defined quantitatively in terms of each other, but a certain limited number of these fundamental factors must be arbitrarily assumed as a starting point. Furthermore, the choice of units in which these basic or primary factors are measured and expressed is likewise completely arbitrary. The fundamental units which have been adopted as primary in scientific and technical work are those of time, mass (quantity of matter), distance and temperature. The second is ordinarily chosen as the unit of time, although the hour is occasionally employed. The following table shows the usage in the four more common systems, including the important secondary unit of force.

TABLE I.—FUNDAMENTAL UNITS
(Unit of time = second in all cases)

Name of system	Mass	Length	Force	Temperature
Centimeter-gram-second (c.g.s.)	Gram	Centimeter	Dyne	Deg. C.
English Absolute...............	Pound	Foot	Poundal	Deg. F.
English Gravitational....	"Slug"	Foot	Pound	Deg. F.
English Engineering...........	Pound	Foot	Pound	Deg. F.

One must remember that the fundamental law of motion is not $F = Ma$, but $F = \alpha Ma$, where α is a proportionality constant which the physicist has arbitrarily chosen to make unity in the first three of these systems by appropriate choice of units. This will be clear from study of Table I.

The mechanical and the civil engineer find no serious difficulty in using the engineering system, despite the intellectual confusion that cannot fail to result from the use, often in the same breath, of the word "pound" to describe two such fundamentally different entities as mass and force; this is primarily due to the fact that engineers are rarely interested in amount of matter as such, but only in terms of its force effects (such as its weight and the corresponding structure that must be supplied to support it). To the chemical engineer, on the contrary, *quantity of matter i.e.*, mass, is vitally important, serving as it does as the basis of every material balance and chemical equation. For him the best solution would be the use of the pound as a unit of mass only, using the poundal as the unit of force. However, he does in fact use the pound as a unit of mass or quantity of matter, and at the same time uses the pound (or rather its weight, the force of attraction of the earth upon it) as a unit of force. His scales read in pounds (mass) and his pressure gauges in pounds (force) per square inch. This is allowable if he will at the same time use the proper value of α,* which is obviously $1/g_0$, where g_0 is the arbitrarily chosen, so-called standard value of the earth's attraction, assumed to be constant at sea level at 45° latitude:†

$$F(\text{in lb. force}) = \frac{1}{g_0}M(\text{in lb. mass}) \ a \ (\text{in ft./sec.}^2).$$

This text will express final equations in engineering units, but wherever ambiguity can arise will distinguish between pound mass and pound force. It is easier to make derivations in absolute units (*e.g.*, mass in pounds, force in poundals) and transform the final expressions into engineering units. The data of the chemical engineer will often be found in various system of units and he must be able to disentangle them. The burden of straight thinking is upon him and he must be able to avoid the confusion induced by the terminology employed by brother engineers.

Once these fundamental units are assumed, units for the measurement of all other interrelated physical properties can be derived and expressed in terms of them. The secondary or derived properties are, in general, defined in terms of power functions of the basic quantities, and the degree to which each of the basic factors enters into the term in question is called its *dimensions*. Thus, the dimensions of density, mass per unit volume, are M/L^3. The dimensions of a quantity are always the same in all systems using the same primary factors (*e.g.*, all those in Table I), despite diversity in units.

* However, having done this, the value of α must be carried through into all equations based on the fundamental relation: $F = \alpha Ma$. When working in the English Engineering System with time in seconds, g_0 is 32.2 ft./sec.^{2}, but, when time in hours is employed, g_0 becomes $32.2 \times (3600)^2 = 4.18 \times 10^8$ ft./hr.^{2}

† Where gravity plays a part, its value g, taken at the place the measurements in question are made, should appear. However, the variation in g with elevation and latitude rarely exceeds one-quarter of 1 per cent; hence in ordinary engineering works no distinction is made between g_0 and g, and the working equations usually show merely the symbol g, regardless of whether the term is serving merely as a conversion factor or whether gravity is really involved in the phenomenon.

Only similar quantities, hence those of the same dimensions, can be submitted to the operations of addition and subtraction. Thus an equation cannot be universally valid unless it is dimensionally homogeneous, *i.e.*, all its separate terms have the same dimensions. Similarly, a sum or difference, even a differential, has the dimensions of its parts. The numerical value of any dimensionless quantity is independent of the system of units in which it is evaluated, provided the system is consistent

TABLE II.—FUNDAMENTAL DIMENSIONS OF VARIOUS QUANTITIES IN TERMS OF MASS (M), LENGTH (L), TIME (θ) AND TEMPERATURE (t)

Quantity	Net Dimensions
Acceleration	L/θ^2
Area	L^2
Coefficient (surface) of heat transfer	$M/\theta^3 t$
Coefficient of volumetric expansion	$1/t$
Density	M/L^3
Diameter, or hydraulic radius	L
Energy (work, heat)	ML^2/θ^2
Friction factor	Dimensionless
Force	ML/θ^2
Kinematic viscosity	L^2/θ
Mass rate of flow	M/θ
Mass velocity	$M/L^2\theta$
Pressure, force per unit area	$M/L\theta^2$
"Roughness" of surface	L
Specific heat	$L^2/\theta^2 t$
Surface tension	M/θ^2
Thermal conductivity	$ML/\theta^3 t$
Thermal "diffusivity"	L^2/θ
Velocity	L/θ
Viscosity (absolute)	$M/L\theta$

throughout. This fact is often of convenience, enabling one to evaluate one dimensionless ratio in one system and another, intimately correlated with the first, in a second.

Conversion of Units.—Given any two systems of measurement using the same primary factors, in both of which all arbitrary constants (*e.g.*, α in $F = \alpha Ma$) are unity (or numerically equal), whatever the differences in the magnitude of the units in the two systems, the conversion factor to transform any quantity in one system into the other can be found by multiplying together the corresponding conversion terms for each primary unit, each raised to a power equal to the exponent on the dimensions in question. Where the arbitrary constants of the two systems differ, proper allowance must be made in conversion. Several illustrations follow.

A certain process tested in the laboratory yields 2800 c.c. of hydrogen/gm. of the coal employed. Since the coal has a density of ρ gm./c.c., 1 c.c. of coal yields 2800ρ c.c. of hydrogen. Consequently, if the identical process is operated in a plant, it will yield 2800ρ cu. ft. of hydrogen/cu. ft. of the coal employed. Since 1 cu. ft. of water is 62.3 lb., and water has a density of 1 gm./c.c., 1 cu. ft. of the coal would be 62.3ρ lb. Consequently, the yield of gas in the plant would be $2800\rho/62.3\rho$ or 45 cu. ft. of hydrogen/lb. of the coal consumed. It will be noted that the density of the coal cancels out.

Consider an orifice through which a liquid is flowing at the rate of w gm./sec. At a given instant of time, its rate of discharge is changing at the rate of $dw/d\theta$, whose units are mass over time squared. It is desired to express this in engineering units, lb./sec.^{2} Since the time units are the same in both systems, and since there are 454 gm. in the pound, the conversion factor is $\frac{1}{454}$.

However, while surface tension likewise has the units M/θ^2, the corresponding conversion factor from c.g.s. to engineering units is not the same. Surface tension is force per unit length. Hence the factor $\frac{1}{454}$ will convert dynes/cm. (c.g.s. units) to poundals per foot (English absolute units), but this in turn must be divided by g_0 to convert to pounds of force per foot (engineering units).

Dimensional Similitude.—It seems to be a universal rule in physical phenomena that, however complicated the functional relationships between the physical variables, the variables themselves, whether dependent or independent, are involved only in the form of dimensionless ratios. An alternative statement of the rule is that it is possible to express all natural interrelationships in terms of functions and coefficients that are universal in form and numerical value, completely independent of the arbitrary system of units which may be employed in making the measurements themselves, provided the system is inherently consistent. This generalization is termed the *principle of dimensional similitude*. It is most conveniently expressed in the form of the equation, $\phi(p, q, r, \text{etc.}) = 0$, in which p, q, r, etc., are *dimensionless ratios* of the fundamental physical variables. The function ϕ represents a universal relation, independent of the system of units, which, however, need not necessarily be expressible in terms of known functions. It is often best presented in graphical form.

The number of independent dimensionless ratios in the function ϕ depends on the number of physical factors involved in the problem in hand and the number of fundamental dimensions involved in these factors. In general, the number of dimensionless ratios is best determined by an algebraic procedure developed on page 75, although in simple cases the number may be obtained by inspection.

The principle of dimensional similitude, while of great help, is characterized by sharp limitations. It does not assist in selecting the fundamental factors influencing a given problem; these must be determined by the judgment of the investigator, exercised in the light of such knowledge of the mechanism as is available. However, once the number of these factors is assumed, the principle reduces the relationships to a definite number of completely independent variables. The conclusions must now be tested experimentally. If the experimental results are obviously more complicated than the principle would indicate, relevant fundamental factors have been overlooked in the analysis; if less variables than predicted will correlate the data, certain factors have mistakenly been assumed significant. The principle throws no light on the character of the functional relationships of the dimensionless ratios or their relative importance; this must be determined on the basis of the experimental data.* It does, however, show the simplest and most comprehensive way of presenting results, graphically or otherwise, namely, as functions of the dimensionless ratios. Furthermore, it offers the soundest known method of correlating the results obtained under widely diversified conditions and of extrapolating results obtained under one set of conditions to fit different circumstances.

One of the most important applications of the principle of dimensional similitude is in the construction and use of experimental models as tools in engineering design. Suppose a given operation, involving n significant dimensionless ratios, carried out in each of two structures, one an accurate scale model of the other. Suppose, furthermore, that the operation as conducted

---

* The function is often assumed as a product of powers of the ratios, but this is an empirical and in no sense general relation. Surprisingly, the experimental data often indicate that the relation is a product of functions of the individual ratios of the form $\phi_1(r)\phi_2(p)\phi_3(q)$, etc. $=$const., where ϕ_1 is a function of r only, etc., but this too is undoubtedly no general rule.

in the small model is so modified by changes in operating variables other than size that the numerical value of each of $n-1$ of the significant dimensionless ratios is identical with that of the same ratio in the operation of the larger structure. The principle of similitude requires that the values of the final ratio must also be identical in the two operations. Grant, now, that the large-scale structure has not been built but is in process of design, and, furthermore, that the last ratio includes some factor which the designer must be able to predict, but which is not readily or accurately found by direct computation. Clearly, experimental determination of this ratio on the model, constructed and operated with all other ratios identical in value with those corresponding to the performance of the full-size unit, will enable the designer readily to compute the value of the unknown factor in the final operation.

It will be noted that, in the preceding illustration, an experimental model was employed solely to determine the performance of a large dimensionally similar unit. Obviously, the model can be employed to determine experimentally the influence of changes in all operating variables other than relative linear dimensions, and, by modification of the model, this last factor, subject as it is to almost infinite variation, can be investigated. The method has been developed and used with outstanding success in such fields as aerodynamics, hydrodynamics, marine engineering, heat transfer, absorption and the like, and there is growing appreciation of its importance and value in chemical engineering work.

References

BRIDGMAN, P. W., "Dimensional Analysis," Yale University Press, 1922, 1931.

BUCKINGHAM, E., *Phys. Rev.*, **4**, 345 (1914).

GIBSON, A. H., *Engineering (London)*, **117**, 325, 357, 391, 422 (1924).

CHAPTER II

FLUID FILMS

It has long been known,* though not generally appreciated, that, when a gas or a liquid moves over a solid surface or when a gas moves across a liquid surface, there exists a film of the moving substance upon the surface of the stationary one. This fluid film forms a boundary or zone between the portion that is rapidly moving and that which is still, which acts toward the transportation of heat, vapor and matter as though it were a separate material. Its properties are so controlling in many engineering processes that its presence and characteristics must be clearly recognized.

Consider the case of continuous flow through a conduit. A plot of the motion of the gas as determined by the distance from the containing wall is shown in Fig. 6. At the boundary wall itself there is no motion of the fluid. As one progresses from the wall, the velocity of motion of the fluid increases, but in the neighborhood of the wall each element† of the fluid flows in a path parallel to the wall, having essentially no component of velocity at right angles to the wall. As one goes farther from the wall, not only does velocity increase but also a point G is finally reached at which the character of the motion changes. The elements of the fluid now begin to travel in forward-moving spirals. The net motion is still parallel to the surface, but the path of any one particle has a large average component at

---

* The first mention of the water film was made by Peclet, "Traité de la Chaleur," Chap. VIII, p. 131, 1844. Since that time the presence and properties of such films have been verified by others, more particularly by Langmuir in 1912 (*Phys. Rev.*, **34,** 421), who, working with gases, demonstrated the effect of velocity upon the thickness of the film and upon heat transfer.

† Such an element is a very small body of the fluid but contains many molecules. Each molecule has its own irregular motion, but the whole group of molecules composing the fluid element moves as a unit, just as a raindrop falls vertically through quiet air, despite the irregular motion of the water molecules in the drop.

right angles to the surface. This complex motion obviously has a marked mixing effect on neighboring layers of the fluid and is described as turbulent.

Hence there exists on the boundary surface of a moving fluid a creeping film, traveling parallel to the surface at a speed considerably less than the average velocity of the fluid relative to the surface, but characterized preeminently by the fact that the bulk motion in this film is parallel to the surface and with little turbulent or mixing motion of the fluid elements. Consequently motion through this film at right angles to the surface must be by the slow processes of molecular diffusion. While all

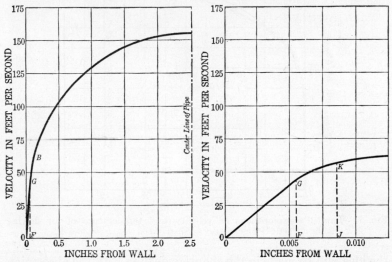

Fig. 6.—Velocity distribution for isothermal flow in a circular pipe. Based on data of reference 1 at end of chapter.

parts of this film other than that in immediate contact with the surface actually creep along the wall, it is easier to visualize the film as a stationary body of fluid and practically always allowable to do so. Where the motion of the main body of liquid past the surface is appreciable, this film is usually very thin.

Vapor from liquids (or solids) can escape through this gas film only by diffusion. A molecule is thrown off from the surface of the liquid and must work its way through the molecules of the gas forming the film until it reaches the outside of the film and can be caught up and carried away by the convection currents there existing.

Upon increasing the velocity of the main body of the fluid, the increased turbulence at the surface of the boundary film will wear away or rub off a portion of it, causing convection currents to strike more deeply into it. The thickness of the film is thereby decreased and any action resultant upon the presence of the film will be influenced accordingly.

This concept of a film of gas or liquid is useful in the majority of operations in chemical engineering. Detailed applications of

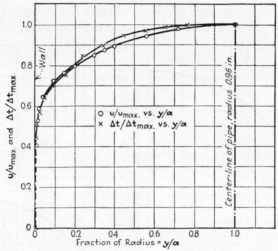

FIG. 7.—Pannell's explorations of velocity and temperature of air flowing inside a vertical pipe, $u_{max.} = 87$ ft./sec., $\Delta t_{max.} = 33.5°F$.

the idea will be made in the chapters dealing with the absorption of gases from gaseous mixtures by liquid absorbing agents, the removal of volatile from nonvolatile material by passing through it a stream of air or other gas, the solution of solids by liquids and the transfer of heat in its many forms. Such phenomena are best explained by the assumption of the existence of the resistant film.

Figure 7[2]* shows the results of temperature and velocity explorations across an air stream flowing upward in turbulent motion in an electrically heated vertical brass pipe having an inside diameter of 1.92 in. The ratio of local to maximum velocity $u/u_{max.}$ is plotted *vs.* the position ratio y/a, where u is

* Reference 2 at end of chapter.

the local velocity at distance y from the wall and a is the radius. This plot also shows the ratio of local to total temperature difference $(t_w-t)/(t_w-t_0)$ plotted vs. y/a, where t_w, t_0 and t are the temperatures at the pipe wall, at the center line of pipe and at the position y, respectively. It is to be noted that the curves of distribution of velocity and temperature differences are very similar. The gas film should be that zone in which the relationship between $\Delta t/\Delta t_{max.}$ and y/a is essentially linear. In this case approximately 50 per cent of the total temperature drop occurs in the film which has a thickness less than 1 per cent of the radius of the pipe. However, it should be noted that even at a velocity of 87 ft. per sec. the convective mixing in the pipe is so imperfect that one-half the total temperature drop is necessary for the transportation of the heat through the main body of the gas.

A theoretical consideration of the flow of gas through a capillary tube led Poiseuille to formulate a law which states that the volume of gas flowing through such a tube varies directly as the fourth power of the inside diameter of the tube. The derivation of this law is based upon the assumption, first, that the main body of the gas assumes streamline flow rather than rolling or turbulent motion; second, that the friction is proportional to the relative slip of one layer of the gas on the next one to it; and, third, that there is no slip at the boundary wall. The fact that careful experiments with very narrow capillary tubes show this law to be quantitatively exact proves that the assumptions are correct, whence it follows that there is no flow in immediate contact with the wall.

Consider the mechanism of the diffusion of water vapor from a mixture of water vapor and air in contact with concentrated sulfuric acid, the operation being conducted at constant total pressure. In Fig. 8 the line OA represents a section of the surface of the liquid in contact with the air. The line OB represents the distance out into the air from the surface of the liquid and the line HK represents the outer surface of the air film. In the direction OA, starting at the point O as an origin, the partial pressure of the water vapor is plotted. The equilibrium partial pressure of the vapor at the surface of the liquid is indicated by the point C. The partial pressure of the vapor in the main body of the air is, however, higher, as indicated by the point E. In the main body the gradient *ED* is necessary for the transportation of the vapor by convective mixing. The vapor then passes through the gas film by diffusion under the influence of the partial pressure gradient *DC*, and is absorbed by the acid.

Let the total pressure in the space be represented by the horizontal line *LM*. Since at the surface of the liquid the partial pressure of the vapor is equal to *OC*, the partial pressure of the air must be equal to *OL* minus *OC* or *OW*. Similarly, in the main body of the air the partial pressure of the air will be equal to *OL* minus *OE* or will be represented by the line *PQ*. The partial

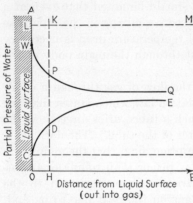

pressure of the air in the surface film will therefore be represented by the line *WP*. In other words, the partial pressure of air at the surface of the liquid is greater than its partial pressure farther out from the surface. Despite the existence of this pressure gradient, there is no net transfer of air through the film, because of the impact against the air molecules of the

Fig. 8.—Absorption of water vapor from air by sulfuric acid.

vapor molecules driving in towards the surface. This pressure gradient of air is maintained by a dynamic equilibrium controlled by the frictional resistance offered by the air film to the vapor molecules diffusing inward through it.

The movement of matter through this stationary film requires diffusion. The diffusional velocities of gases and vapors are proportional to the square root of the sum of the reciprocals of the molecular weights of the diffusing and nondiffusing gases and inversely proportional to the sum of the cross-sectional areas of the two types of molecules. Small particles of solids or liquids suspended in the gas (*i.e.*, dust and fogs) may be considered as having relatively high cross-sectional areas and therefore negligible diffusion velocities. It is obvious that the gas film will effectively insulate such particles from the surface of liquid or solid in contact with the gas, so that interaction is difficult to secure.

Thus, whereas, if one will bring either ammonia gas or dilute hydrochloric acid gas into contact with water, both will be absorbed with great rapidity, on the other hand, if one allows these two to interact in the gaseous state, forming a cloud of solid ammonium chloride particles, it is almost impossible to dissolve the latter. One can draw air containing such a cloud through a series of wash bottles, highly effective for the absorption of gases, with almost no results.

This offers the explanation of the difficulty of absorbing sulfur trioxide made in the contact process. If one attempts to dissolve the trioxide in water or dilute sulfuric acid, the trioxide vapor first comes in contact not with the liquid but with the water vapor which has evaporated from the liquid into the gas. It reacts with this vapor, producing minute droplets of sulfuric acid in the form of a fog, and these droplets are effectively insulated from the absorbing liquid by the gas film. One must therefore use as an absorbent a liquid, the water-vapor pressure of which is negligible, *i.e.*, strong sulfuric acid. This is the reason that for absorption one must use acid between 97 and 98 per cent. If more dilute, the pressure of water vapor is sufficient to produce a fog; if more concentrated, the partial pressure of SO_3 over it is great enough to prevent complete absorption. Fog formation is not necessarily dependent on chemical combination. Thus if air containing a high concentration of hydrochloric acid gas is brought into contact with water, the acid may combine with the water vapor and condense as a fog, which will likewise fail to be absorbed by the main body of the water.

These facts explain the difficulty of removal of tar fog from illuminating gas and producer gas, of cement dust and arsenic fume from stack gases, of carbon black formed by incomplete combustion of natural gas, and the like (see pages 313 to 317).

References

1. Stanton, Marshall, and Bryant, *Proc. Roy. Soc.*, Ser. A, **97**, 413 (1920).

2. Pannell, *Brit. Aero. Research Comm.*, *Rept.*, Memo 243, June, 1916, H. M. Stationery Office, London.

CHAPTER III

FLOW OF FLUIDS

The major problem of fluid dynamics is to develop, for any given apparatus or structure and fluid of definite properties flowing through it, quantitative relations between rate of flow and pressure difference. One can thus determine the power requirement of the system. The results also furnish the basis of important methods of measuring rates of flow. Problems of secondary significance are the mechanical reactions of flowing fluids and the effects of conditions of flow on other phenomena, such as diffusion. The fundamental relationships will be treated in this chapter but their applications will be found throughout the text.

The principles underlying the analysis of every problem of fluid flow are, first, the conservation of matter; second, the conservation of energy; and third, the laws of fluid friction. The first is employed in the form of a material balance and the second in the form of an energy balance for the operation in question. The first as applied to fluid flow is sometimes called the *law of continuity*.* The stream of fluid may be visualized as divided into a number of filaments or "tubes of flow." Although the energy balance may be formulated without knowledge of the equation of state and the thermal properties of the fluid, these data are required for the evaluation of the energy balance.

MATERIAL BALANCE FOR STEADY FLOW

Consider an apparatus of any sort, *e.g.*, one such as depicted in Fig. 9, focusing attention on the part between sections 1 and 2. Between these sections no fluid is entering or leaving the

---

* This term is preferably reserved to describe the fact, usually implicitly assumed, that the paths of flow of the individual particles are smooth nonintersecting curves and that there exists a cross section orthogonal to the direction of motion completely filled by the moving fluid.

40

apparatus. Under steady conditions the mass* rates of flow at each section must be identical, since otherwise there would be a progressive accumulation or depletion of fluid within the apparatus between the two sections. This relation is expressed in the equation

$$w = \frac{V_1 S_1}{v_1} = \frac{V_2 S_2}{v_2} = G_1 S_1 = G_2 S_2 \tag{1}$$

where w represents the mass rate of flow; S the area of cross section; V the average velocity, equal to the volumetric rate of flow q divided by the cross section; v the specific volume, *i.e.*, volume per unit mass, at the point in question; and G the mass velocity, equal to the mass rate of flow divided by the cross section. A general nomenclature table is given on page 97.

TOTAL ENERGY BALANCE FOR STEADY FLOW

Considering steady flow in the apparatus of Fig. 9, take as a basis of calculation the length of time required for 1 lb. of fluid

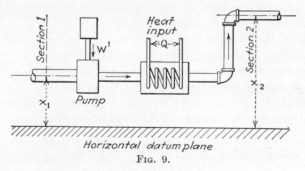

FIG. 9.

to enter and also to leave the space between the sections. The pound entering at section 1 brings in with it a certain amount of energy, existing in various forms. Thus, because of its elevation, x_1 ft. above any arbitrarily chosen horizontal datum plane, it possesses a *potential energy* of x_1 ft.-lb., which could be recovered by allowing the pound of fluid to fall from the level of section 1 to that of the datum. Because of its velocity u_1, the pound possesses and brings into the apparatus at section 1 an amount of *kinetic energy*, $u_1^2/2g$ ft.-lb. It also brings its so-called *internal energy*, thermal, chemical and otherwise, E_1. Further-

* See p. .29.

more, the pound of fluid in question entering at section 1 is forced into the section by the pressure of the fluid behind it and this form of mechanical energy must also be evaluated. The amount of this energy is the force exerted by the following fluid times the distance through which it acts, and the force is clearly the pressure per unit area, p_1, times the area S_1 of the cross section. The distance through which the force acts is the volume v_1 of the pound of fluid divided by the cross-sectional area S_1. Since the work done is the force times the distance, *i.e.*, $(p_1 S_1)(v_1/S_1) = p_1 v_1$, the energy expended is the product of the pressure times the volume of a pound of fluid.*

While the terms just discussed comprise all forms of energy brought in through section 1 by the flowing fluid, and while it has been assumed that no material leaves or enters between sections 1 and 2, this does not preclude exchange of energy with the surroundings between the sections. This energy interchange may be in the forms of both heat and work. Call the former Q and the latter W, each expressed per pound of flowing fluid, the positive sign indicating addition of energy from the surroundings to the apparatus.

Clearly, the flowing fluid carries out of the apparatus at section 2 energy in the four forms brought in at section 1. Clearly, also, conservation of energy requires equality of the sum of all forms of energy entering to that of those leaving. Expressing all terms in the same units, *e.g.*, foot-pounds of energy per pound of fluid flowing, this results in the **total energy balance**:

$$x_1 + p_1 v_1 + \frac{u_1^2}{2g} + E_1 + Q + W = x_2 + p_2 v_2 + \frac{u_2^2}{2g} + E_2. \qquad (2)$$

The importance of this equation is difficult to overestimate. Based only on the laws of conservation of matter and of energy, its validity for the conditions assumed is beyond question.

While this equation is fundamentally valid, evaluation of specific terms often involves complications, which fortunately are rarely serious. Thus, unless the section is horizontal, theoretically the x-term should be integrated for the mass of fluid entering at each level, and variations in the pv-product should be similarly allowed for, but these corrections are almost always so small that they are beyond the precision of the other

* This is sometimes called *flow work*.

data. Variations in the point velocity over the sections of flow must be considered.* Theoretically one could avoid these difficulties by applying the equation only to a differential tube of flow, but this usually makes it impossible properly to evaluate the other terms. The term Q must be the *total net* heat added between the sections per pound of flowing fluid; but it includes only heat passing into the fluid through the walls of the containing vessel from an external source. This excludes heat generated by friction, fluid or otherwise within the equipment, since such heat must come from dissipation of forms of energy already allowed for. Positive addition of heat involves no necessity of temperature rise, for the energy can find outlet in other forms. Indeed, addition of heat accompanied by temperature drop is not uncommon.

The external work energy W, like the heat Q, must come through the retaining walls. While it could conceivably enter in other ways, in practice it is always supplied by some form of moving mechanism, such as a pump, which may, however, be of diverse types, *e.g.*, piston, centrifugal, gas lift, etc. Where the mechanism withdraws work energy from the flowing fluid, it is described as an engine, prime mover, etc. In the absence of such a mechanism, the term W disappears. Furthermore, its effect is completely localized at the mechanism. The term should include the net work done on the flowing fluid by the mechanism. Occasionally it may be preferable to use the total external work done on the mechanism and include in Q any heat losses from this energy which do not get into the fluid stream.

The internal energy term E corresponds to the usual thermodynamic definition, determinable only by difference. If desired,

---

* By definition, the kinetic energy of a small filament of fluid having *local* velocity u is $u^2/2g$ ft.-lb. per lb. If the local velocities at all points in the cross section were uniform, V would be equal to u and $V^2/2g$ would be the correct value of the kinetic energy. Ordinarily there is a velocity gradient across the passage, and hence the use of $V^2/2g$ introduces an error, the magnitude of which depends on the nature of the velocity gradient and the shape of the cross section. For the usual case where the velocity is approximately uniform, the error in using $V^2/2g$ is not serious, and, since the error tends to cancel because of the appearance of $V^2/2g$-terms on each side of the energy balance equations, it is customary to use $V^2/2g$ as the kinetic energy. Where the velocity distribution is parabolic, it can be shown that the correct value of the kinetic energy is V^2/g, not $V^2/2g$. This is further discussed on p. 80.

however, it may be defined by this equation, all other terms being subject to direct experimental measurement. Both E and pv are clearly properties of the flowing fluid, uniquely determined by point conditions. For convenience their sum is often treated as a single function called **enthalpy,** heat content or total heat, $h = E + pv$. It too is a property of the fluid, uniquely determined by its point conditions. Like E, its absolute value cannot be determined. Differences in value are often given above an arbitrary datum.*

Provided flow conditions are steady, there is no need of homogeneity in the flowing fluid. Furthermore, correction for multiplicity of streams is easy since the energy content of each stream is proportional to its quantity and the principle involved is a balance of total energy. The following example illustrates the application of the total energy balance to a problem involving calculation of heat loss from a pipe carrying superheated steam.

Illustration 1.—Superheated steam is flowing at constant mass rate through a horizontal insulated pipe. At the first section the average linear velocity of the steam is 250 ft./sec., the temperature is 600°F. and the absolute pressure is 2 in. of mercury. At a second section the absolute pressure is 1 in. of mercury and the temperature is 590°F. Under these conditions the steam behaves as a perfect gas, since on a Mollier diagram the lines of constant enthalpy are parallel to those for constant temperature. Using 0.48 as the specific heat of the steam at constant pressure, calculate the heat loss to the surroundings, expressed as B.t.u./lb. of steam flowing.

Solution.—Since the pipe is horizontal, x_1 equals x_2, and, with no pump between sections, W is zero. Hence, Eq. 2 becomes

$$(C_p)_{\text{av.}}(T_1 - T_2) + \frac{V_1{}^2 - V_2{}^2}{2gJ} = -Q = \text{heat loss to surroundings.}$$

Since under these conditions superheated steam deviates little from the gas laws, the material balance reduces to

$$V_2 = V_1 \frac{v_2}{v_1} = V_1 \left(\frac{T_2}{T_1}\right)\left(\frac{p_1}{p_2}\right) = 250 \left(\frac{1050}{1060}\right)\left(\frac{2}{1}\right) = 495 \text{ ft./sec.}$$

Substitution of these values in the total energy balance gives

$$(0.48)(600 - 590) + \left[\frac{(250)^2 - (495)^2}{(64.3)(778)}\right] = 4.8 - 3.65 = 1.15 \text{ B.t.u./lb.} = -Q.$$

If the heat equivalent to the increase in kinetic energy had been neglected, as in the usual "heat balance," the heat loss would have been taken as 4.8

* While in general the enthalpy change is read from tables of data, for a perfect gas, where dE equals $C_v \, dT$ and $d(pv)$ equals $R \, dT$, dh equals $C_p \, dT$.

B.t.u./lb., and the error so introduced would have been $(100)(4.8-1.15)/$ $1.15 = 317$ per cent of the actual heat loss to the surroundings.

MECHANICAL-ENERGY BALANCE FOR STEADY FLOW

For steady flow of essentially noncompressible fluids under conditions where friction is negligible, in the absence of external work effects it is found experimentally that there is little error in an energy balance involving only the terms for the mechanical forms of energy. However, in corresponding cases involving the flow of compressible fluids, the total mechanical energy appearing at the outlet often greatly exceeds that at the earlier section, particularly where there are large pressure drops between sections. Analysis of the situation makes it clear that any given element of the moving fluid is undergoing an expansion, in the course of which it does mechanical work. Clearly, this work must be expended on the fluid immediately ahead of it, but the fluid element in question also picks up an equivalent amount of mechanical energy from that behind it. The net result is an increase in the mechanical energy at the expense of the internal energy of the fluid or of externally derived heat. Granting reversibility of expansion, this self-expansion work is $\int_1^2 p \, dv$, which should be included in a mechanical-energy balance. Applying this correction in the cases cited, the mechanical-energy output, while it may in special cases closely approximate the input, is always less. In order to balance the equation, another term, ΣF, must be introduced, the equation becoming

$$x_1 + p_1 v_1 + \frac{u_1^2}{2g} + \int_1^2 p \, dv = x_2 + p_2 v_2 + \frac{u_2^2}{2g} + \Sigma F.$$

The term ΣF represents total friction due to fluid flow. It is best defined as the term necessary to balance this equation—a definition entirely compatible with the statement that fluid friction is mechanical energy rendered nonavailable owing to irreversibilities in the processes of flow. If between sections 1 and 2 a pump actually delivers W' ft.-lb. of mechanical work to the fluid, this term must appear on the left-hand side of the equation,*

---

* Owing to the friction F_p in the pump, W' is less than the term W defined in connection with Eq. 2: $W' = W - F_p$.

which thus assumes its general form:

$$x_1+p_1v_1+\frac{u_1{}^2}{2g}+\int_1^2 p\ dv+W'=x_2+p_2v_2+\frac{u_2{}^2}{2g}+\Sigma F.$$

This is known as **Bernoulli's theorem.** Together with the total energy balance, it serves as the fundamental basis for the solution of problems in fluid flow. This chapter deals almost exclusively with its applications in special cases. The student must appreciate it thoroughly in every detail.*

Since $\int_1^2 p\ dv+p_1v_1-p_2v_2$ equals $-\int_1^2 v\ dp$, the above equation is more compactly written

$$W'-\int_1^2 v\ dp=x_2-x_1+\frac{u_2{}^2-u_1{}^2}{2g}+\Sigma F. \tag{3}$$

In evaluating $\int p\ dv$ the expansion was assumed reversible, differences being thrown into ΣF. However, the integral, unlike E, pv and h, is not a point function of the conditions, but depends on the path of expansion or compression, *i.e.*, on the history of the fluid during its passage through the apparatus. This often renders evaluation difficult. It is not uncommon to assume a path that is at least approximately correct and throw the difference into friction.

The equations are readily and often helpfully expressed in differential form, *i.e.*, for sections a differential distance apart. In this case the W-term falls out, since this effect is in its nature inherently localized.

$$\text{Total energy balance:}\ dQ=dx+\frac{u\ du}{g}+dh. \tag{2a}$$

$$\text{Bernoulli's theorem:}\ -v\ dp=dx+\frac{u\ du}{g}+dF. \tag{3a}\dagger$$

---

* Disappearance of the friction term from Bernoulli's theorem is a criterion of mechanical but not necessarily of thermodynamic reversibility, since it does not imply reversibility of the heat effects. The equation as here written assumes the absence of energy effects such as electrical, magnetic and the like. If present, they must be allowed for, as by inclusion in W. An adequate appreciation of the underlying significance of Bernoulli's theorem cannot be had except in the light of the second law.

† This equation is derived by writing the mechanical-energy balance, corrected for transformations:

Disappearance of the terms for friction, external work and velocity yields the criterion of static equilibrium in a fluid.* A fundamentally important and more complex problem is the evaluation of ΣF. Occasionally this can be done by analysis of mechanism, but the usual approach is empirical.

Illustration 2.—A centrifugal exhauster is taking in dry air from a room where the temperature is 40°F. and the barometer is normal. The axis of the horizontal discharge pipe (12 in. i.d.) is 1 ft. above that of the intake pipe (16 in. i.d.). The air in the discharge pipe is at a pressure of 1.2 in. of water above normal barometric pressure. The air then flows through a meter and the rate of flow is found to be 2.5 lb./sec. The power input to the drive shaft of the exhauster is 0.8 hp. The specific heat of air may be taken as 0.24 B.t.u./(lb.) (deg. F.). (*a*) Neglecting heat exchange with the room, calculate the temperature of the air in the discharge pipe. (*b*) Neglecting friction, calculate the work theoretically required.

Solution.—(*a*) The actual work input W is $550(0.8)/(2.5) = 176$ ft.-lb./lb. Section 1 will be taken in the room at the elevation of the axis of the suction pipe; hence x_1 is zero and V_1 is zero. The specific volume of the air in the room is $(^{359}\!\!/_{29})(^{509}\!\!/_{492}) = 12.58$ cu. ft./lb. The specific volume of the air in the discharge pipe, where both the pressure and temperature have changed by small amounts, will be assumed the same as in the room. Hence $V_2 = 2.5(12.58)/(0.785) = 40.2$ ft./sec. Since under these conditions air behaves as a perfect gas, the increase in $E + pv$ equals $(C_p)_{av.}(T_2 - 40)$. Expressing all terms in ft.-lb./lb., Eq. 2 becomes $0.24(778)(T_2 - 40) = 176 - 1 - (40.2)^2/64.3$, whence the temperature rise, $T_2 - 40$, is found to be 0.8°F.

(*b*) Using Eq. 3, assuming v constant and neglecting friction,

$$W' = v\int_1^2 dp + (x_2 - x_1) + \frac{V_2{}^2 - V_1{}^2}{2g} = \frac{(12.58)(1.2)(62.3)}{(12)} + 1 + \frac{(40.2)^2 - (0)^2}{64.3}$$
$$= 78.5 + 1 + 25.1 = 104.6 \text{ ft.-lb./lb.}$$

The item $176 - 104.6 = 71.4$ ft.-lb./lb. represents friction in the fan and piping. The overall efficiency of the fan and short ducts is then $100(104.6/176) = 59.4$ per cent.

Illustration 3.—Referring to Illustration 1, page 44, estimate the friction term.

$$x + pv + \frac{u^2}{2g} + p\,dv = x + dx + pv + d(pv) + \frac{(u + du)^2}{2g} + dF$$

which reduces to the form given above. It may also be obtained by differentiating Eq. 3, noting that the term

$$\int_1^2 p\,dv + p_1 v_1 - p_2 v_2 = -\int_1^2 v\,dp.$$

* It is interesting to compare this with the usual derivation of static relationships, *e.g.*, in determining change of barometer with the height.

Solution.—Calculations will be based on Eq. 3, with all terms expressed in ft.-lb./lb. By the perfect gas law, v equals $1543T/Mp$, where the molecular weight M is 18.02. Calling T constant, integration gives

$$\frac{1543T_{av.}}{M} \ln \frac{p_1}{p_2} - \left(\frac{V_2{}^2 - V_1{}^2}{2g}\right) = \Sigma F.$$

Since the increase in kinetic energy was found to be 3.65 B.t.u., the mechanical equivalent is 778(3.65) or 2840 ft.-lb./lb. Taking $T_{av.}$ as 1055, ΣF is found to be $62,400 - 2840 = 59,560$ ft.-lb./lb., or $59,560/778 = 76.6$ B.t.u./lb.

DEFINITIONS

Fluid Head.—Any kind of pressure exerted by a fluid (gas or liquid) at any point may be expressed in terms of the height of a column of fluid of equal density. The height of such a column is defined as the fluid head. Assume a vertical pipe attached to the apparatus at the point where the fluid head is to be measured. The fluid will obviously rise in this pipe until the weight of the column of fluid exactly counterbalances the pressure above that of the atmosphere.* The height of such a column is called the *fluid head,* and it follows that this head multiplied by fluid density equals pressure per unit area in excess of atmospheric, *i.e.*, a 10-ft. head of water (density of 62.3 lb. per cu. ft.) is equivalent to a pressure (above atmospheric) of 623 lb. per sq. ft. At a given point in a stationary fluid the pressure (or its equivalent, the fluid head) is the same in all directions. In a moving fluid this is no longer true, but the observed pressure varies as described below with the direction of the opening or orifice. Therefore, fluid head cannot be interpreted unless one knows the direction of motion of the fluid relative to the plane of the opening through which the head is transmitted for measurement.

Static Pressure.—In a moving fluid, the intensity of the pressure exerted on a plane parallel to the direction of flow is called the *static pressure*, or simply the *pressure*. The pressure-measuring device (piezometer) is ordinarily attached at the wall of the conduit, where the velocity is normally negligible. The piezometer connection should not be located near bends or other obstructions that cause flow toward the wall, as otherwise additional pressure effects arise owing to the kinetic energy.

* This assumes the fluid to be of constant density and immiscible with air.

Impact Pressure.—When the plane of the opening of a pressure tap is placed at right angles to the direction of fluid flow, the pressure on the opening is called the *impact pressure*.

Subscripts.—The upstream and downstream sections are indicated by subscripts 1 and 2, respectively.

PRESSURE GAUGES AND MANOMETERS

Piezometer Ring.—It is sometimes necessary to measure static pressure at a cross section of a conduit where the pressure is not uniform. Instead of measuring the pressure at a number of points and averaging the values, an equal number (usually four or more) of symmetrically located small piezometer holes *a* are made in the wall, and these are connected by means of a ring, from which the average pressure is obtained (see Fig. 10). The holes are made very small ($\frac{1}{64}$ in.) because it is easier both to make the planes of the openings parallel to the walls of the conduit and to offer substantial resistance to flow from one opening to another. It is preferable to measure the pressure at a straight section sufficiently far from bends or other sources of disturbance so

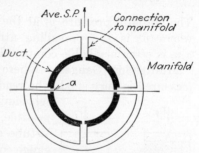

Fig. 10.—Piezometer ring.

that the lines of flow are parallel to the wall, in which case a single pressure tap at the wall is adequate.

Pressure Gauges.—For measuring pressure of both gases and liquids when the pressure is considerably above or below atmospheric pressure, the well known Bourdon-type gauge is used. Such instruments should indicate a zero reading for the prevailing atmospheric pressure.*

Open Manometers.—In the case of *liquids* it is sometimes convenient to measure the pressure by attaching a vertical pipe in which the liquid rises a distance x such that the pressure ρx due to the vertical column just balances the gauge pressure, $p - p_a$, in the apparatus. A U-tube may be partially filled with a second heavier liquid immiscible with the one flowing, and should

* Normal atmospheric pressure corresponds to an absolute pressure of 14.69 lb. per sq. in. or 2115 lb. per sq. ft.

be placed below the point of attachment to the apparatus to avoid gas pockets in the lead.

With *gases*, a vertical U-tube, partially filled with a liquid and with one arm open to the atmosphere, may be attached to the apparatus. To avoid the accumulation of water or other liquid that may condense from the gas, the U-tube is placed above the point of attachment to the apparatus, as indicated in Fig. 18.

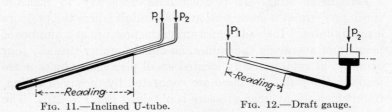

FIG. 11.—Inclined U-tube.   FIG. 12.—Draft gauge.

The absolute pressure p_1 at the point 1 is then $\rho_G x_G + \rho_L x_L + p_a$, where p_a is the prevailing atmospheric pressure. The term $\rho_G x_G$ is often negligible compared to the product $\rho_L x_L$.

Multiplying Gauges.—Where the pressure difference to be measured is very small, the reading may be multiplied by some

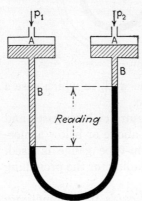

FIG. 13.—Multiplying gauge.

mechanical device to make precision possible. Figure 11 shows an inclined U-tube and Fig. 12 illustrates the draft gauge commonly used in the boiler room, both of which make the readings much greater than the difference in levels produced; the readings may easily be made 10 times the difference in levels.

Figure 13 shows a "multiplying gauge," in which the lower part of the vertical U-tube contains a liquid having a density only slightly greater than the one above it and not miscible with it. The relation between the reading and the actual difference in pressure is best determined by calibration, although it may be calculated from the cross sections S_A and S_B and the densities ρ_H and ρ_L of the two liquids, using the equation

$$p_1 - p_2 = (x - x_0)\left(\rho_H - \rho_L + \frac{\rho_L}{S_A/S_B}\right) \tag{4}$$

where x is the differential reading (vertical distance) and x_0 is the reading when no pressure difference is applied. The pair of liquids chosen for use in a gauge of this type should give a flat meniscus and neither of the liquids should tend to stick to the walls of the tube B. It is not safe to assume that the pair chosen will be absolutely insoluble in each other; hence the two liquids should be thoroughly agitated and the densities of the two resulting saturated solutions should be accurately observed before placing them in the manometer. Although the effect of temperature on density is small, in this case it must not be overlooked as the effect on density difference may be large. For example, if S_A/S_B is 100/1, if the specific gravities of the solutions are 0.8315 and 0.7905, and if the deflection $(x-x_0)$ is 1 ft., the pressure difference (p_1-p_2) would be 3.05 lb./sq. ft., or $3.05/62.3 = 0.0489$ ft. of water; the reading is hence $1/0.0489 = 20.4$ times what would have been obtained had the pressure difference been measured directly in terms of feet of water. Failure to employ the correction for the ratio of cross sections would have given a computed pressure difference 16.4 per cent lower than the true value.

MEASURING DEVICES BASED ON VELOCITY CHANGE

Granting horizontal flow of a fluid in the absence of both external work effects and friction, but involving a definite change in velocity, Bernoulli's theorem reduces to $-\int_1^2 v\, dp = (u_2^2 - u_1^2)/2g$. If conditions are such that change in fluid density is negligible or if use of an average value is allowable, this becomes $v(p_1-p_2) = (u_2^2 - u_1^2)/2g$, or $H = \Delta(u^2/2g)$, where H is the difference in the fluid head corresponding to $v(p_1-p_2)$. Finally, if conditions can be chosen so that a stream of velocity u is brought substantially to rest, or so that the velocity u is imparted to a stream of negligible velocity, the expression for the head equivalent to the velocity u simplifies to $v(p_1-p_2) = \pm u^2/2g$. The idea underlying this simple relation is the basis of a series of important devices for measuring the rate of fluid flow, including the Pitot tube, Venturi meter, various types of orifices and nozzles, weirs, etc.

Since by proper choice of conditions it is allowable to use this simple equation unmodified, at least as a good and often excellent approximation, it offers a valuable method of orientation in engineering work. However, one frequently finds it desirable to use measuring instruments under conditions deviating so widely from those assumed that major corrections are needed. Furthermore, for the highest accuracy it is almost always necessary to apply such corrections, though they may be small; hence methods of correlating the corrections are important. Where practicable, it is best to determine the corrections by careful experimental calibration of the specific instrument. The more important factors causing deviations for which allowance must be made are variations in velocity and direction of motion at different points of the sections of flow, particularly at the section of high velocity; uncertainty as to the actual area of the orthogonal cross sections of flow; friction against the walls and within the fluid, whether due to turbulence or to streamline motion; variations in density; and uncertainty as to the proper points between which to measure pressure differences.

PITOT TUBE

Consider a stream of fluid flowing as indicated by the arrows of Fig. 14. Insert into the stream a small rod B, held stationary by mechanical support at its right-hand end. Consider that tube

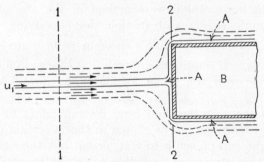

Fig. 14.—Derivation of relation: $p_2 - p_1 = \rho u_1^2/2g$.

of flow AA, bounded by the full lines shown, which supplies the fluid in the immediate neighborhood of the end of B. The cross section of AA enlarges greatly as it approaches B, so that its velocity falls from its initial value u_1 to a negligible amount. Furthermore, friction between it and its neighboring tubes of flow, shown by dotted streamlines, is slight because all are traveling at substantially the same velocity. Applying Bernoulli's theorem to the tube AA, $(p_1-p_2)/\rho=0-(u_1^2/2g)$ or $p_2-p_1=\rho u_1^2/2g$. This increase in pressure p_2-p_1 can be measured by replacing the rod B by a hollow tube and measuring the excess pressure necessary to prevent flow of fluid through it. The instrument using this principle is the *Pitot tube* or impact tube.

The cross section of the hollow tube B should be kept as small as practicable to reduce disturbance of the streamlines and thus minimize interfilamental friction. The face of B should be exactly normal to the direction of flow, as otherwise the velocity past its face will not be negligible. If the direction of flow past B is reversed, it is clear that a corresponding deficiency of pressure in the tube should develop. In this event, however, the only way in which velocity in the tube of flow AA beyond B can be generated is by the dragging forward of that tube by friction against its neighbors. Since this friction inevitably involves dissipation of mechanical energy, it is not surprising to find that the pressure deficiency resulting from reversal of direction of flow is found to be considerably less than

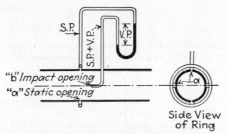

Side View of Ring

Fig. 15.—Impact tube and piezometer ring.

that calculated by reversing the sign of the above equation. The static pressure at the same elevation as the impact opening is obtained at the wall of the conduit, using either a simple pressure tap ground flush with the inside wall or one or more pairs of such taps connected by a piezometer ring, the two taps in each pair being attached to the pipe in diametrically opposite positions (Fig. 15).

To facilitate the exploration of velocity in a conduit, the impact and static openings are often combined in a single instrument known as a Pitot tube. One form of Pitot tube consists of two concentric tubes containing a 90-deg. bend as shown in Fig. 16, the impact opening b being at the open end of the inner tube, and one or more static openings

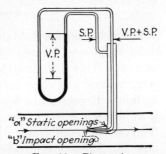

Fig. 16.—Pitot tube.

a in the outer tube. The difficulty with this arrangement lies in the fact that the very insertion of the Pitot tube itself deflects the fluid stream, thus obviously interfering with the accurate determination of static pressure.   Figure 16 illustrates an attempt to avoid this evil by the use of four static openings, with the idea that if the pressure is too high on one of them it will be too low on some of the others and thus a true average static pressure will be obtained.   Certain manufacturers offer Pitot tubes in which this counterbalancing of errors on the static orifices is not satisfactorily accomplished, but in such cases the makers usually furnish a coefficient for their particular type of instrument; the calibration of such instruments is essential.

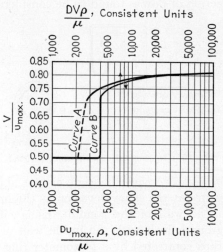

Fig. 17.—Ratio of average to maximum velocity in circular pipes.   (*From Stanton and Pannell.*[6])

The velocity of a fluid flowing in any conduit always varies at different points in a section taken at right angles to the direction of flow.   This variation is extremely erratic in or near bends, tees, valves and any point of contraction or enlargement of section.   Experiments have shown that this variable behavior is minimized if the observations are taken at a section not less than 50 diameters from any point of disturbance, so that normal flow conditions are closely approached.   For such normal flow in smooth pipes, the ratio of the average velocity over the entire cross section to that at the axis $V/u_{max.}$ is found experimentally to depend only on the numerical value of a dimensionless ratio $Du_{max.}\rho/\mu$.   Curve B of Fig. 17[6] is useful for predicting the average velocity $V(=q/S)$ based on measurement of $u_{max.}$ by means of a Pitot tube located at the *axis* of the pipe.* Curve A, based on the same data, is used to predict $u_{max.}$ when $DV \rho/\mu$ is known.

Pitot tubes are used for exploration purposes to measure the flow in apparatus already built, as the instrument can be inserted through a small hole in the conduit, which can later be closed. In certain cases, for example, where a fan is placed in the middle of a short air duct drawing from and delivering into an open space, the gas flow is so erratic that it is necessary to determine the velocity at many points in a cross section, and for this purpose the instrument is of great value.

The disadvantage of the Pitot tube when used for gases is the fact that, owing to the low gas density, the readings at moderate velocities are very small and liable to error. Thus, the differential reading where air at 70°F. and atmospheric pressure is flowing at a velocity of 10 ft. per sec. is only 0.0224 in. of water, and when flowing at 30 ft. per sec. is 0.202 in. of water. Where such low readings are encountered, the differential pressures are best measured by an inclined gauge or by a multiplying gauge. When water flows at these same velocities, owing to its greater density, the readings are $62.3/0.075 = 832$ times the above. There is no appreciable power loss due to the presence of a Pitot tube in a fluid stream.

Illustration 4 (Gas).—A commercial Pitot tube similar to the one shown in Fig. 16 is inserted at the center line of a horizontal 12-in. i.d. galvanized iron pipe carrying dry air at 70°F. at a static pressure of 2 in. of water above atmospheric pressure, and the horizontal deflection on a U-tube (inclined 10 in. horizontal to 1 in. vertical and connected to the impact and static openings) shows 2 in. of water. The Pitot tube is at a distance of 50 pipe diameters (50 ft.) from any obstruction in the pipe. Calculate (*a*) the actual velocity of air as ft. per sec. at the point where the reading is taken, (*b*) the average velocity as ft./sec. at this cross section, (*c*) the rate of flow as cu. ft./min., and (*d*) as lb./hr. The barometer is 29.75 in. of mercury.

Solution.—The density of the gas at the point of reading is

$$\rho = \frac{(29)(492)[29.75 + (2/13.6)]}{(359)(530)(29.9)} = 0.0750 \text{ lb./cu. ft.}$$

The horizontal deflection on the inclined U-tube is 2 in., but owing to the 10-to-1 inclination the actual difference in levels is only 0.2 in. of water.

* At values of $Du_{max.}\rho/\mu$ below 4200 or of $DV \rho/\mu$ below 2100, $V/u_{max.}$ is constant at $\frac{1}{2}$.

The velocity pressure is then $(0.2/12)(62.3-0.075)$ or 1.04 lb./sq. ft. Hence

$$u_{max.} = \sqrt{2gH} = \sqrt{(64.3)\left(\frac{1.04}{0.075}\right)} = 29.9 \text{ ft./sec.}$$

at the point where the reading was taken, namely, the center line of the pipe.

From Fig. 225, it is seen that the absolute viscosity of air at 21°C. is 0.018 centipoises, which must be multiplied by 0.000672 to convert it into lb./(sec.) (ft.). The value of $Du_{max.}\rho/\mu$ for this case is then (1) (29.9) $(0.075)/(0.000672 \times 0.018) = 185,000$, and from Fig. 17, $V = 0.815u_{max.}$.

Hence $V = (0.815)(29.9) = 24.4$ ft./sec.

Since the cross-sectional area is $\pi/4$ or 0.785 sq. ft., the rate of flow is $(24.4)(60)(0.785) = 1150$ cu. ft./min., or $(1150)(60)(0.075) = 5200$ lb./hr

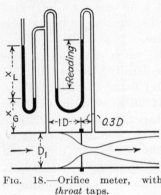

Fig. 18.—Orifice meter, with *throat* taps.

STEADY FLOW OF FLUIDS THROUGH ORIFICES AND NOZZLES

One of the common methods of determining the rate of flow of gases, vapors and liquids is to measure the pressure drop caused by the insertion of a restricted opening into the line. When the fluid passes through the restriction, there is necessarily an increase in the velocity, and hence, in kinetic energy. With this increase of the kinetic energy of the fluid in passing from the entrance section of the meter to the restriction, a decrease in static pressure occurs. Combining the mechanical-energy balance with the material balance and the equation of state of the fluid makes it possible to determine the rate of flow in terms of the measured pressure drop and properties of the fluid flowing.

The construction of an orifice meter is shown in Fig. 18. Two pressure taps are inserted in the pipe, one on the upstream side of the orifice plate, the other on the downstream side. The square-edged orifice (Fig. 19A) is merely a very short cylindrical passage bored in a thin metal plate. Where the pressure drop is to be high, a thick plate, beveled on the downstream side, may be used. In a properly constructed square-edged orifice, the walls of the aperture meet the upstream face of the orifice plate at right angles and the surfaces are carefully smoothed to remove burrs and other irregularities. Figure

19*C* shows a "rounded-edge orifice." This type of orifice is more difficult to construct than the square-edged; therefore it is not so commonly used. Since the *square-edged* orifice is easily constructed and the meter as a whole is simple and comparatively inexpensive, its use is widespread.

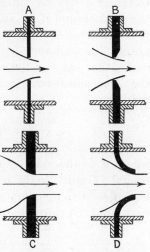

As shown in Fig. 20, the fluid begins to converge at some distance upstream from the orifice and continues to converge for some distance downstream from the orifice. Since the cross section of the stream is continuously varying from the section where convergence begins to the section on the downstream side of the orifice where the fluid again completely fills the pipe, the velocity also varies continuously. Hence the pressure readings for a given rate of flow will depend on the position of the pressure taps relative to the orifice plate. Since the

FIG. 19.—*A*, sharp-edged orifice in thin plate; *B*, sharp-edged orifice in thick plate; *C*, rounded orifice in thick plate; *D*, nozzle.

mechanical-energy balance contains the term $\int v\,dp$, the functional relation between p and v must be known. For simplicity the case of liquids will be first considered, where the specific volume is substantially constant.

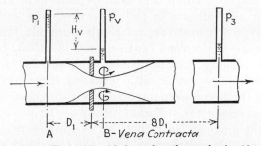

FIG. 20.—Flow of liquid through a sharp-edged orifice.

Liquids.—Consider the orifice of Fig. 20 and focus attention on sections *A* and *B*, the first upstream a distance above the orifice sufficient so that the streamlines of the flowing fluid are parallel to the axis, and the second downstream at the *vena contracta* where the streamlines have again become parallel. Consider a specific differential filament of flow separated from the fluid around it by an imaginary surface across which no net flow occurs. Assume furthermore that friction of the fluid against the wall and of the various filaments of the fluid against each other can for the moment be neglected. One can apply the mechanical-energy balance to this individual filament, writing

$$-\int_1^v v \, dp = v(p_1 - p_v) = \frac{u_v^2}{2g} - \frac{u_1^2}{2g} \tag{5}$$

where u_v is the velocity of the small filament at the vena contracta. Grant for the moment that the *upstream velocity u_1 is negligible* in comparison with the downstream velocity u_v. The equation then simplifies to the expression

$$v(p_1 - p_v) = H_v = \frac{u_v^2}{2g}$$

wherein the difference in head $v(p_1 - p_v)$ or H_v is the difference in liquid levels in the manometers. Inspection of this relation shows that the downstream velocity u_v of the filament for any specific setup and liquid density is determined solely by the upstream and downstream pressures. Keeping in mind the fact that at neither of the sections in question can there be a radial pressure gradient (since otherwise there would be radial flow), it follows that the initial and final pressures, p_1 and p_v, are identical for all filaments in the respective cross sections, and consequently, where upstream velocity is negligible, the velocities of all filaments at the vena contracta are identical, *i.e.*, at this section the velocity distribution is *uniform*. In fact, a substantially frictionless orifice with relatively large pressure drop offers one of the best known methods of securing a stream of flow in which the velocity is uniform. Study of the preceding paragraph should make it clear that, for conditions of frictionless flow and negligible upstream velocity, the conclusion of uniform downstream velocity is valid irrespective of velocity distribution upstream and therefore irrespective of the type of upstream flow, whether streamline or turbulent. The conclusion does, however, depend on the assumption of negligible friction between the sections. Inspection of Fig. 20 makes it clear that friction of the fluid against the walls can be appreciable only in the immediate neighborhood of the sharp edge of the orifice, since at other points the velocity of fluid past the wall is low. Since the area of high friction is so restricted, the magnitude of its effect is correspondingly reduced. On the other hand, it is not improbable that the outer filaments of the flowing stream are retarded significantly relative to the inner ones, although the percentage effect may be negligible. If the liquid is in streamline flow throughout, interfilamental friction may become serious. However, its effect tends to be reduced by the fact that adjacent filaments are flowing at widely different velocities only in the neighborhood of the *upstream* section, where the corresponding frictional effect is low because of the low velocities. At the downstream section they all tend to flow at identical velocities, correspondingly reducing the interfilamental friction at the point where it would otherwise be high.

As the cross section of the stream of flowing fluid enlarges beyond the vena contracta, the friction tends to be low until the enlarged stream again fully fills the downstream section of the pipe. Consequently even up to this point the velocity distribution tends to remain substantially uniform. Beyond this point, however, friction at the pipe wall retards the filament of flow in its neighborhood and develops a velocity distribution curve that will be characteristic of the type of flow there existing.

In order to work in terms of *average* velocity V, rather than local velocity u, the energy balance for the filament of differential cross section should be integrated over the cross section of flow. Since the velocity u is uniform at the vena contracta, $u_v^2/2g$ may be replaced by $V_v^2/2g$. However, since the upstream velocity is not uniform, owing to friction set up at the walls of the pipe upstream of section 1, $u_1^2/2g$ is replaced by $V_1^2/2g\alpha_1$, where α_1 is a dimensionless factor allowing for the nature of the velocity gradient at section 1.* The mechanical-energy balance, Eq. 3, then becomes

$$-\int_1^v v\,dp = v(p_1 - p_v) = H_v = \frac{V_v^2}{2g} - \frac{V_1^2}{2g\alpha_1} \qquad (5a)$$

* For streamline flow the kinetic energy is V^2/g, not $V^2/2g$; hence α_1 equals one-half; for turbulent flow, where the velocity is more nearly uniform, the kinetic energy approaches $V^2/2g$ and α_1 approaches unity.

wherein the term $v(p_1 - p_v)$, the decrease in fluid head, is represented by H_v. By a material balance $V_1 = V_v S_v / S_1$, and Eq. 5a becomes

$$V_v = \frac{\sqrt{2gH_v}}{\sqrt{1 - (S_v^2/S_1^2 \alpha_1)}}.$$ (5b)

In order to work in terms of the average velocity V_0 through the orifice rather than with V_v, one substitutes $V_0 = V_v S_v / S_0$, giving

$$V_0 = \frac{q}{S_0} = \frac{S_v \sqrt{2gH_v}}{S_0 \sqrt{1 - (S_v^2/S_1^2/\alpha_1)}}$$ (5c)

where q is the volumetric rate of flow through the orifice having cross section S_0. Equation 5c is modified in use to the form*

$$V_0 = \frac{q}{S_0} = \frac{c\sqrt{2gH_v}}{\sqrt{1 - (S_0^2/S_1^2)}}.$$ (6)

The so-called coefficient of discharge, c, is seen to depend upon α_1 and the ratio of the cross section of the vena jet to that of the orifice and to that of the pipe. Since the numerical value of those factors depends on the type of fluid flow, which in turn depends upon a dimensionless ratio known as a *Reynolds number*,† experimentally measured values of c are plotted against a Reynolds number $D_0 V_0 \rho / \mu$ for each of a number of values of the ratio of diameters of orifice and pipe.‡ The data for sharp-edged orifices with *throat connections* (where the upstream pressure tap is one pipe diameter from the upstream side of the orifice plate and the downstream tap is one-third of one pipe diameter from the downstream side) are satisfactorily repre-

---

* It will be noted that $c = \dfrac{S_v}{S_0} \dfrac{\sqrt{1 - \dfrac{S_0^2}{S_1^2}}}{\sqrt{1 - \dfrac{S_v^2}{S_1^2 \alpha_1}}}.$ Where the diameter of the up-

stream chamber is at least five times that of the orifice, c reduces to S_v/S_0; since the latter is the ratio of the cross section of the vena jet to that of the orifice, this ratio is called the *coefficient of contraction*, c_c.

† The significance of this factor is discussed in detail on pages 82 to 84.

‡ From dimensional considerations, since $c = \phi(D_0/D_1, \ D_0 V_0 \rho / \mu)$, it is immaterial whether the values of c for each diameter ratio are plotted vs. $D_0 V_0 \rho / \mu = (D_1 V_1 \rho / \mu)(D_1/D_0)$ or vs. $D_1 V_1 \rho / \mu$.

sented by the curves shown in Fig. 21. For each diameter ratio, at small Reynolds numbers the coefficient of discharge is very small, but as Re_0 increases the curve goes through a maximum, finally becoming asymptotic to c equals approximately 0.61 at orifice-Reynolds numbers above 30,000. Hence, when

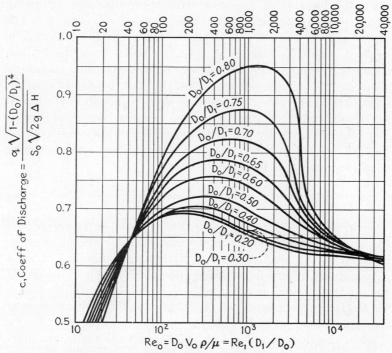

FIG. 21.—Coefficients for sharp-edged orifices with throat taps. (*From Tuve and Sprenkle.*[1])

$D_0 V_0 \rho/\mu$ is above 30,000, the results with throat taps may be predicted from the approximate relation for sharp-edged orifices

$$V_0 = \frac{q}{S_0} = \frac{0.61\sqrt{2gH_v}}{\sqrt{1 - \dfrac{S_0^2}{S_1^2}}}, \tag{6a}$$

alternatively written as

$$\sqrt{V_0^2 - V_1^2} = 0.61\sqrt{2gH_v}. \tag{6b}$$

Since the data from various sources may show discrepancies of several per cent in the coefficients of discharge, for accurate work an orifice should be calibrated, although the values given in the curves are satisfactory as first approximations.

In a given experiment if the pressure is measured at a number of points along the downstream chamber, inspection of Fig. 20 makes it clear that the pressure p_2 so measured will depend upon the location of the downstream pressure tap. Starting on the downstream side of the plate, p_2 decreases slightly as the tap is moved downstream until the vena contracta section is reached, where p_2 reaches a minimum value since the jet has attained its minimum cross section and corresponding maximum velocity and kinetic energy. As the tap is moved farther downstream, the pressure gradually rises, although never reaching equality with the initial upstream pressure because of friction loss caused mainly by the agitation of the downstream pool by the jet. Consequently, if one arbitrarily uses the following equation, analogous to Eq. 6,

$$q = \frac{c_1 S_0 \sqrt{2g(p_1 - p_2)v}}{\sqrt{1 - (D_0/D_1)^4}} = \frac{c_1 S_0 \sqrt{2gH_2}}{\sqrt{1 - (D_0/D_1)^4}} \tag{6c}$$

wherein p_2 has replaced p_v and c_1 has replaced c, it is clear that the numerical value of c_1 will be larger than c except when p_v is taken at the vena contracta. Hence the numerical value of c_1, as defined by Eq. 6c, depends upon the location of the downstream tap, as well as upon both D_0/D_1 and Re_0. Curves of c_1 vs. Re_0 for various values of D_0/D_1 are available for the several arrangements of pressure taps.*

Since at values of Re_0 above 30,000 the values of c_1 are independent of Re_0, the values of c_1, for various values of D_0/D_1, may be plotted vs. the location of the downstream tap. For convenience the data are shown plotted in Fig. 22[(2)] in terms of a new coefficient of discharge c', defined by the relation

$$V_0 = \frac{q}{S_0} = c' \sqrt{2gH_2} \tag{6d}$$

wherein the difference in head H_2 represents the term $v(p_1 - p_2)$.†

* The ordinates of Fig. 21, within an error of 1.5 per cent, may be used as both c and c_1 for sharp-edged orifices, regardless of whether *throat taps* (Fig 20) or *flange taps* are used.

† Upon comparing Eqs. 6c and 6d it is found that

$$c' = \frac{c}{\sqrt{1 - (D_0^4/D_1^4)}}.$$

For the small values of the ratio D_0/D_1, it is seen that the coefficient c' varies but little with the location of the downstream tap, whereas at the high values of D_0/D_1 the location of the tap has a substantial effect on c'. The point of maximum contraction, *i.e.*, the vena contracta, varies from 0.3 to 0.7 pipe diameters downstream from the plate as D_0/D_1 varies from 0.84 to 0.22.

Equations 6*c* and 6*d* are the two common forms of the orifice equation.

The data of Fig. 21 are convenient where it is desired to predict the pressure differential for a fixed rate of flow through an existing orifice meter, but their use leads to trial-and-error calculation when it is desired to calculate the rate of flow corresponding to an observed pressure differential. This trial-and-error work may be avoided by rearranging the dimensionless ratios so that V_0 will appear only in one coordinate, *i.e.*, one can plot

$$\frac{D_0 V_0 \rho}{\mu} = \frac{4 q \rho}{\pi \mu D_0}$$

vs.

$$\left(\frac{D_0 \rho}{\mu}\right) \sqrt{\frac{2gH}{[1 - (D_0{}^4/D_1{}^4)]}} = \frac{Re_0}{c}$$

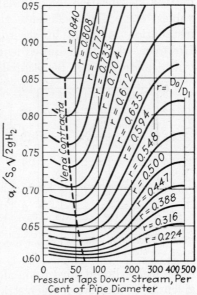

FIG. 22.—Effect of location of downstream tap on $c' = q/S_0\sqrt{2gH_2}$ for sharp-edged orifices where Re_0 exceeds 30,000. (*From Spitzglass.*[2])

Owing to the discharge of the rapidly moving jet into the slower moving pool of fluid in the downstream chamber, a considerable portion of the kinetic energy of the jet is converted by impact and internal friction into internal energy and hence lost as mechanical energy, the remainder appearing as mechanical energy in the moving stream at the downstream section. This permanent loss of mechanical energy, compared to the pressure drop across the orifice itself, decreases as the diameter of the orifice approaches that of the pipe, as shown in Fig. 23.* When D_0/D_1 is small, the lost energy may become so important that it is more economical to employ another type of apparatus

* p_1 is measured one pipe diameter upstream, p_2 at three-tenths of one pipe diameter downstream and p_3 at eight pipe diameters downstream.

(Venturi meter), which, although it has a higher initial cost than the orifice, gives only approximately one-eighth the permanent loss for equal readings of the instruments.

The proper location of orifices in lines has been studied extensively by the A.S.M.E. Committee on Fluid Meters, which has drafted specification for installations in the vicinity of fittings, valves, etc. The coefficients given here are valid only if the installation is made in accordance with such specifications. However, when the required length of straight pipe ahead of an orifice meter cannot be secured, the insertion of straightening vanes in the pipe at least six pipe diameters above the orifice will satisfactorily correct the flow. A bundle of small tubes fastened in the pipe forms a convenient straightening-vane installation.

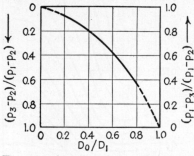

FIG. 23.—Overall pressure losses across sharp-edged orifices.

Orifice plates are sometimes constructed with off-center orifices. For example, the orifice opening may be tangent to the bottom of the pipe in cases where liquid must drain along a gas line. The coefficients given here, however, are restricted to orifices centered in the pipe.

An ingenious installation of flange-tap orifices has been developed which permits removing the orifice plate and replacing it with another without shutting down the gas line. This equipment is particularly useful for permanent orifices metering large flows where corrosion of the plate or a change in the magnitude of flow may require changing of the orifice plate.

The usual orifice coefficients are not applicable in cases where pulsations of some magnitude are encountered, as from a reciprocating compressor near the orifice. Problems of this type can usually be solved only by eliminating the pulsation or calibrating the orifice for the specific condition. Damping the pulsation in the leads to the metering device is of no benefit, and may actually increase the error of the reading.

Well-rounded orifices (Fig. 19C) and flow nozzles (Fig. 19D) should be calibrated for accurate work; for approximate calculations the curve for the Venturi meter (Fig. 25) may be used in estimating c in Eq. 6.

Gases, Small Per Cent Pressure Drops.—The pressure loss caused by an orifice in a permanent meter installation usually represents a significant operating expense for power, and large ratios of D_0/D_1 are therefore favored. When the pressure drop is only a few per cent of the upstream pressure, the usual hydraulic equations (6c) and (6d) may be used with v replaced by v_{av}. based on the arithmetic-mean pressure.

Illustration 5.—Oil is flowing through a standard $1\frac{1}{2}$-in. steel pipe in which is inserted a 1.00-in. square-edged orifice with taps, respectively, one pipe diameter upstream and 0.3 diameter downstream of the orifice plate. Pressure differential across the orifice is indicated by two parallel vertical open tubes into which the oil rises from the two pressure taps. The oil is at 100°F.; its specific gravity is 0.87 and its viscosity 20.6 centipoises.

Calculate the reading on the gauge described, when oil is flowing at a rate of 400 gal./hr.

Solution.—The velocity in the orifice, $V_0 = (400)(144)(4)/(7.48)(3600)(\pi)$ $=2.72$ ft./sec.; $D_0V_0\rho/\mu = (\frac{1}{12})(2.72)(0.87\times62.3)/(0.000672\times20.6)=890$; $D_0/D_1=1.00/1.61=0.62$; from Fig. 21, $c=0.76$. By Eq. 6,

$$H_v=\frac{V_0{}^2}{2gc^2}\left[1-\left(\frac{D_0}{D_1}\right)^4\right]=\frac{(2.72)^2}{64.3(0.76)^2}(1-0.62^4)=0.170 \text{ ft.}$$

Illustration 6.—Natural gas consisting of practically pure methane flows through a long straight standard 10-in. steel pipe in which is inserted a square-edged orifice 2.50 in. in diameter, with pressure taps, each 5.0 in. from the orifice plate. Just above the orifice the gas is at 80°F. and 5.0 lb./sq. in. gauge. A differential manometer inclined at an angle of 15 deg. with the horizontal, attached across the orifice, reads 6.18 in. of water. What is the weight rate of flow of gas through this line?

Solution.—The ratio of orifice to pipe diameter is $2.50/10.19=0.245$. Assuming the Reynolds number in the orifice to be over 30,000, the coefficient c' is 0.61, from Fig. 22. The average pressure of the gas in the orifice is

$$p_{av.} = 19.7-\frac{6.18\times62.3 \sin 15°}{2\times12\times144}=19.67 \text{ lb./sq. in. abs.}$$

and the average density of the gas in the orifice is therefore

$$\rho = \frac{16}{359}\times\frac{19.67}{14.7}\times\frac{492}{540}=0.0540 \text{ lb./cu. ft.}$$

$$H_2=\frac{6.18 \sin 15°}{12}\times\frac{62.3}{0.0540}=153.7 \text{ ft.}$$

Then, by Eq. 6d

$$V_0=0.61\sqrt{64.3\times153.7}=60.7 \text{ ft./sec.}$$

Using this result, the Reynolds number in the orifice is

$$Re_0 = \frac{D_0 V_0 \rho}{\mu} = \frac{2.50 \times 60.7 \times 0.0540}{12 \times 0.011 \times 0.000672} = 92{,}800,$$

whence determination of c' from Fig. 22 was permissible.

The weight rate of flow is

$$W = 60.7 \times \frac{\pi}{4} \times \frac{2.50^2}{144} \times 0.0540 \times 3600 = 403 \text{ lb./hr.}$$

For somewhat higher per cent pressure drops, it is worth while to allow for the variation in the specific volumes, and the material balances become $V_v S_v/v_v = V_0 S_0/v_0$ and $V_1 S_1/v_1 = w$, where w represents the mass rate of flow. These relations, combined with Eq. 5a, give

$$w = \frac{S_v}{v_0} \sqrt{\frac{2g(p_1 - p_v)v_{\text{av.}}}{\dfrac{v_1^2}{v_2^2} + \dfrac{v_1^2 S_v^2/S_1^2}{v_0^2 \alpha_1}}}.$$

Since this equation is so unwieldy, and since it is a convenience to be able to employ the coefficients of discharge of Fig. 21, the equation is written in a form analogous to Eq. 6c.

$$w = c_1 Y S_0 \sqrt{\frac{2g(p_1 - p_2)}{[1 - (D_0/D_1)^4]v_1}} \tag{7}$$

The dimensionless term Y is found[4] by calibration to be a function of p_1, p_2, D_0/D_1 and of k, where k^* is the ratio of specific heat at constant pressure to that at constant volume:

$$Y = 1 - \left(\frac{p_1 - p_2}{p_1 k}\right)\left[0.41 + 0.35\left(\frac{D_0}{D_1}\right)^4\right]. \tag{7a}$$

For sharp-edged orifices with either throat or flange taps, this equation holds for D_0/D_1 ranging from 0.2 to 0.75. For small pressure drops the factor Y approaches unity and Eq. 7 reduces to Eq. 6c for incompressible fluids. Equation 7 is accurate within 1 per cent for p_2/p_1 not less than 0.8, and does not involve serious error when p_2/p_1 approaches the critical ratio (see page 67).

Gases, Large Per Cent Pressure Drops, Rounded Orifices and Nozzles.— When a perfect gas expands under conditions where there is no heat interchange between the gas and its surroundings, the expansion is said to be "adiabatic." The pressure-volume relations for a *frictionless* adiabatic change are expressed by $p_1(v_1)^k = p_2(v_2)^k$, where k is the ratio of the specific heat of the gas at constant pressure to that at constant volume. Employing Eq. 5a, integration gives

$$\frac{V_t^2}{2g} - \frac{V_1^2}{2g\alpha_1} = \frac{(p_1 v_1)(k)}{k - 1}\left[1 - \left(\frac{p_t}{p_1}\right)^{\frac{(k-1)}{k}}\right]$$

* Values of k are given in Table IV, p. 694.

where subscript t refers to the throat, or smallest section of the nozzle. With a large orifice chamber $(D_1/D_0 = 5/1)$ the square of the velocity in the chamber can be neglected when compared to the square of the velocity in the orifice. Making this simplification, introducing a coefficient of discharge as before and solving for the mass flow rate w, remembering that $V_t = V_1(p_1/p_t),^{\frac{1}{k}}$ one obtains:

$$w = \frac{q_t}{v_t} = c'' S_t \sqrt{\frac{2gkp_1}{(k-1)(v_1)}\left[\left(\frac{p_t}{p_1}\right)^{\frac{2}{k}} - \left(\frac{p_t}{p_1}\right)^{\frac{(1+k)}{k}}\right]}. \tag{8}$$

Equation 8 for adiabatic flow contains the function

$$\left(\frac{p_t}{p_1}\right)^{\frac{2}{k}} - \left(\frac{p_t}{p_1}\right)^{\frac{(1+k)}{k}}. \tag{8a}$$

Where there is no flow through the orifice, $p_t/p_1 = 1$, and, as the ratio of p_t/p_1 decreases from unity, p_1 remaining constant, the quantity (8a) and consequently the flow given by Eq. 8 increase from zero, reaching a maximum when

$$\left(\frac{p_t}{p_1}\right)_{\text{crit.}} = \left(\frac{2}{1+k}\right)^{\frac{k}{(k-1)}}. \tag{8b}$$

After p_t/p_1 falls below the "critical" value given by Eq. 8b, which calls for maximum flow, the flow through a given nozzle might be expected to decrease according to Eq. 8. Experiments have shown that the flow does correspond to Eq. 8 above and at the critical-pressure ratio, but that it remains constant for further decrease in the pressure ratio. This apparent discrepancy is explained as follows: Until the critical throat pressure is reached, the throat and downstream pressures are nearly the same, but as the downstream pressure is further decreased the throat pressure (and velocity also)* remains constant; since the throat pressure is the controlling factor, the rate of flow remains unchanged. Therefore, the quantity (8a) has a constant value when the pressure ratio of p_t/p_1 is equal to or less than the critical value given by Eq. 8b, and under such conditions Eq. 8, which was predicated on a large orifice chamber, reduces to

$$w_{\text{max.}} = c'' S_t p_1 \sqrt{\frac{gkM}{1543T_1}\left(\frac{1+k}{2}\right)^{\left(\frac{1+k}{1-k}\right)}}. \tag{8c}$$

Since k for *air* is 1.405, Eq. 8c becomes

$$w_{\text{max.}} = \frac{0.533c'' S_0 p_1}{\sqrt{T_1}} = \text{lb. air/sec.} \tag{8d}$$

* At the critical-pressure ratio the linear velocity in the throat attains the velocity of sound and hence the upstream chamber is screened from the pressure in the downstream chamber.

when the downstream pressure is not greater than 0.53 times the initial pressure above the orifice and when, as before, the area of the orifice chamber is at least 25 times that of the orifice. This special case is known as *Fliegner's equation.* For steam, k increases with T in such a way that they approximately offset each other in Eq. 8c, which reduces to the well-known *Napier equation* for saturated *steam*, when the absolute back pressure is less than 55 per cent of the initial absolute pressure:

$$w_{max.} = \frac{c''S_0 p_1}{70} \qquad (8e)$$

Inasmuch as these simple equations (8c), (8d) and (8e) hold whenever the ratio p_t/p_1 is sufficiently low and the orifice chamber is sufficiently large compared to the orifice, it is highly desirable to secure these conditions where the percentage drop in pressure is large. For well-rounded orifices and flow nozzles the values of c'' may be estimated from Fig. 25, but for accurate work the orifice in question should be calibrated.* When it is not feasible to make p_t/p_1 fall below the critical value, the more complicated Eq. 8 applies.

If the pressure drop is not more than 20 per cent of the initial pressure, Eqs. 7 and 7a apply.

Flowmeters.—The term *flowmeter* is sometimes used to designate any restricted opening or tube through which the rate of flow has been determined by calibration. For example, a 2-in. pipe may be bushed down to ½ in. and then enlarged to 2 in.; the pressure drop through this opening is a measure of the rate of flow, but this relation should be determined by calibration.

For laboratory work, where the rate of flow of gas is small, capillary tubes of 1 to 12 in. length are used to produce the pressure drop, indicated on a U-tube connected by tees to chambers at both ends of the capillary. Usually they are calibrated over the desired range, as by measuring the volume of water displaced (gasometer method). Flowmeters for liquids similar to those described for gases are cheaply made both for laboratory and for plant use.

VENTURI METERS

The Venturi meter operates on the same principle as the orifice, and indicates the decrease in static pressure due to an increase in the velocity of a fluid stream caused by a known reduction in the cross section of the path. The striking difference in the form of the standard orifice (Fig. 18) and Venturi meter (Fig. 24) lies in the fact that the changes in cross section are sudden in

---

* The coefficient of discharge may exceed unity owing to the occurrence of supersaturation.

the former and gradual in the latter.   Since the cross section of the pipe is *gradually* reduced to that at the throat, the convergence of the streamlines is not nearly so marked in the Venturi meter as in the square-edged orifice, and hence c is larger for the former than for the latter.   In the square-edged orifice, the section is suddenly enlarged from that of the orifice to that of the downstream chamber or pipe, with the result that the greatest proportion of the velocity head (created in the orifice at the expense of the static pressure in the upstream chamber) is not reconverted to static pressure in the downstream chamber, but is lost by impact and internal friction.   The Venturi meter possesses a great advantage over the standard orifice in that the

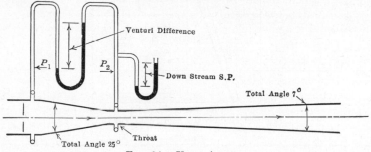

FIG. 24.—Venturi meter.

permanent reduction in the static pressure is small, because the velocity head is largely reconverted to static pressure by the gradual enlargement of the section to its original size.

The construction of the Venturi meter is shown in Fig. 24. The throat diameter is usually from one-half to one-quarter the upstream diameter, and the throat length should not exceed one throat diameter.   The total angle of divergence of the two tapered sides should not exceed 25 deg. on the upstream side or 7 deg. on the downstream side.   In order to minimize the friction loss and to insure a high coefficient of discharge, the throat should be lined with bronze and accurately bored to size and finished. Under these conditions the permanent loss in static pressure is only one-tenth to one-eighth of the Venturi reading.   Pressure taps are located as indicated in Fig. 24 and are connected to piezometer rings, care being taken that the connections to the static openings do not project into the sections; otherwise serious errors in the readings will result.   Since it is necessary to make the total angle of divergence small in order to obtain a value of c near unity in the turbulent region, the length of the Venturi meter is great relative to the diameter of the line in which it is inserted. The Venturi meter is used in the illuminating-gas industry and elsewhere with great success.

The equations for Venturi meters are the same as those for orifices, and in the usual range of operation ($D_1 V_1 \rho_1 / \mu_1$ above 10,000) the coefficients of discharge are higher than for sharp-edged orifices, since, when the Venturi meter is properly con-

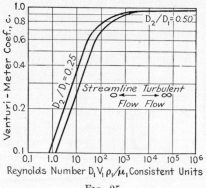

FIG. 25.

structed and operated, the fluid substantially fills the throat of the meter. The coefficients of discharge of Fig. 25[3] were determined for liquids and are defined by Eq. 6c. The coefficients of Fig. 25 may be used as estimates for gases flowing with a small per cent drop in pressure, using v as the arithmetic mean of v_1 and v_2.

WEIRS

Visualize a liquid flowing at steady rate over a vertical dam placed across an open channel. At the distance x above the top of the dam the volumetric rate of flow dq through the cross section $y\,dx$ may be calculated from the orifice equation: $dq = c(y\,dx)\sqrt{2gx}$, wherein the velocity of approach is neglected. The total volumetric rate of flow q_0 is obtained by integrating from 0 to x_0, giving $q_0 = (\tfrac{2}{3})(cy)\sqrt{2g}x_0^{3/2}$. In practice the head x_0 is measured as the vertical distance from the top of the dam to the free surface of the liquid sufficiently far upstream to include the immediate drop in liquid level on the upstream side of the dam. Using f.p.s. units and replacing the term $\frac{2}{3}c\sqrt{2g}$ by a constant taken equal to 3.33,* one obtains the familiar Francis equation

$$q_0 = 3.33yx_0^{\frac{3}{2}} \tag{9}$$

for the so-called suppressed weir, where the width of the discharging sheet is substantially equal to the width y of the dam. This equation gives an accuracy of approximately 3 per cent with water if x_0 is at least 0.3 ft.; y is at least twice x_0, and the velocity of approach does not exceed 1 ft. per sec. More complex equations are available for less restricted cases. Weirs are sometimes used to measure rates of flow of water or of aqueous solutions of low viscosity, but, unless the weir in use corresponds closely to one for which experimental data are available, calibration is desirable.

For inward flow over circular weirs such as the overflow weirs in plate-type rectifying columns (page 548), the Gourley[5] equation

$$q = 3.0yx_0^{1.4} \tag{9a}$$

is often quoted for heads up to one-fifth the diameter of the circular weir. However, owing to waves in the pool on the plate and the existence of froth in some cases, this equation should be used only as a rough approximation for the flow over weirs in rectifying columns. A logarithmic plot of q vs. x may show breaks in slope, and calibration is advisable.

OTHER MEASURING DEVICES

1. Gasometers and Receivers.—A gasometer is an inverted vessel, usually a cylindrical metal one, placed concentrically inside another vessel containing a liquid, generally water. When the gasometer is empty, the inner vessel is full of liquid, and, as the gas is fed in through a pipe projecting up through the bottom of the outer tank, the inner vessel rises by an amount proportional to the quantity of gas admitted. Gasometers are used widely in the illuminating-gas industry.

The changes in the amount of gas in a constant-volume storage tank may be measured by observing the changes in the pressure

---

* It is noted that this factor has the dimensions of the square root of the acceleration due to gravity, and corresponds to an orifice coefficient of 0.623.

and temperature, or in weight. The constant-volume receiver is employed for high pressures, as in the determination of the rate of discharge of air from a compressor. The measurement of gases by weight is usually unsatisfactory because the weight of the tank is so great, relative to that of the gas, that results obtained by difference may have little accuracy unless the gas is under high pressure.

2. Addition (or Removal) of Energy, or Foreign Material.— The amount of matter flowing past a given section may be determined by injecting a measured amount of a substance into the stream and measuring the concentration of it in the final product after perfect distribution has been attained. Knowing the amount of the substance admixed and the concentration before and after the addition, it is possible to calculate the amount of material to which it is added. For example, the rate of chlorine evolution from an electrolytic cell may be determined by feeding air at a known constant rate into the gas as it leaves the cell and by analyzing the gas before and after the air has been added. Again, the amount of air passing a humidifier or drier may be calculated from the known evaporation and the humidities of the entering and of the exit air.

It is sometimes convenient to add or remove heat in the form of electrical energy at a known rate and to measure the change in temperature. The Thomas gas flowmeter is based on this principle. In an enlargement of the pipe are inserted first a thermometer of the electrical resistance type, then electrical resistance wire properly distributed across the whole section of the pipe, in which a known amount of electrical energy is transformed into heat, and finally, on the downstream side, a mixing device and another thermometer similar to the first. The Thomas meter automatically controls the electrical input so as to maintain a constant small temperature rise between the thermometers and measures the necessary wattage. This electrical input is proportional to the amount of gas passing the section, since the specific heat of any gas is constant over the temperature range involved, and the heat equivalent to kinetic-energy changes is negligible compared to the increase in enthalpy. However, the operation must be automatic in order to get satisfactory results, because under ordinary conditions the temperature fluctuations of the entering gas are large compared with the rise in the temperature of the gas in the meter. Hence an attempt to measure the quantity of gas by admitting a constant amount of energy and determining the temperature rise is highly unsatisfactory. Thomas meters are usually of the "integrating" type, *i.e.*, the instantaneous rate is integrated with respect to time, giving the total flow over a period of time.

The rate of heat loss from a small electrically heated wire placed in a stream of fluid is a function of the local velocity past the wire and the temperature of the wire and the fluid. When these relations have been obtained by calibration, such an instrument, known as a *hot-wire anemometer*, may be used for determining unknown velocities, usually of gases.

3. Mechanical Gas Meters.—The amount of gas flowing past a section may be measured by the insertion of a mechanical meter, of which various recording types are obtainable. Such meters should be carefully standardized, generally against a gasometer or other apparatus. They are expensive and liable to get out of order, but they are employed where larger quantities of gas are to be measured constantly, as in the illuminating-gas industry. Such meters have the advantage that they record the total flow over a period of time; the average rate may be determined by taking readings at desired intervals.

4. Anemometers.—The anemometer is a small windmill, the friction of which is reduced to a minimum and the rate of rotation of which should therefore be proportional to the velocity of the gas current in which it is placed. It consists of a light vane wheel fixed on a shaft, the rotation of which is recorded by a counting mechanism. Such instruments must be standardized with the greatest care at velocities as nearly as possible equal to those to be measured, and even when so treated are liable to wide variations in behavior; while very convenient, the instruments are unsatisfactory on this account. However, they are useful for exploration work, and, unless very sensitive multiplying gauges are used with the Pitot tube, at gas velocities below 5 ft. per sec. they give greater accuracy than does the latter. Anemometers are seldom made for gas velocities higher than 40 or 50 ft. per sec. Obviously the usual types cannot be used in corrosive atmospheres or hot gases.

When *liquids* are to be measured, the gasometer is replaced by a measuring tank or by a weighing tank.

The principle of measuring the change in the concentration of a foreign material in water may be applied to continuous evaporation.* The rates of feed and discharge may be calculated from the rate of condensation and the analysis of the entering and exit solutions; or the rate of evaporation may be calculated from the rate of feed and entering and exit concentrations. The rate of liquid flow through a cooler may be calculated from the specific heat of the liquor, the entering and exit temperatures of the liquid and the heat picked up by the cooling water. In both cases, correction should be made for heat interchange with the surroundings.

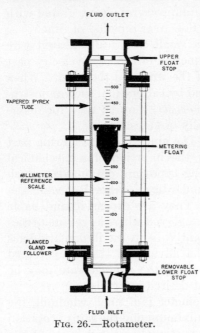

FLUID OUTLET

UPPER FLOAT STOP

TAPERED PYREX TUBE

METERING FLOAT

MILLIMETER REFERENCE SCALE

FLANGED GLAND FOLLOWER

REMOVABLE LOWER FLOAT STOP

FLUID INLET

Fig. 26.—Rotameter.

There are various types of water meters, as described in the literature.

5. Rotameter.—When liquid flows upward through the glass tube of this device, shown in Fig. 26,† the plummet rotates, owing to the flow of liquid through spiral grooves in the vertical wall of the flange on the plummet, and "floats" at a position that is indicative of the instantaneous rate of flow.

FRICTION DUE TO FLUID FLOW

Liquids differ greatly in resistance to flow. A measure of the resistance can be obtained by placing a thin film of liquid of thickness L' between two horizontal planes, each having a surface area A, the upper capable of sliding over the lower fixed surface. Such sliding is found to require the exertion of shearing force τ upon the upper surface, in direction parallel to it, the magnitude

* The test period should be sufficiently long to make negligible depletion or accumulation due to change in liquor levels.

† Courtesy of Schutte and Koerting, Philadelphia.

of the force being directly proportional to the area of the sliding surfaces and to the linear rate of slip of one surface past the other, and inversely proportional to the thickness of the layer of liquid between the surfaces. The factor μ converting this proportionality into an equality is found to be, under given conditions, a specific property of the fluid. It is called the *viscosity* of the fluid, defined by the equation

$$\tau = \frac{\mu A u}{L'}$$

for conditions equivalent to those just outlined. It is a measure of the internal friction of the fluid molecules slipping past each other, the internal resistance to fluid motion. Viscosity data are given on pages 687 to 690.

Friction Due to Steady Flow in Straight Pipes of Circular Section.—The following treatment deals primarily with conditions of steady flow. Unsteady operation is complicated, but such problems can be solved by integration of the equation for steady flow, allowing for the variations in conditions inherent in the specific case. A generalized treatment sufficiently inclusive to cover the extreme variety of conditions encountered in practical work seems undesirable.

Consider the case of steady flow of a fluid through a straight pipe of circular section, from the point of view of dimensional similitude. The friction will certainly be influenced by diameter, length of pipe and fluid velocity. Furthermore, viscosity cannot fail to play a part. One would also anticipate that fluid density will be important, as it will affect the kinetic reaction of the moving fluid. The pressure and temperature of the fluid are relevant, but probably not independent variables, since their effect is likely to be covered by those of the density and viscosity of the fluid. The friction can be expressed in terms of a corresponding pressure drop. Since change in pressure will affect density and velocity, and possibly viscosity, one must consider point conditions, expressing length and pressure drop as differentials. The factors certainly involved are, therefore, $-dP'$, dN, D, ρ, μ and V. These six factors have the dimensions $M/L\theta^2$, L, L, M/L^3, $M/L\theta$ and L/θ.* Let z be any dimensionless

* A table of dimensions is given on p. 30

ratio of these variables. In general terms each ratio can be expressed as

$$z = (-dP')^a (dN)^b D^c \rho^e \mu^h V^k$$

or substituting the dimensions

$$0 = \left(\frac{M}{L\theta^2}\right)^a L^b L^c \left(\frac{M}{L^3}\right)^e \left(\frac{M}{L\theta}\right)^h \left(\frac{L}{\theta}\right)^k.$$

In order to be dimensionless, the exponents are subject to the following limitations:

$$\Sigma M = 0: \ 0 = a + e + h.$$
$$\Sigma L = 0: \ 0 = -a + b + c - 3e - h + k.$$
$$\Sigma \theta = 0: \ 0 = -2a - h - k.$$

There are too few equations to give numerical solution for all the unknowns, but in this case one can solve for any three in terms of the others. Solving one finds $e = -a - h$, $k = -2a - h$, and $c = -b - h$. Substituting these values in the equation for z gives

$$z = (-dP')^a (dN)^b D^{-b-h} \rho^{-a-h} \mu^h V^{-2a-h} =$$
$$\left(\frac{-dP'}{\rho V^2}\right)^a \left(\frac{dN}{D}\right)^b \left(\frac{\mu}{DV\rho}\right)^h. \quad (10)$$

The exponents a, b and h are arbitrary, except that all cannot be zero. For the moment assume $a = 1$, $b = h = 0$, whence one of the ratios is $-dP'/\rho V^2$. Now assume $b = 1$, $a = h = 0$, whence $z = dN/D$. Finally let $h = 1$, $a = b = 0$, whence $z = \mu/DV\rho$, the reciprocal of the Reynolds number. These three ratios (or three others obtained by rearranging these three) may constitute the physically important dimensionless ratios sought, but the actual significance of each must be determined experimentally.

This technique is generally applicable. The number of independent dimensionless ratios in a given case is limited to the number of independent exponents (three in the illustration given) shown by the method employed. If the equations show all exponents zero or incompatible, the original analysis is defective, usually due to error in choice of variables.

This result is equivalent to requiring that, in this case, the relation* between the pressure drop due to friction and the operating variables be expressed as $\phi''(-dP'/\rho V^2,\ dN/D,\ DV\rho/\mu)=0$, or, alternatively,

$$-dP'/\rho V^2 = \phi'(dN/D,\quad DV\rho/\mu). \tag{10a}$$

While this is the final result obtainable by dimensional analysis alone, it is physically obvious that, other things equal, friction will be proportional to length of pipe, *i.e.*, $-dP'$ must be directly proportional to dN. It therefore follows that

$$\frac{-dP'}{\rho V^2} = \frac{dN}{D}\phi\left(\frac{DV\rho}{\mu}\right) \tag{10b}$$

or, rearranging,

$$-dP' = \frac{\rho V^2\,dN}{D}\phi\left(\frac{DV\rho}{\mu}\right).$$

Converting pressure drop into engineering units by dividing by g,

$$-dp' = \frac{\rho V^2\,dN}{gD}\phi\left(\frac{DV\rho}{\mu}\right).$$

This drop in pressure due to friction can be expressed as the friction loss by dividing by density,

$$dF = -\frac{dp'}{\rho} = \frac{V^2\,dN}{gD}\phi\left(\frac{DV\rho}{\mu}\right) \tag{10c}$$

This relation is frequently met as the so-called **Fanning equation**:

$$dF = 2f\left(\frac{V^2}{g}\right)\left(\frac{dN}{D}\right) \tag{11}$$

where $2f = \phi(DV\rho/\mu)$.

While this analysis throws no light on the nature of the function f (or ϕ), it indicates that f is a unique function of $DV\rho/\mu$, *i.e.*, that, if one will plot f against $DV\rho/\mu$, the points will fall on a single curve, no matter how diverse the relations between the independent variables involved. Figure 27† is

---

* To avoid confusion in dimensions, it will probably be best to use an absolute system of units at this point.

† Plotted logarithmically because of the enormous range of the variables involved.

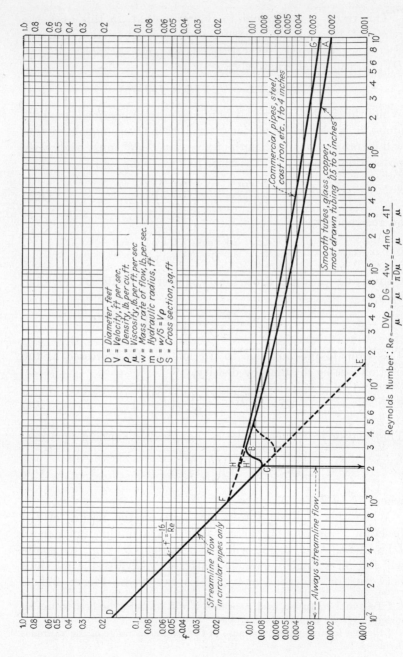

FIG. 27[7].—Friction factors for long, straight, clean, round pipes.

based on more than 1000 points, each representing the experimental results of a separate test.* The measurements were made by independent investigators or groups, using fluids whose densities varied 83,000 per cent, viscosities 375,000 per cent, velocities 160,000 per cent and pipe diameters 12,000 per cent. The maximum deviation of any of the points from the mean curve among them is about 5 per cent. Results such as this leave no doubt that the relation between the variables represented by this figure is fundamentally sound.

Inspection of Fig. 27 shows that the curve representing the points is broken up into two distinct parts, a 45-deg. line at the left and a very flat portion at the right. One would anticipate that the differences in quantitative interrelations thus indicated would correspond to some fundamental physical

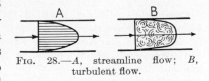

Fig. 28.—*A*, streamline flow; *B*, turbulent flow.

difference in the nature of the flow. If one will conduct the flow in transparent tubes, using clear fluids in which dust particles are suspended to make visible the character of the motion, or, preferably, will introduce minute colored filaments of fluid at various points in the moving stream, the differences immediately become apparent to the eye. At low velocities corresponding to the 45-deg. line at the left of the diagram, each filament of liquid flows in a straight line, parallel to the axis of the tube, moving at progressively higher velocity as the center of the pipe is approached. At high velocities, in the flat part of the curve, each individual filament travels in a sinusoidal path, developing irregular whirling eddies, unstable and yet continuously reforming. The former type of motion is called *streamline* or viscous, and the latter *turbulent*.

Streamline motion, as thus visually observed in a full tube at low velocities, obviously involves smooth slippage of one liquid layer past another, of the type postulated in the definition of viscosity already given; it should be amenable to quantitative treatment by the analysis there developed. However, two differences must be faced. In the first place, the thin laminae of moving fluid slipping past each other are not plane but cylindrical, so that their areas of contact vary from point to point from the

* Such a plot is shown in reference 6. The curves are shown in Fig. 27.

center of the pipe; in the second place, the shearing force is not applied at the outer lamina alone, but is the result of the pressure gradient along the axis of the pipe, and is effective progressively over the whole cross section. Consequently the fundamental equation for streamline flow must be applied to point conditions. Since the rate of slip is varying, one must replace u/L' by du/dL', which in this case becomes du/dr. Since both area and force vary with radius, the whole equation must be differentiated, giving

$$d\tau = d\left(\mu A \frac{du}{dr}\right).$$

Consider a cylindrical shell of fluid having radii r and $r+dr$, and length ΔN. Since the area of slip is $2\pi r \,\Delta N$, the difference in tractive forces is $d\tau = d(\mu 2\pi r \,\Delta N\, du/dr)$. The force impelling the annulus forward is the pressure drop $\Delta P'$ operating over the cross-sectional area of the annulus, $2\pi r \,dr$, giving $d\tau = \Delta P'\, 2\pi r\, dr = d(\mu 2\pi r \,\Delta N du/dr)$. Integration gives $\Delta P' r^2/2 = \mu \,\Delta Nr du/dr + c_1$. The constant c_1 must obviously disappear, since otherwise velocity at the center must be infinite. Again integrating, $\Delta P' r^2/4 = \mu \Delta Nu + c_2$. Assuming no slip at the pipe wall, *i.e.*, $u_1 = 0$, this becomes $-\Delta P'(r_1^2 - r^2)/4 = u \,\Delta N\mu$, or

$$u = \frac{-\Delta P'}{4\mu \,\Delta N}(r_1^2 - r^2) \tag{12}$$

which is the equation for velocity distribution, parabolic for this case, as shown in Fig. 28A. Since the volumetric rate of flow must be

$$q = \int_{r=0}^{r=r_1} u 2\pi r \,dr = -\frac{\pi r_1^4 (\Delta P')}{8\mu \,\Delta N}$$

and the average velocity V is $q/\pi r_1^2$,

$$V = -\,\Delta P' r_1^2/8\mu \,\Delta N \tag{12a}*$$

* It is interesting to calculate the *average* kinetic energy for streamline flow in pipes. At the local radius r consider the fluid flowing through the small annulus of thickness dr. By definition the local kinetic energy is $dM\, u^2/2g$, where dM is the mass rate of flow through the annulus. In unit time the mass of fluid flowing through this annulus is $2\pi r \,dr\, u\rho$. The velocity distribution is given by the parabolic relation: $u = 2V(r_1^2 - r^2)/r_1^2$, obtained from Eqs. 12 and 12a. Hence the corresponding kinetic energy is

$$d(\text{K.E.}) = \frac{dM\, u^2}{2g} = \frac{(2\pi r \,dr\, u\rho)u^2}{2g}$$

and the integral of this expression, divided by the mass flowing through the entire cross section of the pipe, is the *average* kinetic energy per pound flowing:

or

$$-\Delta P' = 32\mu V \Delta N/D^2. \tag{12b}$$

Converting to engineering units by dividing by g, and noting that $-dp'$ equals $\rho \, dF$,

$$-dp' = \rho \, dF = 32\mu V dN/gD^2. \tag{12c}$$

This equation is known as **Poiseuille's law.** Its validity has been established by careful extensive experimentation.*

In the relation already developed dimensionally for this type of flow, $dF/dN = 2fV^2/gD$, it was found experimentally that $2f$ equals $a\mu/DV \rho$, where a is a universal constant. Substituting this value of $2f$, one obtains $dF/dN = a\mu V/g\rho D^2$ in contrast with $dF/dN = 32\mu V/g\rho D^2$, as required by Poiseuille's law. Clearly, the constant a must be 32.

In other words, the two methods of approach to the problem of friction of flow give in this case identical results so long as the motion is streamline, with the exception that the dimensional approach, other than establishing the number of independent variables involved, leaves evaluation of the functional relations entirely to experimental determination, whereas the analytical method derives explicitly both the functions and the constants involved in them in terms of the conditions of flow and the physical properties of the fluid. However, the analytical method has so far not proved effective in dealing with the problem of turbulent motion.

Comparison of the relations for the two types of flow is instructive. Thus, whereas in streamline flow pressure drop due to friction is proportional to viscosity, in turbulent it is relatively independent of viscosity, indicating that in the latter slip of fluid layers past each other is not the major mechanism of energy dissipation. On the other hand, in streamline motion density

---

$$\frac{\text{K.E.}}{\text{lb.}} = \frac{\int d(\text{K.E.})}{\pi r_1^2 V \rho} = \frac{8V^2}{gr_1^8}\int_0^{r_1}(r_1^6 r \, dr - 3r_1^4 r^3 \, dr + 3r_1^2 r^5 \, dr - r^7 \, dr)$$

$$= \frac{8V^2}{gr_1^8}\left(\frac{r_1^8}{2} - \frac{3r_1^8}{4} + \frac{3r_1^8}{6} - \frac{r_1^8}{8}\right) = \frac{V^2}{g}.$$

This is the relation mentioned in the footnote on page 43.

* This validity, especially in the case of small diameters and large pressure drops, confirms the assumption of no slip of the fluid past the solid pipe wall, since it is easily shown that in such case a small slip would greatly change influence of diameter on flow.

is not a factor.   Its presence to the first power in the turbulent
equation, especially in connection with the appearance in that
equation of V raised to the second power, points toward dissipation of kinetic energy by impact of mixing elements of fluid as
the probable source of energy degradation—a mechanism which
analysis shows is clearly absent from the other type of flow.
Transition from one type to the other must be mainly a matter
of the relative importance of the different forms of loss.

In streamline flow the ratio of the maximum velocity, which
occurs at the axis, to the average over the cross section, is
found by comparing Eqs. 12 and 12a to be $\frac{1}{2}$.   For turbulent
flow, since the degree of turbulence or mixing increases with
increase in the Reynolds number, the ratio V/u_{max} increases
as shown by the curves of Fig. 17, page 54, based on experimentally determined data.[6]

Figure 27 shows that the nature of the motion and the extent
of the friction in smooth pipes are determined by the dimensionless ratio $DV\rho/\mu$, the so-called Reynolds number Re.   This
ratio is usually one of the first things to evaluate in any study
of fluid friction.   It is found that the curve DC for streamline
flow and the curve AB for turbulent motion are joined with a
looped section, such as CB.   This means that with a Reynolds
number less than approximately 2100 (at C) the flow in long
straight pipes is always streamline in character, and that at
Reynolds numbers greater than, say, 3000 (at B) the flow is
turbulent.   The zone CB is a transition zone in which the flow
is changing from one type to the other.   Under some conditions
streamline flow occurs at a Reynolds number greater than
2100, and the looped section CB is displaced to the right, as
shown, giving a wider dip in the critical region.   At present no
general rules are available regarding the location of the curve CB
for various sets of conditions.*   Because of these uncertainties,
it is recommended in design that calculations be based on curve
BH' rather than on BC.   The Reynolds number corresponding
to C is called the "lower critical Reynolds number" and the
corresponding linear velocity is called the "lower critical velocity."   If the curve AB is extrapolated to the left, it intersects
curve D at a Reynolds number of 1050; the corresponding linear

* A review of the experimental data in the critical region is given in
reference 8.

velocity was formerly termed a "critical velocity" but is now called the "fictitious critical velocity," since, as the velocity is gradually increased by small steps, streamline flow persists at least until C is reached.

When it is desired to predict the capacity of a given pipe line operating with a fixed pressure drop on a given fluid, trial-and-error calculation is involved when using Fig. 27, since the

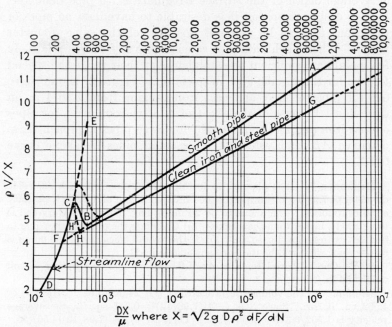

FIG. 29.—Chart for estimating rate of flow from pressure gradient. The ordinate $\rho V/X$ also equals $4y\rho/\pi D^2 X$.

unknown velocity occurs in *both* coordinates. This difficulty is avoided by replotting the data as the dimensionless ratio $\rho V/X$ vs. the dimensionless ratio DX/μ, where X represents the term $\sqrt{2g\,D\rho^2\,dF/dN}$, having net units of pounds per second per square foot. Figure 29 shows such a plot.*

The striking relations just developed were based on certain assumed limitations; modification of these conditions cannot fail to introduce complications, particularly by the introducing

* Prepared from Fig. 27, noting that $\rho V/X$ equals $1/\sqrt{4f}$ and DX/μ equals $Re\sqrt{4f}$.

of new independent variables.   The cross section of the conduit is obviously significant.   It is perhaps surprising, however, to find that the *roughness* of the surface is of importance in turbulent flow, particularly at high Reynolds numbers, but relatively slight in effect in streamline flow (see Fig. 27).   Effort has been made to correlate curves of f vs. Re on the basis of a roughness factor, assumed dimensionless, of the nature of the ratio of average depth of the surface irregularities to pipe diameter; but for design at present it is desirable to have data on pipes of the exact type to be used—if possible, of the same diameter range.   Where such data plot consistently as f vs. Re, relatively few points are sufficient to establish over their range the special f-curve for the specific type in question.   Figure 27 shows curve *GH* for pipes of steel and cast iron ranging from 1 to 4 in. in diameter.   Because of the effect of relative roughness, for pipes of cast iron and steel, values of f for large pipes approach those of curve *AB*, and values of f for small pipes lie above curve *GH*.*

Illustration 7.—It is planned to install a steel pipe line with an inside diameter of 7.98 in. to transport 24,000 bbl. per day of oil having a viscosity of 50 centipoises.   The line is to be 20 miles long, and the delivery end is to be 100 ft. higher than the intake.   (*a*) Calculate the pressure drop due to friction, expressed as lb./sq. in.   (*b*) If the overall efficiency of the pump is 60 per cent, what will be the horsepower required?

Data.—One oil barrel contains 42 U.S. gal. or 5.62 cu. ft., and the oil weighs 56 lb./cu. ft.

Solution.   a. The volumetric rate of flow q is $24,000(5.62)/(24)(3600)$ or 1.562 cu. ft./sec.   Since S is $(\pi/4)(7.98/12)^2 = 0.347$ sq. ft., the average velocity is $1.562/0.347 = 4.50$ ft./sec.   Then $DV\rho/\mu$ is $(7.98/12)(4.50)(56)/(0.000672)(50) = 5000$, and, reading midway between curves *AB* and *GH* of Fig. 27, page 78, f is approximately 0.010.   By Eq. 11,

$$F = \frac{4fNV^2}{2gD} = \frac{(4)(0.010)(20)(5280)(4.50)^2}{(64.3)(7.98/12)} = 1990 \text{ ft.-lb./lb.}$$

and the corresponding pressure drop is $1990(56)/144 = 775$ lb./sq. in.

b. Since the line is so long, end losses and the creation of kinetic energy are negligible compared to $1990+100 = 2090$ ft.-lb./lb. required to offset friction and the change in elevation.   The prime mover driving the pump would require $2090(1.562)(56)/(550)(0.6) = 553$ hp.

Effect of Heat Transfer on Fluid Friction in Pipes.—Consider a long vertical pipe, the lower section being bare and the upper section provided with a

* Reference 9 gives detailed tables and charts for pipes of various commercial materials.   See also reference 7.

steam jacket. Liquid, initially at room temperature, enters at constant rate at the bottom, and flows in *streamline* motion in the unheated section. As shown on page 80, the velocity gradient will be parabolic in shape, as indicated by curve A of Fig. 30. When this liquid enters the heated section, a temperature gradient will be established in the liquid, with a high temperature near the wall and a low temperature at the axis. Near the wall, owing to the reduced viscosity, the layer of liquid in the heated section will flow more rapidly than in the unheated section. Since the total mass flow rate is the same at both sections, some of the liquid from the center of the pipe must flow toward the heated wall. Hence the heating of the liquid develops a radial component of the velocity, distorting the parabola and giving a velocity gradient such as curve B of Fig. 30.*

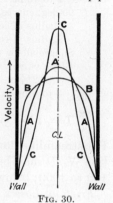

Fig. 30.

Superimposed on the effects just mentioned would be natural convection effects, *i.e.*, flow of fluid due to differences in density. In a horizontal pipe the natural convection effects would cause circulation in a vertical direction, which, combined with the horizontal component of velocity due to the flow through the pipe, tends to develop motion in forward-moving spirals. The derivation of a general equation for predicting the friction loss accompanying nonisothermal streamline flow is difficult, owing to the complicated mechanisms involved, and at present the problem is handled empirically. Thus, when heating or cooling certain oils in a horizontal pipe, so long as DG/μ is less than 2100, the friction factor is given by the relation $f = 17.6\mu'/DG$, in which μ' is taken at

$$t' = t + [(t_w - t)/4] \tag{13}$$

where t_w is the temperature of the wall and t is the average or bulk temperature of the liquid, when mixed. Where the values of DG/μ are above 2500, the observed values of f agree well with those read from curve AF of Fig. 27, provided the abscissas are considered to be DG/μ_f, where μ_f corresponds to

$$t_f = t + [(t_w - t)/2]. \tag{13a}$$

Flow through Bends, Fittings, Etc.—It is usual to evaluate empirically the effects of bends and pipe fittings, such as elbows, valves, and the like, in terms of a fictitious equivalent length (N_e) of straight pipe, of the diameter they are made to fit,

* If the liquid were cooled, a curve such as C (Fig. 30), would be obtained. For gases, since viscosity increases with increase in temperature, heating would give results similar to curve C, although the distortion of curve A would not be so marked for heating a gas as for cooling a liquid, since for gases the rate of change of viscosity with temperature is normally much less than for liquids.

which would develop the same friction drop, and to add this equivalent length to the length of actual straight pipe. Values of the ratio N_e/D are tabulated below.

TABLE I.—N_e/D RATIOS FOR STANDARD FITTINGS (FOR TURBULENT MOTION)

90-deg. elbows:

1 to 2½ in.	30
3 to 6 in.	40
7 to 10 in.	50

90-deg. curves, inside diameter unchanged:

Radius of center-line curve = diameter of pipe	20
Radius of center-line curve = 2 to 8 diameters	10
Square elbow (intersection of two cylinders)	50

Globe valve:

1 to 2½ in.	45
3 to 6 in.	60
7 to 10 in.	75
Tees, 1 to 4 in., full-size branch	60

For streamline flow in standard 90-deg. elbows, as an approximation N_e/D may be taken as $DG/25\mu$ in the range of DG/μ from 100 to 1000; below DG/μ of 10, N_e/D is 2.5.

Friction Losses Accompanying Enlargements and Contraction in Cross Section.—Flow through orifices throws light on losses in head caused by sudden enlargement or contraction of section. The conditions of flow accompanying *sudden increase* in pipe diameter (Fig. 31) are clearly analogous to those beyond the throat of

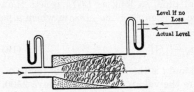

Level if no Loss

Actual Level

Fig. 31.—Enlargement effects.

a rounded orifice or beyond the vena contracta of a sharp-mouthed orifice, except for the character of the initial velocity distribution. The losses are mainly due, not as in flow through pipes to a friction drag against the wall, but to the turbulence engendered by impact of the high-velocity stream into the pool of more slowly moving fluid beyond it. On this account, the energy thus dissipated must depend, again except for questions of velocity distribution, not on the absolute velocities but on the difference in their initial and final values, $V_1 - V_2$. Since the effect disappears in absence of a change in section, *i.e.*, for $V_1 - V_2 = 0$, one may assume for the moment that the relation can be expressed as a power function, $F_e = a(V_1 - V_2)^n$.

For the special case of indefinitely large downstream sections, where V_2 is negligible, the analysis of orifices makes it clear that all the upstream (in this case, throat or vena contracta) kinetic energy, $V_1^2/2g$, is dissipated in turbulence, since in this situation there can be no appreciable pressure difference between the point of minimum cross section of upstream and downstream points. The function given can reduce to this specific value only if $a=1/2g$ and $n=2$. The losses in sudden enlargement are therefore computed by the expression

$$F_e = \frac{(V_1 - V_2)^2}{2g}. \tag{14}$$

The data to substantiate the use of this formula are unfortunately meager. It should not be depended upon outside the turbulent range, as this would certainly invalidate the assumption of similarity of velocity distribution, on which it is based. Attention is called to the fact that the expression can be written

$$F_e = \left(1 - \frac{S_1}{S_2}\right)^2 \frac{V_1^2}{2g}, \tag{14a}$$

indicating that the *fraction* of the initial kinetic energy dissipated by turbulence is independent of its magnitude, but determined solely by the fractional enlargement of section. This is in accord with the suggested mechanism of loss.

Upon substituting the enlargement loss into the Bernoulli equation, one obtains

$$-\int_1^2 v\,dp = v_{\text{av.}}(p_1 - p_2) = \frac{V_2^2 - V_1^2}{2g} + \frac{(V_1 - V_2)^2}{2g}$$

$$= \frac{V_2}{g}(V_2 - V_1) \tag{14b}$$

from which it is clear that, since V_2 is always less than V_1, p_2 will exceed p_1. In other words, in spite of the enlargement loss, the pressure rises, but the rise is less than if there had been no friction. Where the upstream section is negligible compared with the downstream section, the enlargement loss is just equal to the upstream kinetic energy, and hence p_1 equals p_2.

For *gradual enlargement* of section, no general relation is available, but for turbulent flow of water in circular conical sections (uniformly tapered) and for angles of divergence β between the two sides of the section, ranging from 7.5 to 35 deg., the following equation has been recommended:[14]

$$F_e = 3.5\left(\tan\frac{\beta}{2}\right)^{1.22}\frac{(V_1-V_2)^2}{2g}. \qquad (15)$$

It will be noted that the correction factor to the expression for an equivalent sudden expansion is in the form of a shape factor. For highly turbulent conditions it may still prove a good approximation for other fluids.

Loss in head on *sudden contraction* (Fig. 32) can be approached similarly. The action is analogous to that of a sharp-edged

orifice placed at the point of contraction, beyond which the stream expands from the vena contracta, not to the upstream cross section S_1, but only to that of the orifice itself, S_2. Granting high turbulence and large contraction, from the characteristics of orifices one would anticipate that up to the vena contracta energy dissipation would be slight. However, the area of the stream at this point is about 0.6 times that of the orifice. Dissipation must therefore occur predominantly beyond this point, as an enlargement effect. This can be estimated by Eq. 14 as $[(1/0.6)-1]^2 = 0.44$, or 44 per cent of the kinetic energy at the final section. The actual loss, experimentally determined, is for this limiting case a little higher than this,* about 50 per cent of the kinetic energy at the final section. It likewise is a function of the area ratio S_2/S_1; the loss is calculated from the expression

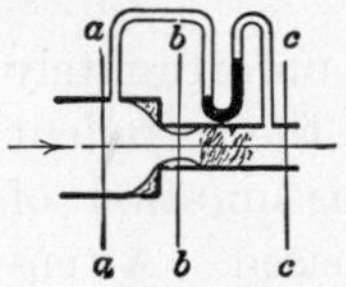

Fig. 32.—Contraction effects.

$$F_c = \frac{KV_2{}^2}{2g} \qquad (16)$$

where K, the fraction of the final kinetic-energy content that is dissipated, is the function of S_2/S_1 shown in Fig. 33, experimentally determined.†

These expressions are undoubtedly too general to be ultimately valid, as they show no correction for Reynolds number or its

---

* The limited enlargement in this case, relative to that in orifice chambers from which the coefficient 0.6 was derived, will certainly modify the orifice performance, *e.g.*, its coefficient of contraction, and render the above estimate an approximation only.

† The value of K is given closely by the expression $K = 1.5(1-r)/(3-r)$, where $r = S_2/S_1$.

equivalent. However, as long as conditions are decidedly turbulent, this factor may, as in friction in pipes, be of minor effect. In actual use Eq. 16 is combined with the Bernoulli equation, giving

$$-\int_1^2 v \, dp = \frac{V_2{}^2}{2g} - \frac{V_1{}^2}{2g} + K\frac{V_2{}^2}{2g} \tag{16a}$$

and, since V_1 is always less than V_2, the right-hand side is always positive and p_1 will exceed p_2.

Overall Friction.—In calculating total friction through a system, it is usual to calculate the skin friction by the Fanning equation or some modification of it, using the total length of straight pipe and adding to this the friction due to enlargements and contractions, fittings, etc. From this procedure one must not conclude that these latter effects are localized at the points in question. Irregularities in flow exist which extend far into the neighboring conduit of uniform section. This effect is observed both upstream and downstream

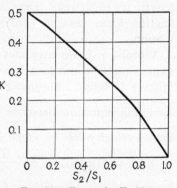

FIG. 33.—Factor for Eq. 16.

for surprising distances. It is probably due to irregular turbulence caused by the disturbance of the lines of flow. Because of it, dependable measurements of pressure gradients cannot be made in the neighborhood of irregularities in section. Thus it is a common rule in measuring pressure gradients for determining friction coefficients in conduits to measure pressures at points at least 50 diameters from bends or other sources of disturbance of the lines of flow.

Pressure Change Due to Flow in Conduits.—The problem of calculating the pressure change due to steady flow in conduits of constant cross section arises so frequently that it will be considered here. It will be recalled that the term dF in the Fanning equation ($dF = f \, dN \, V^2/2gm$) represents the friction loss that appeared in the Bernoulli equation written for a differential length dN of the conduit:

$$-v\,dp = dx + \frac{V\,dV}{\alpha g} + dF$$

where α is one-half for isothermal streamline flow (page 81) and is nearly unity for turbulent motion.

In the case of *liquids* or gases flowing under conditions where the specific volume and the friction factor change but little, average values may be taken for v and f, and integration from section 1 to section 2 gives

$$v_{\text{av.}}(p_1 - p_2) = x_2 - x_1 + \frac{V_2{}^2 - V_1{}^2}{2\alpha g} + \frac{f_{\text{av.}}N'V_{\text{av.}}{}^2}{2gm} + \Sigma F_c + \Sigma F_e \quad (17)$$

where N' is the length of straight pipe plus the equivalent length N_e of fittings (page 85) and ΣF_c and ΣF_e represent the friction losses due to contractions and enlargements in cross section.

A problem frequently met is the turbulent flow of gases and vapors under conditions where the fractional change in specific volume is large. Assuming the conduit to be horizontal, the Bernoulli equation becomes $-v\,dp = \dfrac{V\,dV}{\alpha g} + \dfrac{fV^2\,dN}{2gm}$. Since the mass velocity G is constant and equals V/v, elimination of V and dV gives $-v\,dp = \dfrac{G^2 v\,dv}{\alpha g} + \dfrac{fG^2 v^2\,dN}{2gm}$. Dividing through by v^2 to obtain separation of variables in the friction term gives $-\dfrac{dp}{v} = \dfrac{G^2\,dv}{v\alpha g} + \dfrac{fG^2\,dN}{2gm}$. Where the specific volume is proportional to T/P, using a suitable gas constant R', $v = R'T/p$, and elimination of v from the first term gives

$$\frac{-p\,dp}{R'T} = \frac{G^2\,dv}{\alpha gv} + \frac{fG^2\,dN}{2gm}. \tag{18}$$

If the temperature is approximately constant, μ will vary but little and f, which in the turbulent region changes very slowly with large change in $4mG/\mu$, will be substantially constant. Integration gives

$$\frac{p_1{}^2 - p_2{}^2}{2(R'T)_{\text{av.}}} = \frac{G^2}{\alpha g}\ln\frac{v_2}{v_1} + \frac{f_{\text{av.}}G^2 N}{2gm}. \tag{18a}$$

In the rather rare case where fractional variation in $R'T$, *i.e.*, in the pv-product, is large, Eq. 18 is combined with the appropriate heat-transfer equation and the resulting equation is integrated, graphically or otherwise.

Where v does not vary more than twofold, the equation $-\dfrac{dp}{v} = \dfrac{G^2\,dv}{v\alpha g} + \dfrac{fG^2\,dN}{2gm}$ may be multiplied by v and integrated with little error by calling v constant in the last term, giving

$$p_1 - p_2 = \frac{G^2}{\alpha g}(v_2 - v_1) + \frac{f_{\text{av.}}G^2 N v_{\text{av.}}}{2gm}. \tag{18b}$$

In case the nature of the velocity gradient changes as the fluid flows through the conduit, it may be important to allow for variation in α. For example, consider the case of *streamline* flow of a fluid in a horizontal pipe supplied from a large tank connected to the pipe by a well-rounded entrance. Owing to the shape of the entry, the velocity is substantially uniform and the kinetic energy is $V^2/2g$. After the fluid flows a sufficient distance* N through the pipe, the normal parabolic velocity gradient will be established, and the kinetic energy will be V^2/g. Since the pressure drop is caused not only by the fluid friction but also by increase in kinetic energy from $V^2/2g$ to V^2/g, the pressure drop will be higher than calculated from Poiseuille's law. Figure 34[12] is a plot of $\left(\dfrac{p_1 - p_2}{\rho V^2/2g}\right)$ vs. $\left(\dfrac{N/D}{DG/\mu}\right)$ where p_1 is the pressure in the tank at the height of the center line of the pipe and p_2 is the pressure of the fluid at distance N from the entrance section. When the pipe is not level, the ordinates of Fig. 34 are

$$\frac{p_1 - p_2}{\rho V^2/2g} + \frac{x_1 - x_2}{V^2/2g}$$

where x_1 is the height of the axis of the entrance section above the datum plane and x_2 is the height of the center line at length N.

Illustration 8.—Air is flowing at constant-weight rate inside the straight horizontal tubes of a cooler, at a mass velocity of 2 lb./(sec.)(sq. ft. of cross section). The air enters the tubes at 500°F. and normal barometric pressure, and leaves at 180°F. The tubes have an actual inside diameter of 2.00 in. and are 19 ft. long. Calculate (a) the pressure drop in the tubes, expressed as inches of water, and (b) the overall pressure drop between upstream and downstream chambers, if these have cross sections twice those of the steel tubes.

Solution. a. From Fig. 225, page 687, the viscosity of air, expressed as lb./(sec.)(ft.), is 0.0000195 at 500°F. and 0.0000141 at 180°F. Since DG is $(2/12)2$, the values of $Re = DG/\mu$ are 17,100 and 23,600, and, from Fig. 27,

---

* According to Boussinesq, for a pipe with a rounded entrance, the length of straight pipe necessary to establish normal streamline flow is $0.065D$ (DG/μ).

page 78, the corresponding values of f are 0.0077 and 0.0072, with $f_{av.} =$ (0.0077+0.0072)/2 = 0.0075. The hydraulic radius $m = D/4 = \frac{1}{24}$ ft. The average molecular weight of air is 29.0, *i.e.*, 29 lb. of air occupy 359 cu. ft.

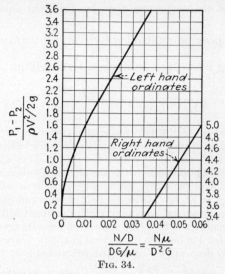

Fig. 34.

at 32°F. and normal atmospheric pressure.

$$v_1 = \frac{359}{29}\left(\frac{500+460}{492}\right) = 24.1 \text{ cu. ft./lb.}$$

Assuming that the final absolute pressure is substantially normal barometric pressure,

$$v_2 = (359/29)(640/492) = 16.1 \text{ cu. ft./lb.}$$
$$v_{av.} = (24.1+16.1)/2 = 20.1.$$

The values of v, V and G are illustrated by Fig. 35.

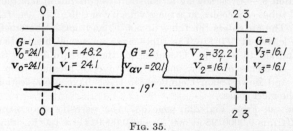

Fig. 35.

By Eq. 18b,

$$p_1 - p_2 = \frac{(2)^2}{32.2}(16.1-24.1) + \frac{(0.0075)(19)(2)^2(20.1)}{64.3(1/24)}$$
$$= -0.993 + 4.27 = 3.28 \text{ lb./sq. ft.}$$

or $(3.28)(12/62.3) = 0.63$ in. of water. In this case the pressure increase due to change in kinetic energy in the tube was roughly 23 per cent of the pressure drop due to friction, or approximately 30 per cent of the net drop in pressure. However, the change in kinetic energy is only 0.033 per cent of the net heat input:

$$Q = 0.24(500-180) + \frac{(32.2)^2 - (48.2)^2}{778(64.3)} = 76.8 - 0.0257 \text{ B.t.u./lb.}$$

b. The entrance loss $F_c = KV_1^2/2g$, and from Fig. 33, page 89, $K = 0.3$, whence, by Eq. 16a, page 89,

$$p_0 - p_1 = \frac{V_1^2 - V_0^2}{2gv_{av.}} + \frac{KV_1^2}{2gv_{av.}} = \frac{(48.2)^2 - (24.1)^2}{(64.3)(24.1)}$$
$$+ \frac{0.3(48.2)^2}{(64.3)(24.1)} = 1.12 + 0.45 = 1.57 \text{ lb./sq. ft.}$$

By Eq. 14b, page 87,

$$p_2 - p_3 = \frac{V_3^2 - V_2^2}{2gv_{av.}} + \frac{(V_2 - V_3)^2}{2gv_{av.}} = \frac{(16.1)^2 - (32.2)^2}{64.3(16.1)}$$
$$+ \frac{(32.2-16.1)^2}{64.3(16.1)} = -0.75 + 0.25 = -0.5 \text{ lb./sq. ft.}$$

SUMMARY

Differences	Lb./sq. ft.	In. of water
$p_0 - p_1 = 1.12 + 0.45$...............	+1.57	+0.301
$p_1 - p_2 = -0.99 + 4.27$.............	+3.28	+0.630
$p_2 - p_3 = -0.75 + 0.25$.............	-0.50	-0.096
$p_0 - p_3$.......................	4.35	0.835

Since 1 atmosphere is equivalent to a pressure of $14.69(144) = 2115$ lb./sq. ft., little error was made in neglecting the change in p when calculating v_2. Assuming 500 air tubes, the volumetric rate of flow at the exit would be $500(3.14)(1/144)(32.2) = 351$ cu. ft./sec. at normal pressure. With the fan at the exit, the power theoretically required would be $351 (4.35)/550 = 2.77$ hp.

Flow in Conduits of Noncircular Section.—For specific sections the integrations have been made for isothermal streamline flow (see page 94), but general correlations are not available. For turbulent flow, the following quasi-empirical correlations have been found extremely useful. The only frictional drag on the flowing liquid as a whole must certainly occur at the wall of the conduit and be more or less proportional to the wall surface. This is proportional to the perimeter Z of the cross section times the length dN of conduit under consideration. Since the amount flowing at a given velocity is proportional to the area of the cross section S, the frictional drag per unit amount flowing should be inversely proportional thereto. In other words, from the point of view of effect of shape of section, friction should be proportional to $Z\,dN/S$. For circular sections, this function reduces to $2dN/r = 4dN/D$. It will be noted that dN/D does in fact occur in the equation developed for turbulent flow in circular pipes. The logical step is to generalize the friction equation by use of S/Z, the ratio of cross section to perimeter, called m, in place of D; the equation thus becomes $dF/dN = fV^2/2gm$, since for circular pipes $m = D/4$. The term m is called the mean *hydraulic radius*. For conduits with uniform cross section of the shapes ordinarily encountered, this equation is remarkably dependable as long as flow is turbulent. In evaluating f, the Reynolds number may be written $Re = 4mV\rho/\mu$, and the resulting values may be used as abscissas in Fig. 27.* As is to be anticipated from the above discussion, in flow of liquids through conduits only partially filled, only wetted perimeter and section actually filled with liquid are used in evaluating m.

By a procedure similar to that used in obtaining Poiseuille's law, equations have been derived for the friction loss due to isothermal *streamline* flow in variously shaped passages:

Streamline Flow between Infinitely Broad Parallel Plates:

$$\frac{dF}{dN} = \frac{12\mu V}{\rho g a^2} \qquad (19)$$

where a is the clearance.

Streamline Flow in Square Cross Section, Side = y:

$$\frac{dF}{dN} = \frac{28.6\mu V}{\rho g y^2}. \qquad (19a)$$

It is noted that an equation of the type $dF/dN = \beta\mu V/\rho g m^2$ covers the case of the circular cross section and the two cases given above, but that different values of β are required: 2.0, 3.0 and

---

* Since by definition $m = \dfrac{S}{Z}$ and $V\rho = \dfrac{w}{S}$, $Re = \dfrac{4mV\rho}{\mu} = \dfrac{4}{\mu}\left(\dfrac{S}{Z}\right)\left(\dfrac{w}{S}\right) = \dfrac{4w/Z}{\mu}$,

which means that, for a given w/Z, Re is independent of the cross section filled by the fluid. The term w/Z, the mass-flow rate per unit perimeter, is sometimes designated by Γ, and hence $Re = 4\Gamma/\mu$.

1.78, respectively. In other words, the use of the hydraulic radius m would not permit the use of a fixed value of β for the three shapes.

Streamline Flow in Annulus, Diameters D_3 and D_4:

$$\frac{dF}{dN} = \frac{32\mu V}{\rho g \left(D_4{}^2 + D_3{}^2 - \frac{(D_4{}^2 - D_3{}^2)}{\ln \frac{D_4}{D_3}} \right)}. \tag{19b}$$

While Fig. 27 applies directly only to flow through pipes of uniform circular section, and while flow through many other forms of structure is extraordinarily complicated, there is one universal parallelism, namely, that, whatever the structure or flowing fluid, at velocities sufficiently low the friction is quantitatively proportional to the velocity, while, as velocity is increased, a point is reached at which the resistance becomes approximately proportional to the square of the velocity. Furthermore, the point of transition is influenced as much by the viscosity and density of the fluid and the scale of the structure as by velocity itself, *i.e.*, is determined by a modified Reynolds number, $4mV\rho/\mu$, where m is an empirical "hydraulic radius," proportional to scale so long as shape of the resisting body remains unchanged. The transition in friction doubtless corresponds to a change from streamline to turbulent flow. If the channels are small, the pressure gradient necessary to maintain reasonable rates of flow may be great enough to distort the structure (or even collapse it), masking the relations. If the channels are variable in size, transition from one type of flow to the other may be retarded. Usually, the quantitative relations must be determined experimentally for the case in question; sometimes this can be done by dimensional models. Cases in point include flow through porous solids, around staggered pipes, etc.

Friction in Packed Towers.—An analysis analogous to that in the case of fittings indicates that friction losses due to flow of gases through beds of dry granular solids of uniform size, as in tubes packed with catalysts, may be estimated by the use of Fig. 36[10] and the modified Fanning equation

$$\frac{dF}{dN} = \frac{4f'f''V_0{}^2}{2gD_p} \tag{20}$$

where F represents the friction loss, N the depth of packing, D_p the diameter of packing and V_0 the superficial velocity of the gas, based on the cross section of the empty tower; f' and f'' are friction factors and wall-effect factors (see Fig. 36); D represents the inside diameter of the tower. Since the equation is dimensionless, any consistent units may be employed.

Inadequate data are available for the effect of the rate of flow of liquid over the packing, but the increased friction loss due to circulating liquid, expressed as per cent Y of the results given by Fig. 36, may be roughly estimated by the empirical equation $Y = 3.3/D_p$, where D_p is expressed in feet.

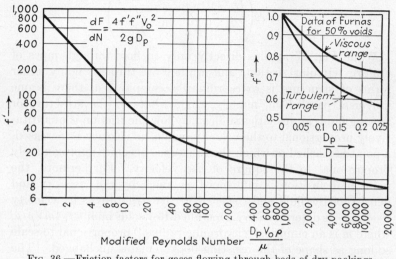

Fig. 36.—Friction factors for gases flowing through beds of dry packings.

For hollow packings the friction factors f', shown in Fig. 36, are multiplied by f''' given by the relation $f''' = b/\sqrt{D_p}$, taking f'' as 1. The factor b* is 0.069 for Raschig or Lessing rings and 0.038 for Berl saddles.

Friction Due to Fluid Flow Normal to Staggered Tubes.—Data for the *turbulent* flow of air at right angles to banks of staggered pipes are correlated[11] by the modified Fanning equation:

$$F = \frac{4f' n V^2_{max.}}{2g}; \quad f' = 0.75\left(\frac{aV_{max}\rho}{\mu}\right)^{-0.2} \tag{21}$$

where F represents the friction loss, n the number of rows over which the gas flows, $V_{max.}$ the linear velocity based on the *minimum* free cross section, ρ the gas density, μ the fluid viscosity and a the clearance between adjacent pipes taken normal to the gas stream. These equations are based on $aV_{max.}\rho/\mu$ ranging from 40 to 15,000, and a variety of arrangement of tubes.

For *streamline* flow, the data were correlated by the empirical dimensionless equation

$$F = \frac{53\mu' N' V_{max.}}{gD_e^2} \tag{22}$$

* Based on data of A. M. WHITE, *Trans. Amer. Inst. Chem. Eng.*, **31**, 390–408 (1935).

where N' represents the depth of the tube bank in the direction of fluid flow; D_e the equivalent diameter, equal to four times the free volume divided by the surface of the tubes; μ' the viscosity taken at the temperature t', defined by Eq. 13 (page 85), the other factors are defined above. This equation is based on the flow of liquids at right angles to tube banks having tubes spaced at the apices of equilateral triangles, with $D_e V_{max.}\rho/\mu$ ranging from 1 to 100.

Nomenclature
Definition of Symbols (F.p.s. Engineering Units)

A = surface, measured in direction of flow, sq. ft.

a = clearance between parallel plates, ft.

b = factor in the relation: $f''' = b/\sqrt{D_p}$.

C_p = specific heat at constant pressure, B.t.u./(lb.) (deg. F.).

C_v = specific heat at constant volume, B.t.u./(lb.) (deg. F.).

c, c', c_1 = coefficient of discharge, dimensionless.

c_c = contraction coefficient.

D = inside diameter of circular pipe, ft.

D_e = equivalent diameter, ft.

D_p = diameter of packing, ft.

d = prefix, indicating differential.

E = internal energy of fluid, ft.-lb./lb.

F, ΣF = friction loss, ft.-lb./lb.

F_e, F_c = friction loss due to sudden enlargements and contractions, respectively, ft.-lb./lb.

f = dimensionless friction factor in Fanning equation: $dF/dN = fV^2/2gm$.

f', f'', f''' = factors in modified Fanning equation, dimensionless.

G = mass velocity, lb/(sec.) (sq. ft. of cross section): $G = w/S$.

g = acceleration due to gravity, 32.17 ft./(sec.) (sec.).

H, H_2 = difference in static head $= v(p_1 - p_2)$, ft.

H_v = difference in static head, between upstream and vena sections.

$h_2 - h_1$ = increase in enthalpy, ft.-lb./lb.

J = mechanical equivalent of heat, 778 ft.-lb./B.t.u.

K = coefficient in contraction loss equation, dimensionless.

k = dimensionless ratio, C_p/C_v.

L, L' = linear dimension, layer thickness, respectively.

ln = logarithm to the natural base e, equal to 2.303 times the logarithm to the base 10.

M = average molecular weight of a perfect gas; mass, in dimensional analysis.

m = hydraulic radius, ft., equals cross section of stream, sq. ft., divided by wetted perimeter, ft.

N = actual length of straight pipe or duct, ft.

N_e = equivalent frictional length of fitting, ft.

N' = depth of tube bank, ft.

n = number.

p =absolute static pressure, measured at the wall in a plane parallel to the direction of fluid flow, lb./sq. ft.; p_a is measured above normal atmospheric pressure.

$\Delta P'$ =pressure drop due to friction, absolute units.

$\Delta p'$ =pressure drop due to friction, engineering units.

Q =heat input from an external source, ft.-lb./lb. of fluid.

q =volumetric rate of flow, cu. ft./sec. $= VS = w/\rho = wv$.

R, R' =gas constants, $pv = RT/M = R'T$, where R is 1543 ft.-lb./(lb.-mol) (deg. F. abs.), or 1.985 B.t.u./(lb.-mol) (deg. F. abs.).

Re =abbreviation for Reynolds number, $4mV\rho/\mu$, dimensionless.

r =radius of a chosen point, ft.

r_1 =radius of circular pipe, ft.

S =cross section at right angles to axis of conduit, sq. ft.

T =absolute temperature, deg. F. abs.

t, t', t'' =thermometric temperatures, deg. F.

u =local (actual) velocity of a small filament of fluid at a chosen point, ft./sec.

V =average linear velocity, ft./sec. $= q/S = w/\rho S$.

V_0 =superficial velocity, based on the total cross section, ft./sec.

v =specific volume, cu. ft./lb. $= 1/\rho$.

$v_{av.}$ =average specific volume, cu. ft./lb.

W =shaft work, gross work input from surroundings, ft.-lb./lb.

W' =mechanical work imparted to the fluid from an external source, ft.-lb./lb.

w =mass rate of flow, lb./sec.

X =symbol representing the term $\sqrt{2g\ D\rho^2\ dF/dN}$, having net dimensions of lb./(sec.) (sq. ft.).

x =elevation or vertical distance above datum, ft.

Y =a function.

y =width of weir, ft.; side of square, ft.

Z =wetted perimeter, normal to direction of flow, ft.

z =a dimensionless ratio.

Greek Symbols

α =alpha, dimensionless factor.

β =beta, angle of divergence, deg.

Γ =gamma, mass rate of flow per unit wetted perimeter, w/Z.

∂ =prefix, indicating partial derivative.

Δ =delta, prefix to indicate finite difference.

θ =theta, time.

μ =mu, absolute viscosity of fluid, lb./(sec.)(ft.) $=0.000672$ times viscosity in centipoises $=0.0672$ times viscosity in poises.

π =pi, 3.1416.

ρ =rho, fluid density, lb./cu. ft. $= 1/v$.

Σ =sigma, a summation.

τ =tau, tractive force or "viscous drag"; $\tau = \mu A\ du/dr$, ft.-lb./sec.^{2}

ϕ =phi, function.

Subscripts

1 refers to upstream section.
2 refers to downstream section.
max. refers to maximum.
c refers to a critical condition.
G refers to gas.
L refers to liquid.
O refers to orifice.
s refers to a standard liquid.
t refers to narrowest section of throat.
v refers to vena contracta section.
x refers to any liquid other than the standard one.

References

1. TUVE and SPRENKLE, *Instruments*, **6**, 201–206 (November, 1933).
2. SPITZGLASS, *Trans. Amer. Soc. Mech. Eng.*, **44**, 919 (1922).
3. SMITH, E. S., JR., *Trans. Amer. Soc. Mech. Eng.* HYD-52-7b, 89–135 (1930).
4. BUCKINGHAM, *Bur. Standards J. Research*, **9**, 61 (1932).
5. GOURLEY, *Proc. Inst. Civ. Eng.*, Part 2, 297 (1910).
6. STANTON and PANNELL, *Phil. Trans. Roy. Soc. (London)*, A214, 199 (1914).
6a. BLAUSIUS, *Mitt. Forschungsarb.*, **131**, 1 (1913); DREW, KOO and McADAMS, *Trans. Amer. Inst. Chem. Eng.*, **28**, 56 (1932).
7. DREW and GENEREAUX, *Quart. Trans. Amer. Inst. Chem. Eng.*, **32**, 17 (1936).
8. SCHILLER, *Physik. Z.*, **26**, 566 (1925).
9. KEMLER, *Trans. Amer. Soc. Mech. Eng.*, HYD-55, 7–32 (1933).
10. CHILTON and COLBURN, *Trans. Amer. Inst. Chem. Eng.*, **26**, 178 (1931); *Ind. Eng. Chem.*, **23**, 913 (1931).
11. CHILTON and GENEREAUX, *Trans. Amer. Inst. Chem. Eng.*, **29**, 161 (1933).
12. SCHILLER, *Z. angew. Math. Mech.*, **2**, 96 (1922).
13. LAMB, "Hydrodynamics," 5th ed., Cambridge University Press, London, 1924.
14. GIBSON, "Hydraulics and Its Applications," Van Nostrand Company, Inc., New York, 1930.

CHAPTER IV

FLOW OF HEAT

Introduction.—Chemical reactions are accompanied by characteristic and unavoidable heat effects; hence, in most problems in chemical engineering design, provision must be made for the satisfactory transference of the heat quantities. Furthermore, even in processes which involve practically no chemical changes, problems of heat transfer usually arise. The laws governing the flow of heat through bodies and from one body to another are therefore of great importance.

Mechanism of Heat Transmission.—It is well understood that heat may flow by three mechanisms:

1. *Conduction* is the transfer of heat from one part of a body to another part of the same body, or from one body to another in physical contact with it, without appreciable displacement of the particles of the body.

2. *Convection* is the transfer of heat from one point to another within a fluid, gas or liquid, by the mixing of one portion of the fluid with another. The motion of the fluid may be entirely the result of differences in density resulting from the temperature differences, as in natural convection; or the motion may be produced by mechanical means, as in forced convection.

3. *Radiation.*—A hot body gives off heat in the form of radiant energy which is emitted in all directions. When this energy strikes another body, part is reflected. Part may be transmitted unchanged through the body, depending on its degree of opacity. The remainder is absorbed and quantitatively transformed into heat.*

PART I. CONDUCTION

In the majority of cases arising in engineering practice, heat flows from some medium into and through a solid retaining

* Except in the cases where photochemical reactions are induced, or energy is consumed in other special ways.

wall and out into another medium. The flow through each is, therefore, but one step in a more complicated process, and the resistance offered by the retaining wall is only one of a series of resistances. The necessity for a clear insight into the mechanism of this process is obvious, and the ability to apply constructively a knowledge of it to many problems cannot be attained until the character and significance of each of the individual steps involved are studied and appreciated.

A. FLOW THROUGH HOMOGENEOUS SOLIDS

Fourier's Law.—Consider a solid body, such as a rod, hot at one end and cold at the other, protected in some way against heat losses from the sides. There will be a flow of heat along this body from the high to the low temperature end, accompanied by a progressive drop in temperature in the direction of the length L. Consider a section across the body at some point, at right angles to its length and the direction of flow of the heat. Call the area of the cross section at this particular point A. In the differential time interval $d\theta$, an amount of heat dQ will flow through this section. The fundamental law of conduction is that the rate of heat flow, or heat current, $dQ/d\theta$, is proportional to the area of cross section A and to the temperature gradient $-dt/dL$, both taken at the point. The proportionality factor k is called the *thermal conductivity*, defined by the equation

$$\frac{dQ}{d\theta} = -kA\frac{dt}{dL}. \tag{1}$$

The differential equation is general for unidirectional conduction.* In this text k will be expressed† as

$$\frac{\text{B.t.u.}}{\text{(Hr.)(sq. ft.)(deg. F./ft.)}} = \text{(B.t.u.)(hr.)}^{-1}\text{(ft.)}^{-1}\text{(deg. F.)}^{-1}.$$

It is found experimentally that for a given isotropic substance the thermal conductivity depends essentially on its temperature.‡

* Both heat current and temperature gradient are vectors and may be compounded in the usual way.

† Factors to convert values from one set of units to another are shown on p. 697.

‡ For perfect gases, pressure is without effect (except at very high vacua) despite changes in density. However, for most substances, the thermal conductivity rises as the pressure is increased above atmospheric.

Furthermore, except for certain special cases, the conductivity changes relatively slowly with the temperature. Since the accuracy of measuring conductivities is not high, it is usually satisfactory to express the conductivity as a linear function of the temperature. A substance may have a definite conductivity even though the substance itself is not homogeneous, *e.g.*, concrete of a definite composition and structure. Furthermore, the conductivity does not depend on composition alone but also on structure. For example, the porosity influences the conductivity very greatly. Small amounts of impurities may affect it substantially; particularly in the case of metals this may result in serious uncertainties. For different substances the thermal conductivity differs greatly (pages 694 to 697), the value of k for copper being approximately 10,000 times that for cork.

Thermal Conduction in the Steady State.—Steady conditions of heat flow, under which a constant quantity of heat passes each section of path per unit of time and the temperature at each point in the system remains unchanged, will be first discussed. Since the rate of heat flow is constant, independent of time, $dQ/d\theta$ is identical with Q/θ, frequently designated by q, and Eq. 1 becomes

$$q = -kA \ dt/dL. \tag{1a}$$

Rewriting Eq. 1a in the form

$$q \ dL/A = -k \ dt, \tag{1b}$$

it follows that the equation is separated into one expression involving as variables only the shape and dimensions of the body and into a second expression involving only functions of its temperature. Given the dimensions of the body and k as a function of t, integration is immediately possible. Where k is linear with the temperature,

$$-\int_{t_1}^{t_2} k \ dt = k_{av.}(t_1 - t_2)$$

where $k_{av.}$ is the value of k at the arithmetic-mean temperature, $(t_1 + t_2)/2$. The integral of dL/A must be evaluated for the specific case. Frequently, it is convenient to call it $(L_2 - L_1)/A_{av.}$, or simply $L/A_{av.}$, in which a proper value of $A_{av.}$ is employed. Mathematically expressed

$$q\int_{L_1}^{L_2}\frac{dL}{A}=q\frac{(L_2-L_1)}{A_{\text{av.}}}=k_{\text{av.}}\Delta \tag{1c}$$

where Δ represents the temperature difference t_1-t_2. Equation 1c is often written

$$q=\frac{k_{\text{av.}}A_{\text{av.}}\Delta}{L}=\frac{\Delta}{L/k_{\text{av.}}A_{\text{av.}}}. \tag{2}$$

The proper value of $A_{\text{av.}}$ is readily obtained by integration of the term dL/A, solving for $A_{\text{av.}}$ by means of Eq. 2. When the cross

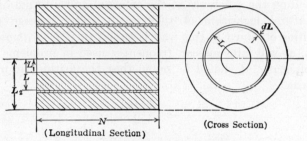

(Longitudinal Section)   (Cross Section)

FIG. 37.—Diagram of hollow cylinder.

section A is constant, as in flow of heat through flat walls, Eq. 2 reduces to

$$q=k_{\text{av.}}A\Delta/L. \tag{3}$$

Equation 3 is the simplest form of the conduction law and is frequently given as the formal expression of the law itself, rather than the differential equation, from which it is derived for this special case.

Where heat is flowing through the sides of a closed cylindrical body of circular section, as in lagged pipes or insulated wires, the direction of flow being at all points radial and perpendicular to the axis, the cross section of the path is proportional to the distance from the center of the cylinder. Considering the flow through a section of thickness dL (Fig. 37) at a distance L from the center, the cross section of path A equals $2\pi LN$, where N is the length of the cylinder. Substituting and integrating Eq. 1c gives

$$\frac{1}{2\pi N}\ln_e\frac{L_2}{L_1}=\frac{L_2-L_1}{A_{\text{av.}}}$$

or

$$A_{\text{av.}} = \frac{2\pi N (L_2 - L_1)}{\ln_e (L_2/L_1)} = \frac{A_2 - A_1}{\ln_e (A_2/A_1)} = \frac{A_2 - A_1}{2.3 \log_{10} (A_2/A_1)}. \quad (4)$$

For cylinders of circular cross section the rule is exact; for elliptical sections the equation may be used as an approximation, but for rectangular forms other more exact expressions have been determined.[1]*

Equation 4 requires that the average area of cross section, through which the heat is flowing in such a case, be computed by dividing the difference of the external and internal areas by the natural logarithm of their ratio. The average of two quantities obtained in this way is called their *logarithmic* mean and is, as will later appear, frequently used in problems on the flow of heat.   It should be noted that the arithmetic mean of the areas

$$A_{\text{av.}} = \frac{A_1 + A_2}{2} \quad (5)$$

gives a value for the average area differing from that of the logarithmic mean by not more than 4 per cent when the value of the expression A_2/A_1 is 2 or less, an accuracy considered sufficient for most problems in heat flow.

B. Potential Concept—Conduction through Several Solids in Series

Many transformations of both matter and energy can be conceived as controlled by two factors, one a potential and the other a resistance, the rate being in general proportional to the quotient of the two.   Inasmuch as the direction of transformation is controlled by the potential, the condition of equilibrium is zero potential difference.   The application to electrical phenomena is familiar; electricity does not flow except under a potential difference, the direction of flow is determined by it, and the rate of flow, *i.e.*, the current, is proportional to it.   Similarly, temperature is the potential function of heat.   Heat will not pass from one body to another, or from one point to another, except under the influence of a temperature difference.   The direction of flow is determined by the sign of the temperature difference,

* Reference 1 at end of chapter.

and the rate of flow of heat is proportional to its magnitude. Equation 2 for steady conduction may be written as

$$q = \Delta/R \qquad (6)$$

where the individual resistance term R represents the ratio $L/(k_{av.}A_{av.})$. Where heat is conducted at a rate q through a multiple wall, *e.g.*, the solids a, b, and c (Fig. 38), writing Eq. 6 for each resistance gives

$$\Delta_1 = qR_1, \quad \Delta_2 = qR_2, \quad \Delta_3 = qR_3.$$

By addition, noting that the sum of the individual temperature differences equals the overall temperature difference $\Sigma\Delta$, one obtains

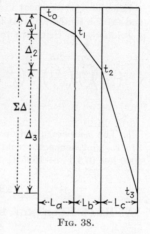

Fig. 38.

$$q = \frac{\Delta_1 + \Delta_2 + \Delta_3}{R_1 + R_2 + R_3} =$$

$$\frac{\Sigma\Delta}{(L/k_{av.}A_{av.})_1 + (L/k_{av.}A_{av.})_2 + (L/k_{av.}A_{av.})_3}$$

$$= \frac{\Sigma\Delta}{\Sigma R} \qquad (7)$$

where ΣR is the overall resistance. In other words, thermal resistances, like electrical, are additive.

C. Flow from Solid to Solid

When heat passes through a surface from one solid to another in good contact with it, it is probable that at the boundary no temperature drop is found. However, this requires perfect contact between the solids, and also the absence of gases or vacant spaces caused by blowholes, bubbles, rough surfaces, etc., which are very likely to be present where two solids are brought together. Even traces of poorly conducting material between metals, such as oxide films on the surface, will cause abrupt drops in the temperature. It is usually impossible to estimate the thickness of such films, but their effects may be serious. In order to allow for the conductivity of the mortar bond in brick walls, for example, an experimental wall is generally made up in the laboratory and the heat loss determined. The resulting conductivity of the type of wall in question thus includes the conductivity of the mortar.

Illustration 1.—The vertical flat walls of the combustion chamber of a furnace consist of 7½ in. of refractory $k_{av.} = 0.75$, 3 in. of insulation $k_{av.} = 0.08$, and ¼ in. of steel $k_{av.} = 26$. The average surface temperatures of the inner face of the refractory and the outer face of the steel are 2000 and 220°F., respectively.

Calculate (a) the heat loss expressed as B.t.u. per hour per square foot, and (b) the temperature at the cold side of the refractory.

Solution. a. Using the resistance concept, Eq. 7,

$$\frac{q}{A} = \frac{\Sigma\Delta}{\left(\frac{L}{k_{av.}}\right)_a + \left(\frac{L}{k_{av.}}\right)_b + \left(\frac{L}{k_{av.}}\right)_c} = \frac{2000 - 220}{\frac{0.625}{0.75} + \frac{0.25}{0.08} + \frac{0.021}{26}} =$$

$$\frac{1780}{0.833 + 3.13 + 0.0008} = \frac{1780}{3.96} = 450 \text{ B.t.u./(hr.) (sq. ft.).}$$

b. The temperature drop through the refractory is 1780 (0.833/3.96) or 375°F., and hence the cold side of the refractory is at a temperature of 2000 less 375°F. or 1625°F.

PART II.   CONVECTION

A. Heat Exchange between Solids and Fluids (Liquids and Gases)

The interchange of heat between a fluid and a solid surface with which it is in immediate contact is an engineering problem of major importance. It can be mastered only in the light of clear concepts of the mechanisms involved, but even so the extraordinary complexity of the interrelationships is at first discouraging. However, there is no other major field in which methods of engineering calculations and design have made greater progress during recent years, owing largely to extensive use of the methods of dimensional analysis.

Let AB be the fixed interfacial surface of contact between a solid G and a fluid EF, flowing parallel to the surface (Fig. 39) without change in state. Assume steady conditions and the temperature of the wall at C equal to t_w, hotter than the fluid. Heat must be flowing from the wall into the fluid. In conse-- quence, there must be a temperature rise of the fluid in the direction EF, resulting in change of fluid properties and hence probably in modification of heat exchange between wall and fluid.

To avoid the complication this causes in the analysis of the problems, first limit consideration to the differential interfacial area dA in the immediate neighborhood of a given point on the contact surface. Clearly, heat exchange between surface and fluid at this point will be determined, other things being equal, by the surface temperature t_w, irrespective of the mechanism by which this temperature is maintained by energy supply from the left of surface AB. The conventional approach is to assume that the corresponding differential rate of flow of heat between solid surface and fluid can be expressed by the equation

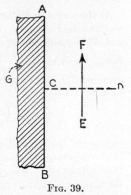

$$dq = h(t_w - t)\ dA = h\Delta\ dA, \qquad (8)$$

better written $dq/dA = h\Delta$, treating the differential coefficient dq/dA (*i.e.*, the current density, or rate of heat flow per unit contact area) as a single quantity. The numerical value of the coefficient h must ultimately be determined experimentally. Because it is based on interfacial contact area, h is called the *surface* or *film* coefficient of heat transfer. Since in the practical problem there is usually more than one such interfacial surface, it is often called the *individual* coefficient. It is designated *point* or *local* coefficient to distinguish it from averaged coefficients often employed. In the following, h is always expressed in B.t.u./(hr.) (sq. ft. of contact surface) (deg. F. temperature difference between surface of the solid wall and the fluid). The equation is frequently written

Fig. 39.

$$q = \frac{Q}{\theta} = hA\Delta, \qquad (9)$$

but this fails to emphasize the fact that it is limited to point conditions.

Study of the equation in the light of the conditions symbolized in Fig. 39 makes it clear that the numerical value of t and hence also of Δ is uncertain because of the necessary existence, along the normal CD, of some sort of temperature gradient in the fluid, which must be hot next the wall and progressively colder farther from it. In any event, t must be some sort of average fluid temperature, but specific choice is arbitrary, since such choice will merely define h. The engineer is usually interested in the total net effect of flow on the fluid flowing through a given equipment, or up to a given point in it, and this depends on the temperature that the fluid will possess if allowed to discharge from the equipment at the point in question and then mix thoroughly. This is defined as the *bulk* temperature of the flowing fluid i. Unless otherwise specifically stated, the fluid temperature used in Eq. 8, and hence in defining Δ, is t.

At the variable distance L along the normal CD, let u, ρ, C_p and t' represent the fluid velocity, density, specific heat and temperature, respectively, and dS the differential cross-sectional area normal to the direction of fluid flow. Since $w = \left(\int_{L=0}^{L=L_1} u\rho \ dS \right)$ is the total mass rate of flow past the plane of CD, the bulk temperature t is defined by the relation in which T

$$\int_{L=0}^{L=L_1} \left(\int_{T=T_0}^{T=t'} C_p \ dT \right) u\rho \ dS = w \int_{T=T_0}^{T=t} C_p \ dT \tag{10}$$

represents the general variable temperature, T_0 is an arbitrarily selected base temperature for calculation of enthalpies, and L_1 is the total width of the fluid stream. Where variation of ρ and C_p over the section are negligible, the above equation reduces to

$$t \int_{L=0}^{L=L_1} u \ dS = \int_{L=0}^{L=L_1} t'u \ dS. \tag{10a}$$

The bulk temperature is readily measured experimentally by allowing the fluid to discharge adiabatically, determining its temperature after complete mixing.

It is clear that in the practical engineering problem one will usually be forced to integrate the equation $dq/dA = h\Delta$ in the direction parallel to the surface of contact, over the range of changing conditions of temperature and fluid properties involved. Furthermore, the integration must be made in the light of the influence on operating conditions of the source of the energy supply to the contact surface. In the following, discussion of this step of integration is preceded by analysis of point conditions for certain important cases. For others, however, point conditions are so completely determined by the history of the fluid at other points of the contact surface that segregation of the two steps of analysis loses utility; in these cases, the whole treatment is given under the second heading.

Influence of Point Conditions on h

Film Concept.—It must be kept in mind that, when a liquid or a gas is in contact with a solid, there is strong evidence to show the presence of a relatively slowly moving film* of fluid on the surface of the solid, a film which becomes thinner as the velocity of the fluid parallel to the surface increases. Through such a film, heat can be transmitted by *conduction* only, although once the heat has penetrated the film the hot molecules are picked up and carried away mechanically by the swirling motion of the main body of the fluid, *i.e.*, the transfer is then mainly a matter of *convection.*† Since most liquids and gases are exceedingly poor conductors of heat, one finds a large resistance to heat flow at the boundary of a fluid and a solid, and also at the boundary of a liquid and a gas.

From the mechanism of the transmission, it is not surprising that the coefficient *h* is by no means constant, even for a given fluid, but is a complex function of a number of variables such as the physical properties of the fluid, the nature and shape of the solid surface, and the velocity of the fluid past the solid boundary. In cases of engineering importance, *h* varies for different fluids over 20,000-fold. Frequently, the capacity of heat-transfer apparatus is limited by the thermal resistances of the fluid films rather than by that of the retaining wall, and hence the magnitudes of the individual film resistances become controlling factors in the size of apparatus needed for a given heat-transmission capacity. In all attempts to reduce the boundary resistance between fluid and solid, experience has proved that the most effective means are those tending to reduce the thickness of the surface film. Thus a rapid movement of the body of the liquid or gas past the surface can greatly reduce the resistance by reducing the thickness of the insulating film of fluid.

Fluids in Circular Pipes.—The general approach can best be appreciated by considering a specific case, that of fluids

---

* See chapter on Fluid Films, and Figs. 6 and 7, pp. 35 and 36.

† Actually the resistance $1/h$ equals the sum of the conduction resistance L/k of the true film and the thermal resistance R' of the fluid lying outside the true film. If desired, h may be visualized as equal to k/B, where B is the so-called "effective" or "fictive" thickness of the film. Except where R' is negligible compared with L/k, B exceeds L.

flowing through pipes of circular section. One wishes to be able to determine the density of the heat current, dq/dA. This will certainly be influenced by temperature difference and, in view of the film concept, by the absolute thermal conductivity k of the fluid. It will likewise depend upon factors influencing the character of flow:* diameter D, density ρ, velocity u and viscosity μ. Furthermore, the heat-carrying capacity of a given quantity of the moving fluid must be relevant. This is clearly proportional to its specific heat C. It seems unsafe to omit any one of these factors from consideration, despite the fact that their number apparently involves complication to the point of confusion.

However, the problem can be simplified by preliminary analysis. In the first place, the total effect of dq/dA and Δ has been arbitrarily expressed as $h = dq/\Delta\ dA$, so that h may be chosen as a single factor combining all effects of these two. Since temperature varies across the section, there is corresponding variation in the properties of the fluid, particularly ρ and μ. Friction induces a similar variation in u (see page 79). One must therefore decide what values of all these variables to employ. However, it is not unlikely that at least the major effect of velocity and density may be expressed in terms of their product, the mass velocity $G = \rho u$ (*e.g.*, as they appear in the Reynolds number), thus eliminating all uncertainty as to the value of ρ and u to be employed.† This reduces the assumed ultimate variables to the following list: h, D, G, C, μ and k. Upon applying dimensional analysis, as shown on page 75, one finds that three dimensionless ratios are involved. For the case under discussion, the ratios usually chosen are DG/μ, $C\mu/k$ and, for the third, h/CG or hD/k, the last equaling the product of the other three. The group $C\mu/k$ is called the **Prandtl number.**

If one wishes to use these ratios as the independent variables in the attempt to correlate experimental data, one is immediately faced with uncertainty as to the value of μ to be employed, varying as it does with the temperature of the fluid, which in turn varies across any given section of the pipe.‡ This difficulty

---

* Pressure and temperature are probably without effect except as they influence properties of the fluid.

† Variation in μ is further discussed below.

‡ Variation in C and k due to radial temperature gradient is a theoretical difficulty, but almost always too small numerically to be significant.

can be met in part by choice of experimental conditions of low temperature difference to minimize variation in temperature and hence in viscosity, but a radial temperature gradient is inseparable from heat flow.   However, in view of the mechanism of heat exchange which has been presented, one would expect as the major effect of viscosity its influence on the thickness of the film.   This in turn should depend largely on the viscosity of the film itself.   This is still not specific because of the temperature gradient through the film, but use of an average film viscosity μ_f, corresponding to arithmetic-mean temperature between that of the wall and the bulk of the flowing fluid, cannot be far in error.

When the mass of data available is analyzed on this basis, an extraordinarily effective correlation is discovered, which can be given the empirical form

$$(h/C_pG)(C_p\mu_f/k)^{2/3} = 0.023(DG/\mu_f)^{-0.2}. \tag{11}$$

This remarkable equation enables one to calculate for a given set of conditions a value of h that shows a maximum deviation from the most carefully collected data of various investigators of perhaps 50 per cent and a probable error of roughly one-third as much.   This is all the more striking when one remembers that h varies over a thousand-fold from case to case, the Reynolds number one-hundred-fold, the Prandtl number forty-fold, and pipe diameter twelvefold.   It is conveniently used in graphical form and is plotted as curve AC on Fig. 40.

The equation is unfortunately often inconvenient in use (*e.g.*, where wall temperature is the unknown sought).   If one will use in the formula, instead of μ_f, the viscosity μ, corresponding to the bulk temperature of the fluid, one will obviously compute a value of h that is too high if the fluid is being cooled and too low if heated.   An attempt has been made to compensate for this by modification of the function, writing

$$(h/C_pG)(C_p\mu/k)^n = 0.023(DG/\mu)^{-0.2} \tag{12}$$

where $n = 0.6$ if the fluid is being heated and $n = 0.7$ if it is being cooled.   This equation gives satisfactory correlation if the ratio of the film viscosity to the main-body viscosity does not differ too greatly from unity.   For μ_f/μ outside the range, Eq. 11 is more dependable, although even in such cases Eq. 12 may be used for preliminary orientation.   Upon multiplying both sides of Eq. 12 by DG/μ, one obtains the familiar form

$$(hD/k)(C_p\mu/k)^{n-1} = 0.023(DG/\mu)^{0.8}. \qquad (12a)$$

However, one must not lose sight of the limitations of these equations for turbulent flow, where Re exceeds 2100.*   Knowl-

Curve	Fluid flow	y	x
JK	Normal to banks of staggered tubes	$(h/C_p G_{max})(C_p\mu_f/k_f)^{2/3}$	DG_{max}/μ_f
ELF	Parallel to a plane	$(h/C_p V_\infty \rho_\infty)(C_p\mu/k)^{2/3}$	$NV_\infty \rho_\infty/\mu$
GH	Normal to a single cylinder	$(h/C_p G)(C_p\mu_f/k_f)^{2/3}$	DG/μ_f
ABC	Turbulent flow inside tubes	$(h/C_p G)(C_p\mu_f/k)^{2/3}$	DG/μ_f

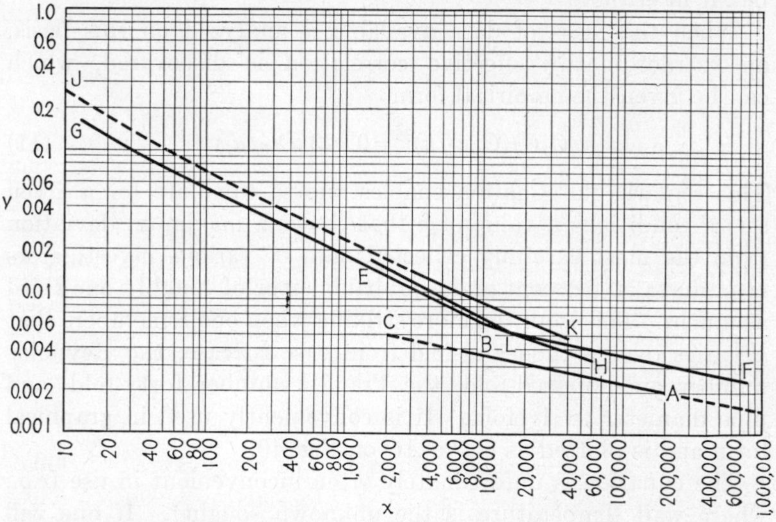

Fig. 40.—Heating and cooling of fluids by forced convection (and conduction).

edge of the true surface temperature of the wall is assumed. They have no corrections for end effects, and are probably in error when applied to very short tubes.   These equations are based on results for smooth tubes, and the effect of surface roughness is uncertain.   Even more important, they apply strictly only to a given cross section of a tube and must be integrated or averaged when used for the tube as a whole.

For the common gases the physical properties involved in this equation are so related that for them Eqs. 11 and 12 may

* In the neighborhood of the critical value of the Reynolds number. irregularities develop which are discussed on pp. 123 to 130.

be simplified to give the following *dimensional* equation:

$$h = 0.0144 C_p G^{0.8} / D^{0.2}. \tag{12b}$$

For water at ordinary temperatures, Eq. 12 may be simplified to the dimensional equation

$$h = 160(1 + 0.01t)(V_s)^{0.8} / (D')^{0.2} \tag{12c}$$

where t represents the average water temperature in degrees Fahrenheit; V_s the average water velocity in feet per *second*, based on a density of 62.3 lb. per cu. ft.,* D' the actual inside diameter, expressed in *inches;* and as, usual, h is expressed in B.t.u./(hr.) (sq. ft. of inside surface) (deg. F.).

Analogy between Heat Transfer and Friction.—Extensive theoretical study of the relation between heat transfer and friction has led various investigators to conclude that h/CG should be proportional to the friction factor f and some function of $C_p \mu_f / k$, the exact form of the latter being in doubt. Indeed, inspection of Eq. 11 shows that h/CG is inversely proportional to the 0.2 power of Re_f and study of Fig. 27, page 78, indicates that, in the range of turbulence, f falls off with increase in Re at about the same rate, an approximate empirical equation for the friction factor being $f = 0.046 Re_f^{-0.2}$. Substituting in Eq. 11 gives[2]

$$(h/C_p G)(C_p \mu_f / k)^{2/3} = f/2. \tag{11a}$$

Flow of Liquid in Layer Form $Re > 2100$.—Instead of allowing the liquid to fill the pipe, it is often advantageous to allow the liquid to flow by gravity in layer form down the inside or outside wall of a vertical pipe. Where the layer flows in turbulent motion, *i.e.*, where Re exceeds, say, 2100, one would expect Eq. 11a to apply, and comparison with data[3,4] shows that this is a fair approximation. It will be recalled that the Reynolds number based on film viscosity is $4mG/\mu_f$, that the mass velocity equals w/S and that the hydraulic radius m equals S/p', where p' is the wetted perimeter. Hence Re_f equals $4w/p'\mu_f$, ordinarily written $4\Gamma/\mu_f$, where Γ represents the ratio w/p'. Therefore, with a given film viscosity, mass-flow rate and wetted perimeter, Re_f is the same regardless of whether or not the pipe is full.

* That is, $V_s = G/(3600 \times 62.3)$.

Since for turbulent flow the relation between the friction factor and the Reynolds number is approximately the same both for full pipes and for flow in layer form down vertical walls, the right-hand side of Eq. 11a will be the same in both cases. Because the physical properties C_p, μ_f and k are the same, it is clear from Eq. 11a that the values of h/G will be the same in both cases. Since the cross section S of the fluid stream is less for flow in layer form than when the pipe is full, the mass velocity $(G = w/S)$ and consequently the coefficient of heat transfer between pipe wall and fluid is greater for flow in layer form. As the mass-flow rate w is increased, this advantage gradually disappears.

Since in the falling-film case the friction loss equals the tube height, the Fanning equation reduces to $fG^2/\rho^2 = 2gm$. Noting that G equals w/S and that m equals S/p', one obtains

$$G = \left(\frac{2g\rho^2 w}{fp'}\right)^{\frac{1}{3}}. \tag{11b}$$

This equation will break down as G approaches $4w/\pi D^2$. The heat-transfer coefficients predicted by combining Eqs. 11a and 11b

$$\frac{h}{C_p\sqrt[3]{2g\rho^2\Gamma}} = \frac{1}{2}f^{\frac{2}{3}}\left(\frac{k}{C_p\mu_f}\right)^{\frac{2}{3}} \tag{11c}*$$

agree satisfactorily with experimental data[3,4] for heating water flowing at Reynolds numbers ranging from 3000 to 60,000 down the vertical walls of a clean 2-in. pipe   Since f is approximately proportional to $(4\Gamma/\mu_f)^{-0.2}$, h should be proportional to $\Gamma^{0.2}$.

The analytical and experimental study of heat interchange between homogeneous fluids inside pipes and pipe wall has been far more extensive than for other types of contact of fluid and solid. The problems involved in these latter will probably be solved ultimately by methods analogous to those just presented. Meanwhile, one must use the best approximations available, even though these may not be so dependable as one would desire. The following is a summary of what is considered to represent best engineering practice at the present time.

Flow of Liquids and Gases Outside and Parallel to Tubes.— Few data are available for these conditions, but, as would be

---

* In evaluating g, one should remember to use the *same* unit of time as employed in evaluating G, w and Γ.

expected by analogy with the case of flow inside tubes, the data for *turbulent* flow in the annular spaces between concentric pipes are approximated by using the relations for turbulent flow inside tubes, with D interpreted as an equivalent diameter equal to four times the hydraulic radius (page 94).

Flow Normal to Tubes.—Data for *single* tubes are of value in connection with the interpretation of pyrometer readings obtained with the gas and surroundings at unequal temperatures (page 163). Curve GH of Fig. 40 shows the recommended relation for the heating or cooling of gases flowing normal to a single tube. For air at ordinary temperatures, and with DG/μ_f above 1000, a simplified *dimensional* equation is

$$h = 0.03 G^{0.56}/D^{0.44}. \tag{13}$$

Data for the important case of the heating or cooling of a gas or liquid flowing normal to a bank of *staggered tubes* are tentatively correlated[2] by curve JK of Fig. 40, page 112, in terms of dimensionless ratios. For air flowing normal to a bank of staggered tubes, an approximate dimensional equation[5] is

$$h = 1.75 T^{0.3}(G'_{\max.})^{\frac{2}{3}}/(D')^{\frac{1}{3}} \tag{14}$$

where T represents gas (not film) temperature in degrees Fahrenheit absolute, $G'_{\max.}$ is expressed in pounds per *second* per square foot of minimum cross section, and D' is in *inches*.

Other cases are discussed later.

Overall Coefficients.—In case of interchange of heat between a fluid and a solid through an interfacial surface, the heat current is frequently maintained by flow through a second interface from or into a second fluid, as shown diagrammatically in Fig. 41. D represents the cross section of the solid wall separating the fluids. F is the main body of the fluid receiving heat and E the surface film of this fluid. The temperature gradient normal to the surface at the point in question is indicated. The bulk temperature of the colder fluid is t_7, although parts of it are at the somewhat lower temperature, t_8. The colder side of the wall is at t_5. However, the continuous loss of heat from the wall surface demands a corresponding supply which is maintained by the temperature drop, $t_4 - t_5$, through the solid wall. Considering a differential area dA of the wall surface beneath the fluid film E, the corresponding heat current dq equals $h' dA \Delta$, where

$\Delta = t_5 - t_7$. Similarly, this same heat current must be given by the equation $dq = k\ dA\ \Delta'/L$, where k is the conductivity of the wall, L its thickness and dA' its average area of cross section (see page 104), and $\Delta' = t_4 - t_5$. Similarly, the film coefficient of the fluid at the left of the wall being designated by h'' and the corresponding area as dA'', one may write $dq = h''\ dA''\ \Delta''$, where $\Delta'' = t_0 - t_3$. Solving these equations for the individual temperature drops and adding the equations, noting that the same heat current flows through the various parts of the path, gives

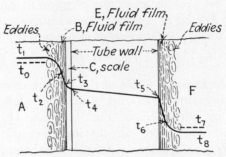

Fig. 41.—Diagram illustrating temperature gradients in transferring heat from fluid A through the wall D to fluid F.

$dq = \Delta_0/\Sigma R$, where Δ_0 equals the overall-temperature difference $t_0 - t_7$, and ΣR equals the total resistance, $\Sigma R = (1/h'\ dA) + (L/k\ dA') + (1/h''\ dA'')$. Indeed, assuming the existence of a deposit C (*e.g.*, a film of corrosion products or scale), granting that it has the conductivity k_s, and thickness L_s, its resistance $L_s/k_s\ dA''$, can be added into the total, giving:

$$dq = \frac{\Delta_0}{\Sigma R} = \frac{\Delta_0}{\dfrac{1}{h'\ dA} + \dfrac{L}{k\ dA'} + \dfrac{L_s}{k_s\ dA''} + \dfrac{1}{h''\ dA''}}. \qquad (15)$$

Instead of dealing with the total resistance, its reciprocal can be treated as a conductance $U\ dA$, whence

$$dq = U\ dA\ \Delta_0. \qquad (15a)$$

The overall coefficient of heat transmission U for a case of this type is defined by the equation:

$$1/U\ dA = \Sigma(1/h\ dA) + \Sigma(L/k\ dA) \qquad (15b)$$

where the indicated summation involved the addition of all

thermal resistances in the path of flow of the heat. Frequently, *e.g.*, where wall thickness is small compared with diameter, the relative differences in the various areas involved may be neglected, and one may write $1/U = \Sigma(1/h) + \Sigma(L/k)$.

From the discussion of individual film coefficients, it is clear that the overall coefficient U must be an extraordinarily complex function of operating conditions. Wherever possible, it should be evaluated by determination of the individual film coefficients for the case in question, together with the resistances of the intervening solids as determined by their physical properties. While the use of such overall coefficients is frequently allowable and extremely convenient, one should never lose sight of their complex nature as defined by the above equations.

Integration in the Direction of the Surface

It has been emphasized that heat transmission through an intervening wall from one fluid to another almost universally involves modification of the conditions from point to point, *i.e.*, change in temperature of one or both of the fluids with corresponding changes in properties, and hence in film coefficients, and consequently in overall coefficients used. This demands integration along the total area of the intervening wall in order to determine the total heat-transmission effect.

The heat current at a given point on the wall surface is $dq = U\Delta \, dA$, where U is determined by Eq. 15b. Inspection of that equation shows that the major variables in U are usually the film coefficients h, which depend upon the properties of the fluids, which in turn are frequently determined by their temperatures. Now, in the great majority of cases the temperatures and other properties of the two fluids at a given cross section can be determined by a combination of energy and material balances on the equipment up to the section in question. This is equivalent to saying that both U and Δ are known or determinable functions of q. Consequently, one can separate the variables by writing the differential equation as $dq/U\Delta = dA$, so that immediate integration is possible, graphically or otherwise. Fundamentally, this is the proper approach to the solution of any problem of heat transmission between fluids, through an intervening wall and under steady conditions of operation. This ultimate solution is frequently tedious, but there are certain special cases in which the integration leads to relatively simple practical rules of importance. However, the student must always keep in mind the fact that these rules are merely short-cut practical methods of performing the integration and, furthermore, that they are applicable only in certain specific circumstances, the existence of which must be established before the rules are employed.*

Single-phase Fluids Flowing through Uniform Cross Section.— In the case of a fluid flowing steadily past the surface without change in phase, the cross section perpendicular to the direction of flow being constant, inspection of the equation for point conditions shows that variations in U from point to point in the apparatus must be due to variations in the physical properties of the flowing fluid. As long as changes in temperature and pressure of the fluid are moderate, the specific heat and thermal conductivity usually change but little, and in many cases even the viscosity is reasonably constant. If the variation in the physical properties is in fact negligible, it follows that the value of U is also substantially constant. If, now, these conditions obtain on both sides of the intervening wall in both fluids flowing through an equipment, one can neglect variations in both the film coefficients. If, furthermore, wall thickness and its conductivity are likewise constant, and one can neglect either interfering deposits or their variations from point to point in the equipment, it follows that one can use a single constant value of U, applicable throughout the equipment. The problem reduces itself to the allowance for variation in temperature difference from point to point in the equipment, using the basic differential equation, $dq/U\Delta = dA$. While this problem can be treated under the general case and must be so handled when the variation in Δ is complex, it can be solved in simple form for the special case in which change in temperature difference is proportional to the amount of heat transferred.

*Logarithmic-mean Temperature Difference.—*In the case of heat exchange between two fluids under steady conditions of flow,

---

* Where the cross section of flow of the fluid varies progressively through a piece of apparatus, this results in variation of velocity, which in turn may result in variation in individual film coefficients. In such case, direct separation of the geometric variables comprised in the term dA, from the thermal variables segregated in the expression $dq/U\Delta$, may be impossible, but indirect methods of integration of the differential equation are available.

either parallel or countercurrent, call dq the heat transferred per unit time from one fluid to the other through the differential contact area dA. The contact may be either direct or indirect. Designating conditions of one fluid by primes and of the other by double primes, an energy balance requires that $dq = C'w' \, dt = \pm C''w'' \, dt''$, the sign of the last expression depending on relative directions of fluid flow. Because conditions are steady, w' and w'' are constants. If C' and C'' can also be assumed constant,* it follows that both t' and t'' are linear in q, as shown in Fig. 42. Since $\Delta = t' - t''$, Δ is also linear in q. From a study of the plot of Δ vs. q, one may write

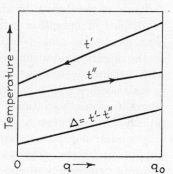

FIG. 42.—Diagram used in derivation of logarithmic-mean temperature difference.

$$\frac{d\Delta}{dq} = \frac{(\Delta_2 - \Delta_1)}{q_0}, \quad \text{or} \quad dq = q_0 \frac{d\Delta}{(\Delta_2 - \Delta_1)}.$$

Equating this to the rate equation, $dq = U\Delta \, dA$, and rearranging gives $d\Delta/U\Delta = (\Delta_2 - \Delta_1) \, dA/q_0$. If U can be assumed constant through the apparatus, integration from 0 to A and from Δ_1 to Δ_2 gives:

$$\ln(\Delta_2/\Delta_1) = UA(\Delta_2 - \Delta_1)/q_0. \tag{16}$$

This is the integrated overall expression for the case in hand, but it is ordinarily used in a slightly modified way. Granting one prefers to use the heat-flow equation in the form $q_0 = UA_0\Delta_{m.}$, where Δ_m is the *mean* temperature difference, inspection shows this procedure is correct if one will define

$$\Delta_{m.} = \frac{\Delta_2 - \Delta_1}{\ln \dfrac{\Delta_2}{\Delta_1}}. \tag{16a}$$

the so-called *logarithmic-mean temperature difference*.

Study of this equation shows that the logarithmic mean becomes identical with the arithmetic as the relative difference

---

* Constancy of temperature on one side, *e.g.*, a monovariant change in state, is equivalent to an infinite value of C. In this event, direction of fluid flow is immaterial.

between Δ_2 and Δ_1 becomes small. For $\Delta_2/\Delta_1 = 2$, the difference between the two means is only 4 per cent; since this is within the accuracy of much engineering work, one often uses the simpler arithmetic mean for lower ratios. The logarithmic mean is of especial value where the ratio Δ_2/Δ_1 is high, *i.e.*, for large fractional variation in temperature difference in the apparatus, under which conditions the arithmetic mean is useless.

Study of the derivation shows that it assumes steady adiabatic conditions of operation in a given apparatus and constancy of heat capacities and overall coefficient U. However, the use of the logarithmic-mean temperature difference in conjunction with arithmetic average values of the heat capacities and the overall coefficient is a good approximation, frequently employed, where fractional variation in the quantities mentioned is moderate but that in temperature difference is large.

A similar derivation shows that the logarithmic mean Δ also applies to batch operation, where time is the variable, again assuming constancy of specific heats and overall coefficient and adiabatic operation.

The factor that most frequently rules out the use of the logarithmic mean, in cases where it is otherwise applicable, is variation in U. However, if U is linear in Δ (or, what is equivalent, linear in t' or t''), a derivation similar to the above gives the relation

$$\frac{q_0}{A_0} = \frac{U_1\Delta_2 - U_2\Delta_1}{\ln(U_1\Delta_2/U_2\Delta_1)} \tag{17}$$

for parallel or counter current conditions of steady flow; and for batch operations $Q_0/\theta = A_0(U_1\Delta_2 - U_2\Delta_1)/\ln(U_1\Delta_2/U_2\Delta_1)$. Frequently it is a satisfactory approximation to assume U linear in Δ, calculating the values of U_1 and U_2 carefully for the case in hand, but one should also check one or two intermediate values to make sure the linear assumption is not seriously in error.

Illustration 2.—It is desired to heat 13,400 lb./hr. of a hydrocarbon oil from 80 to 217°F., while flowing through a horizontal standard 2-in. steel pipe externally heated by dry saturated steam condensing at 227°F. Calculate the length of pipe required.

Data.—The oil has a mean specific heat of 0.47, and the following overall coefficients U, based on the inside surface, have been calculated from Fig. 40. with the aid of a curve of viscosity *vs.* temperature.

t	80	95	110	130	160	190	217
U	29.5	38	47	51	70	81.5	91.7

Solution.—Upon plotting U vs. Δ three approximately straight lines are obtained from 80 to 110, 110 to 160, and 160 to 217°F. The equation (17) is then applied to *each* of the three zones in which U is linear in t, and the total inside surface is found to be 37.9+59.8+143 or 241 sq. ft., corresponding to 445 lin. ft. of pipe having an inside diameter of 2.07 in. An alternative method would have been to plot $1/U\Delta$ vs. t, noting that the area under the curve was A/wC, but the method illustrated is more convenient in this case.

Multi-pass Flow of Fluids without Change in Phase.—As already indicated, from the point of view of effective utilization of heat, it is almost always preferable in transferring heat from one fluid to another without change of phase to use counterflow, although in specific cases parallel flow may be desirable for other reasons. However, the practical construction of equipment for either true countercurrent or parallel flow is often quite difficult. Instead it is usually convenient to enclose a large bundle of tubes within a single cylindrical shell in such a manner that one fluid passes through the tubes and the other outside them but within the shell. In order to establish the fluid velocities compatible with the economic transfer of heat, it is frequently necessary to arrange the paths of flow so that either or both of the fluids must reverse directions one or more times in passing through the unit. In such equipment, the flow is seldom truly countercurrent or parallel but a combination of the two, called *reversed flow*.

That the logarithmic-mean temperature difference is generally inapplicable to the design of such units can be easily shown. Visualize a heat exchanger consisting of a U-tube placed inside a pipe with its return bend upstream to the fluid flowing through the jacket. If the colder fluid is passed through the U-tube, operating conditions could be such that this fluid is heated in the entrance pass of the tube and actually cooled in the return pass. Obviously, calculation of the length of the U-tube required to produce a given temperature change in either of the two fluids under fixed conditions of flow and inlet temperatures might be seriously in error if calculated by the usual methods employing the logarithmic-mean temperature difference. Failure to recognize this fact often leads to performance specifications on such a unit which are thermodynamically impossible.

Assume such an apparatus in which the distance through it in the direction of the flow of the fluid entering the U-tube is x (see Fig. 43). Call the mass of fluid entering the U-tube w, its specific heat C_1, its temperature at any point in the first pass t' and that in the exit pass t''. Designate the mass of the other fluid flowing always in the $-x$ direction by W, its specific heat by C_2 and its temperature at any point by T. Call the wall area per unit length of apparatus a'. Assume that the specific heats of the fluids and the overall coefficient of heat transfer U are constant and that the shell-side

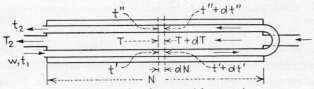

FIG. 43.—Diagram of exchanger with two tube passes.

fluid is at a uniform temperature over any cross section. Focusing attention on a differential length of the exchanger dx, it is clear that the following relations apply:

$$wC_1\,dt' = U(a'/2)(dx)(T - t').$$
$$-wC_1\,dt'' = U(a/2)(dx)(T - t'').$$
$$WC_2\,dT = wC_1(dt' - dt'').$$

Solution of these simultaneous equations in terms of $\Delta_{m.}$, defined by the equation $q_0 = wC_1(t_2-t_1) = Ua'N\Delta_{m.} = UA\Delta_{m.}$, gives[7a]

$$\Delta_{m.} = \frac{\sqrt{(T_1-T_2)^2+(t_2-t_1)^2}}{\ln\dfrac{T_1+T_2-t_1-t_2+\sqrt{(T_1-T_2)^2+(t_2-t_1)^2}}{T_1+T_2-t_1-t_2-\sqrt{(T_1-T_2)^2+(t_2-t_1)^2}}}. \qquad (17a)$$

Thus it can be seen that the true mean temperature difference $\Delta_{m.}$ can be quite different from the logarithmic mean, $\Delta_{l.m.}$ However, where the temperature of either fluid remains constant (*i.e.,* $T_1 = T_2$ or $t_1 = t_2$), the above expression reduces to the logarithmic-mean temperature difference. For the more complex flow paths, the expressions for the mean temperature difference become even more complicated.

Many commercial exchangers conform essentially to the description above, although there may be many U-tubes connected in parallel through common headers at both ends, as in Fig. 44. Units of this type may have a single pass on the shell side and two passes on the tube side; more tube-side passes are formed by connecting groups of the parallel-connected U-tubes in series. More complex flow paths are encountered where several tube bundles of this type are enclosed in a shell divided into compartments by longitudinal baffles, giving two or more shell-side passes with two or more tube-side passes per shell pass.

For these cases, mathematical relationships between the true mean temperature difference and certain dimensionless ratios have been obtained, based on the assumptions of constant overall heat-transfer coefficient and specific heats, of uniform

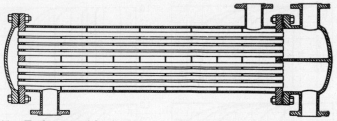

Fig. 44.—Exchanger with two passes in the tubes and one pass in the baffled shell. (*Courtesy of Struthers-Weils Co.*).

temperature of shell-side fluid at any cross section of each pass* and of equal heating surface per pass. These relationships are plotted in Figs. 45a,[7] 45b,[7] 45c,[7c] 45d,[7c] and 45e,[7c] in terms of *F*, the ratio of the true mean to the counterflow logarithmic-mean temperature difference. Similarly Fig. 45f[7b] shows values of *F* for the case in which the shell-side fluid flows at right angles to a single-pass tube bundle and in which the shell-side fluid is at a uniform temperature at any cross section normal to its direction of flow.

Although these reversed flow arrangements give a smaller mean temperature difference than is obtainable with true counterflow, yet their use is often justified by the increase in *U* due to the higher velocities. The disadvantage of reversed or cross flow may be partially offset by placing a number of units in series with counterflow of fluids through the battery.

Streamline Flow in Tubes $(DG/\mu < 2100)$.—If there is flowing through a straight pipe at low *Re* a fluid whose viscosity changes but little with temperature, the radial change in properties may be negligible, even though it is being heated or cooled through

* This uniformity is closely approached by heavily baffling the shell side.

the pipe wall, provided the temperature difference is small. In such event, the flow will practically follow Poiseuille's law. The heat transmission is by pure conduction, and, since the velocity distribution is known (page 80), one can set up the

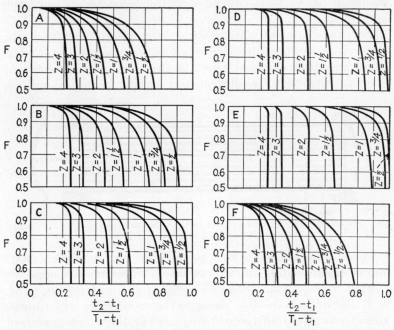

Fig. 45.—*A*, one shell pass and two or more tube passes (reference 7); *B*, two shell passes and four or more tube passes (reference 7); *C*, three shell passes and six or more tube passes (reference 7*c*); *D*, four shell passes and eight or more tube passes (reference 7*c*); *E*, six shell passes and twelve or more tube passes (reference 7*c*); *F*, cross flow, one shell pass and one tube pass (reference 7*b*).

Nomenclature

T_1 = inlet temperature of hotter fluid.
T_2 = outlet temperature of hotter fluid.
t_1 = inlet temperature of colder fluid.
t_2 = outlet temperature of colder fluid.
$Z = (T_1 - T_2)/(t_2 - t_1)$.
F = ordinate = $\dfrac{\text{true mean temperature difference}}{\text{logarithmic-mean temperature difference for counterflow}}$.

differential equations for heat flow, treating the problem purely theoretically, as in analysis of streamline flow itself. These have been integrated for the specific case of constant wall temperature but can be evaluated only if the radial temperature distribution is known at some section. Granting uniform temperature at inlet, the rise in bulk temperature at any section of the straight pipe at distance N is found to be the product of a series function of the dimensionless ratio Wc_p/kN and the initial temperature difference Δ_1. It is usually easier to work in terms of h, particularly so if one may employ an arithmetic-mean temperature difference, $\Delta_{a.m.}$. From the above relation it follows algebraically that, using $\Delta_{a.m.}$ and an equivalent coefficient, $h_{a.m.}$, $h_{a.m.}D/K$ is a modified function of wC_p/kN. The complicated theoretical function is approximated for normally encountered values of wC_p/kN by the empirical form[8] usually employed:

$$h_{a.m.}D/k = 1.65(wC_p/kN)^{1/3}. \tag{18}*$$

If, however, one assumes a long tube (large N) and low rate of flow (small w), equivalent to assuming a very low value of wC_p/kN, the fluid is exposed to a large surface for a long time and hence will come practically to wall temperature ($\Delta_2 = 0$). Since, by definition, $Q/\theta = wC(t_2 - t_1) = h_{a.m.}\pi DN\Delta_a$, and in this case $t_2 = t_w$, then $h_{a.m.}D = 2wC_p/\pi N$, or

$$h_{a.m.}D/k = (2/\pi)(wC_p/kN). \tag{19}$$

In the range in which this equation applies it is obvious that change in the operating conditions makes no change in the useful result (*i.e.*, temperature change of the fluid). In this sense it has no direct utility.

Both these equations are only special cases, but, in addition to their value in limiting the field of variation, they disclose the significance of the ratio wC_p/kN in heat transfer† and its general effect in streamline flow; for, if it is the determining independent variable in the limiting case, it must so appear in the general case as to reduce to the forms given above on elimination of other variables.

For large and even moderate temperature differences, these equations must obviously be modified. The theoretical approach now becomes more complicated, and unfortunately the amount of dependable experimental data available is limited. The following is a tentative correlation of these. Comparing two viscous liquids, identical in properties and conditions of flow, except that the first has a low temperature coefficient of viscosity

---

* The term N is defined in Fig. 43, p. 122.

† Note that this constitutes an additional method of discovering a significant dimensionless ratio in the general analysis of a problem.

and the second a high one, the first will conform approximately to Eq. 18. The second, however, if heated, drops in viscosity near the wall, and hence fluid velocity will increase in that neighborhood, resulting in increased heat transmission, *i.e.*, increased h. Cooling the liquid obviously has an opposite effect. To allow for this behavior, introduction of the ratio μ/μ_f has been suggested; the data indicate that, in Eq. 18, wC_p/kN should be multiplied by it. A second, more involved phenomenon is the convective mixing, the swirling circulation induced by change in density of the liquid with temperature, which can completely distort the streamlines and correspondingly hasten distribution of heat through the fluid. This must depend primarily on the volumetric coefficient of thermal expansion of the fluid β. Its effect will be proportional to the temperature differences involved, measured by Δ, and to the gravitational or other field of force which alone induces the circulation, *i.e.*, to g. The density ρ of the fluid is significant in that both the density differences developed (which in turn are the effective cause of the phenomenon) and any inertia effects are proportional to it. Fluid viscosity should damp the action but tube diameter increases its scope. The magnitude of the effect must depend on the inclination of the tube. All these factors but the last are combined in the dimensionless ratio $(D^3\rho^2g/\mu_f^2)(\beta\Delta)$, known as the *Grashof* number, Gr, film viscosity being used since the major effects are probably near the wall. Because its effect must vanish at $\Delta=0$, Gr cannot be used as a multiplier in Eq. 18. The data indicate that for horizontal pipes $h_{\text{a.m.}}D/k$ is proportional to the term $1+0.015\sqrt[3]{Gr}$. The working equation[2] recommended therefore becomes

$$\frac{h_{\text{a.m.}}D}{k}=1.65\left(\frac{wC_p}{kN}\right)^{1/3}\left[\left(\frac{\mu}{\mu_f}\right)^{1/3}\left(1+0.015\sqrt[3]{Gr}\right)\right]. \qquad (20)$$

This equation is presented graphically as curves A, B, C and D of Fig. 46, where $\phi^{1/3}$ represents the term $[\sqrt[3]{\mu/\mu_f}(1+0.015\sqrt[3]{Gr})]$. Curve EF corresponds to Eq. 19, and represents the asymptote which the preceding form approaches at low values of wC_p/kN. In the case of gases, streamline motion requires such low rates of flow that in tubes of ordinary length the low values of wC_p/kN make curve EF a good approximation, *i.e.*, the gases practically reach tube-wall temperature.

While these equations are based on the assumption of constant tube-wall temperature, since in their final form they become an expression for the coefficient $h_{a.m.}$, it seems probable that they may be used dependably to estimate average values of $h_{a.m.}$, even in cases in which wall temperature changes from point to

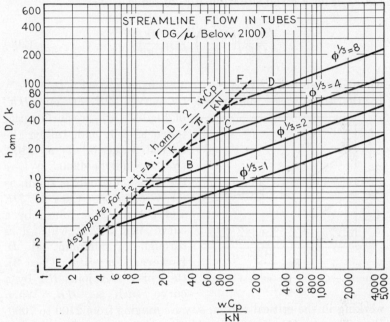

FIG. 46.—Curves A, B, C, and D are based on Eq. 20; curve EF is based on Eq. 19. The term N is defined in Fig. 43, p. 122.

point, provided there is not undue variation in the individual factors appearing in them.

For liquids of high viscosity, such as viscous oils, flowing in tubes of ordinary diameter, the Grashof number is small and the term $1.65(1+0.015\sqrt[3]{Gr})$ becomes approximately 2.0. The effect of viscosity gradient may be expressed conveniently in terms of the ratio μ/μ_w, giving [8a]

$$\frac{h_{a.m.}D}{k} = 2.0\left(\frac{wC_p}{kN}\right)^{\frac{1}{3}}\left(\frac{\mu}{\mu_w}\right)^{0.14}. \tag{20a}$$

Critical Region.—In order to compare Eq. 20 for streamline flow with Eq. 11a for turbulent flow, both equations are plotted to logarithmic scales in Fig. 47[2] with the term $(h/C_pG)(C_p\mu_f/k)^{2/3}$ as ordinates versus Re_f as abscissae. The range of strong turbulence ($Re >$ ca. 7000) is represented by curve AB based on Eq. 11a, the ordinates being equal to $f/2$. Since wC_p/kN equals $(\pi/4)(D/N)(C_p\mu_f/k)(DG/\mu_f)$ and hD/k equals $(h/C_pG)(C_p\mu_f/k)$ (DG/μ_f), for a given situation Eq. 20 reduces to

$$\left(\frac{h_{a.m.}}{C_pG}\right)\left(\frac{C_p\mu_f}{k}\right)^{2/3} = \alpha\left(\frac{DG}{\mu_f}\right)^{-2/3}. \qquad (20b)$$

where α equals $1.5(D/N)^{1/3}(\mu/\mu_f)^{1/3}(1+0.015\sqrt[3]{Gr}) = 1.5(D/N)^{1/3}\phi^{1/3}$. In the three cases illustrated by curves DE, FG and HK,

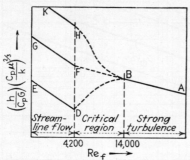

Fig. 47.—Curves for critical region, for μ/μ_f of 2.

of Fig. 47, μ/μ_f was arbitrarily taken as 2/1, and, taking the critical value of Re as 2100, $(Re_f)_c$ would be 4200. Where the Grashof group is small, as for viscous oils (Case 1), DE and BA must be joined by a curve such as DB, which goes through a minimum at D. However, for water (Case 3), the curve HK joins BA by a curve such as HB. When working in the critical region, say Re ranging from 2100 to 7000, Eqs. 20a and 11 are used in this way to estimate the probable values of h.* The natural convection mixing that accompanies a large Grashof number is important in the streamline region (cf. HK and DE), but the effect fades out asymptotically in the region of strong turbulence.

When working with viscous oils in the critical region, where Re lies between 2100 and 7000, the substantial effect of heated length, shown by Eq. 20a for streamline flow, fades out asymptotically at high Re, as shown in Fig. 48.[8a]

Résumé for Single-phase Flow inside Tubes.—Summarizing, the recommendations for predicting the heat-transfer coefficient for flow inside tubes are as follows:

* Of course, if the apparatus is overdesigned, so that Δ_2 is nearly zero, Eq. 19 would replace Eq. 20.

1. If DG/μ is above 7000, use Eq. 11 or 11a or curve AB of Fig. 40, or Eqs. 12 to 12c as approximations.

2. If DG/μ is below 2100, use Fig. 46, which is based on Eqs. 19 and 20, or Eq. 20a for viscous oils.

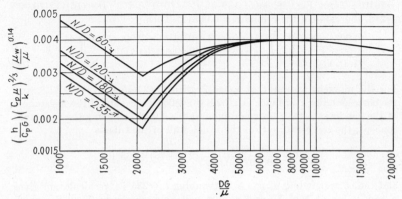

Fig. 48.—Heating and cooling of viscous oils flowing inside tubes. The curves for Re below 2100 are based on Eq. 20a.

3. If DG/μ lies between 2100 and 7000, use the procedure illustrated in Fig. 47, based on Eq. 20b and 11, or Fig. 48 for viscous oils.

Illustration 3.—It is desired to heat 81,000 lb./hr. of a hydrocarbon oil in a tubular exchanger from 75 to 200°F. with steam condensing at 240°F. The oil is to be pumped through the tubes at a velocity of 3 ft./sec. Tubes are to be 16 ft. long, made of Admiralty metal, 1 in. o.d. and 0.902 in i.d. Calculate the number of tube passes and the total heating surface required.

Data.—Over this range of temperatures, the specific heat of the oil may be taken as constant at 0.52 B.t.u./(lb.)(deg. F.), the density at 56.4 lb./cu. ft., the thermal conductivity at 0.091 B.t.u./(hr.)(sq. ft.)(deg. F./ft.). The viscosity of the oil at several temperatures is:

Deg. F..............	60	80	100	120	160	200	240
μ lb./(hr.)(ft.)........	66	40	26.5	18	10	6.2	4.2

Assuming that the combined coefficient for steam and scale is 1000 based on the outside tube area, the overall resistance, $1/U_i$, based on the inside area, is

$$\frac{1}{h}+\frac{0.049/12}{60(0.951/0.902)}+\frac{1}{1000(1.00/0.902)}=\frac{1}{h}+0.00097$$

where h is the individual coefficient for the oil film. The coefficient h, and hence U, will vary from one end of the exchanger to the other as the viscosity of the oil changes with temperature. At the oil inlet the oil temperature is 75°F., and from a plot of μ vs. temperature its viscosity is 45.4 lb./(hr.) (ft.); the corresponding Reynolds number is $(0.902/12)(3)(56.4)(3600)/45.4$ $=1010$. From Fig. 48, page 129 at $Re=1010$ and $N/D=(16)(12)/0.902$ $=213$, the value of the ordinate is 0.0031. Then

$$h=\frac{(0.0031)(C_pG)}{(C_p\mu/k)^{2/3}}\left(\frac{\mu}{\mu_w}\right)^{0.14}=\frac{(0.0031)[(0.52)(3\times3600\times56.4)]}{(0.52\times45.4/0.091)^{2/3}}\left(\frac{45.4}{\mu_w}\right)^{0.14}$$
$$=24(45.4/\mu_w)^{0.14}.$$

For the moment assume that $\mu_w=4.7$; then $h=24(45.4/4.7)^{0.14}=32.8$, and the corresponding resistance is $1/32.8=0.0305$. The sum of the resistances of the condensate film, scale and pipe wall is 0.00097. Using the resistance concept, the temperature t_w of the inside wall of the tube is

$$240-\frac{0.00097}{0.00097+0.0305}(240-75)=235°F.$$

and the corresponding μ_w is 4.5. Assuming $t_w=235°F.$, recalculation gives a new value of h of 33 and a new wall temperature of 234.9°F., which satisfactorily checks the assumed value. At h of 33, $1/U_i=0.00097+\frac{1}{33}$, whence $U=32$. By a similar process the following table was prepared:

t, deg. F.	75	80	100	110	120	140	160	180	200
U_i......	32	31.5	30	29	42	64	82	96	108

In order to calculate the total length of each fluid path through the exchanger, the equation $wC\,dt=U(dA)(T-t)$ may be integrated graphically by plotting $1/U(T-t)$ vs. t. The area under the curve, which is equal to A/wC, is found to be 0.0235. Taking one fluid path as a basis, w equals $(3600\times3)(56.4)(\pi/4)(0.902/12)^2$ or 2700 lb./hr., whence A equals (0.0235) $(2700)(0.52)$ or 33 sq. ft. The corresponding length of the fluid path is 140 ft. Since each tube is to be 16 ft. long, $^{140}\!/_{16}=8.75$ passes are required 9 passes would be used.

The total number of fluid paths in parallel would be $81,000/2700=30$, and the total inside tube area is $30\times33=990$ sq. ft.

Gravity Flow of Liquids in Layer Form $(Re<2100).$—This case is analogous to that of streamline flow in full pipes, and the theoretical method of attack is the same. The results are apparently not substantially affected by natural convection, since the fluid flowing down the inner walls fills only a small fraction of the total cross section and the fluid velocities are consequently much higher than with the same rate of fluid flow in full pipes. The data are best correlated graphically by the curve[4] of Fig. 49, which involves the dimensionless coordinates hL/k and $CL\Gamma/kN$, and the parameter μ/μ_w. The latter term allows for the distortion of the velocity gradient, owing to the fact that μ varies with the temperature. Over the range where

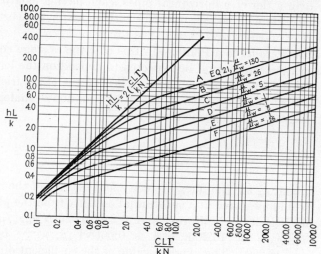

FIG. 49.—Gravity flow of liquid in layer form down vertical walls, based on Eqs. 21 and 21a, $4\Gamma/\mu < 2100$.

the curves A to F are straight, they may be represented by the equation

$$\frac{h_{\mathrm{a.m.}}L}{k} = 1.0\left(\frac{CL\Gamma}{kN}\right)^{\frac{1}{3}}\left(\frac{\mu}{\mu_w}\right)^{\frac{1}{4}} \tag{21}$$

where $L = \sqrt[3]{3\mu\Gamma/\rho^2 g}$. The 45-deg. curve, which is the asymptote of curves A to F inclusive, is the analogue of Eq. 19 for full pipes and corresponds to the equation

$$\frac{h_{\mathrm{a.m.}}L}{k} = \frac{2(CL\Gamma)}{kN}. \tag{21a}$$

Figure 49 and Eqs. 21 and 21a apply to liquid layers flowing down the inside or outside of *vertical* pipes, where $4\Gamma/\mu$ is less than 2100.

Under certain operating conditions in the streamline region, higher coefficients are obtained with gravity flow of layers down the walls of vertical pipes than with full pipes. For example, in heating an oil flowing at the rate of 100 lb. per hr. through a pipe having an inside diameter of 1 in. and a length of 6 ft., given $\mu = 40$, $k = 0.0826$, $C = 0.455$ and $\mu/\mu_w = 2$, the average coefficient for the falling-film case is 26 compared to 9 for the full pipe, a ratio of approximately 3 to 1.

For the so-called trombone cooler, where the liquid flows by gravity over a tier of n horizontal pipes, each having length N', the available data agree satisfactorily with those for the vertical pipes if N is taken as $n\pi D/2$, and Γ is taken as $w/2N'$.

Gas Flow Parallel to a Plane.—In this case the average coefficient of heat transfer would be expected to depend on the length of travel of the fluid along the plane, as is also true of the friction factor for flow along a plane. Indeed an equation[2] analogous to Eq. 11a, page 113, may be employed:

$$\left(\frac{h_{\text{av.}}}{C_p V_\infty \rho_\infty}\right)\left(\frac{C_p \mu}{k}\right)^{2/3} = \frac{f}{2} \tag{22}$$

where V_∞ and ρ_∞ are the linear velocity and density of the main stream of fluid measured at a substantial distance from the plane, where the velocity is uniform; and $f/2$ is $0.036(NV_\infty\rho_\infty/\mu)^{-0.2}$ above $NV_\infty\rho_\infty/\mu$ of 16,200, and is $0.66(NV_\infty\rho_\infty/\mu)^{-0.5}$ below $NV_\infty\rho_\infty/\mu$ of 16,200. The average value of the coefficient of heat transfer is based on the temperature difference between the surface of the plane and the average temperature of the main gas stream, *i.e.*,

$$\frac{q}{A} = h_a(t_w - t_\infty).$$

Equation 22 is shown graphically as curve EF on Fig. 40, page 112.

Natural Convection from Tubes and Planes.—A study of the variables involved leads to the dimensionless groups: hL'/k, $C_p\mu/k$, $\beta\Delta$ and $L^3\rho^2 g/\mu^2$, where L' is a shape factor having linear dimensions. The bulk of the experimental study of natural convection has been devoted to single horizontal cylinders, ranging in size from small wires to large pipes, exposed to gases or liquids. These data are well correlated by the equation

$$y = \phi x \tag{23}$$

where y equals hD/k_f and x equals the complex term $(D^3\rho_f^2 g/\mu_f^2)$

$(\beta\Delta)(C_p\mu/k)$, which is the product of the Grashof and Prandtl groups. The coordinates of the logarithmic plot follow:

$\log x$	-4	-2	0		4	6	8
$\log y$	-0.31	0.18	-0.035	0.325	0.73	1.21	1.71

For heat loss from pipes to the air of a room, this function reduces to the dimensional equation:

$$h = 0.42\left(\frac{\Delta}{D'}\right)^{0.25}. \tag{23a}$$

For the heat loss from various shapes to the air of the room the following simplified equations are available:

$$\text{Long vertical pipes, } h = 0.4(\Delta/D')^{0.25} \tag{23b}$$
$$\text{Small vertical plates, } h = 0.28(\Delta/H)^{0.25} \tag{23c}$$
$$\text{Large vertical plates, } h = 0.3\Delta^{0.25} \tag{23d}$$
$$\text{Horizontal plates, facing } upward, h = 0.38\Delta^{0.25} \tag{23e}$$
$$\text{Horizontal plates, facing } downward, h = 0.2\Delta^{0.25} \tag{23f}$$

In these simplified equations, $(23a)$ to $(23f)$, which are not dimensionless, it is necessary to use the units of the nomenclature table on page 143, noting that D' is expressed in *inches* and the height H in *feet*.

B. Condensing Vapors

When a pure saturated vapor comes into contact with an inert surface maintained at lower temperature, condensation ensues. If the surface is wettable by the condensate, a continuous film of liquid tends to form. Further condensation can occur only on the outer surface of this film. Moreover, because the heat of condensation is released entirely at the locus of change of phase, the process can continue only as the heat is transmitted through the film. Since most liquids are poor conductors of heat, the film offers the major if not the only thermal resistance between the vapor and the cooling surface. If, on the other hand, the surface is nonwettable, surface tension draws the condensate into isolated drops which soon grow large enough to fall off unless the surface is horizontal. This keeps a large fraction of the cooling surface bare and hence available for condensation of additional vapor, resulting in far higher coefficients of heat transfer between cooling surface and vapor.*

1. Film-type Condensation of Pure† Vapor.—Visualize a *vertical* tube, the wall surface of which, in contact with a pure saturated vapor, is maintained at a constant temperature below that of the vapor and is wetted by the condensate.‡ Focus attention first on the surface near the top of the tube. The condensate will flow down the tube wall under gravity, but, because there is but little liquid at this point, the film will be thin and its motion streamline.§ At points progressively lower on the tube surface the cumulative amount of condensate flowing past the point is larger and the film of liquid correspondingly thicker. The heat of condensation being absorbed from the vapor must, therefore, flow through the thicker film of condensate, resulting in progressively lower value of the surface coefficient h. While one can deal with the value of h at a given point, it is usually more convenient to consider an average value, $h_{av.}$, for the tube as a whole.

Take as basis unit horizontal width measured along the periphery of the condensing wall, and consider a point N ft. below the point where condensation starts, motion still being streamline. The total amount of condensate formed vertically above the point and flowing past it is Γ lb. per unit time. Call the thickness of the liquid film at this point, L. If one may neglect variation of physical properties of the liquid, particularly viscosity, due to temperature gradient through the film, from Eq. 19, page 94, the average velocity of the liquid is $u = \rho g L^2/3\mu_f$, whence $\Gamma = \rho u L = \rho^2 g L^3/3\mu_f$. However, because there is no turbulence, the heat goes through the film by pure conduction, *i.e.*,

$$h = \frac{k}{L} = k\left(\frac{\rho^2 g}{3\mu_f \Gamma}\right)^{\frac{1}{3}}. \tag{24}$$

The rate of condensation $d\Gamma$ in the area dN is $d\Gamma = h\Delta\, dN/r$, as defined by the

---

* Occasionally one part of a given surface may be wettable and another not.

† What follows is equally applicable to condensation of a constant boiling mixture of miscible liquids. Immiscibility of the condensing constituents would obviously interfere with flow.

‡ The vapor may be either outside or inside the tube, but preferably the former, since in the latter case all vapor condensed in the tubes must enter at the ends, tending to develop a pressure gradient interfering with condensation.

§ This may not be true if the rate of condensation is excessive and the velocity of approach of vapor to the surface correspondingly high.

heat-transmission equation, where r is the latent heat of the material condensing. Differentiation of the above flow expression gives $d\Gamma = {}_f{}^2gL^2\,dL/\mu_f$, and integration (noting that L equals 0 at N equals 0) gives $N = rg\rho^2L^4/4k\,\Delta\mu_f$. However, granting one may use an average surface coefficient from the top to the point in question, this will be defined by the equation, $h_{\mathrm{av.}} = \Gamma r/N\Delta$, or, since $\Gamma = \rho^2gL^3/3\mu_f$, $h_{\mathrm{av.}} = rg\rho^2L^3/3\mu_fN\Delta$. Eliminating L from the expressions for $h_{\mathrm{av.}}$ and N and rearranging in dimensionless groups, one obtains the Nusselt equation[9]

$$\frac{h_{\mathrm{av.}}N}{k} = 0.94\sqrt[4]{\frac{rg\rho^2N^3}{k\mu_f\Delta}} \tag{25}*$$

which may be rearranged as

$$h_{\mathrm{av.}} = \frac{4k}{3}\sqrt[3]{\frac{g\rho^2}{3\mu_f\Gamma}} = 0.925k\sqrt[3]{\frac{g\rho^2}{\mu_f\Gamma}}. \tag{25a}$$

Comparing the equations for the local and average coefficients, Eqs. 24 and 25a, it is found that, at any distance N from the point where condensation starts, the local coefficient is three-quarters of the average coefficient for the length N.

For a single *horizontal* tube, condensation occurring on the external surface and dripping off, analogous reasoning[9] leads to the expression†

$$\frac{h_{\mathrm{av.}}D}{k} = 0.73\sqrt[4]{\frac{rg\rho^2D^3}{k\mu_f\Delta}} \tag{26}$$

equivalent to

$$h_{\mathrm{av.}} = 0.76k\sqrt[3]{\frac{g\rho^2}{\mu_f\Gamma}}. \tag{26a}$$

For n horizontal tubes lying in a vertical bank, so that the condensate drips from one tube to the next below, one is obviously increasing the effective vertical height. Inspection of Eq. 26 shows that in that case $h_{\mathrm{av.}}$ is inversely proportional to the fourth root of the vertical height. Hence for horizontal tubes vertically banked one uses Eq. 26 and divides the value of $h_{\mathrm{av.}}$ thus obtained by the fourth root of n. Staggered tube arrangements are frequently equivalent to vertical banks in this sense.

---

* One must remember to use the *same* time unit in evaluating g, μ and k.

† This equation is far less plausible than the preceding one, *e.g.*, because it neglects the distortion of the film by surface tension, likely to be considerable, particularly on the undersurface of the pipe.

In each case the first form of the equations is convenient in problems in which Δ is known, and the second in those in which the total condensation per unit horizontal length (tube length for horizontal tubes or perimeter πD for vertical ones) is given.

Analysis of the equations shows that a tube of given dimensions is more effective in a horizontal than in a vertical position for the usual case where $N/Dn > 2.76$. Thus, if N/Dn is 100, horizontal tubes give an average surface coefficient approximately 2.5 times that for the vertical tubes.

The longer the vertical travel, the more condensate passes a given point and the thicker the film. This will finally develop turbulence, after which these equations must break down. This probably occurs in the neighborhood of $Re = 4mu\rho/\mu = 2100$. The expression for Reynolds number reduces to $Re = 4\Gamma/\mu$ for either a vertical or a horizontal tube. As Re increases above 2100, the total thickness of the condensate layer increases, but so does turbulence; the result is a decrease in the thickness of that portion of the layer which flows in streamline motion and an increase in the local individual coefficient of heat transfer. Provided the region beyond the critical point is not great, for a vertical tube it is safe to assume that the local h is constant at its critical minimum value, *i.e.*, at $h = k\sqrt[3]{g\rho^2/3\mu_f(2100\mu/4)} = k\sqrt[3]{g\rho^2/1575\mu^2}$. It will be recalled that this is 75 per cent of the value of $h_{av.}$ for the streamline region up to the critical point. A similar analysis breaks down for horizontal tubes because of the variability in slope of the surface. However, for conditions in the beginning of the turbulent range in banks of superimposed tubes, one will probably not be greatly in error in assuming, by analogy, the turbulent coefficient to be three-fourths of $h_{av.}$ for streamline flow at the critical limit.

In practical engineering work tube-wall temperature is never constant, so that one must integrate for its variation, as well as that of film thickness. In the important case of vertical tube condensers, operating under steady conditions, cooled by a fluid of substantially constant heat capacity over the temperature range involved, flowing in such a way that variation in the surface coefficient h of the cooling medium may be neglected and ignoring sensible relative to latent heat abstracted from the condensate, this is readily done.

Denoting by Δ_1 the overall temperature difference between condensing vapor and cooling fluid at the top of the tube, overall temperature difference is clearly $\Delta = \Delta_1 \pm b\Gamma$, where b is a constant equal to the ratio of the latent heat of the vapor to the product of mass rate and specific heat of the cooling fluid, and where the sign is positive if cooling fluid flows upward, negative if downward.

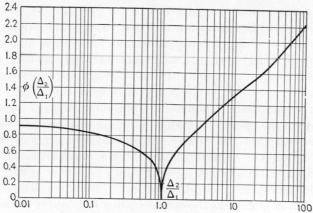

Fig. 50.—Function appearing in Eq. 27.

Likewise, the overall coefficient U is given by the relation, $\dfrac{1}{U} = \dfrac{1}{h\alpha} + \dfrac{L' \ln \alpha}{k'(\alpha - 1)} + \dfrac{L}{k}$, where h is the cooling-fluid surface coefficient, α is the ratio of cooling to condensing-wall area, L' is wall thickness; k' is wall conductivity, L is condensate film thickness and k is its conductivity. Calling $\dfrac{1}{h'} = \dfrac{1}{h\alpha} + \dfrac{L' \ln \alpha}{k'(\alpha - 1)}$, $U = \dfrac{kh'}{(k + h'L)}$. Integrating in the manner employed on page 135 one obtains

$$h'N\Delta_{\text{log mean}} = r\Gamma\left[1 + \frac{h'}{k}\sqrt[3]{\frac{3\mu_f\Delta_1}{g\rho^2 b}}\phi\left(\frac{\Delta_2}{\Delta_1}\right)\right] \tag{27}$$

where the values of $\phi(\Delta_2/\Delta_1)$* are shown in Fig. 50. The second term in the bracket is obviously the correction for the effect of the film of condensate.

Condensation of a Single Superheated Vapor.—As brought out by the work of Merkel and of others, with corresponding steam pressures and wall temperatures, superheated steam transfers heat at only a slightly higher rate than saturated steam. The rate per unit area, q/A, is obtained approximately by multiplying h for the saturated vapor by the difference between the saturation

---

* Calling $z = \dfrac{b\Gamma}{\Delta_1}$, $\phi\left(\dfrac{\Delta_2}{\Delta_1}\right) = \pm\dfrac{1}{\ln(\Delta_2/\Delta_1)}\displaystyle\int_{z_1}^{z_2}\dfrac{\sqrt[3]{z}\,dz}{1 \pm z}$, a negative sign indicating down-flow of cooling fluid.

temperature t_s and that of the wall t_w. Of course, if the wall temperature is above the saturation temperature, no condensation results and the steam is merely desuperheated, the coefficient being given by Eq. 11a, page 113.

2. Dropwise Condensation of Pure Vapor.—Impurities, often of the nature of fatty acids, which are sometimes accidentally present in boiler steam, or which are purposely added, such as benzyl mercaptan, are found to favor dropwise condensation.[10] While a complete list of the action of various compounds on the various metals and the amounts of promoter required to produce dropwise condensation for stated periods of time are not available, it is known that the coefficients of heat transfer h with fine-grained dropwise condensation of steam range from 11,000 to 17,000 B.t.u./(hr.) (sq. ft.) (deg. F. diff.) on copper or chromium-plated tubes[3] and 3000 to 4000 with brass.[11] These coefficients are so large, and the corresponding resistances are so small compared with the other resistances usually encountered, that the other resistances tend to be of controlling importance. In surface condensers with copper tubes where the velocity of the cooling water is 6 ft. per sec., the overall coefficient U is increased roughly 70 per cent when the steam condenses in dropwise fashion instead of forming a continuous film.

Allowance for Scale Deposits.—Clearly the thermal resistances of scale deposits will depend upon the nature and thickness of the deposit. In the absence of specific information, the following "scale-deposit factors" $h_s = k_s/L_s$, expressed in B.t.u./(hr.) (sq. ft.)(deg. F. diff.), are suggested for use in Eq. 15, page 116:

> For condensing steam: 3000.
>
> For condensing petroleum vapors: 500.
>
> For heating clear water: 3000.
>
> For heating muddy water: 600.
>
> For heating topped crude or petroleum residue: 200.

Illustration 4.—It is desired to design a tubular surface condenser to handle 300,000 lb./hr. of dry saturated steam condensing at an absolute pressure of 1.5 in. of mercury. It is planned to use Admiralty-metal tubes, $k = 63$, having outside and inside diameters of 1.00 in. and 0.902 in., respectively. Clean cooling water is available at 70°F., and it is planned tentatively to permit the cooling water to rise 15°, and to employ a water velocity of 7 ft./sec. The following items are to be calculated: (a) gal./min. of cooling water, (b) number of tubes in parallel, and (c) length of each tube.

Solution. *a.* Using data from the steam tables and neglecting heat losses and changes in kinetic energy, the cooling water rate is found to be $300,000(1041)/(15)(8.33)(60)$ or 41,500 U. S. gal./min.

b. At the specified water velocity, each tube handles $(0.785)(0.902/12)^2$ $(7)(60)(7.48)$ or 13.94 gal./min., and the number of tubes in parallel is hence $41,500/13.94$ or 2970.

c. By Eq. 12*c* the water-side coefficient is $160(1+0.75)(7)^{0.8}/(0.902)^{0.2} =$ 1350. Using a steam-side coefficient of 3000 and "scale-deposit factors" k_s/L_s of 3000 on both steam and water sides, by the resistance concept:

$$\frac{1}{U_1} = \frac{A_1}{h_v A_v} + \frac{L_s A_1}{k_{s,v} A_v} + \frac{L_m A_1}{k_m A_{\mathrm{av.}}} + \frac{L_s A_1}{k_{s,w} A_2} + \frac{A_1}{h_w A_w}$$

$$= \frac{1}{3000} + \frac{1}{3000} + \frac{0.049}{12(63)(0.951)} + \frac{1}{3000(0.902)} + \frac{1}{1350(0.902)}$$

$$= 0.000333 + 0.000333 + 0.000068 + 0.000369 + 0.000822 = \tfrac{1}{520}.$$

The terminal temperature differences are $91.8 - 70 = 21.8$ and 6.8. Since the overall coefficient is substantially constant, the logarithmic-mean temperature difference (12.9°F.) applies. By the heat-transfer equation the total outside surface is $300,000(1041)/(520)(12.9)$ or 46,500 sq. ft.

The external surface per tube equals $46,500/2970$ or 15.7, which corresponds to a tube length of $15.7(12/\pi) = 60$ ft. Since this length is longer than convenient, three or four passes could be used on the water side. Because the temperature of one of the fluids is substantially constant, the use of reversed flow would not reduce the mean temperature difference. In practice other water velocities and temperature rises would be investigated to determine those at which annual charges would be a minimum.

3. Condensation in Presence of a Noncondensable Gas.—

Except in the unusual cases where the presence of a small concentration of noncondensable gas causes a shift from film to dropwise condensation, the presence of the inert gas seriously reduces the coefficient of heat transfer, owing to the presence of the gas film of low thermal conductivity. For this reason vapor-heated apparatus should be well vented to prevent the accumulation of inert gas.

If the cooling surface is at a temperature below the dew point or saturation temperature, condensation results even though the main body of the mixture is highly superheated. Owing to a difference in partial pressures, the condensable vapor diffuses through the gas film and liquefies at the interface between the gas and condensate films. Owing to a temperature difference, sensible heat is transferred through the gas film. Both sensible and latent heat quantities are transferred through the condensate film and the tube wall to the cooling medium on the other side.

Quantitative treatment[12] of this case involves the vapor-diffusion equation, heat-transfer equation and material and energy balances, as developed in Chap. XVIII.

C. Boiling Liquids

Forced Circulation Type.—In this type of evaporator the unevaporated liquid from the vapor-liquid separator is recirculated by a pump through vertical or inclined tubes, usually

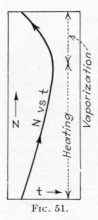

externally heated by condensing vapor. Although the liquid is at the temperature corresponding to the boiling point at the pressure in the overhead separator, the pressure at the bottom of the tubes is greater than this, owing to the fluid head and friction loss in the tubes, and hence as the liquid flows through the first part of the tubes only sensible heat is transferred, unless boiling should occur in the film next to the walls of the tube. As the liquid progresses up the tube, it becomes warmer and the pressure decreases, and it finally reaches a point where boiling occurs. Since above this

Fig. 51.

point the pressure drops off even faster than before, because of increased friction due to increased volume, the temperature will fall. This analysis is supported by the data of Fig. 51,[13] wherein the temperatures of both the fluid and the inner wall of the tube are plotted *vs.* the height of the vertical tube. If most of the tube length was used for warming the fluid, it would be expected that the coefficients would be of the general order of magnitude of those given by Eq. 12 for heating fluids without vaporization. This was found to be the case for data on sugar solutions[13] and a number of organic liquids, including aqueous solutions of methanol.[14]

In forced-circulation types involving horizontal tubes, the situation must be similar to that for the vertical types, except that the decrease in pressure is due only to friction and increase in kinetic energy.

Natural Circulation Evaporators.—As noted on pages 393 to 399, there are many types of natural-circulation evaporators, but general equations for h in the various types of evaporators are not available. However, since with aqueous solutions of low viscosity the individual coefficients are large and the corresponding resistance is small, the effect of scale deposits is apt to reduce materially the overall coefficient.   Substances such as calcium sulfate, which become less soluble with increase in temperature, are notorious as scale formers.

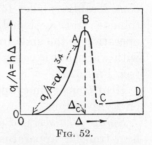

FIG. 52.

In the range of small to moderate temperature differences (2 to 20°), the individual coefficients from tube to liquid are found by several observers to increase with the 2.4 power of the temperature difference from tube to liquid.*   However, as the temperature difference is further increased, this rule eventually breaks down before the maximum

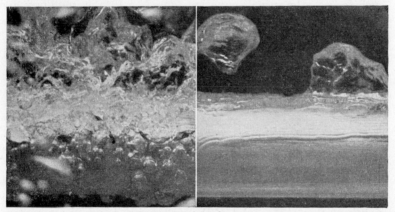

FIG. 52.*a*—Boiling of ethyl acetate at atmospheric pressure by a steam-heated aluminum tube. The left-hand picture was taken when the steam pressure was 12 lb. per sq. in. gauge, the overall temperature difference Δ was 73°F., and the heat-transfer rate was 41,000 B.t.u. per hr. per sq. ft. The right-hand picture was taken when the steam pressure was 40 lb. per sq. in. gauge, the overall temperature difference was 104°F., and the heat-transfer rate was 5800 B.t.u. per hr. per sq. ft. These data were taken from the recent work of E. T. Sauer (S.M. Thesis in Chemical Engineering, Massachusetts Institute of Technology, 1937). Photographs were taken with an exposure of 1/100,000 sec. by W. B. Tucker, using the Edgerton technique.

heat current density is reached, at B in Fig. 52.   In the zone CD where the heating surface is insulated from the liquid by a

* For a given small temperature difference from metal to liquid, the individual coefficient from metal to boiling water was the highest of 11 liquids tested [15] and n-butanol gave less than 1 per cent of that result.

nearly continuous film of vapor, the rate of heat transfer by conduction and radiation through the vapor film is relatively small. The so-called "critical temperature difference" Δ_c is considerably smaller for some organic liquids, such as benzene, toluene and methanol, than for water,[16] and consequently operation in the undesirable range CD is infrequently encountered with water but is easily obtained with low-boiling organic liquids (see Fig. 52a).

Heat transfer in evaporators is further discussed in the chapter on Evaporation.

Spray Chambers, Packed Towers, Etc.—In some types of heat-transfer apparatus the two fluids are brought into direct contact in an apparatus where the exact extent of the heat-transfer surface is difficult or impossible to evaluate. To handle such cases, the usual equation $dq = U \, dA \, \Delta$ is modified by substituting the relation $dA = aS \, dN$, where a represents the square feet of heat-transfer surface per cubic foot of apparatus, having the volume $S \, dN$ cu. ft., where S is the cross section and dN the length. This gives

$$dq = (Ua)(S \, dN)(\Delta) \tag{28}$$

and the product of the two unknowns, U and a, is evaluated as a single term Ua, being expressed as B.t.u./(hr.) (cu. ft.) (deg. F. diff.). This concept of a coefficient on a volumetric basis is applied in later chapters.

Optimum Velocity (Economic Balance).—In the above equations it will be noted that velocity is an important variable and one largely within the control of the designer. Thus, in air heaters for ventilating systems, driers, humidifiers, etc., one may use a high air velocity, thereby securing a high coefficient of heat transfer, but this is done at the expense of a high pressure drop. If desired, one may go to the other extreme and use a very low air velocity, requiring therefore a large heating surface but involving a low pressure drop and accordingly only a small power consumption. The decision as to the velocity to be employed in a given case requires an economic balance between cost of power and cost of heating surface. The curves in Fig. 53 have been calculated for the heating of 10,000 cu. ft. per min. of air from 70 to 150°F., using steam condensing at 220°F. in a heater made of staggered standard 1-in. pipes. The coefficients were determined from Fig. 40, page 112, and the pressure drops from Eq. 21, page 96. The cost of heating surface was taken as $1.40 per sq. ft. including all installation costs. The cost of power delivered to the air, corrected for efficiencies of fan and motor, was assumed to be 5 cents per kw.-hr. The drier for which this apparatus was designed operates 7200 hr. per year, *i.e.*, 300 days. The annual charge against the heating surface for depreciation, interest, taxes, maintenance, etc., was taken as 15 per cent.

It will be noted that the point of lowest total cost corresponds to a linear velocity of only 8 ft. per sec. through the minimum clear area. The explanation for this result is that the percentage charged off against depreciation is lower than is justifiable under other than exceptional condi-

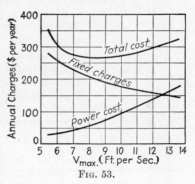

Fig. 53.

tions. High fixed charges demand high velocities; high power cost, the reverse. There is often a tendency on the part of the designer to reduce initial investment by an installation that is in reality uneconomical because of excessive operating costs.

Nomenclature

(The units are based on feet, pounds, hours, degrees Fahrenheit and B.t.u. Any other consistent set may be used in the dimensionless relations given, but for the few dimensional equation. the units of this table must be used.)

A = area of heat-transfer surface, sq. ft.

$A_{av.}$ = average value of A, sq. ft.

a = heat-transfer surface per unit volume of apparatus, sq. ft./cu. ft.

a' = a ratio, A/N, sq. ft./ft.

B = effective thickness of film, ft.; $B = k/h$.

b = a constant.

C, c = specific heats.

C_p = specific heat at constant pressure, B.t.u./(lb.) (deg. F.).

d = prefix, indicating differential.

D = diameter, ft.

$D_{eq.}$ = equivalent diameter, ft.

D' = diameter, inches.

e = base of natural logarithms, 2.718.

F =ratio of true mean temperature difference to that for counterflow.

f =friction factor in Fanning equation, dimensionless.

G =mass velocity, equals w/S, lb./(hr.)(sq. ft. of cross section occupied by fluid).

$G_{max.}$ =mass velocity through minimum free area in a row of pipes normal to the fluid stream, lb./(hr.)(sq. ft.).

$G'_{max.}$ =mass velocity, lb./(sec.)(sq. ft.).

g =acceleration due to gravity, 4.18×10^8 ft./(hr.)(hr.).

H =height of vertical plane, ft.

h =local individual coefficient of heat transfer, equals $dq/dA \; \Delta$, B.t.u./(hr.)(sq. ft.)(deg. F. diff.).

$h_m.$ =mean value of h for entire apparatus, based on $\Delta_m.$.

$h_{a.m.}$ =average h, arbitrarily based on arithmetic-mean temperature difference.

h_s =scale factor =conductivity of scale/thickness of scale.

k =thermal conductivity of fluid, B.t.u./(hr.)(sq. ft.)(unit temperature gradient, deg. F./ft.).

$$k_{av.} = \int_1^2 \left(k \; dt \right) \div (t_2 - t_1).$$

$k_f = k$ at the "film" temperature, $t_f = (t + t_w)/2$.

L =linear dimension; thickness of conductor, ft.

M =mass.

m =hydraulic radius, ft.; equals S/p'.

N =length of heat-transfer surface, heated length, ft.   See Fig. 43.

n =number, dimensionless.

p' =perimeter in contact with fluid, ft.

Q =quantity of heat, B.t.u.

q, q_0 =rate of heat flow, B.t.u./hr.

R =individual thermal resistance, $L/k_{av.}A_{av.}.$.

Re = Reynolds number, $4mG/\mu = 4\Gamma/\mu$.

$Re_f = Re$ at film temperature t_f, where $t_f = (t + t_w)/2$.

r =latent heat of condensation, B.t.u./lb.

S =cross section, filled by fluid, in plane normal to direction of fluid flow, sq. ft.

T =temperature, deg. F. abs.

T_1, T_2 =inlet and outlet bulk temperatures, respectively, of *warmer* fluid, deg. F.

t =bulk temperature (based on heat balance), deg. F.

t_s =saturation temperature of vapor, deg. F.

t_w =wall temperature, deg. F.

t_1, t_2 =inlet and outlet bulk temperatures of *colder* fluid, deg. F.

t_∞ =temperature of stream of great depth, ambient temperature, deg. F.

t =temperature difference (in discussion of dimensions).

t', t'' =bulk temperature of fluid at any point in entrance and exit passes, respectively, of U-tube in discussion of $\Delta_m.$ in multi-pass exchangers.

U =overall coefficient of heat transfer, B.t.u./(hr.)(sq. ft.) (deg. F.).

V, u =average velocity, volumetric rate divided by cross section filled by fluid, ft./hr.

V_∞ =velocity of stream of great depth, ft./hr.

V_s =value of V, ft./sec.

W, w =mass rate of flow per tube, lb./(hr.)(tube).

x, y, z =variables.

$Z = (T_1 - T_2)/(t_2 - t_1)$.

α =alpha, a ratio.

β =beta, volumetric coefficient of thermal expansion, having units of reciprocal of temperature.

Γ =gamma (capital), mass rate of flow, lb./(hr.)(ft. of wetted periphery measured on a plane normal to direction of fluid flow); $w/\pi D$ for a vertical and $w/2N$ for a horizontal tube.

γ =gamma (lower case), surface tension, lb./hr.[2]

Δ =delta, temperature difference, deg. F., either overall or individual.

$\Delta_{a.m.}$, $\Delta_{l.m.}$ =arithmetic and logarithmic means of terminal temperature differences, respectively, deg. F.

Δ_m =true mean value of the terminal temperature differences, deg. F.

∂ =delta, partial derivative.

θ =theta, time, hr.

μ =mu, viscosity at bulk temperature, lb./(hr.) (ft.); equals 2.42 times centipoises.

μ_f =viscosity, lb./(hr.)(ft.), at arithmetic mean of wall and fluid temperatures.

μ_w =viscosity at wall temperature, lb./(hr.)(ft.).

π =pi, 3.1416.

ρ =rho, density, lb./cu. ft.

ρ_∞ =density of stream of great depth, lb./cu. ft.

ϕ =phi, function defined by $\phi^{1/3} = (\mu/\mu_f)^{1/3}(1 + 0.015\sqrt[3]{Gr})$.

ψ =psi, function.

PART III. RADIATION

Introduction.—All bodies emit radiant energy and the rate of energy emission always rises with the temperature of the body.[*] Furthermore, the spectra of the radiation emitted by solids and liquids are always continuous. When radiation strikes a body, part of it is absorbed and quantitatively transformed into heat, part is reflected, and part may be transmitted unchanged if

[*] The type of radiation under discussion is called *thermal* radiation, in contradistinction to fluorescence, phosphorescence, radiation excited by electric discharge, and the like.

the body is not completely opaque. The **total emissive power** E of a surface is the total radiant energy emitted per unit time from a unit area. If the surface is exposed to uniform radiation from a source that fills the field of view of the surface, the fraction of the incident radiant energy which is absorbed is termed the hemispherical absorptivity of the surface, hereinafter called merely the **absorptivity** a; similarly, the fraction reflected is called the **reflectivity.** For opaque bodies, to which all later treatment is restricted, the sum of absorptivity and reflectivity equals unity. Certain bodies, such as lampblack or a surface coated with it, absorb nearly all the radiation falling upon them. An ideal body which absorbs all the radiation striking its surface is defined as the **black body.** No actual surfaces are absolutely black in this sense, but many nonmetallic bodies absorb approximately 90 per cent of the incident radiation. The **emissivity** p of an actual surface is defined as the total emissive power E of the surface divided by the emissive power of a black body at the same temperature, $p = E/E_B$.*

Visualize two parallel plane surfaces, S_1 and S_2, having areas that are large relative to the distance between them. Both surfaces are maintained at the same temperature; S_1 is a black body, absorbing all the radiation falling upon it; the other, S_2, has an absorptivity less than unity. The space between is evacuated so there is nothing to interfere with the travel of radiant energy. The absorption of energy from the black body by the surface S_2 is $E_B a$, and the reflection from S_2 to S_1 is $E_B(1-a)$. The emission from S_2 is $E_B p$ and must be of such magnitude that the sum of it and the reflected energy must equal the emission E_B from S_1, since otherwise there would be a net transfer of heat between two bodies at the same temperature. Therefore, $E_B(1-a)$ plus $E_B p$ equals E_B, and *the absorptivity a equals the emissivity p* under these isothermal conditions. Since the absorptivity of a surface can never exceed unity, the above relation indicates that the emissivity can never exceed unity. *i.e.,* no surface can emit more radiation than a black body at

---

* The reader is cautioned to bear in mind the frequent loose use of terms in the literature, where for example "absorptive power" is sometimes used to cover the term herein called "absorptivity." "Absorptive power" connotes an actual amount of energy per unit time. Absorptivity and reflectivity are merely numerical ratios.

the same temperature, and hence the black body is sometimes called the perfect radiator.

In the light of the preceding paragraph, it is clear that, if a small peephole were made in the surface of the black body in the above case, the amount of energy per unit time streaming through this peephole (the sum of emission and reflection from the non-black surface) must be equal to that emitted from a black body at the same temperature. A more detailed analysis shows that this conclusion is valid regardless of the shape or material of construction of the enclosure, so long as it is isothermal. Indeed, the isothermal enclosure provided with a peephole serves as the basis of all temperature standards above the range of the gas thermometer.

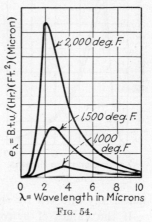

Investigation of the spectra of black-body radiation gives curves such as those shown in Fig. 54. These curves, which show the distribution of radiant energy throughout the range of wavelength, are fixed at any given temperature and are a function of temperature only. The energy lying between the

FIG. 54.

wavelengths λ and $\lambda+d\lambda$ is obviously proportional to $d\lambda$ and equals $e_{\lambda B}\, d\lambda$ where $e_{\lambda B}$ is the **monochromatic emissive power** of the black body per unit wavelength, expressed as energy per unit time per unit area and per unit wavelength. The value of $e_{\lambda B}$ always reaches a maximum at a characteristic wavelength λ_m dependent on the temperature; expressing wavelength in microns and temperature in degrees Fahrenheit absolute, λ_m equals $5200/T$. As the temperature rises, the whole curve rises and the maximum moves in the direction of shorter wavelength (see Fig. 54). It is clear that the total emissive power E_B of the black body at any given temperature is the integral of the area under the corresponding curve, *i.e.*, E_B equals $\int_0^\infty e_{\lambda B}\, d\lambda$.

The ratio of the monochromatic emissive power e_λ of an *actual* surface to that of the black body at the same temperature is called the **monochromatic emissivity**, *i.e.*, $p = e_\lambda / e_{\lambda B}$. The statements made as to the equality of emissivity and absorptivity of a given surface as applied to radiation of all wavelengths must apply likewise to each individual wavelength, since otherwise the character of the black-body spectrum would depend on the surface.   Hence the monochromatic emissivity p_λ equals the monochromatic absorptivity a_λ for any wavelength and depends only upon the character of the specific surface and its temperature. Because the radiation from a black body, both monochromatic

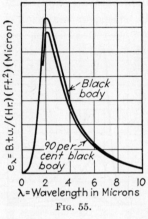

and total, is fixed at a given temperature, the value of p_λ or of p at that temperature fixes definitely the energy emitted from the surface. On the other hand, the amount of energy absorbed by a surface is a function of the nature and intensity of the radiation to which it is exposed as well as of the surface absorptivities a_λ and a. The character and temperature of the surface are therefore inadequate to define fully the energy received by *absorption*.   There is no experimental evidence that the absorptivity is materially affected by the intensity of the incident radiation.

FIG. 55.

If the values of p_λ for an actual body were constant at all wavelengths, its spectral distribution curve, e_λ vs. λ, would be similar in shape to that for a black body at the same temperature, and at each wavelength the height of the curve, e_λ, would be the same fraction of $e_{\lambda B}$ (Fig. 55).   Such a body is defined as a **gray body.***   In the treatment of gray bodies one can deal directly with total emissive power and ignore the monochromatic effects when considering total energy exchange.   While the phenomena of radiation are extraordinarily complex, fortunately, under the conditions encountered in most engineering work, the interrelationships can be greatly simplified.   Thus, the temperature levels encountered in engineering practice are such that the bulk of the energy lies in the infrared spectrum in contrast to sunlight

* Since experimental evidence indicates that p_λ, the emissivity at any wavelength, is but little affected by temperature, a truly gray body will have a total absorptivity a and a total emissivity p unaffected by temperature.

which has its maximum intensity in the visible spectrum.* The great majority of solids except polished metals, approximate the gray-body state under such conditions of infrared radiation and can be reasonably treated as gray bodies. Reliable data on p and a are meager, and factors such as differences due to surface roughness and degree of glazing cause variations in the results obtained. However, for most surfaces except polished metals,† p and a are high and range from 0.7 to 0.97, indicating the use of a value of 0.9 where other data are unavailable.

With polished metals the values of a and p are low at low temperatures and increase with temperature, owing to considerable variations of a_λ and p_λ with wavelength. Despite this, for many problems a single average value for a and p for a given metal is a workable approximation.

Stefan-Boltzmann Radiation Law for Black Bodies.—Based on Tyndall's measurements of the emission of radiation from platinum black, Stefan noted in 1879 that the rate of energy emission was proportional to the fourth power of the absolute temperature. A few years later Boltzmann deduced this relation for black bodies by thermodynamic reasoning. The relation known as the Stefan-Boltzmann law for black bodies is $E_B = \sigma T^4$, in which σ is the Stefan-Boltzmann constant, revised several times as experimental technique improved. The present value of σ is 0.173×10^{-8} when E_B is expressed in B.t.u. per hour per square foot and T is expressed in degrees Fahrenheit absolute.‡ Employing these units, the Stefan-Boltzmann law becomes:

$$E_B = 0.173\left(\frac{T}{100}\right)^4. \qquad (29)$$

Let A represent the surface of the black body expressed in square feet and q the rate of emission in B.t.u. per hour. If all parts

* At a given temperature the absorptivity of a surface for sunlight may be considerably different from its absorptivity for the longer wavelengths predominating in low-temperature radiation.

† Unoxidized aluminum plate and foil have emissivities of 0.04 to 0.06; even when oxidized at 1100°F.; because of the transparency of the thin coating of oxide, p is only 0.2.

‡ When E_B is expressed in gram calories per second per square centimeter, and T in degrees centigrade absolute, σ is 1.37×10^{-12}.

of the black emitting surface are at a uniform temperature, $q = E_B A$; if the surface temperature varies, $q = \int E_B \, dA$.

Interchange between Black Surfaces

If one observes at a distance the thermal radiation from a black body of any shape whatever, the result is identical with the radiation one would receive from another black body, at the same temperature, whose actual surface in position and area is identical with the projected area of the first body. It is frequently assumed that the same is true for bodies that are not black bodies, assuming that the projected surface is identical in character with the actual one. This is approximately true in the case of many industrial surfaces that have high emissivities, but breaks down in the case of the polished metals. This rule is capable of mathematical formulation in terms of the important cosine law.

Derivation of General Differential Equation.—Consider a small black-surface element dA_1 of total emissive power E_B radiating in all directions from one side. The problem is to determine what portion of its radiation is intercepted by some other small black surface of element dA_2. Figure 56 presents the details of the problem. Obviously the radiation per unit time $dq_{1\to2}$ from dA_1 intercepted by dA_2 is proportional to the *apparent* area dA_1' as viewed from dA_2. Furthermore, the interception of the emitted beam is proportional to the *apparent* area dA_2' of dA_2 taken normal to the beam. Also the radiation received at dA_2 will vary inversely as the square of the distance or radius r separating dA_1 and dA_2. Algebraically stated, these relations give the equation

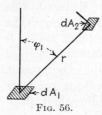

Fig. 56.

$$dq_{1\to2} = i_1(dA_1')(dA_2')/r^2 \qquad (30)$$

where i_1 is a proportionality constant. This is the "square-of-the distance law" familiar from physics experiments in illumination. Since dA_1' equals dA_1 cos ϕ_1* and dA_2' equals dA_2 cos ϕ_2, this may be written

$$dq_{1\to2} = i_1(dA_1 \cos \phi_1)(dA_2 \cos \phi_2)/r^2. \qquad (30a)$$

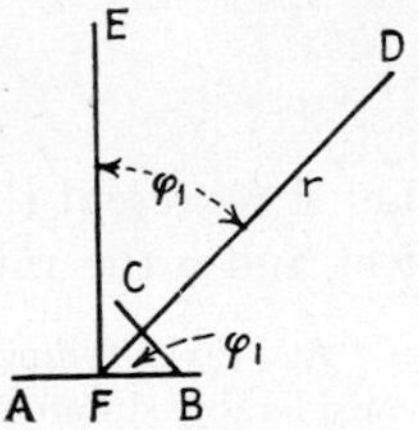

Fig. 57.

This equation is sometimes expressed in a different form. Let the small

* This may be seen from Fig. 57, which shows an enlarged view of dA_1 having side AB, and of dA_1' having side BC. Since AB and BC, enclosing angle ABC, are, respectively, perpendicular to EF and DF, BC/AB equals cos ABC. Since BC/AB equals dA_1'/dA_1, dA_1' equals dA_1 cos ϕ_1.

solid angle subtended by dA_2 at dA_1 be called $d\omega_1$ (see Fig. 58). By definition a solid angle is numerically the area subtended on a sphere of unit radius, or, for a sphere of radius r, the intercepted area divided by r^2. Hence one may write $d\omega_1 = dA_2'/r^2 = dA_2 \cos \phi_2/r^2$, and Eq. 30$a$ becomes

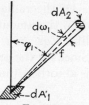

$$dq_{1\rightarrow 2} = i_1 \, dA_1 \cos \phi_1 \, d\omega_1. \qquad (30b)$$

Since Eq. 30a is symmetrical with respect to dA_1 and dA_2, and to $\cos \phi_1$, and $\cos \phi_2$, a third way of writing Eq. 30a is

$$dq_{1\rightarrow 2} = i_1 \, dA_2 \cos \phi_2 \, d\omega_2. \qquad (30c)$$

The various forms of Eq. 30 are completely equivalent; the choice among them in subsequent use will depend on the particular problem. The proportionality factor i_1 will be referred to as the **intensity of radiation** from the surface dA_1.

Fig. 58.

The rate of radiation dq_1 in *all* directions from one side of dA_1 is given by integration of Eq. 30b over the complete hemi-spherical angle $\pi/2$ above dA_1; $dq_1 = dA_1 i_1 \int d\omega_1 \cos \phi_1$. Since by definition E_{B1} equals dq_1/dA_1, the relation between E_{B1} and i_1 is obtained by

$$E_{B1} = i_1 \int_0^{\frac{\pi}{2}} \cos \phi_1 \, d\omega_1. \qquad (30d)$$

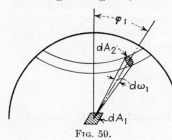

Referring to Fig. 59, describe a hemisphere of radius r around dA_1. Let dA_2 be a small surface element of the surface of the hemisphere, the radius r making the angle ϕ_1 with the normal to dA_1. Considering as an element of area of the hemisphere, a ring of width $r \, d\phi_1$ and a length of $2\pi r \sin \phi_1$, the area dA_2 is $2\pi r^2 \sin \phi_1 \, d\phi_1$. Substitution

Fig. 59.

of this value of dA_2 in Eq. 30d gives

$$E_{B1} = 2\pi i_1 \int_0^{\frac{\pi}{2}} \sin \phi_1 \cos \phi_1 \, d\phi_1 = i_1 \Big(\sin^2 \phi_1 \Big)_0^{\frac{\pi}{2}} = \pi i_1.$$

Thus the intensity i of the cosine law is found to be the total emissive power of a black body, divided by π:

$$i = \frac{E_B}{\pi} = \frac{\sigma T^4}{\pi}. \qquad (30e)$$

The same result is obtained by considering the upper surface to be an infinite plate parallel to dA_1, rather than the hemisphere considered above.

Of the radiation emitted per unit time by the black element dA_2, the amount $dq_{2\to1}$ intercepted by dA_1 is given by equations like Eqs. 30a, 30b and 30c, except that i_1 is replaced by i_2. Since for the present case of black bodies all radiation intercepted is absorbed, the net rate of interchange, dq_{net}, or $dq_{1\to2}$, minus $dq_{2\to1}$,

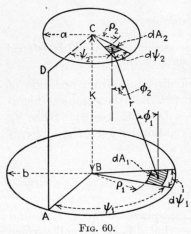

FIG. 60.

is given by equations like Eqs. 30a, 30b and 30c, except that i_1 is replaced by i_1-i_2, which equals $(E_{B1}-E_{B2})/\pi$.

Net Rate of Radiation between Two Finite Black Bodies.—The application of this relation to the evaluation of the *net* interchange between finite black surfaces will be illustrated by a simple case, that of two parallel disks directly opposed, separated by the distance K. Figure 60 shows the details of the problem. The larger and smaller disks have radii a and b, and areas A_1 and A_2, respectively. The angles ψ_1 and ψ_2 are measured from the reference plane $ABCD$. The elementary surfaces dA_1 and dA_2 lie at local radii ρ_1 and ρ_2, respectively. Equation 30, with the replacement of i by the term $(E_{B1}-E_{B2})/\pi$, is convenient to use:

$$dq_{net} = \frac{(E_{B1}-E_{B2})\,dA_1 \cos\phi_1\,dA_2\cos\phi_2}{\pi r^2} \tag{30f}$$

By examination of Fig. 60, the terms in this equation may be identified as follows:

$$dA_1 = d\rho_1\,\rho_1\,d\psi_1; \quad dA_2 = d\rho_2\,\rho_2\,d\psi_2;$$
$$\cos\phi_1 = K/r; \quad \cos\phi_2 = K/r;$$
$$r = \sqrt{\rho_1{}^2 + \rho_2{}^2 - 2\rho_1\rho_2\cos(\psi_2-\psi_1) + K^2}.$$

Substituting these five relations in Eq. 30f and inserting limits to cover the whole area of each disk give the relation:[17]

$$q_{net} = (E_{B1}-E_{B2})\int_0^{2\pi}\int_0^{2\pi}\int_0^a\int_0^b \frac{\rho_1\rho_2 K^2\,d\rho_1\,d\rho_2\,d\psi_1\,d\psi_2}{\pi[\rho_1{}^2+\rho_2{}^2-2\rho_1\rho_2\cos(\psi_2-\psi_1)+K^2]}$$
$$= (E_{B1}-E_{B2})\left\{\frac{\pi}{2}[(b^2+a^2+K^2-\sqrt{(b^2+a^2+K^2)^2-4a^2b^2})]\right\}. \tag{31}$$

Since the radiant-heat interchange between the disk of area A_1 and an infinite parallel plane replacing A_2 is $(E_{B1} - E_{B2})A_1$, it is seen that the bracket in Eq. 31 represents $A_1 F_{1 \to 2}$, where $F_{1 \to 2}$ represents the fraction of the radiation leaving one side of A_1 in all directions, which is intercepted by disk A_2. By the symmetry of the problem, the bracket may alternatively be considered to be represented by $A_2 F_{2 \to 1}$. Since either $A_1 (= \pi b^2)$ or $A_2 (= \pi a^2)$ may be factored out of the bracket, the choice of A_1 gives one value to $F_{1 \to 2}$ and the choice of A_2 another value of $F_{2 \to 1}$.

The general equation of radiant-heat interchange between two black surfaces is consequently

$$q_{net} = (E_{B1} - E_{B2})AF_A = 0.173A \left[\left(\frac{T_1}{100} \right)^4 - \left(\frac{T_2}{100} \right)^4 \right] F_A \quad (31a)$$

in which A is the area of one of the surfaces and F_A is a geometrical factor dependent only on the shape of the system and on which of the two surfaces is used for evaluating A.

In the case of a small black body of area A_1 and temperature T_1 completely enclosed, it is obvious that all the radiation leaving A_1 in all directions is intercepted by the walls of the enclosure at T_2, i.e., $F_{1 \to 2}$ is unity. The net exchange is then

$$q_{net} = (E_{B1} - E_{B2})A_1 = 0.173A_1 \left[\left(\frac{T_1}{100} \right)^4 - \left(\frac{T_2}{100} \right)^4 \right]. \quad (31b)$$

The value of F_A corresponding to the case of finite disks considered in detail above is presented as curve 1 of Fig. 61 for the special case of disks of equal radius. Figure 61 also includes as curve 2 the factor F_A for squares. The factors for many other shapes of industrial importance are available in algebraic or graphical form.

Interchange between Gray Surfaces

Analysis of the problem of interchange between surfaces makes it clear that structures having identical surface characteristics, relative temperature distributions and shape factors, but differing in dimensions will have at all points identical rates of total radiation interchange per unit area at corresponding points. Since this is true, the total rate of energy interchange over a given area will be proportional to that area, despite the possibility of considerable variations from point to point in the area.

Granting that the heat exchange is due predominantly to the maintenance of a relatively uniform high temperature T_1 over one portion of the area of the structure and a relatively constant lower temperature T_2 over another, and that net energy quantities transferred from other areas are negligible, this is equivalent to saying that the total energy interchange per unit time can be expressed by an equation of the form

$$q = 0.173A\left[\left(\frac{T_1}{100}\right)^4 - \left(\frac{T_2}{100}\right)^4\right]F_{AE} \tag{32}$$

in which q represents the net rate of heat radiation, B.t.u. per hour; A the area of one of the two surfaces, square feet; F_{AE} a factor which allows for the average angle throughout which one surface views the other and is dependent on which surface is chosen to use in the area term A, and also makes allowance for the emissivities p_1 and p_2 of the two surfaces. From the character of the preceding discussion it should be clear that for any structure of a specific geometrical shape, built of surfaces of specific radiation characteristics, it ought to be possible to evaluate the function F_{AE} by integration of the fundamental equation given. However, it is not surprising to find that the integrations themselves are extraordinarily complicated. Indeed, in many cases one can only make approximations, which are not too accurate. However, these integrations have been carried out for a relatively large number of cases of engineering importance. It has been found possible to approximate the factor F_{AE} of Eq. 32 by the product of two factors: the geometrical factor already discussed, and a factor F_E to allow for the nonblack character of the surfaces. Equation 32 then becomes

$$q = 0.173A\left[\left(\frac{T_1}{100}\right)^4 - \left(\frac{T_2}{100}\right)^4\right]F_A F_E. \tag{32a}$$

The factors F_A and F_E are tabulated for a number of important cases in Table I, accompanied by Figs. 61 and 62. For other cases occasionally encountered one must go to the literature. Since in the expression for F_E the factor p must serve as the emissivity of the surface and as its absorptivity for radiation from the other surface (which is at a different temperature). and since absorptivity depends more on the "temperature" of the radiation being absorbed than on the temperature of the absorber, the value of p for the sink should be evaluated at the temperature of the *source*. Since the radiation emitted by the sink is small compared to that from the source, the emissivity of the source is more important than its absorptivity for radiation of a lower "temperature"; hence the value of p for the source should also be evaluated at the temperature of the *source*. The

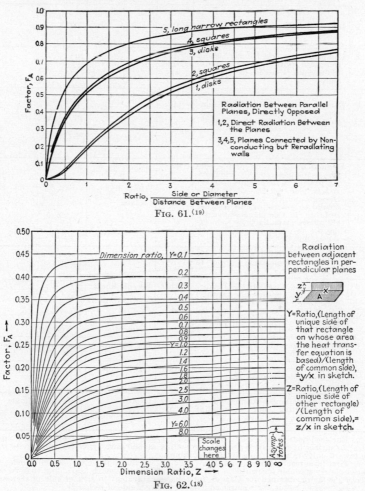

Fig. 61.[19]

Fig. 62.[18]

approximation here involved is well within the precision with which emissivities are known for most industrial surfaces. The use of Eq. 32a with values of F_A and F_E of Table I is theoretically restricted to cases where the source and sink are at a uniform temperature.

TABLE I.[18]—RADIATION BETWEEN SOLIDS.   FACTORS FOR USE IN EQ. 32a
(*Hottel*)

Case	Surfaces between which radiation is being interchanged	Area, A	Angle factor, F_A	Emissivity factor, F_E
1	Infinite parallel planes............	Either	1	$\dfrac{1}{\dfrac{1}{p_1}+\dfrac{1}{p_2}-1}$
2	Completely enclosed body, small compared with enclosing body. (Subscripts 1 refer to enclosed body.)	A_1 (Note a)	1	p_1
3	Concentric spheres or infinite cylinders. (Subscripts 1 refer to enclosed bodies, 2 to surroundings.)	A_1	1	$\dfrac{1}{\dfrac{1}{p_1}+\dfrac{A_1}{A_2}\left(\dfrac{1}{p_2}-1\right)}$, or $\dfrac{1}{\dfrac{1}{p_1}+\dfrac{1}{p_2}-1}$ (Note b)
4	Element dA and semi-infinite surface, latter generated by line moving parallel to its original position and to plane of dA. Pass plane through normal to dA, perpendicular to generating line of other surface. In this plane ϕ' and ϕ'' are angles made by lines connecting dA to edges of surface, with the normal to dA.	dA	$\dfrac{\sin\phi'-\sin\phi''}{2}$ Only plane angles are involved	p_1p_2
5	Two equal parallel circular disks with centers on same normal to their planes.	Either	Fig. 61, line 1	$p_1p_2 < F_E$, $\dfrac{1}{\dfrac{1}{p_1}+\dfrac{1}{p_2}-1} > F_E$ (Note d)
6	Two equal squares in parallel planes and directly opposite one another.	Either	Fig. 61, line 2	(Note f)
7	Two equal rectangles in parallel planes and directly opposite one another.	Either	$F_A = \sqrt{F_A'\times F_A''}$ (Note c)	
8	Two rectangles with a common side, in perpendicular planes.	Either	Fig. 61	p_1p_2, approximate (Note f)
9	Parallel squares or disks, connected by nonconducting but reradiating black walls.	Either	Fig. 61, line 3	p_1p_2, approximate (Note f)
10	Parallel rectangles connected by nonconducting but reradiating black walls.	Either	(Note e)	p_1p_2, approximate (Note f)

a. Enclosed body must contain no negative curvature if A_1 is used.   Replace any "dimples" in surface by equivalent planes in evaluating A_1, and raise "effective" emissivity from p_1 toward unity in proportion to depth of dimple.

b. First form results from assumption of completely diffuse reflection, second if reflection is completely specular (mirrorlike).   True value will be very much nearer first than second.

c. F_A' = factor obtained for Case 6, for squares equivalent to smaller side of rectangle. F_A'' = same factor, for squares equivalent to larger side of rectangle.

d. Exact treatment is dependent on kind of reflection, when areas are small compared to distance apart, F_E is nearer p_1p_2; when areas are large or close together, F_E is nearer $\dfrac{1}{\dfrac{1}{p_1}+\dfrac{1}{p_2}-1}$.

e. Obtained from Case 9 as Case 7 is obtained from Case 6.   See Note c and Fig. 61.

f. An exact formulation is impossible unless the entire system is completely described. However, where p_1 and p_2 are 0.8 or higher, the approximations given are satisfactory.

Enclosures at Nonuniform Temperature.—Although it is beyond the province of this book to treat fully the complex cases of enclosures of nonuniform temperature, certain simplified cases will be considered to indicate the method of attack. If an enclosure consisting of black surfaces can be divided into a number of zones, each at a uniform temperature, the fraction of the total radiation from any one of the zones, which is intercepted by one of the other zones, may be evaluated by suitable integration or by the use of plots giving the geometrical factor F_A for Eq. 32a. Generally in a design problem the temperature of not more than two of the zones will be specified, the source and the sink. Other zones will take up equilibrium temperatures obtainable by a heat balance on the zone, which may involve allowance for external heat losses. The sole objective in a problem is frequently the determination of the net interchange between the source and the sink, including both direct interchange and reradiation from other surfaces. This need not always involve a determination of the temperatures of the other surfaces present.

In some enclosures the temperature varies continuously along the wall. Certain cases of this type may be treated exactly, such as the interchange between two disks at uniform but different temperatures, connected by nonconducting but reradiating walls. Although the solution of this problem is quite complex, the results can be presented in simple form (curve 3, Fig. 61). It is found that the actual heat interchange per unit area is a fraction of that which would occur if the two disks were separated by an infinitesimal distance (*i.e.*, the case of infinite parallel planes), and that this fraction is independent of the temperatures of the disks and completely determined by the ratio of their diameter to distance apart. This factor of interchange between planes is presented in Fig. 61 as curves 3, 4 and 5. It is clear that the case just discussed covers such industrial cases as the loss of heat through furnace peepholes and the interchange of heat in certain types of electric furnaces.

Illustration 5.—A muffle-type furnace, in which the carborundum muffle forms a continuous floor of dimensions 15 by 20 ft., has its ultimate heat-receiving surface in the form of several rows of tubes above and parallel to the muffle, the distance from the muffle top to the lowest row of tubes being 10 ft. The tubes fill the furnace top, equal in area to that of the carborundum floor. The average temperature of the upper surface of the floor is 2100°F.; the tubes are at 600°F. The side walls of the chamber are assumed substantially nonconducting but reradiating, and are at some equilibrium temperature between 600° and 2100°F., such that they radiate just as much heat as they receive. The tubes are steel, oxidized. Find (a) the total net radiation between the two surfaces, taking into account the reradiation from the side walls and (b) the direct radiant-heat interchange between the tubes and the 15-ft. by 10-ft. back wall, if the latter has an average temperature of 1500°F.

Solution. a. The net radiation between the carborundum and the tubes, with allowance made for the effect of the reradiating side walls, is obtained by evaluating F_A for Case 10 instead of Case 5. From curve 4 (Fig. 61), $F_A' = 0.63$ and $F_A'' = 0.69$. Then $F_A = \sqrt{(0.63)(0.69)} = 0.66$, which means that the carborundum and tubes interchange directly and indirectly, by the aid of the side walls, 66 per cent as much radiant heat as if they were so close together that they could be considered infinite parallel planes, viewing nothing but each other:

$$q = 0.173(300)[(25.6)^4 - (10.6)^4](0.66)(0.9)(0.7) = 8,960,000 \text{ B.t.u./hr.}$$

b. Since the tubes represent a 15- by 20-ft. rectangle, this problem may be classified under Case 8, Table I, interchange between two rectangles, 15 by 20 ft. and 15 by 10 ft., in perpendicular planes, and having a common 15-ft. side. Figure 62 shows that the interchange of heat may be based on either area. Let A equal the plane of the tubes, 15 by 20 ft. Then, $Y = {}^{20}\!/_{15} = 1.33$, $Z = {}^{10}\!/_{15} = 0.67$ and $F_A = 0.13$. If the emissivity of the back wall is assumed to be 0.85,

$$q = 0.173(300)[(19.6)^4 - (10.6)^4](0.13)(0.85)(0.90) = 693,000 \text{ B.t.u./hr.}$$

Illustration 6.—The distribution of radiant heat to the different rows of tubes in a tube nest irradiated from one side falls under Case 4 of Table I. Figure 63 represents the summarized results obtained by the application of the method described in Case 4 to the special problem of radiation from a plane to one or two rows above and parallel to the plane when the tubes are staggered and placed on equilateral triangular centers.

a. Suppose it is desired to consider the case of $4\frac{1}{2}$-in. tubes on 9-in. centers. The heat interchange between two infinite parallel planes will be taken as a basis of comparison. If one plane is replaced by a nest of tubes, many rows deep, the heat interchange will be the same. According to Fig. 63, curve 3, the first row of the tubes will intercept 0.66 of the total. According to curve 1, the second row will intercept 0.21 of the total, leaving $1 - 0.66 - 0.21 = 0.13$ to be intercepted by the remaining rows.

b. Suppose the one plane had been replaced by a single row of tubes with a refractory back wall instead of by a nest of tubes. The fraction 0.66 of the radiation from the other plane would still be intercepted by the row of tubes, the fraction 0.34 going through and being absorbed by the back wall. If it is assumed that there is no external heat loss from the back wall, the latter must take up an equilibrium temperature between that of the tubes and that of the other radiating plane and must radiate back as much heat as it absorbed. This back radiation, 0.34, will be 66 per cent intercepted by the tubes, the other 34 per cent of it returning to the original radiator. The total heat picked up by the tube is, therefore, $0.66+0.66(0.34)=0.88$, a value that could have been read from Fig. 63, curve **5**. **A single tube and back wall will, therefore, be 88 per cent as effective a heat receiver as an infinite number of rows, so far as radiant-heat transmission is concerned.**

c. Suppose the one plane had been replaced by two rows of tubes with refractory back wall, instead of by a single row. According to Fig. 63,

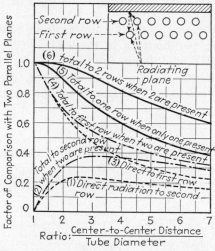

Fig. 63.[17]—Radiation from a plane to one or two rows of tubes above and parallel to the plane. Tubes on equilateral-triangular centers; nonconducting, but reradiating refractory surface above tubes. The ordinates are expressed on the basis of heat transferred from a plane to a plane replacing the tubes or to an infinite number of rows of tubes. Curves 3 and 1 apply to *direct* radiation to the first and second rows, respectively.

curves 4 and 2, the total radiation to the first row is 0.69, to the second 0.29, and to both $0.69+0.29$, or 0.98 as much as to an infinite number of rows (or to a continuous plane).

From Fig. 63, it is seen that only when the tubes are of small diameter, relative to their distance apart, is there any considerable quantity of radiant-heat penetration beyond the second row.

Simplified Equation for Radiation.—As shown on page 107, the heat transfer between solid and gas by convection is given by the equation

$$q_c = h_c A (T_s - T_g) \tag{33}$$

wherein q_c represents the rate of transfer by *convection*, B.t.u.

per hour; A the surface area, square feet; T_s and T_g the temperatures of the surface and of the gas, respectively, in degrees Fahrenheit absolute; and h_c the coefficient of heat transfer by convection, B.t.u./(hr.)(sq. ft.)(deg. F.) (see pages 112 and 115). As shown for Case 2 in Table I, the heat loss by radiation from a body small in size compared to the enclosure, as, for example, a steam pipe in a room, is given by the equation

$$q_r = 0.173pA\left[\left(\frac{T_s}{100}\right)^4 - \left(\frac{T_r}{100}\right)^4\right] \qquad (34)$$

wherein q_r is the rate of heat transfer from pipe to room by *radiation*, B.t.u. per hour; p is the emissivity of the surface of the pipe; and T_s and T_r are the temperatures of the pipe and room, respectively, in degrees Fahrenheit absolute. It is sometimes convenient to evaluate q_r by the *simplified equation for radiation:*

$$q_r = h_r A (T_s - T_r) \qquad (35)$$

wherein h_r is a factor called the coefficient of radiant-heat transfer from solid to solid, expressed in B.t.u./(hr.)(sq. ft.)(deg. F. diff. between surface and room), and is evaluated from a chart or the equation

$$h_r = \frac{0.173p\left[\left(\frac{T_s}{100}\right)^4 - \left(\frac{T_r}{100}\right)^4\right]}{T_s - T_r}. \qquad (36)$$

Figure 64 shows values of h_r for a black body, based on $p=1$. Where both the air and the walls of the room are at the same temperature, $T_g = T_r$, the *combined* heat loss by convection and radiation is obtained by adding Eqs. 33 and 36:

$$q_c + q_r = (h_c + h_r)(A)(T_s - T_r). \qquad (37)$$

The temperature difference in Eqs. 33 and 37 may be expressed in degrees Fahrenheit, which is the same as the difference in the temperatures on the Fahrenheit absolute scale. Observed values of the combined coefficient $h_c + h_r$ have been determined for bare pipes (Fig. 65) and may be employed directly, instead of evaluating h_c and h_r separately.

Heat Losses from Lagged Pipes.—The optimum thickness of insulation is that thickness which gives the maximum net saving, *i.e.*, the difference between the value of the heat saved and the

total charges against the covering. The literature contains
numerous examples of such calculations. Obviously the optimum thickness for a given pipe size varies with the value of heat
and the cost of lagging the pipe.

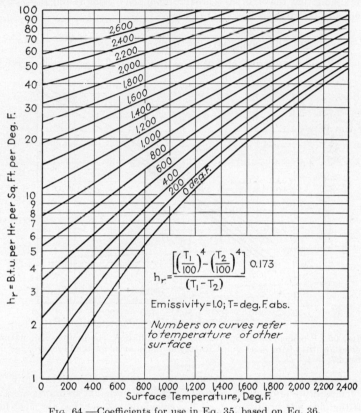

Fig. 64.—Coefficients for use in Eq. 35, based on Eq. 36.

Illustration 7.—Calculate the heat loss from 100 lin. ft. of standard 4-in.
steel pipe carrying saturated steam at 360°F. The pipe is covered with a
1-in. thickness of 85 per cent magnesia lagging ($k = 0.042$ English hour
units), and the temperature of the air surrounding it is 80°F.

Solution.—The internal and external diameters of the pipe are 4.026 and
4.50 in., respectively. Denoting by ΣR the sum of the resistances to heat
flow offered by steam film, metal wall, lagging and air film,

$$q = \frac{\Sigma \Delta}{\Sigma R} = \frac{360 - 80}{\dfrac{1}{h_v A_v} + \dfrac{L_m}{k_m A_m} + \dfrac{L_L}{k_L A_L} + \dfrac{1}{(h_c + h_r) A_a}}.$$

Take h_v as 3000. $A_v = 100(\pi)(4.03)/12 = 105.5$ sq. ft.

$k_m = 26.$ $A_m = 100(\pi)(4.03 + 4.50)/(2 \times 12) = 111.5$ sq. ft.

$k_L = 0.042.$ $A_L = 100(\pi)(4.50 + 6.50)/(2 \times 12) = 144$ sq. ft.

$$A_a = 100(\pi)(6.50)/12 = 170 \text{ sq. ft.}$$

Assuming that the external temperature of the lagging is 130°F., $(h_c + h_r)$ is found to be 2.0 from Fig. 65.   Hence

$$q = \frac{280}{0.00000316 + 0.0000068 + 0.0138 + 0.0029} = \frac{280}{0.0167} = 16,700 \text{ B.t.u./hr.}$$

To check the assumption of 130°F. as the external lagging temperature

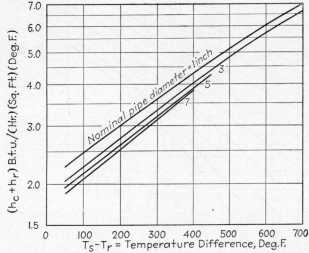

FIG. 65.—Coefficients of heat transfer by radiation, conduction and natural convection from bare steel pipes to surroundings at room temperature, for use in Eq. 37.

note that $\Delta_a = q/(h_c + h_r)A = 16700 \times 0.0029 = 49°F.$, which gives 129°F. as the temperature in question, a good check of the original assumption.

If the pipe had been bare, a similar calculation shows that the heat loss would have 104,000 B.t.u. per hr.   Estimating the value of heat at $0.30 per 10^6 B.t.u., the value of the heat saved per 300-day year is $87,000 \times 24 \times 300 \times 0.30/10^6 = \$188$ per yr.

It is possible to have the heat loss from a pipe increased rather than decreased by putting a layer around it.   However, this can occur only under exceptional conditions involving a combination of poor insulation with small size of pipe.   This principle is exploited by the electrical engineer in insulating wires to secure a combination of electrical insulation with increased cooling effect on an overloaded wire.

Radiation Errors in Pyrometry.—An ordinary mercury thermometer on a thermocouple is often used to measure the temperature of a gas when the temperature of the surroundings is different from that of the gas. Under such conditions the thermometer will indicate an apparent gas temperature somewhere between that of the gas and that of the surroundings; if the gas is the hotter, the thermometer reading will be too low; if the wall is the hotter, the reading will be too high. The factors that tend to develop a large error are: large difference between the true temperature of gas and surroundings, high temperature of either the thermometer or the surroundings, and a small value of h_c.

The mechanism by which the error is developed may be illustrated by considering a thermocouple inserted in the gas stream passing through a duct, the walls of which are hotter than the gas, under conditions such that the true temperatures of the walls and gas remain constant. The walls radiate heat to the couple, which tends to raise its temperature, but the couple loses heat to the gas stream by conduction through the gas film on the couple and thence by convection to the main body of the gas. These two opposing factors soon counterbalance, thereby establishing a constant reading on the couple. Under this condition of dynamic equilibrium the rate of heat flow by radiation must be exactly equal to that by conduction and convection, as otherwise the temperature of the couple would change. Algebraically stated,

$$\frac{q}{A} = 0.173 p_c \left[\left(\frac{T_w}{100} \right)^4 - \left(\frac{T_c}{100} \right)^4 \right] = h_c (T_c - T_g) \qquad (38)$$

in which the temperatures are expressed in degrees Fahrenheit absolute. The method of calculation is simple; the observations required are the temperatures of the wall and thermocouple, the gas velocity, and the diameter of the thermocouple or the tube housing it, the latter item being required in the estimation of the coefficient h_c between gas and couple. The auxiliary data necessary are the emissivity p of the couple and an equation from which h_c may be calculated. Estimation of the error is often worth while, as it may be as high as several hundred degrees in some cases. For the ordinary glass and mercury thermometers, at temperatures not above 800°F., a value of

p of 0.96 is suggested, while for thermocouples covered with a film of oxide the value of 0.9 is recommended.

Radiation from Nonluminous Gases.—In the preceding pages interchange of thermal radiation between surfaces was treated as independent of the nature of the intervening fluid. In the range of wavelengths important in engineering practice, gases with symmetrical molecules, such as oxygen, nitrogen and hydrogen, have not been found to show absorption bands, and hence the treatment given is adequate for the purpose; however, certain gases with asymmetrical molecules, such as carbon dioxide, water vapor, sulfur dioxide and ammonia, show absorption bands of sufficient importance to merit allowance for this factor.[20] Thus in the economizer sections of pipe stills, where the gas velocities and consequently convection coefficients are small, a large fraction of the heat absorbed by the tubes is transferred by radiation from carbon dioxide and steam in the flue gases. The general problem of heat transfer in combustion chambers is treated elsewhere.[21]

Derivation of Differential Equation for Unsteady-state Conduction.—The differential equation for unsteady-state conduction of heat is obtained from the familiar equation for the conduction of heat in one direction, $dQ = -k(dt/dL)(A)(d\theta)$. Using rectangular coordinates x, y and z, consider an element of volume $dx\ dy\ dz$. The heat entering along the x-axis, at right angles to the area $dy\ dz$, is $(dQ)_{in}$ and the heat leaving along the x-axis is dQ_{out}. The net heat remaining in the element is

$$(dQ)_r = (dQ)_{in} - (dQ)_{out} = \frac{\partial}{\partial x}\left(k\frac{\partial t}{\partial x}\right)(dy)(dz)d\theta\ dx.$$

Along all three axes the heat remaining is equated to the heat stored in the element:

$$dx\ dy\ dz\left[\frac{\partial}{\partial x}\left(k\frac{\partial t}{\partial x}\right)+\frac{\partial}{\partial y}\left(k\frac{\partial t}{\partial y}\right)+\frac{\partial}{\partial z}\left(k\frac{\partial t}{\partial z}\right)\right]d\theta = (dx\ dy\ dz)\left(\rho C_p\frac{\partial t}{\partial \theta}\right)d\theta,$$

giving the *general* differential equation for unsteady-state heat conduction, expressed in rectangular coordinates:

$$\frac{1}{\rho C_p}\left[\frac{\partial}{\partial x}\left(k\frac{\partial t}{\partial x}\right)+\frac{\partial}{\partial y}\left(k\frac{\partial t}{\partial y}\right)+\frac{\partial}{\partial z}\left(k\frac{\partial t}{\partial z}\right)\right] = \frac{\partial t}{\partial \theta}. \tag{39}$$

For a homogeneous and isotropic solid, k is taken outside the parenthesis, giving the term $k/\rho C_p$, called the *thermal diffusivity*, α, which has the dimensions L^2/θ.

The desired temperature-time-position relations for the heating or cooling of various shapes are obtained by integration of Eq. 39, substituting the appropriate boundary conditions. Where the heat flow is unidirectional, Eq. 39 reduces to

$$\alpha\left(\frac{\partial^2 t}{\partial x^2}\right) = \frac{\partial t}{\partial \theta}.$$

Consider a slab of thickness $2R$, heated from both sides and having a negligible surface resistance corresponding to an infinite value of the surface coefficient h_T. The initial temperature is uniform at t_1. The boundary conditions are then $t = T$ at $x = 0$ and at $x = 2R$; $t = t_1$ at $\theta = 0$; and $t = T$ at $\theta = \infty$. A solution is given by the rapidly converging infinite series:

$$\frac{T - t}{T - t_1} = \frac{4}{\pi}\left(e^{-\beta}\sin\frac{\pi x}{2R} + \frac{1}{3}e^{-9\beta}\sin\frac{3\pi x}{2R} + \frac{1}{5}e^{-25\beta}\sin\frac{5\pi x}{2R} + \cdots\right) \qquad (40)$$

where β represents the dimensionless term $(\pi/2)^2\alpha\theta/R^2$. Since for this special case the time and the square of the thickness enter only as a ratio, this means that the time required to attain a given temperature distribution is directly proportional to the square of the thickness and inversely proportional to the thermal diffusivity.

The total heat Q absorbed by the slab up to any time θ is obtained by evaluating the integral of $(t - t_1)\rho C_p A\, dx$, from 0 to $2R$, giving

$$\frac{Q}{2RA\rho C_p(T - t_1)} = 1 - \frac{8}{\pi^2}\left(e^{-\beta} + \frac{1}{9}e^{-9\beta} + \frac{1}{25}e^{-25\beta} + \cdots\right). \qquad (41)$$

In the general case of a finite surface resistance, corresponding to a definite and constant value of h_T, the boundary conditions become

$$-k\left(\frac{\partial t}{\partial x}\right)_{x=0} = h_T(T - t_s); \quad k\left(\frac{\partial t}{\partial x}\right)_{x=2R} = h_T(T - t_s);$$

$t = t_1$ at $\theta = 0$; and $t = T$ at $\theta = \infty$. For given values of T, t_1, R, h_T and α, integration leads to a relation between these factors and the variables, t, x and θ. Similar integrations have long been available for various solid shapes, and the results are conveniently plotted in terms of a number of dimensionless ratios.[22] Less restricted cases are readily solved by an approximate method.[23]

Nomenclature for Radiation

A = area of surface, sq. ft.

a = *absorptivity*, *i.e.*, the radiant energy absorbed and converted into heat, expressed as a fraction of the radiation incident on the surface.

$a\lambda$ = value of a, considering energy of any wavelength λ.

a, b = radii of disks.

d = prefix indicating differential.

$d\omega_1$ = small solid angle.

E = radiant *emissive power*, B.t.u./(hr.) (sq. ft.), equals

$$\int_0^\infty e_\lambda\, d\lambda.$$

E_B = value of E for the ideal *black body*, equals $\displaystyle\int_0^\infty e_{\lambda B}\ d\lambda$, equals σT^4.

e_λ = radiant energy of a wavelength λ emitted per unit time per unit area, B.t.u./(hr.)(sq. ft.)(micron).

$e_{\lambda B}$ = value of e_λ for the ideal *black body*.

F_A = *geometrical* factor, dependent on the shape of the system and on which of the two surfaces is used for evaluating A.

F_E = *emissivity* factor, a function of the emissivities of the surfaces involved.

F_{AE} = a function of the shape of the system and the emissivities of the surface.

h_c = coefficient of heat transfer by conduction and convection, B.t.u./(hr.)(sq. ft.)(deg. F.).

h_r = coefficient of heat transfer by *radiation* in simplified equation for radiation, B.t.u./(hr.)(sq. ft.)(deg. F.).

$h_c + h_r$ = combined coefficient of heat transfer by conduction and convection and by radiation, B.t.u./(hr.)(sq. ft.)(deg. F.).

i = *intensity* of black-body radiation, B.t.u./(hr.)(sq. ft.), equals E_B/π.

K = normal distance between parallel disks, ft.

p = *emissivity*, equals E/E_B.

p_λ = monochromatic emissivity, equals e_λ/e_B.

$q,\ q_r$ = radiant energy per unit time, B.t.u./hr.

q_c = rate of heat transfer by conduction and convection, equals $h_c A \Delta$.

r = normal distance between two surface elements, ft.

T = absolute temperature, deg. F. abs.

t = thermometric temperature, deg. F.

$T_c,\ T_g,\ T_r,\ T_s,\ T_w$ = values of T of pyrometer, gas, room, surface and wall, respectively.

$x,\ Y,\ y,\ Z,\ z$ = items defined in Fig. 62, page 155.

Greek Letters

λ = lambda, wavelength, microns.

λ_m = wavelength at which $e_{\lambda B}$ reaches a maximum, at the temperature involved, λ_m equals $5200/T$.

π = pi, 3.1416.

ρ = rho, local radius.

σ = sigma, Stefan-Boltzmann constant, equals E_B/T^4.

ϕ = phi, plane angle.

ψ = psi, plane angle.

References

1. LANGMUIR, ADAMS, and MEIKLE, *Trans. Amer. Electrochem. Soc.*, **24,** 53 (1913).

2. COLBURN, A. P., *Trans. Amer. Inst. Chem. Eng.*, **29,** 174–210 (1933).

3. BAYS, G. S., and L. M. BLENDERMAN, S. M. Thesis in Chemical Engineering, Massachusetts Institute of Technology, 1935; S. BAUM, *ibid*, 1936.

4. BAYS, G. S., D.Sc. Thesis in Chemical Engineering, Massachusetts Institute of Technology, 1936.

5. MONRAD, C. C., *Ind. Eng. Chem.*, **24**, 505–509 (1932).

6. COLBURN, A. P., *Ind. Eng. Chem.*, **25**, 833–850 (1933).

7. NAGLE, W. M., *Ind. Eng. Chem.*, **25**, 604–609 (1933).

7a. UNDERWOOD, A. J. V., *J. Inst. Petroleum Tech.*, **20**, 145–158 (1934).

7b. SMITH, D. M., *Engineering (London)*, **138**, 479–481, 606–607 (1934).

7c. BOWMAN, R. A., *Ind. Eng. Chem.*, **28**, 541–544 (1936).

8. DREW, T. B., *Trans. Amer. Inst. Chem. Eng.*, **26**, 26–117 (1931).

8a. SIEDER, E. N., and G. E. TATE, *Ind. Eng. Chem.*, **28**, 1429–1435 (1936).

9. NUSSELT, W., *Z. Ver. deut. Ing.*, **60**, 541, 569 (1916).

10. NAGLE, W. M., and T. B. DREW, *Trans. Amer. Inst. Chem. Eng.*, **30**, 217–255 (1933–34); T. B. DREW, W. M. NAGLE and W. Q. SMITH, *Trans. Amer. Inst. Chem. Eng.*, **31**, 605–621 (1935); W. M. NAGLE, G. S. BAYS, L. M. BLENDERMAN, and T. B. DREW, *Trans. Amer. Inst. Chem. Eng.*, **31**, 593–604 (1935); W. M. NAGLE, U. S. Patent 1,995,361.

11. FITZPATRICK, J. P., S. M. Thesis in Chemical Engineering, Massachusetts Institute of Technology, 1936.

12. COLBURN, A. P., and O. A. HOUGEN, *Ind. Eng. Chem.*, **26**, 1178–1182 (1934).

13. LOGAN, L. A., N. FRAGEN and W. L. BADGER, *Ind. Eng. Chem.*, **26** 1044–1047 (1934).

14. ROBEY, N. T., S. M. Thesis in Chemical Engineering, Massachusetts Institute of Technology, 1936; R. D. SCOTT, JR., *ibid.*, 1935.

15. CRYDER, D. S., and E. R. GILLILAND, *Ind. Eng. Chem.*, **24**, 1382 (1932); *Refrigerating Eng.*, **25**, 78 (1933).

16. BLASZKOWSKA-ZAKRZEWSKA, H., *International de l'Académie polonaise, Bull.* A (1930), No. 4/5, 188–191; S. NUKIYAMA, *J. Soc. Mech. Eng., Japan*, **37**, 367–374 (1934).

17. HOTTEL, H. C., *Trans. Amer. Soc. Mech. Eng.*, FSP 53-19b, 265 (1931).

18. HOTTEL, H. C., *Mech. Eng.*, **52**, 699 (1930).

19. HOTTEL, H. C., and J. D. KELLER, *Trans. Amer. Soc. Mech. Eng.*, I.S., **55**, No. 15, 39–50 (1933).

20. HOTTEL, H. C., and H. G. MANGELSDORF, *Trans. Amer. Inst. Chem. Eng.*, **31**, 517–549 (1935).

21. PERRY, J. H., "Chemical Engineers' Handbook," Sec. **7**, by H. C. Hottel.

22. GURNEY, H. P., unpublished monograph, Massachusetts Institute of Technology Library; H. P. GURNEY and J. LURIE, *Ind. Eng. Chem.*, **15**, 1173 (1923).

23. SCHMIDT, E., "Föppls Festschrift," p. 179, Julius Springer, Berlin, 1924; M. FISHENDEN and O. A. SAUNDERS, "The Calculation of Heat Transmission," pp. 77–83, H. M. Stationery Office, London, 1932; A. SCHACK, "Industrial Heat Transfer," translated by H. Goldsmith and E. P. Partridge, pp. 54–56, 305–308, John Wiley & Sons, Inc., New York, 1933.

CHAPTER V

FUELS AND POWER

The commercially important *sources* of energy are fuels and water power; the commercially important *forms* of energy are heat, mechanical energy and electrical energy. The energy content of fuels is always first transformed into heat energy, which may be utilized directly, or transformed into mechanical energy by the use of either the steam engine or the internal-combustion engine. The mechanical energy may be transformed into electrical energy and then finally into either chemical energy or heat. The utilization of water power is always carried out through the production of mechanical energy, which may then be transformed into electrical or heat energy if desired.

FUELS

The basis of the commercially important fuels is carbon and its compounds with hydrogen. They are classified, first, into primary or natural fuels, such as wood, lignite, coal, crude petroleum and natural gas, and, second, into secondary or prepared fuels, such as charcoal, coke, fuel oil, water gas and producer gas. A second classification frequently met, although of minor importance, is based upon whether the fuel considered is solid, liquid or gaseous. The natural fuels have similar origin and represent progressive stages of the transformation that vegetable matter slowly undergoes when protected from complete oxidation.

Upon ultimate analysis these fuels are found to contain carbon, hydrogen, sulfur, nitrogen, oxygen and ash, the mineral constituents (other than sulfur) being grouped together under the last head. It is not definitely known how these elements are combined, but it is convenient for purposes of calculation to arrange the analytical results as follows:

1. Moisture (loss in weight at 100°C.).
2. Combined water.
3. Carbon.
4. Free hydrogen (other than that in moisture and combined water).

5. Sulfur, nitrogen, etc., in small amounts.

6. Ash.

In fuel calculations, the sulfur and nitrogen are often neglected, though usually present in amounts from 1 to 3 per cent. Since the hydrogen content is always in excess of that necessary to form water with the oxygen, it is often assumed for purposes of calculation and comparison that all the oxygen is in the form of water of chemical combination, and the excess of hydrogen may be termed "free" or "net" hydrogen. The carbon content of coals increases and the percentage of oxygen (or combined water) decreases in the following order: lignites, brown, sub-bituminous, bituminous and anthracite coals.

The usual approximate method of expressing the composition of a fuel is to assume it to consist of moisture, combustible matter and ash. Upon ignition in the absence of air under specified conditions of time and temperature (covered platinum crucible), the fuels lose all the combined water and hydrogen and a large proportion of carbon in the form of volatile hydrocarbons, leaving the ash and the residual carbon. This loss upon ignition is called "volatile combustible matter." The combustible left after this ignition is called "fixed carbon." The ash is the residue left from the complete combustion of the sample in the open air, the sum of moisture, volatile combustible matter, fixed carbon and ash being 100 per cent. The coals mentioned above decrease in content of volatile combustible matter in the order named.

The ultimate analysis of coal is difficult and is often omitted. *Bureau of Mines Bulletin* 29 contains the analyses of coals from practically all American fields of importance. Where the origin of the coal in question is known, it is usually safe to assume the ultimate analysis of its *combustible matter* to be identical with that given for the same field. The same bulletin shows that the heating value of a coal is within narrow limits a function of the ratio of its carbon content to oxygen plus ash. The curve given in that bulletin can be satisfactorily represented by the following equation,

$$\text{B.t.u.} = 16{,}750 - \frac{17{,}230}{r + 0.98}$$

or

$$r = \frac{17{,}230}{16{,}750 - \text{B.t.u.}} - 0.98.$$

r is the ratio of carbon to oxygen plus ash.   The equation may be applied to a coal on either a wet or dry basis and is often useful in estimating the carbon content of a coal.

Comparison of the Commercial Sources of Mechanical Energy.—The commercially important primary sources of mechanical energy are water power and solid, liquid and gaseous fuels.   The two latter are capable of direct utilization for the production of mechanical energy in internal-combustion engines with an energy efficiency as high as 20 or 25 per cent.   On the other hand, the price of liquid and gaseous fuels is excessive except in certain localities, and their use for industrial work is usually restricted on this account.   Furthermore, internal-combustion engines have certain disadvantages which will be pointed out on page 172.   As a result relatively small amounts of commercial power are developed from primary liquid and gaseous fuels.

The major commercial sources of mechanical energy are therefore water power and solid fuels.   The energy of the latter can be obtained in mechanical form by the use of either the steam engine or the internal-combustion engine, and a comparison of water power with the two latter is therefore essential.

The energy utilized by harnessing water costs nothing directly, and it is therefore frequently assumed that water power must in consequence be cheap.   As a matter of fact, while water power is the source of the cheapest mechanical energy known, the conditions where such cheap energy is available from water are relatively rare and very frequently water power fails to compete with fuel power.   Water power is cheap where a large storage supply is available, insuring constancy of flow throughout the year, where the mechanical development can be made at small expense by the construction of a relatively small dam with short transportation of the water to the wheels, where the expense of costly water rights is not involved, and where effective industrial utilization of the power is possible at the point of generation.

If constancy of flow throughout the year is not assured, it is necessary to shut down the industrial plants depending upon this power when water is low or else to provide a fuel plant capable of handling the load.   This involves an investment for a fuel plant which will lie idle a large fraction of the year.   The mechanical development of a water power is often very expensive where proper foundations are not available and large dams and expensive penstocks are required. Most especially is it true that water rights are likely to tie up very large amounts of capital, and finally, while modern high-tension distribution is relatively efficient from an energy point of view, it is none the less expensive in money cost. So rarely does a water power meet all these requirements that the cases where water power can compete with fuel are surprisingly few.

Since large-scale distribution of power is usually electrical, power costs are generally quoted in electrical units. The cheapest powers known are certain developments in Scandinavia, Iceland and Canada, costing from \$3.50 to \$5 per kilowatt-year* at the generating switchboard. Niagara power probably costs under \$10, though on account of the demand in the immediate district it cannot be bought for that figure. Through the rest of the United States \$20 to \$25 represents an extremely cheap water power, and such figures can be realized only in large installations; \$40 to \$60 may be taken as normal for powers of moderate size, and \$75 is rarely exceeded. †

Where fuel is to be transformed into mechanical energy, a choice must be made between the two methods of transformation, *i.e.*, between the steam engine or turbine and the internal-combustion engine. For the use of the latter, solid fuel must be gasified by one of the methods given above, almost always by the generation of producer gas. The steam turbine will under the best conditions give a thermal efficiency of over 20 per cent, but from 10 to 15 per cent is satisfactory. On the other hand, the internal-combustion engine will, under the best conditions, give a fuel efficiency of over 25 per cent, and 20 per cent is not infrequently realized. This being the case, it would at first seem that the steam engine or turbine cannot possibly compete with the gas engine. This is, however, by no means true. In

---

* Note that this is a unit of *energy*.

† No commodity sold commercially varies more in selling price than electrical energy. It is available in quantity in Norway at less than a twentieth of a cent a kilowatt-hour. It is sold to householders as lighting power at around 10 cents, 200 times as much. The sale of it in the form of dry cells is an important industry and in this form the price is over \$10 per kilowatt-hour. Thus the variation in market price of it is over 20,000-fold. The fact of the matter is that the commodity sought is not so much energy itself as that factor which the power engineer calls "readiness to serve."

the first place, for a given output the investment in a gas-engine plant is much greater than that in a steam-engine plant. In the second place, a gas-engine plant possesses very little overload capacity, because neither the gas producer nor the gas engine can be forced much beyond its normal rating; on the other hand, the steam-engine plant, both the boiler and the engine, is capable of overloads even exceeding 200 per cent. Furthermore, for moderate overloads the efficiency of the steam-engine plant does not decrease greatly.   Inasmuch as a plant must be designed for its maximum load, this means that in any plant subject to occasional excessive overloads the investment required for a gas-engine plant is very much larger than that necessary for a steam plant.   Again, the wear and tear and consequently the depreciation in a gas-engine plant are heavier expenses than in a steam-engine plant. Against all these disadvantages is the single advantage of fuel economy, and the result is that the gas engine is utilized as a prime mover where fuel is high or where load conditions are unusually uniform, but where fuel is relatively cheap and loads fluctuate it is unable to compete with steam generation.   In exceptional cases, however, where large amounts of cheap gas are available, as in the steel industry, gas engines are used extensively.

Where oil is sufficiently cheap, Diesel engines are used for power generation.

CHAPTER VI

COMBUSTION

Fuels are substances capable of combining with oxygen with evolution of heat, and their utilization for energy production almost always involves a reaction with air. All combustion reactions are therefore gas reactions, and the characteristics of all gas reactions apply to them and control combustion processes. The major reactions involved are

1. $C + O_2 \quad = CO_2 + 94,300$ cal.*
2. $CO_2 + C \quad = 2CO - 41,000$ cal.
3. $2C + O_2 \quad = 2CO + 53,300$ cal.
4. $2CO + O_2 = 2CO_2 + 135,300$ cal.
5. $2H_2 + O_2 = 2H_2O + 115,500$ cal.
6. $H_2O + C \quad = CO + H_2 - 31,100$ cal.
7. $2H_2O + C = CO_2 + 2H_2 - 21,200$ cal.
8. $CO + H_2O = CO_2 + H_2 + 9900$ cal.
9. $2OH + H_2 = 2H_2O + 127,500$ cal.

The heat quantities quoted apply to the combination of the number of gram mols of reacting substances indicated on the left-hand side of each equation, at room temperature (60°F.), at constant pressure. The symbol H_2O indicates *gaseous* water in all cases. The reaction heats change with the temperature, the change being calculable from the specific heats of the reacting substances.

The following facts must constantly be kept in mind in regard to all combustion processes.

1. Equilibria.—*All these reactions are reversible.* In the case of most reversible reactions that liberate heat, equilibrium is displaced backward by a rise in temperature (principle of Le Chatelier). The first reaction, it is true, does not reverse directly, but CO_2 breaks down first into CO and O_2 by the reversal of the fourth reaction. This dissociation of CO_2 is scarcely measurable

---

* This heat of combustion is for carbon as graphite; an average value for carbon as in coke is 97,000.

below 1400 or 1500°C., but above this temperature it increases. Carbon monoxide decomposes into carbon and oxygen by the reversal of the third reaction, beginning at approximately 2500°C. and increasing with the temperature.* The point at which this reaction is nearly reversed is not, however, known. The combination of the reversal of reactions 4 and 3 accomplishes the reversal of reaction 1. Reaction 2 goes to the right only at high temperatures, nearly quantitatively above 1000°C., but rapidly reversing below that temperature, so that at 500°C. it is almost quantitatively reversed. In other words, above 1000°C. only carbon monoxide can exist in appreciable amounts at equilibrium in the presence of carbon, the fraction of carbon dioxide being very small, while at low temperatures carbon is incapable of reducing carbon dioxide to carbon monoxide except to a slight extent. Reactions 5 and 9 begin to reverse appreciably at about 1300°C. and at 1600° or 1700°C. the reversal is distinct. Neither the sixth nor the seventh reaction is complete, nor can it take place by itself alone, but in the presence of water and carbon the CO and CO_2 produced by both these reactions interact with the excess carbon according to reaction 2. Reaction 2 or 6 is important in the production of secondary gaseous fuels. The conclusions of Lewis and von Elbe[1] as to the equilibrium constants of these reactions as functions of the temperature,

---

* This stability of CO is one of the important reasons for the value of the oxyacetylene flame. Acetylene is very rich in carbon, and, if burned with enough oxygen to form CO only, gives reaction products stable up to 2500°C. Were more oxygen used, much more heat would be set free *at low temperatures*, but above 1500 to 1800° the CO_2 and H_2O formed would dissociate, reabsorbing the heat evolved by their formation, and serve as diluents to keep down the reaction temperature. While, therefore, the production of CO evolves less heat, it is available at a much higher temperature. Fortunately, too, acetylene has a negative heat of formation from the elements, carbon and hydrogen, and upon combustion this is available in addition to the heat of formation of CO, thereby increasing the heat effect. Furthermore, the flame produced under these conditions, consisting mainly of CO and H_2, is strongly reducing in character, so that metals heated with it are protected from oxidation. This is because the affinity of carbon for oxygen (to form CO, though not to form CO_2) is so much greater than the affinity of most of the metals for oxygen. Finally, the affinity of carbon for oxygen is also so much greater than that of the metals for carbon that very little carbon is absorbed by the metal from the flame, thus avoiding the brittleness and other evils resulting from the formation of metallic carbides.

based on a critical survey of all data in the literature, are shown in Fig. 66. These curves correspond to equilibrium with carbon in the form of *graphite*.

2. Specific Reaction Rates.—*The rates at which these reactions proceed are of vital importance.* All gas reactions are relatively slow, but some are much more rapid than others.

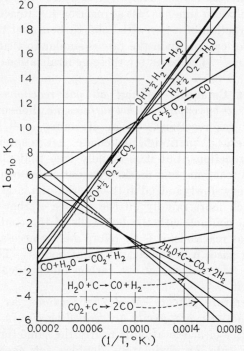

Fig. 66.—Equilibrium constants, K_p, of combustion reactions, carbon as graphite. These constants are in terms of partial pressures, expressed in atmospheres. They are based on the equations as written on the chart. Thus for the reaction $C + \frac{1}{2}O_2 = CO$, $K_p = p_{CO}/\sqrt{p_{O_2}}$.

Reaction 1 is extremely rapid at high temperatures (above 800°C.); reaction 2 is negligible in comparison with reaction 1 at combustion temperatures, though not below 600°C. Both of these reactions involve an interaction of a gas with solid carbon and therefore, other things being equal, the rates are proportional to the surface of carbon exposed. On the other hand, carbon is characterized by the fact that it changes its condition upon prolonged heating, assuming denser and more compact forms. The less dense forms of carbon react with gases far more rapidly than the more compact sorts. Thus charcoal and the carbon from soft coal react rapidly, whereas coke, especially if burned at high temperature, and anthracite coal react relatively slowly. This applies to the interaction of all gases with these different forms of carbon. Reactions 4 and 5 are purely gas reactions, but are relatively slow. The data indicate that reaction 5 is approximately four times as fast as reaction 4. Reactions 6 and 7 involve interaction of a gas with solid carbon, and the influence of the form of carbon upon the rate is similar to that in the first three reactions. The bases for these generalizations will appear later.

3. Contact Catalysis.—*Almost all gas reactions are greatly increased in rate by contact with hot surfaces, i.e.*, hot surfaces act as catalysts of gas reactions. It is, of course, well known that specific bodies, *e.g.*, platinum, nickel, etc., act as specific catalysts for certain reactions, but it is equally true that all hot bodies catalyze gas reactions to a marked degree. Gas reactions which take place very slowly indeed in the interior of a large mass of gas proceed much more rapidly on the surface of that mass where the gas is in contact with the hot walls of the container.* To accelerate gas reactions, it is therefore merely necessary to bring the reacting gases into contact with hot bodies. Thus reaction 8 is capable of catalysis by hot carbon independently of interaction with it.

4. Temperature Effect.—*Most gas reactions*, as with many chemical reactions, *are greatly accelerated by rise in temperature*, and the degree of acceleration is nearly the same for many reactions. The rate approximately doubles for every 10°C. at ordinary temperatures but this rate of increase falls off greatly at high temperatures. Thus at 1000°C. it requires an increase of roughly 100° to double the rate. It is impossible, however, to accelerate any one chemical reaction by rise in temperature without at the same time accelerating all other reactions that are possible under the conditions involved.

5. Interactions of Solids and Gases.—In order for the combustion of a solid fuel to proceed at a rate practicable for the industrial generation of heat, the fuel must be raised to a rela-

* This experimental difficulty is the reason for the lack of data on rates of gas reactions at high temperatures.

tively high temperature—at the very least 700 to 800°C. Before such a temperature is reached, the volatile constituents of the fuel are almost completely distilled* out, so that the *combustion* of the solid fuel is that of carbon itself (coke or charcoal). It should, however, be noted that the gaseous distillation products may burn long before combustion of the solid residue starts.

When coal distills as it is being heated to incandescence, it evolves hydrocarbons which upon further heating themselves thermally decompose ("crack"), with deposition of extremely finely divided carbon (smoke, soot). This carbon, once formed, is swept away in suspension in the gases to zones in the furnace where oxygen concentration is low (and where, as will appear later, it is very desirable to keep it low) and it is consequently very difficult to burn. Fortunately, however, its formation in the first place can be prevented by taking advantage of the observation of Bone[2] that these hydrocarbons, which are formed at temperatures below their ignition point, if heated mixed with oxygen, combine with it, not burning to CO or CO_2 but forming addition products which on thermal decomposition deposit no carbon. The affinity of carbon for oxygen to form CO is so great, that, if oxygen is present in the molecule, it will combine with any carbon that might otherwise be formed on further heating. Hence, to prevent smoke formation it is necessary only to coke the coal in a stream of air. This is especially important in the case of the high-grade (high heating value), high-volatile bituminous coals. In the case of the lignites and brown coal, the volatile matter, though large in amount, is so rich in oxygen (combined water) that carbon formation is less. The smoke from these coals is easier to burn, but unfortunately the furnace temperatures realized are so low that this advantage is largely counterbalanced by the consequent lower reaction rate.

* The volatilization of material from relatively nonvolatile organic substances by the process of thermal decomposition at high temperatures is called *destructive distillation*.

In the case of liquid hydrocarbons the thermal decomposition itself is called *cracking*, whether or not associated with volatilization. The phenomenon must not be confused with ordinary distillation, which takes place without chemical decomposition (see Chap. XVI, p. 514).

Whenever the term *distillation* is employed in this and the next two succeeding chapters, it refers to destructive distillation and not to ordinary distillation.

In high-grade bituminous or anthracite coals the heat absorbed by this distillation is a small fraction of the total heat evolved upon combustion, but fuels containing large quantities of water, either free or combined (lignites, brown coals, etc.), consume a great deal. This heat absorption chills the furnace and accordingly interferes with combustion.

Solid fuels may be burned in two ways: they may be supported upon a grate designed to admit the air necessary for combustion, or finely divided fuel (powdered coal, sawdust or shavings) may be blown into the furnace in such a way that each particle passes through the combustion space along with and surrounded by the air requisite for its own complete combustion. The former is the more usual method, and, because a study of this type of combustion well illustrates the underlying facts and principles, it will be considered in detail here.

Primary Combustion.—Consider a grate upon which rests a bed of coke formed by the distillation of the coal. Through this hot coke rises a stream of air, which supports its combustion. If one samples and analyzes the gases at various points in this fuel bed, and plots the gas analyses as ordinates against the height of the point of sampling above the level of the grate bars, as abscissas, one obtains curves similar to Fig. 67. These curves will vary somewhat with the character of the coal, with its size and with the air velocity. However, wide variations in these controlling conditions cause relatively small changes in the curves, especially in their positions relative to each other. Thus the percentage of oxygen has usually fallen to 2 or 3 per cent within 2 to 4 in. above the grate.

The temperature in the fuel bed is surprisingly uniform. It is, of course, low at the grate because of the cooling effect of the entering air. It rises at first sharply and then gradually to a maximum a few inches below the upper surface of the fuel bed and then decreases slightly. Obviously, the combustion reactions cannot progress until the temperature has reached the ignition point, 600 to 800°C. Although the cold air entering the fuel bed through the grate bars chills the mass at this point, heat flows down through the fuel bed at a very high rate by both conduction and radiation. Furthermore, the instant ignition starts, reaction is so rapid, owing to the high concentration of oxygen, that heat generation at the bottom of the fuel bed is very great. In the case of petroleum coke (very low in ash) these factors keep the temperature at the bottom of the bed so high that it is almost impossible to avoid burning the grate bars. However, with coal and ordinary coke the residual ash protects the grate bars and dilutes the combustible to such an extent that the temperature rise above the grate bars is less sharp. It is general practice in burning petroleum coke to use enough coal to form and maintain a protective bed of ashes on the grate.

Owing to these effects the combustion reactions do not ordinarily start sharply at the grate bars but a little above them. In Fig. 67* the curves starting along the line *BC* are those obtained

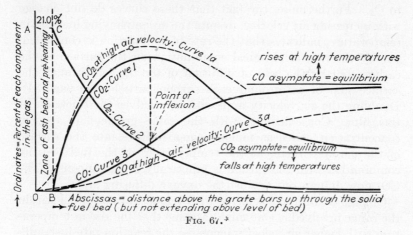

Fig. 67.*

in the burning of petroleum coke without admixed coal, while the curves starting along the line *AO* are the normal type. It will be noted that the two sets of curves become identical a short distance above the grate bars. Because of the absence of complication due to ash, discussion will be limited to the curves starting from *BC*.

For a given coke—whether fired as such or produced on the grate itself by the distillation of the coal—of a given lump size or size distribution (*i.e.*, screen analysis), the O_2 curve and the early part of the CO_2 curve both remain practically unchanged† whatever the air velocity through the fuel bed. Also, at the start each

---

* Based on data of KREISINGER, OVITZ, and AUGUSTINE, *Bureau of Mines. Tech. Paper* 137 (1917).

† Within the experimental error, which is admittedly large.

is symmetrical with respect to the other, the CO_2 curve plotted up being identical with the O_2 curve plotted down from the initial oxygen content of the entering air, 21 per cent. Furthermore, in this region each is a logarithmic curve, *i.e.*, the CO_2 curve is a straight line if plotted directly on semilogarithmic paper, as is also the case if 21 minus the O_2 content be so plotted.

These facts demonstrate that the rates of oxygen disappearance and carbon dioxide formation are equal and each proportional to the oxygen content of the gas at a given point in the fuel bed, *i.e.*, that the primary reaction in the combustion of carbon in air is $C + O_2 = CO_2$, and this reaction is monomolecular with regard to O_2. Furthermore, the fact that these curves do not change with increasing air velocity, despite the accompanying increase in temperature, indicates that the rate of combustion is controlled, not by the rate of chemical combination on the surface of the carbon, but by the rate of diffusion of the oxygen through the surface film of air around each carbon particle (see page 34). Doubling the air velocity approximately halves the thickness of this film. Consequently, with the same gradient in oxygen concentration, twice as much oxygen diffuses into the surface of the carbon, where, at the temperatures of the fuel bed, its combination with the carbon is practically instantaneous. The CO_2 now diffuses out against the oxygen diffusing in.

Change of diffusion velocity with temperature is small within the range involved. One might assume that the rise in temperature with higher air velocity increases the reaction rate just sufficiently to keep the rate of CO_2 formation proportional to velocity, but such exact adjustment of temperature to velocity under the widely varying conditions of heat dissipation seems out of the question. The above facts are compatible with the assumption of CO as the primary product of oxidation, this being oxidized to CO_2 as it diffuses through the air film, but the simultaneous presence of O_2 and CO farther above the grate demonstrates that the rate of combustion of these two is not sufficient to explain the absence of CO at the bottom of the fuel bed. CO_2 is therefore the primary product of combustion.

The CO curve starts out asymptotic to the horizontal axis, and its slope is at all points roughly proportional to the CO_2 content of the gases. It is, however, much flatter than the two preceding curves. At its right-hand end (after O_2 has disappeared) it becomes symmetrical with the CO_2 curve with respect to two horizontal asymptotes corresponding to the equilibrium between CO_2, CO and carbon. If air velocity is increased, the CO curve and the right-hand end of the CO_2 curve both flatten and move to the right, but the displacement to the right is much less than proportional to the velocity. These facts signify that CO is formed by the reaction $CO_2+C=2CO$; that the rate of this reaction is controlled, not by gas diffusion through the gas film around the carbon particles, but by the rate of chemical interaction of CO_2 and carbon; that with the increasing temperature corresponding to increasing air velocity the reaction rate increases, but less rapidly than the air supply; and finally that, even at high temperatures, this reaction is much slower than the formation of CO_2 from O_2, so that equilibrium is approached only with very deep fuel beds and long time of contact of gas and carbon.

It is obviously impossible to operate a fire properly with too thin a fuel bed. It must be at the very least 3 to 6 in. deep to avoid chimneys and thin spots which render proper control out of the question, and it is usually wiser to use much thicker beds. Inspection of these curves shows that the gases leaving the bed carry little or no oxygen, but do contain monoxide, which represents incompletely burned fuel. It is therefore necessary to mix additional air with the gases leaving the fuel bed and to give opportunity for oxidation of this monoxide, of any hydrogen formed by decomposition of water vapor in the air or left in the coke, and of the hydrocarbons formed by initial distillation of the coal. The reactions in the fuel bed itself are spoken of as *primary combustion*, while the burning of the gaseous products evolved is called *secondary combustion*.

Producer Gas.—Gaseous fuels are relatively clean and free from ash, and, mainly because of the limited amount of fuel in the furnace at any one instant, admit of exact control of temperature and heat supply. Of the secondary gaseous fuels, coal gas has the highest heating value and is therefore the easiest to distribute, but its cost is too high for most industrial furnaces. Hard coal or coke can be gasified by decomposition with steam (water gas) but this reaction absorbs heat which has to be supplied by alternately blowing with air. Mere primary combustion of a solid fuel with a thick fuel bed obviously yields combustible gas and this method is sometimes used, but the fuel bed gets very hot at the bottom (where the coke is burning almost quantitatively to CO_2), resulting in trouble from fusion of the ash. One may, however, introduce steam (or occasionally CO_2 in the form of flue gas) with the air, thus absorbing the excess heat yielding *producer gas.* This may be used directly as hot, raw producer gas, or it may be cooled and purified. Raw gas can be used only in a furnace

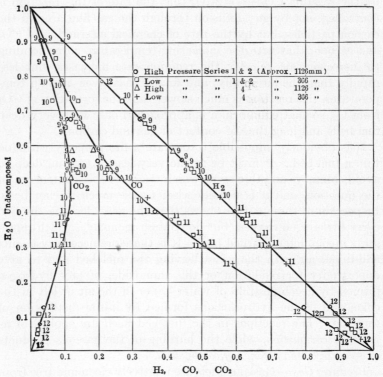

Fig. 68.[3]—Water-gas formation. Bases for ordinates and abscissas are $H_2O + H_2$; numerals represent centigrade temperatures in hundreds of degrees.

directly connected with the producer. The main disadvantage of producer gas is its low heating value, due to the diluent nitrogen from the air, but this can be largely overcome by the use of proper preheating and heat-recovery devices (see page 207).

Since producer gas is formed by the interaction of steam and carbon superimposed upon primary combustion with air, especial attention must be paid to the steam reactions. It is found that, if the reaction products of *steam alone* are plotted as shown in

Fig. 68, the curves obtained are the same whatever the character (fineness, porosity, etc.) of the carbon* or the pressure of the steam or the time of contact of steam with carbon. Furthermore, temperature has only a slight influence. All these variables, however, profoundly affect the extent to which the decomposition goes in a given time.

As just stated, change in pressure of the steam used does not affect these curves. It will be noted, however, that the curves are so plotted as to eliminate as a variable time of contact of the steam with the carbon. The experimental results also show that the time required to get the same identical effect, other things being equal, is inversely proportional to the pressure. These facts demonstrate, first, that, if water vapor takes part in more than one reaction, the order of each of these reactions must be the same with respect to it, since otherwise change in pressure would change the rate of one reaction more than another and therefore throw the net results off the curve; and second, that all these reactions must be monomolecular with respect to water, since otherwise the influence of pressure could not be proportional to the effect of time. It will be noted that the CO_2 and CO curves both have finite slopes at the start. This means that both these gases are produced simultaneously by the *primary* reactions between steam and carbon. This can be explained only on the assumption that the two primary reactions are those given as reactions 6 and 7, page 173:

$$6.\ H_2O + C\ = H_2 + CO.$$
$$7.\ 2H_2O + C = 2H_2 + CO_2.$$

The second reaction must, however, be monomolecular with respect to water as indicated above. This means that the mechanism of this reaction is unknown.

Since these reactions are found to be independent of the amount of carbon surface exposed, the influence of carbon on all reactions taking place simultaneously must be the same. Indeed study of the data shows that time, pressure and surface are substantially equivalent to each other in their effect; *i.e.*, if one doubles the surface at constant pressure, one halves the time required to secure the same results, etc.

* Except that wood charcoal gives entirely different results, with higher CO_2.

These curves can be represented quantitatively with reasonable precision by assuming the following three simultaneous reactions, the reaction rate constants being k_6, k_7 and k_2 respectively, and the ratios of these being substantially constant from 1000 to 1200°C., the approximate temperature range in which they are commercially used.

6. $H_2O + C \rightarrow H_2 + CO$.
7. $2H_2O + C \rightarrow 2H_2 + CO_2$.
2. $CO_2 + C \rightarrow 2CO$.

The usual reaction rate equations are most conveniently set up by assuming one part of entering steam or, what is equivalent to the same thing, a basis of $H_2O + H_2$ in the gas, since this is constant. On this basis call the residual water remaining undecomposed, x; the CO_2, v; and the time θ. Therefore, the rate of disappearance of water is

$$-dx/d\theta = (k_6 + 2k_7)x$$

and the rate of formation of CO_2 is

$$dv/d\theta = k_7x - k_2v,$$

whence

$$\frac{dv}{dx} = \frac{\beta v - x}{\alpha x},$$

where

$$\beta = k_2/k_7 \quad \text{and} \quad \alpha = 2 + (k_6/k_7).$$

The solution of this equation is

$$(\beta - \alpha)v = x - x^{\beta/\alpha}.$$

For the curves of Fig. 68,

$$\beta = 4.18, \quad \alpha = 3.17,$$

whence

$$1.01v = x - x^{1.319}.$$

For the use of these equations, see page 237.

These curves do not, however, tell the story of reaction rates, which increase with temperature and carbon surface. Below 800°C. they are very slow. In the neighborhood of 1000°C.

these reactions approximately double in rate for each 100° rise in temperature, but the temperature increment required to double the rate steadily increases with the temperature (roughly inversely proportionally to the square of the absolute temperature). In producer-gas practice the temperature is kept as high as possible without fusion of the ash in order to keep up reaction rate and secure maximum capacity for the apparatus.

In producer practice reactions 1 and 6 start simultaneously. Reaction 8 plays almost no part. Reaction 1 quickly completes itself, after which reactions 6 and 2 go hand in hand, reaction 6 being much the more rapid.

6. Combustion of Liquids.—All combustible liquids volatilize largely if not wholly before reaching combustion temperature, many of them decomposing thermally (cracking) rather than vaporizing unchanged. Those which vaporize readily without decomposition may be mixed with air before ignition as in internal-combustion engines but in furnace practice the liquid is usually broken up by atomization into an exceedingly fine spray mixed with the air necessary for its own combustion. Under these conditions the processes of distillation, cracking and primary and secondary combustion take place almost simultaneously. Because of the large surface exposed, the combustion rate is extremely high, and, because of the small amount of fuel in the combustion zone at any one instant, control is excellent.

7. Combustion of Gases.—As already stated, the rate of oxidation of all the combustible gases is slow except at very high temperatures and in sufficiently high concentration of the gases and oxygen. Where the concentration of the gas and oxygen is such that combustion following ignition at one point generates enough heat to raise the neighboring portions of the mixture to ignition temperature, it is obvious that a flame once started will propagate itself with great rapidity. This point constitutes the lower explosive limit. If the amount of combustible gas is increased sufficiently, it will itself finally act as a diluent sufficient to prevent combustion, thus determining the upper explosive limit.

In furnace practice the first problem of combustion is complete mixing of the gas and air and the next is the provision of sufficient time for the combustion reactions to complete themselves. These will be discussed in Chap. VII.

It has already been pointed out that hot surfaces serve as catalysts for all gas reactions. It is therefore highly desirable to bring the gases into intimate contact with hot refractory surfaces in order to complete combustion in the least possible time. That combustion by catalysis may be of controlling importance is shown by the fact that at low temperatures the combustion of mixtures of hydrogen and oxygen is proportional, not to the time of exposure of the gases to combustion temperatures, but to the surface of the container. That the mechanism of combustion by surface catalysis is entirely different from that of oxidation in the gaseous phase is demonstrated by the experimentally determined fact that, whereas the combustion of hydrogen catalytically is monomolecular with respect to hydrogen, combustion in the gaseous phase is dimolecular. Quantitatively very little is known concerning the specific reaction rates or the influence of the character of catalytic surfaces upon them.

References

1. Lewis, B., and G. von Elbe, *J. Amer. Chem. Soc.*, **57**, 612–614 (1935).
2. Bone, *J. Chem. Soc.*, **83**, 1074 (1903); **85**, 693 (1904).
3. Haslam, Hitchcock, and Rudow, *J. Ind. Eng. Chem.*, **15**, 115 (1923).

CHAPTER VII

FURNACES AND KILNS

In order to utilize to the greatest advantage the heat energy made available by combustion, it must be set free in an enclosed space made of fire brick or other heat-resistant material, known as a furnace, kiln, retort or oven. Although furnace construction was practiced many centuries before the principles of combustion just presented were understood, the design and operation of modern furnaces in accordance with these principles are an important chapter in the economy of chemical engineering.

Furnaces may in general be divided into two classes according to whether, first, the heat of combustion is transferred by direct contact from the fuel, flame or hot gases to the material to be heated, or, second, the heat is transmitted from the combustion space through some containing wall or partition to the charge, the flame and products of combustion being separated completely from the charge by the use of a muffle, retort, still or other similar container such as sagger or crucible. The first type of furnace has the great advantage of cheaper construction, lower cost of maintenance and operation, and more rapid heating and cooling, and is adapted to maintain a higher temperature. The disadvantages are that the charge is contaminated with the flue dust and other products of combustion which are in many cases objectionable, that the treatment of the charge is limited to chemical conditions compatible with satisfactory combustion of the fuel, and even so is subject to changing conditions of oxidation and reduction resulting from unequal firing, and that any product of the reacting mass which is volatile is lost in the large volume of flue gas. On the other hand, the second type—the muffles, retorts or stills—has the obvious advantages of easy manipulation of the products of the reacting mass and a more uniform control of the temperature and of the chemical conditions of the atmosphere in the furnace. If the temperature is relatively low and the containing wall is of metal, as in a still, low heat-transmission capacity due to poor conductivity is avoided, but in muffles of heavy fire brick construction the temperature drop through the wall is great and for rapid heating the combustion space must be maintained at a much higher temperature than the interior of the vessel, with consequent loss of heat in the flue gases and low heat efficiency.

In some cases the fuel may be mixed directly with the charge and the most intimate contact may be obtained between the source of heat and the object to be heated. This advantage finds its most perfect realization in those electric furnaces in which the charge forms its own resistance; such furnaces, of course, do not use fuel, but, as in the case where fuel is mixed with the charge, the heat is greatest at the point where it is to be utilized. However, in order to maintain through the mass a free passage for the air necessary for combustion, either a strong blast must be used or the charge must remain rigid and lumpy throughout the operation. This type of furnace has, therefore, in the past been limited to such purposes as the blast furnace in metallurgical work, the old-type lime kiln where the fuel was added with limestone, and brick and pottery firing.

A third special type of furnace includes those in which the fuel itself is the only charge (beehive coke ovens, charcoal heaps, etc.).

A second classification of furnaces especially useful as a basis for discussion depends upon the character of the fuel:

1. Furnaces using solid fuels (not powdered or directly admixed with charge),
2. Furnaces using liquid or powdered solid fuel,
3. Furnaces using gaseous fuel,
4. Furnaces using solid (or liquid) fuel directly mixed with charge.

1. FURNACES USING SOLID FUEL ON GRATES; FUEL NOT POWDERED OR DIRECTLY ADMIXED WITH CHARGE

Furnaces of this type must support the fuel on a grate and carry out primary combustion at that point. Steam boilers are by far the most important illustration of this type and well exemplify the problems of design, construction and operation, but, as will appear later, most chemical furnaces must diverge sharply from boiler practice in certain regards.

1. Coking.—The first problem is to bring the fuel up to incandescence and this involves the coking of the coal, which takes place before ignition temperature is reached. This coking must be carried out in a stream of air if smoke is to be avoided (see page 177). Consequently the coal must *not* be coked by throwing it on the incandescent fuel bed, since the gases rising from this are oxygen-free. The air rising through the cold fuel must, however, not be large in amount, as otherwise it will exceed that necessary for secondary combustion. In the case of a hand-fired grate, proper conditions for coking can be maintained by firing the fresh coal on a small area of clean grate bars immediately in front of the fire door, secured by pushing the incandescent fuel back from this area onto the remainder of the fuel bed. This cold fuel is heated by conduction from the incandescent fuel beside it and by radiation from the furnace walls. It distills with an excess of fresh air rising through it, the excess being later available for secondary combustion. When coked, it should be pushed with the hoe back upon the rest of the bed and fresh coal again supplied at this point.

This method is effective in preventing smoke formation but it is laborious in that it requires constant attention to the fire, since it is necessary to add the coal in successive small quantities at frequent intervals. In consequence, it is difficult to get the fireman to use this method, all the more since no recording or even indicating instrument for smoke measurement has been devised, so that there is no check on the operation except when the inspector happens to be looking at the top of the stack. One of the major advantages of mechanical stokers is their solution of this problem. Both the horizontal chain grate and the inclined rocking grate feed the coal slowly and continuously into the furnace, where it cokes with air rising through it. The latter by its motion rolls the coked fuel down over the rest of the fuel bed, keeping this of uniform thickness, a thing the chain grate fails to do. However, both these automatic types have in common with the hand-fired grate (when operated as recommended above) the shortcoming of letting a certain amount of fresh coal fall through the grate bars, where it is difficult to avoid losing it with the ash. The underfed stoker eliminates this difficulty and is peculiarly efficient in the conditions under which it cokes the coal.

2. Maintenance of Fuel Bed and Removal of Ash.—The next problem is to maintain a uniform fuel bed and to remove the ash free from unburned combustible. In a hand-fired furnace, using a coal with nonpacking, nonfusing ash, this is easily done. The bed is kept uniform by poking, and the ash is worked through the grate by shaking, keeping on the grate, however, a layer of ashes sufficiently thick to burn out the carbon completely. If the ash packs, it chokes the draft and the grates must be kept so well shaken that combustible is sure to be lost with the ashes. Conditions are even worse with a fusing ash since the effort to get the clinkers through the grate works combustible through with it. The horizontal chain grate is poor in this regard as it leaves a thin fuel bed at the end of its travel. If operated to burn out all the combustible, it is prone to let through too much air. It is especially unsatisfactory with badly clinkering coals. The inclined grate keeps a very uniform fuel bed but with clinkering ash the grinding of the grates necessary for its removal balls up large amounts of combustible with the fused ash, since the point of grate movement for ash removal is so close to the high-temperature zone of the fuel bed. As high as 50 per cent combustible in the ash has been observed from a furnace of this type. The underfed stoker is especially unsatisfactory in separation of ash from combustible.

3. Combustion Rates.—As indicated on page 180, at furnace temperatures the rate of combination of coke with oxygen to form CO_2 is proportional to the air velocity, so that there is no limit to the amount of coal that can be burned on a given grate surface, provided the draft is sufficient to pull the necessary air through the grate and fuel bed until an air velocity is reached sufficient to blow the coal off the grate.

As air velocity through the grate increases, the amount of heat evolved by primary combustion increases slightly more than proportionally. A substantial fraction of this heat is removed as sensible heat in the gaseous products of primary combustion, and this heat quantity obviously increases with the temperature of those gases. Where, however, there is in the furnace an object to be heated in "sight" of the fuel bed, either directly or by reflection, a great deal of heat flows by radiation from the fuel bed to this object, especially in the former case. In boiler practice the boiler is at a temperature so low in comparison with that of the fuel bed that a large fraction of the total heat of primary combustion reaches the boiler in this way. Furthermore, since radiation rises as the fourth power of the absolute temperature, almost all the excess heat evolved in primary combustion with increasing combustion rate goes to the boilers as radiant energy, and this requires very little increase in temperature of the fuel bed. However, in many chemical furnaces there is no body with adequate heat-absorption capacity available for taking up this radiation and therefore in such cases the temperature of the fuel bed rises rapidly with increase in combustion rate. If not controlled, this will result in localized overheating in the furnace, in fusion of the ash and even in burning out of the grate bars. Consequently, chemical furnaces with limited heat-absorption capacity in "sight" of the fuel bed must, in general, be operated at very carefully limited rates of combustion.

Hand-fired boiler furnaces can be operated successfully at combustion rates of 10 to 20 lb. of coal per sq. ft. of grate area per hr., while mechanical stokers can be forced to 40 or 50 lb. Indeed, combustion rates of 80 lb. have been realized but it is impractical to maintain these commercially. In chemical furnaces the combustion rate is, as stated above, limited by the maximum allowable temperature of the furnace, by its heat-absorption capacity and by the necessity for uniformity of heat distribution. Not infrequently in such furnaces combustion rates must be held below from 2 to 5 lb. of coal per sq. ft. of grate area per hr.

So large is the heat radiation from boiler fires that, where low-grade fuels, such as wet wood waste, tanbark, lignite, etc., are used, it is necessary to construct the furnace so that the boiler cannot "see" the fire, as otherwise the radiation will cool the fire below combustion temperatures. This is done by building the furnaces entirely in front of the boiler and separating the two by a high bridge wall (Dutch-oven construction).

This possibility of an almost unlimited combustion rate on the grate, coupled with the direct transmission of most of the heat evolved by radiation to the point required and its almost complete absorption there, is the basis of the tremendous overload capacity of boiler furnaces. The main disadvantage of thus forcing the boiler is slightly lowered efficiency due to imperfect secondary combustion. Modern practice tends to provide adequate space for secondary combustion to meet this need.

4. Secondary Combustion.—From the fuel bed there rise the distillation products of the volatile combustible matter of the fuel and the gaseous products of primary combustion rich in carbon monoxide and containing some hydrogen from the moisture in the air. In the former gases there should be some oxygen if the fuel has been properly fired but in the latter there is little or none. The potential heat of combustion of these gases represents a large fraction of the heat content of the fuels, and adequate provision must be made for their oxidation.

The first problem is to mix these gases with the proper amount of air. So great is their volume (owing to the large amount of nitrogen) that complete mixing is difficult to secure. In hand-fired furnaces the secondary air (*i.e.*, this air necessary for secondary combustion) is admitted through dampers in the fire door and mixes with the gaseous products of primary combustion as it sweeps over the fuel bed. With both chain and inclined grates a substantial fraction of the secondary air enters through the distilling fuel. In underfed stokers none whatever comes in this way. In stoker-fired boiler furnaces modern practice is developing toward the admission of secondary air through multiple ports in the bridge wall, the air being preheated during its passage through the flues in the wall which conduct it to these ports. In this way it is possible to admit the air at a large number of points, thus improving mixing conditions. The preheating is, as will appear, very desirable from the point of view of secondary combustion.

Secondary combustion itself is a series of purely gas reactions. These reactions are therefore slow compared with those of primary combustion (see page 180) and adequate time must be provided for their completion. In hand-fired boiler furnaces it was formerly the practice to supply from 4 to 5 cu. ft. of combustion space per sq. ft. of grate area and at the combustion rates formerly used (5 to 10 lb. of coal per sq. ft. of grate area per hr.) this was adequate in the case of high-grade coal. When, however, combustion rates were increased with the introduction of mechanical stokers, while the temperature of the combustion gases increased and therefore the rates of secondary combustion also went up, this temperature increase was too slight (see page 191) to secure proper secondary combustion in these limited combustion spaces. As a result, designers have been increasing combustion space progressively during recent years so that today an allowance of 12 to 14 cu. ft. of combustion space per sq. ft. of grate area is not uncommon in new installations that are to be forced to high combustion rates.

Where low-grade fuels are used, the fuel-bed temperature is low, and consequently the temperature of the combustion gases also. This means that the reaction rates of secondary combustion are less, and in such cases additional space must be allowed. One of the advantages of Dutch-oven construction for these low-grade fuels is the provision of increased combustion space coupled with the fact that the products of primary combustion leave the fuel bed at a higher temperature because of absence of radiation from it and therefore burn at a higher rate.

These gaseous reactions can be catalyzed by contact with hot refractory surfaces. For this purpose extensive baffles are frequently introduced in the combustion space of boiler furnaces, against which the gases impinge and around which they have to flow. These baffles aid not merely by catalysis of the gas reactions but by improving mixing with the secondary air and by absorption of heat from the gases, which in turn is radiated to the boiler. Such baffles are not generally used in chemical furnaces but in many cases their introduction would be highly advantageous. For example, in a muffle furnace a part of the heat from the hot gases is picked up by the wall of the muffle itself but another part is absorbed by the remaining walls of the flue and radiated from there to the muffle. Where the muffle is made of refractory material, the temperature difference between it and the remaining walls of the flue is slight because at the high temperature of the furnace the rate of energy interchange between walls and muffle by radiation is very great. If in such a case one will increase the surface area of the remaining walls of the flue, *e.g.*, by allowing alternate bricks to protrude from the wall into the flue, this will furnish additional surface for absorption of heat from the hot gases, which will in turn be radiated to the muffle wall.

In many chemical furnaces a baffle of this sort is superfluous. For example, in an externally fired lime kiln the products of secondary combustion entering the kiln have their combustion catalyzed by the surface of the lime itself. As a result, combustion in these kilns is unusually good.

In order to secure complete combustion one must obviously supply sufficient air, and in practice it is found necessary to furnish a considerable excess. In the limited combustion space of boiler furnaces it is impossible to secure complete oxidation, especially of the CO, even with large amounts of secondary air. Since, when carbon burns to CO, the heat evolution is less than 30 per cent that of combustion to CO_2, CO going up the stack represents a serious heat loss. Formerly the boiler-plant engineer focused attention upon this loss to too great an extent. He determined it by analysis of the flue gases and found that excess air cut down the percentage of CO in it. In fact, however, while excess air does reduce the percentage of CO in the flue gas, it reduces the absolute amount formed from the coal little if at all. In other words, the CO in the flue gas is reduced by dilution with air rather than by oxidation to CO_2, because the *dilution* cuts down the reaction rate, owing to the lowering of the temperature of the gases and the time they are in the combustion space, almost as much as this rate is increased by a higher concentration of oxygen. Furthermore, in furnaces operated under natural chimney draft it is obvious that the use of excess air increases the volume of flue gas and therefore increases the draft necessary to overcome furnace and stack friction. Since this draft comes only through temperature difference between stack gases and the outside air, this means that in such cases stack-gas temperature increases with excess air. Consequently excess air runs up stack losses.

On the other hand, it is not practicable to reduce excess air too greatly. With grate-fired furnaces it seldom pays to cut it below 40 to 50 per cent, since, owing to the imperfect mixing and the extremely low reaction rates of secondary combustion caused by the very low oxygen content of the gases at this point, there will be in the flue gases too much carbon monoxide and in some cases even smoke. The better the provision for mixing of secondary air with the products of primary combustion and the greater the combustion space provided, the less excess air required and the smaller the heat losses up the stack. Fortunately in many chemical furnaces (muffles, retorts, pottery kilns, reverberatory furnaces, etc.) the volume of the combustion space and the temperature in it are sufficient to give perfect secondary combustion.

It frequently happens, especially in chemical practice, that it is desired to distribute the heat energy, produced by the combustion of fuel at a relatively low but necessarily uniform temperature, over a relatively large area. For this purpose it is impracticable to design a coal-fired furnace so as to provide uniform direct radiation from the fuel bed to all the points to be heated. Experience has shown that the problem can be solved by primary combustion of the fuel upon the grate with the production of a combustible gas, the combustion of which can then be completed after the gas is led to the point where the heat is required. By far the best results are obtained if the gas produced will burn with a smoky flame, *i.e.*, will in its combustion generate a large number of exceedingly fine particles of carbon, which will be heated by the

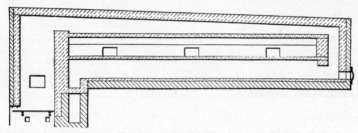

Fig. 69.—Muffle furnace.

combustion reactions to incandescence and will then transmit the energy of combustion to the desired point by radiation. In practice this can best be secured by the use of a high-B.t.u. fuel with a very high percentage of volatile combustible matter, admitting only enough air under the grate to distill off this combustible matter and burn the residual carbon. The volatile matter from such a coal is always rich in carbon and burns with the smoky flame desired, thus generating a large fraction of the total energy of the combustion of the fuel in the form of radiant energy in the gas flame at a point far removed from the grate on which the fuel is fired.

With a fuel high in volatile combustible matter, producing on coking a large volume of combustible gas, the heat generated in the firebox is to some extent absorbed by the endothermic process of distillation of the fuel itself, and an excessive temperature in this part of the furnace is avoided. Combustion of this gas is completed in the body of the furnace, thus carrying the heat from the firebox where it is not needed to the back of the charge, which would otherwise be too cool.

This is the basis of the utility of the "long flame" of wood, which has for many years been the favored fuel for such opera-

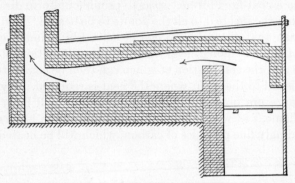

Fig. 70.—Reverberatory furnace, short type.   This type of furnace is employed where it is necessary to bring the whole charge to a uniform high temperature. A large fraction of the heat is transmitted to the charge by radiation from the fuel bed to the arch above the bridge wall, from which it is reflected and radiated to the charge.   The flue gases going to the stack are obviously hot.   It is usually restricted to batch operation.

tions as require a moderate temperature distributed over a large area—such as lime and brick burning.   High-grade high-volatile coals are usually good.   The disadvantage of forcing a furnace of large effective area with a low-volatile coal or coke is very great,

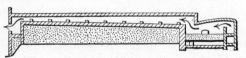

Fig. 70A.—Reverberatory furnace, long type.   This furnace is suitable for preheating the charge when fed through the furnace continuously in a direction counter to the flow of gases.   In this particular furnace the stock is worked through by hand stoking and rabbling.   Furnaces that provide mechanical conveying of the charge are available.   Fuel efficiency is improved by partial recovery of the waste heat from the gases, but contact of the gases with the charge is poor and the heat-transfer coefficient is low in consequence.

if a uniform temperature in the combustion space is desired.   If the fire is forced to heat the remote parts of the furnace, the portion next to the firebox is overheated, and this part of the structure rapidly "burns out."   If a moderate fire is maintained, the output of the apparatus is greatly diminished.   This is particularly true if the charge becomes very corrosive at high temperatures, as in making sodium sulfide; if it is deteriorated, as in burning lime; or if a uniform temperature over a large area is necessary, as when a large iron muffle is to be heated as in the Mannheim process for making hydrochloric acid from niter cake. It is in such cases that an understanding of the principles of combustion discussed in Chap. VI is of great value.

Davis* many years ago showed that the output of a coke-fired furnace for making soda by the LeBlanc process was increased by almost 300 per cent by the simple device of introducing an evenly distributed supply of steam under the grate bars. The endothermic reaction

$$C + H_2O = CO + H_2$$

accomplished three purposes: first, it reduced the excessive temperature of the firebox and that portion of the furnace hearth adjacent thereto, thus increasing its life; second, it furnished a large volume of combustible gas which passed into the body of the furnace to be burned; third, the presence of that portion of the steam which was undecomposed diluted the combustible gases and thus lowered the rate of combustion and produced a flame of lower temperature and greater volume. The net result was that the heat supply was evenly distributed over the entire hearth, the output of the furnace increased, and its life lengthened.

The other common endothermic reaction, $CO_2 + C = 2CO$, can also be utilized for producing these results, and from an energy standpoint is even more economical, as it eliminates the heat necessary to produce the steam. Even so low a content of CO_2 as is present in ordinary flue gas is efficient in distributing the heat generated in a firebox over a large area. Not only is the absorption of heat by the formation of CO and its subsequent combustion of value, but the dilution of combustible gases with the accompanying water vapor and nitrogen diffuses the heat by enlarging the volume of flame as already explained (see page 195). When the flue gas is withdrawn as soon as it leaves the actively heated zone of the furnace, the energy lost by such a procedure is clearly very small compared with the consequent advantages. Eldred used this principle in the efficient operation of lime kilns, and it has been frequently employed in heating large muffles,

---

* DAVIS, *"Chemical Engineering,"* Davis Bros., Manchester, England, 1902.

retorts, annealing boxes and containers of this kind.   A valuable application of these principles has been made in the firing of the

FIG. 71.—Doherty-Eldred lime kiln.   The kiln is externally fired.   The gases at the top of the kiln are quite cool because of the excellent contact between them and the incoming cold charge.   They are piped down to the floor line where the pipe divides, delivering the gas to two blowers, the larger of which discharges most of the gas to the stack, while the other recirculates the rest, delivering it below the grate of the two furnaces with which the kiln is equipped.   The third blower shown supplies the air.   The cut shows only one of the points of entrance of recirculated gas and air, a part of the kiln being cut away to show the interior construction.   The discharge pipe for stack gases is also shown cut off.

ordinary red brick kiln.   A steam pipe with many small openings is placed throughout the length of each firebox.   When the coal fire is well ignited, steam is introduced under the body of the fire. The large volume of low-temperature flame flows around the entire mass of bricks, giving a large yield of marketable brick in a much shorter time.

Greater uniformity of heat distribution can be secured by admitting secondary air, not at the bridge wall, but at successive points along the combustion space, the air supply at each point being capable of control (Semet-Solvay coke ovens, although these are gas-fired).

It must be remembered that those gases formed by modified primary combustion of low-volatile solid fuel do not burn with a luminous flame, and the process is on that account less satisfactory than the use of a highly volatile coal. In certain cases, however, the combustible gases come into intimate contact with the material to be heated and in such cases the surface of the material itself can serve as a contact mass to catalyze the combustion reactions, provided it is sufficiently hot. Since these reactions take place upon the very surface of the material to be heated, the energy due to combustion is thus generated upon that surface itself and consequently is absorbed directly without transmission losses.

If a relatively small area is to be heated to a very high temperature, this dilution of the flame should be avoided, and the fuel and air for combustion must be heated before they combine. It is always possible to preheat the air, but the fuel can be preheated with advantage only when it is a gas. For a localized high temperature even the water vapor present in the air during warm weather has been found to exert a profound influence by the endothermic reaction of its decomposition. Thus, in the iron blast furnace at the entrance point of the air blast, an increased melting capacity of the iron reduced is obtained by removing the water vapor from the air used. An atmosphere richer in oxygen than ordinary air is here desirable (page 219).

2. FURNACES USING LIQUID OR POWDERED SOLID FUELS

Powdered coal was introduced as a fuel over twenty years ago in the burning of cement in rotary kilns. The pulverized coal is injected into the furnace with a powerful blast of air and burns in a flame much the shape of a greatly elongated egg. In large kilns this flame will be from 2 to 4 ft. in diameter at its maximum and 10 to 15 ft. long. Because of the way the fuel is blown in, each particle is surrounded with a layer of air. It is heated to incandescence, partly by conduction but mainly by radiation from the hotter portion of the flame, and therefore the volatile matter distills in the presence of excess air. There is therefore little or no tendency to deposit soot provided sufficient air is present for complete combustion of the fuel. The flame from

Fig. 72.—Pulverized-coal-fired boiler. The semi-Dutch-oven construction is provided to furnish ample combustion space. Certain plants are trying the experiment of injecting the coal directly downward through the top of this Dutch-oven so that the flame is turned back upon itself. The purpose of this is to give to the ash particles a downward component to sling them into the ash pit. This modification is apparently quite successful. (*Courtesy of Fuller-Lehigh Co., Fullerton, Pa.*)

such a burner is exceedingly hot and a large fraction of the heat is given off in the form of radiant energy.

One of the disadvantages of powdered coal is the danger of fires and, on occasion, even of dust explosions. The possibility of the latter can be eliminated by keeping the dust concentration in the air used above the explosive limit. The danger of fires can be reduced by using airtight ducts for transportation of the powdered fuel and exercising great care to prevent ignition. It is inadvisable to hold large quantities of dust in storage, and it is better to use adequate grinding equipment to supply the maximum demand of the furnace rather than to store powdered coal for peak loads. The coal may be transported from the pulverizer to the burner either by screw conveyors or by forcing it along with air pressure (since it flows like a liquid) or by suspending it in air and floating it. In the latter system care must be exercised to keep the air used for floating below the explosive limit.

Liquid fuels are burned much as powdered coal, being atomized by air under pressure or frequently, on account of its convenience, by steam. They too burn with an extremely hot radiant flame. The simplicity of firing and small combustion space required make them very advantageous on shipboard.

Both powdered coal and oil can be mixed with air so perfectly that excess air can be reduced to 10 to 20 per cent without danger of incomplete combustion. With both, the short hot flame tends to overheat that part of the furnace near it, cutting away brickwork and injuring a sensitive charge, and coal ash, if fusible, may flux and ultimately disintegrate the furnace lining. The advantages of lowered flame temperature may be secured without sacrificing furnace efficiency by recycling flue gas into the air used for combustion, although this lowers combustion rate, requiring more combustion space; or Dutch-oven construction may be used and the temperature of the combustion products lowered by adding the recycled gas after combustion is complete. Either method is far superior to lowering flame temperature by excess air. In boiler furnaces it is practicable to install water-cooled surfaces at substantially every point in sight of the flame, thereby increasing heat absorption and eliminating fluxing of the walls of the combustion space. Ash dust carried up the stack is sometimes a problem; it has been proposed to remove it by Cottrell precipitation (see page 315), but the ash is usually so light that the nuisance from it is surprisingly small. The cost of installation and operation of equipment for powdered coal is high in small units, but this in no wise applies to liquid fuels.

3. FURNACES USING GASEOUS FUELS

In the discussion of coal-fired furnaces it was pointed out that uniformity of heat distribution was best secured by suppressing primary combustion so as to increase the gaseous products and burning these as secondary combustion under controlled conditions. In other words, furnace control is best secured with gaseous fuels.

As already stated, coal gas and water gas are too expensive for general use, while natural gas is available only in restricted areas. In consequence, combustion engineers have developed the method of increasing secondary combustion at the expense of primary combustion by isolating the solid fuel furnace and using it for the production of a combustible gas, producer gas (see page 224). This gas is therefore available for almost any sort of furnace operation.

Since a gas-fired furnace contains little fuel at any one time, combustion is under quick and accurate control. Since one can admit the necessary air or gas or both at successive points along the furnace, it is possible to generate the heat exactly where required. Unfortunately none of the cheap gaseous fuels burn with a smoky flame and consequently the heat must be transmitted from the flame to the furnace or charge by conduction rather than by radiation. While this is a disadvantage from the point of view of heat-transmission capacity, it is a great advantage in maintaining uniformity of temperature throughout the furnace. Even this disadvantage can be eliminated by the use of surface combustion.

Surface Combustion.—The combustion of gases is greatly accelerated by contact with hot surfaces. Furthermore, where the gas burns in this way, the heat is generated upon the very surface of the solid and hence raises this solid to incandescence so that, while the gas itself is not radiant, the heat evolved by its combustion can nonetheless be emitted in radiant form. The best way to accomplish this is to mix thoroughly the gas with the air in substantially theoretical proportions and burn this mixture by passing it through a porous mass of refractory material such as fire brick or alundum. The contact mass should be porous and spongy in structure to expose the utmost surface. Where the catalyst is supported horizontally or at not too great an angle, it can consist of a pile of small lumps of crushed refractory. Combustion takes place within the mass and the whole becomes highly incandescent. In this way it has been possible to transmit 1,000,-000 B.t.u. per hr. through a single square foot of surface. Despite the short time of contact, combustion is unusually complete and excess air can be reduced to a negligible quantity. To prevent flash backs the air-gas mixture must be brought through the flues leading to the contact mass at a velocity higher than the rate of flame propagation through the mixture. In small cool tubes the allowable velocity is surprisingly low.

While surface combustion in this narrow sense cannot be universally used, surface catalysis plays an important part in every gas-fired furnace. The catalytic action of the walls of the furnace and its flues and of checkerwork which may be inserted in the combustion space makes it possible to secure complete combustion even at relatively low temperatures. In many furnaces the surface of the charge itself serves this purpose (*e.g.*, pottery, lime and brick kilns, roasting furnaces, etc.).

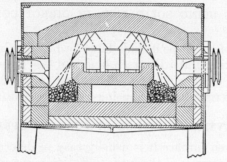

Fig. 73 —Surface combustion furnace. The gas and air mixture enters through the side ports and is directed down upon the coarse mass of refractory material in the bottom of the furnace. From this the heat is radiated up to the arch and down upon the muffle as shown by the broken lines. (*Courtesy of Surface Combustion Co.*)

The pressure drop due to the friction of flow of the gases through gas-fired furnaces can be estimated by the usual equations (pages 77 to 97). In American practice forced draft is seldom used and consequently gas velocities must be kept low. In simple furnaces they are usually between 10 and 15 ft. per sec. but, where the travel is tortuous or the distance is long, these figures must be reduced accordingly.

Gaseous fuel is especially well suited for those furnaces in which the temperatures must be controlled exactly at high temperature levels to secure absolute uniformity of heating (open-hearth steel furnaces, pottery kilns, etc.). In such cases unusual attention must be paid to the introduction of the fuel and to the uniformity of its mixing with the air supply and its distribution through the furnace. In ring furnaces and tunnel kilns (page 209), it is advisable to admit the gas in successive small quantities at a series of points along the furnace. The gas ports must be so located and the furnace so designed as to insure perfect mixing with the air and distribution of the mixture over the charge. The furnace should be so constructed that, if trouble develops, the location of the gas ports and the direction of the gas currents in the furnace can be modified after the furnace has been completed. The ability to control the performance of a furnace in this way is one of the important elements in the skill of a furnace operative.

Three important types of gas-fired furnaces, the ring furnace and the tunnel and the rotary kilns, are discussed on page 207, under Recovery of Waste Heat.

4. FURNACES USING SOLID FUEL IN DIRECT CONTACT WITH CHARGE

Furnaces of this type include kilns for building bricks, the pig-iron blast furnace, the Dietzsch lime kiln (see page 208) and the ring furnace using solid fuel. The most important illustration of the type is the rotary kiln using powdered coal (see page 211).

5. ANALYTICAL CONTROL OF FURNACE OPERATIONS

In any given furnace it is usually easy to determine and control the performance of the furnace, *i.e.*, to measure the quantity of the charge, its temperature rise and such chemical changes as may have taken place in it. On the other hand, a furnace may be giving satisfactory performance so far as the charge is concerned and yet be operating very poorly from the point of view of combustion. Heat losses to the surroundings are not under the control of the operator except as the furnace is redesigned and rebuilt. Lost combustible in the ashes can be determined by proximate analysis (very great care must be exercised in securing a representative sample). However, both these losses are usually small in comparison with those in the stack gases. In consequence, the control of furnace combustion depends upon analysis of the stack gases and determination of their temperatures. For example, almost as much information can be secured with regard to the operation of a boiler from determinations of the heating value of the fuel, of the combustible in the ash and of the temperature and analysis of the stack gases as from a boiler test involving a complete heat balance, at a small fraction of the expenditure of time and labor.

Because of this fact in boiler practice the use of automatic CO_2 recorders is rapidly increasing. Some of these recorders are a mechanically operated Orsat apparatus, while others pass the gas sample in series through two orifices, absorbing the CO_2 between the two with solid soda lime and measuring the CO_2 by the change in pressure drop through the second orifice caused by shrinkage in volume of the gas. In a well-designed boiler furnace the CO will in any case be so completely oxidized by secondary combustion that the CO_2 is a satisfactory measure of the excess air used and the general efficiency of the combustion process. In furnaces so built or operated that this is not the case, CO_2 recorders will not tell the whole story, because one can have the same CO_2 readings with either insufficient or excess air. In the first case there would be considerable CO and perhaps hydrogen in the gas, and in the second case there would be excess oxygen. For this reason CO_2 recorders are by themselves of limited value for gas-fired furnaces. Recorders for CO and oxygen have been developed but have not yet earned wide-spread industrial acceptation.

These recorders are valuable adjuncts in furnace control but offer many mechanical difficulties due to dust, delicacy of the working parts, exhaustion of the chemicals and the like. If their indications are to be depended upon, they must be carefully and intelligently watched and checked against an Orsat analysis.

For the purposes of general experimental testing, the Orsat apparatus or some one of its modifications is preferable to the recording instruments.

Errors in Orsat Analysis

As will appear in connection with computations, a small error in the CO_2 determination in a flue gas will introduce a serious error in the calculated results. The gas sample in an Orsat is ordinarily collected over water. This water dissolves some of the CO_2 and in consequence makes the CO_2 determination in the gas low.* Mercury should always be employed in the burette in

---

* Assume, for example, a gas consisting of 11 c.c. of CO_2 and 90 c.c. of other nonacidic gases. When 101 c.c. are introduced into the Orsat, 1 c.c. of this CO_2 may well dissolve, leaving what is apparently a 100-c.c. sample. There will therefore be a shrinkage of 10 c.c. over caustic. When the sample is returned from the caustic to the burette, the volume will gradually increase owing to the escape of the CO_2 from the water into the gas due to its lowered

gas analyses where precision is desired. The extent of the error can be judged from the following data taken from Bulletin 2 of the U. S. Bureau of Mines.

In boiler test 2, reported by the bureau in this bulletin, the dry coal has an ultimate analysis of 60.15 per cent C, 4.35 per cent H, 21.18 per cent O, 1.07 per cent N, 0.72 per cent S and 12.53 per cent ash. The mols of H_2 per 100 lb. of coal are therefore 4.35/2.016 and the atoms of oxygen, 21.18/16. The difference is 0.833, the mols of net hydrogen (H_2). The ratio of carbon to net hydrogen (C/H_2) is therefore $60.15/(12)\ (0.833) = 6.03$. The ratio of carbon plus sulfur to net hydrogen is 6.06. Since the ash from the furnace was 8.61 per cent of the dry fuel fired and contained 15.1 per cent carbon, 2.16 per cent of the carbon in the fuel remained unburned in the ash. Hence, the ratio of C/net H_2 in the flue gas should be 5.89, or, corrected for sulfur, 5.92.

The flue-gas analysis is given in the table below:

		C	O_2
CO_2	10.04	10.04	10.04
O_2	9.04	.....	9.04
CO	0.10	0.10	0.05
N_2	80.82	.....	.....
		10.14	19.13

O_2 from air $= 80.82(21)/79 = 21.49$

$O_2 \backsim$ net H_2 in fuel $= \quad 2.36$

Net $H_2 = \quad 4.72$

whence

C/net $H_2 = 10.14/4.72 = \quad 2.15$

It is seen that the gas analysis gives a ratio of carbon to net hydrogen less than half the real value. The unburned combustible in the ash gives an error of this sign but to explain its magnitude by such an assumption would mean that 60 per cent of the carbon in the coal remained unburned in the ash. The

---

partial pressure, but on the second or third treatment of the gas with caustic the volume will again return to 90 c.c. This is one cause of the apparently slow absorption of CO_2 in caustic in gas analyses. It will be noted that the analysis is apparently 10 per cent CO_2, whereas actually there were nearly 11 per cent in the sample.

error actually arises from the fact that the CO_2 determination in the flue gas is low by about 1 per cent. If one assumes the CO_2 value higher by that amount, the analyses check. Mercury in the burette would have avoided this error.

Note that, since the amount of the flue gases is figured from a carbon balance, this introduces an error of 10 per cent in calculating them and hence a similar error in getting the stack losses in a heat balance.

A point, which sometimes offers difficulty through failure to appreciate it, is the fact that a gas analysis, even when made over water, is nonetheless an analysis on the dry basis. Since at room temperature the gas measured in a burette above water is over 3 per cent water vapor, this fact is not obvious. It must, however, be remembered that all measurements are made at the same temperature and therefore with the same partial pressure of water vapor in the gas, so that, if half the gas is absorbed by some reagent, half the water vapor in the gas as originally measured will condense. It is as though the analysis were carried out, not at atmospheric pressure, but at a constant pressure equal to atmospheric pressure less the vapor pressure of water at the temperature of the analysis. Where the analysis is carried out with mercury, it is customary to have a drop of water present to keep the gas saturated, since otherwise the partial pressure of water vapor in the gas would vary with that over the absorbents employed.

6. RECOVERY OF WASTE HEAT FROM FURNACES

In every furnace reaction it is required either (1) to heat the charge up to some specified temperature (calcining reactions and the like), or (2) to furnish at such a specified high temperature the heat necessary to carry out some reaction (*e.g.*, decomposition of limestone, fusions, etc.). In either case a definite amount of heat is required at or above a definite temperature. When a fuel is burned, the maximum temperature attainable is limited by either (1) the temperature at which the reversal of the combustion reactions becomes serious, or (2) that temperature to which the heat set free by the combustion will raise the products of combustion. By the use of a given fuel it is impossible to exceed the temperature limit fixed by the first of these conditions but it is possible to avoid the second.

Furthermore, since the oxygen essential for combustion, coming as it does from the air, brings with it nearly four times its volume of inert nitrogen with its large heat-absorption capacity, it is not surprising that very frequently the second of these limiting conditions is the important one.   In illustration, assume a producer gas whose heat of combustion will raise its own combustion products to only 1500°C.   If it is required to use this gas to carry out a reaction at 1400°, it is evident that but a small fraction of its heating value will be usefully available, as most of it will be wasted as sensible heat in the flue gases.   If, however, this waste sensible heat is utilized to preheat the charge, fuel and air to a temperature at least approximately that of the reaction, 1400°, most of this heat may be usefully recovered, and the fuel consumption of the process will be reduced to a small fraction of that otherwise necessary.

COUNTERFLOW

To accomplish this effectively, it is evident that the principle of counter current flow of the materials between which this interchange of sensible heat is desired must be employed, *i.e.*, that the heat content of the waste products, while still very hot, must be used only to attain the final increment in temperature in the incoming materials, while the preliminary heating of these materials must be accomplished by heat flow from the reaction products after the latter have been considerably cooled.

The utilization of this principle of waste-heat recovery is essential in the efficient operation of all high-temperature furnaces. Even in the most common low-temperature furnace—the steam boiler—it is successfully employed in the "economizer" used to preheat the feed water with the waste heat in the stack gases. The simplest means of realizing these conditions is to allow the gaseous combustion products to flow over and through the incoming solid or liquid charge in direction opposite or counter to the motion of the charge, while the air essential for combustion enters in contact with the hot solid or liquid products of the furnace reaction; here again the motions of the two are counter to each other.

DIETZSCH KILN

Such methods of heat regeneration particularly applicable to direct-fired furnaces, which, though effective and much used abroad, have been little employed in the United States, are illustrated by the Dietzsch kiln and the Hoffman ring furnace. The simple shaft furnace in which charge and fuel are fed at the top does not permit effectively preheating the charge and cooling the waste gases, because combustion would start near the top and leave no space for preheating.

The Dietzsch kiln is a shaft furnace so designed that the fuel is admitted halfway down the shaft, and thus premature combustion is avoided.

It consists of a vertical shaft furnace having a horizontal middle portion or shelf as shown in Fig. 74. The charge is introduced at *A* and descends through the shaft to the platform *B*. Here it is mixed with fuel introduced through *D* and drops into the shaft *C*. Air is drawn in through *E*. Active combustion takes place at the top of *C*, the hot flue gases preheating the charge in *A*, while the hot reaction mass descending through *C* to the discharge *E* preheats the incoming air. Tests run on

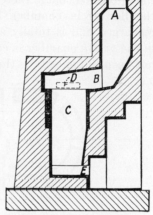

Fig. 74.—Dietzsch kiln.

such furnaces show a very high fuel economy but operating labor costs are excessive.

HOFFMAN RING FURNACE

The Hoffman ring furnace is extremely efficient, and has added advantages in all industries that demand a period of gradual heating up and slow cooling. It is gratifying to note the increasing applications of this arrangement in American industries. As originally developed for solid fuel, it consists of a circular, elliptical or rectangular gallery built around a central flue. This gallery (Fig. 75) is divided into separate chambers, each constructed with side openings *E*, a door on the outside *C* and a flue *D* to the central stack *A*, and is so provided with diaphragms and dampers that any passage may be closed at will.

In operation, combustion is carried on in only one chamber at a time. The two chambers opposite this are in the process of charging and discharging, and all the others are either being heated up to the combustion temperature by flue gases or are themselves cooling and thereby preheating air for combustion. Air enters through the door of the discharging chamber (No. 1 in a series of 14 in the furnace shown) and is drawn through the adjacent chambers in series (2, 3, 4, 5, 6) until it reaches the active one (7); these chambers contain burned product which preheats the air and is itself cooled. From the active chamber the hot flue gases pass through chambers 8, 9, 10, 11, 12 and 13, heating up the unburned charge there, and finally pass to the stack through the flue *D* in chamber 13. Number 14 is meanwhile being recharged and is totally shut off from the rest. After ignition in the active chamber is completed, the adjacent one, which has not been burned (8), is then made active by admitting fuel to it

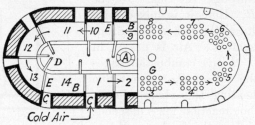

Fig. 75.—Hoffman ring furnace for solid fuel.

through holes in the top; the newly charged chamber (14) is admitted to the series by connecting it to the stack and to 13 and closing the flue from 13 to the stack; the discharged chamber (1) is charged; and the coolest burned chamber (2) is opened to the air and discharged.

It is obvious that very efficient countercurrent action is obtained in this furnace and therefore the heat consumption is exceedingly low. Pre-ignition is avoided by not admitting the fuel until the chamber is ready to be burned. The chief disadvantages encountered are high initial expense and labor costs and the mechanical stresses set up by repeated heating and cooling.

The Hoffman ring furnace is operated most smoothly and efficiently with gaseous fuel, and all modern construction, at least in this country, is of this type. The gas may be admitted to a number of chambers simultaneously, thus avoiding localized overheating. Because of the very efficient preheating of the air used for combustion, high temperatures can be successfully realized even with a fuel of low heating value (producer gas), and the large volume of gas flowing through the chambers gives uniformity of heat distribution. A gas-fired furnace is shown in Fig. 75A.

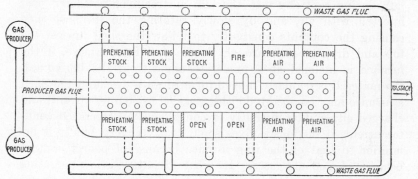

FIG. 75A.—Hoffman ring furnace for gaseous fuel.

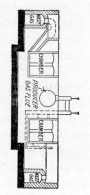

The fuel is distributed through a central flue from which connection is made to the chambers under fire by means of a number of inverted U-tubes, each of which is inserted into a hole in the main flue and into the top of one of the distributing flues around the chambers. The control valves are located in the U-tubes. From each of the latter flues a large number of distributing ports lead to the chamber in order to provide uniformity of gas distribution. Furthermore a number of these distributing flues are fed simultaneously, only a small amount of gas going to each, to avoid localized overheating. From the proper chamber connection is made to the stack by a method similar to that used in distributing the fuel. The holes into which the distributing U-tubes fit are covered when not in use.

All flues must be liberal in size in order to avoid excessive friction with the large amount of air and gases to be handled. In order to insure uniformity of heating and cooling especial care must be exercised in packing the charge and in the construction of the ports in the separating walls between chambers as well as in the distribution of the producer gas delivered to the chambers under fire.

These furnaces must be built carefully to provide for the repeated expansion and contraction in each chamber. Especially where high temperatures are to be employed, only the highest grade refractories should be used in construction.

ROTARY KILN

By the use of powdered coal in a blast of air it has become possible to introduce solid fuel into a furnace with perfect regularity; and by providing a means of passing the flame produced through the charge, efficient heating is realized.   This can be done in a rotary kiln, consisting of a boiler-plate tubular shell from 30 to 220 ft. long, 6 to 12 ft. in diameter and lined with fire brick or other resistant material, the choice of refractory depending upon the reaction to be carried on.   The charge is heated by introducing centrally into the kiln a stream of powdered coal injected with air, and by slowly rotating the furnace, thus causing the contents constantly to follow the shell toward the top and drop or roll through the flame.   Furthermore, if the furnace is inclined at a moderate angle from the horizontal, the material is regularly moved forward until discharged.   Such a furnace may be operated either parallel or countercurrent, and charged either intermittently or continuously.   Operated countercurrent, it obviously gives some heat recovery but it is far inferior to that of the ring furnace because of poorer contact between charge and gases.   Its great advantage is low operating and labor expense and it consequently is of unusual importance in this country where fuel is cheap and labor high.

As discussed on page 191, the most rapid transfer of energy takes place when it is in the form of radiant heat.   Powdered coal furnishes an ideal source of this form of energy and this type of furnace seems to be capable of much larger utility than it enjoys at present.   If the charge is a liquid or a liquid suspension, it may be atomized by a spray nozzle into the combustion space and both evaporation and combustion, calcination or other chemical reaction may be carried on with great rapidity; if it is a fine powder, it may be agglomerated into small pellets or lumps by tumbling it with a small amount of suitable binder such as tar or sodium silicate solution.   The mechanical devices for supporting the shell and for taking up the downward thrust due to rotation, and the driving mechanism have all been thoroughly developed and are easily obtained on the market.

One disadvantage incident to the ordinary type of rotary kiln is the difficulty with which an efficient heat-regeneration system for preheating the air can be employed in connection with it. Such difficulties are, however, by no means insurmountable, and it is but a question of time when the economy in fuel will compensate for the expense of such an installation.

If the clinker and ash from the solid fuel used in these furnaces are objectionable from the point of view of the product, it is obvious that they must be fired by gaseous fuels. Solid fuels may, however, be used by providing a firebox and grate apart from the reaction chamber and by leading the flame over a bridge wall to the charge.

TUNNEL KILN

Another type of furnace which, like the above, gives counter-current flow of charge on the one hand and air and flue gas on the other, and hence offers excellent heat regeneration in the furnace itself, is the *tunnel kiln*. It has been developed in recent years

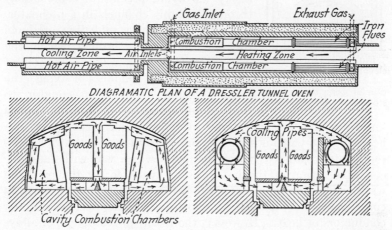

FIG. 76.—American Dressler tunnel kiln. The streams of arrows indicate the "thermo-syphon" circulation of the gases. This reverses direction in the heating and cooling zones.

for firing materials which cannot be tumbled, as in a rotary kiln, yet which require a shorter time of heating and cooling than the cycle of a ring furnace. It consists of a tunnel, through which are pushed a number of trucks carrying the charge. The trucks run on a steel track and running gear, but the whole superstructure on the truck may be of refractory material, and the lower part may be protected from the heat by the shape of the tunnel, or in some cases by the use of a seal consisting of a trough filled with sand, into which dips an apron attached to the body of the truck. These kilns are usually gas fired, the fuel being admitted near the middle of the tunnel. They offer excellent control of the heating operation and are successfully used up to

1400°C. They represent an important phase of modern furnace development.

In cases in which the charge is small in amount, or in which it is inadmissible to bring charge and combustion products into contact because of chemical interaction (as is usually true in the use of muffles and retorts), the sensible heat of the gaseous products of combustion should be employed to preheat the fuel and air. Actual contact is here out of the question, but two means are available to effect the heat recovery. In the first fuel and air may enter separately (to avoid premature combustion) through suitable channels in a preheater, separated from the combustion products by partition walls through which the interchanged heat flows, the motion of the combustion products leaving the furnace being opposite or counter to that of incoming fuel and air. This is known as the "recuperative" system of heat recovery or preheating. Its value is seriously limited by the fact that for high-temperature furnaces no cheap metal which will withstand the corrosive action of the hot gases is available for the partition walls, while the refractory earthenware ducts which must in consequence be employed are expensive, fragile, porous and poor conductors of heat. However, the recent development of alloys capable of withstanding higher temperatures has been attended by a steadily increasing use of recuperation as a means of improving the efficiency of heating operations carried out at high-temperature levels.

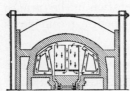

FIG. 76A.—Sectional elevation of Dressler tunnel kiln, showing circulation of gases through the stock.

The other means available for heat recovery in such cases consists in allowing the combustion products to escape through and heat up chambers filled with refractory material in the form of "checkerwork," as large in amount and with as large a surface as possible, while the incoming air and fuel (if gaseous and thermally stable) are preheated by passage through similar chambers previously heated in this same way.

It is necessary to provide only two channels for the fuel gas and two for the air. While one channel of each pair is being heated by the flue gas leaving the furnace, the other two are being cooled by the incoming fuel gas and air. Or, to state it in another way, while the flue gas is giving up its valuable heat to the bricks of two of the chambers, the bricks of the other two are returning the heat to the gas and air to be carried back into the furnace. This is known as the "regenerative" system of heat recovery. By periodically changing the channels from hot flue gas to cold air and fuel gas by the use of "butterfly" valves, a great amount of heat otherwise lost is retained in the furnace cycle. It has the advantage of construction simplicity, but requires constant attention in operation and gives temperature fluctuations caused by the temperature variations of the chambers during each cycle. It would at first appear that this system does not offer the advantages of countercurrent operation, but, if air and fuel gas flow through the chambers in a direction opposite to that of the combustion products, effective countercurrent action is realized. The hot flue gases entering the first end of the chamber bring this end up to a high temperature, but the other end attains only a moderate heat since the flue gases have already cooled to a great degree; upon reversal, the cold air flowing in the opposite direction is first warmed by contact with this other relatively cool end of the chamber, but is finally raised to the highest possible temperature by contact with the hottest bricks in the first end.

In one special case, that of the iron blast furnace, while it is absolutely necessary to preheat the air needed for combustion in order to produce the large quantity of heat required at the high temperature essential for the fusion of the iron, nearly all the sensible heat of the furnace gases is used up in preheating the charge of ore, flux and fuel in the upper part of the shaft of the furnace itself, and little is left to preheat the air. In this case a series of chambers or "stoves" of the regenerative type is used, these being heated by burning in them a part of the waste fuel gas from the top of the blast furnace itself. These stoves are tall cylindrical steel shells, lined with fire brick and filled with fire-checkerwork or flues.

Regenerative furnaces must be carefully built of highly resistant brick, so placed as to secure good contact of brick surface with the gas, yet in such a way as not to introduce too great resistance to flow, and so designed as to resist the expansion and contraction with temperature changes to which they are subjected. Fortunately, as pointed out above, the temperature changes at *any one spot* are not excessive. The regenerators are placed sometimes beneath, sometimes beside the furnace, and are usually rectangular. High heat conductance, produced by high gas velocity, can be secured, though at the expense of increased frictional resistance, by having them long and narrow, but exigencies of construction often make this impracticable.

The effectiveness of regenerative checkers in recovering heat depends directly upon the coefficient of heat transfer between the checkers or flues and the gases that pass through them.

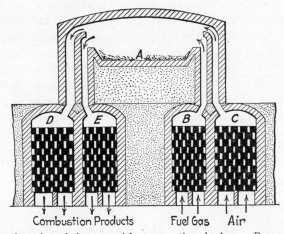

Combustion Products   Fuel Gas   Air

Fig. 77.—Open-hearth furnace with regenerative checkers. Reversing valves and connecting flues are not shown. Attention should be called to the fact that the air chambers are larger than those for gas because of the larger volumes to be ahandled. The design of the furnace itself is of importance in order to secure uniform distribution of the flame throughout the furnace.

During the gas blow the checkers are at a temperature lower than the hot flue gases passing through them to the stack. The heat picked up from these gases and consequently the temperature to which they fall before reaching the stack are determined by the existing temperature difference between the checkers and gas and by the coefficient of heat transfer. Similarly the average temperature to which the checkers fall during the air blow depends upon the heat transfer during this part of the cycle. The periodic reversal of direction of heat transfer makes calculation somewhat complicated.

The curves in Fig. 78 indicate diagrammatically the temperature conditions in a regenerator in which it is assumed that the air enters at the bottom and leaves at the top while the flue gases flow downward in the opposite direction. The upper of each of the three sets of curves indicates the temperature conditions at each particular point in the regenerator at the end of the heating cycle just prior to reversal of the valves or at the beginning of the air blow. The lower curve of each pair indicates the corresponding conditions at the end of the air blow or just after the flue gases are turned through the checkerwork. At the start of the air blow the brickwork is hot and the air temperature curve is therefore high. As the air blow progresses, the brickwork cools off and the air-temperature curve falls correspondingly. The average temperature reached by the air is indicated by point c. After reversal the flue gases entering the cool chamber are lowered in temperature as indicated by the lower of the curves, ad_1. However, as the brickwork rises in temperature, the heat recovered from the flue gas is lessened and tem-

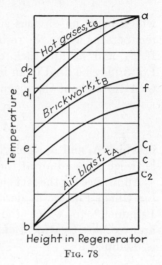

FIG. 78

peratures finally rise to a point indicated by the upper of the two curves, ad_2. The average temperature of the gases going to the stack is d.

It is obvious that the use of regenerators or checkerwork of sufficiently high heat capacity and thermal conductivity and/or the use of very short cycles of operation would cause the brickwork surface temperature to assume a steady value unchanging with time and extending between some such points as e and f of Fig. 78. One could then express the local heat flow *per air period* per square foot of brickwork, Q/A, in terms of h_A, the coefficient of heat transfer from brick to air; t_B, the brick temperature; and t_A, the air temperature, as

$$\left(\frac{Q}{A}\right)_{\text{local}} = h_A \theta_A (t_B - t_A). \tag{1}$$

This same quantity of heat must flow from gas to brickwork during the gas period of duration θ_G hr., from which

$$\left(\frac{Q}{A}\right)_{\text{local}} = h_G \theta_G (t_G - t_B). \tag{2}$$

From Eqs. 1 and 2 the brick temperature may be eliminated to give

$$\left(\frac{Q}{A}\right)_{\text{local}} = \frac{t_G - t_A}{\dfrac{1}{h_A\theta_A} + \dfrac{1}{h_G\theta_G}} = K(t_G - t_A) \tag{3}$$

which bears an obvious similarity to the equation for flow in a recuperator where the resistances to heat flow are truly in series. If h_A and h_G are each constant throughout the regenerator, Eq. 3 may be used in an integration to give the average value of Q/A throughout the regenerator. The resultant relation is

$$\frac{Q}{A} = K\frac{\Delta_1 - \Delta_2}{\ln(\Delta_1/\Delta_2)} \tag{4}$$

in which Δ_1 and Δ_2 signify the average differences in temperature between gas and air at the two ends of the regenerator.

Allowance for the fact that in actual regenerators the conditions for which Eq. 4 was derived do not exist has been treated by Rummel,[*] to which the reader is referred for details. An approximate treatment of the problem indicates that K of Eq. 3. is modified to

$$K = \frac{1}{\dfrac{1}{h_A\theta_A} + \dfrac{1}{h_G\theta_G} + \dfrac{1}{2.5C_p\rho R} + \dfrac{R}{k(\theta_A + \theta_G)}} \tag{5}$$

in which C_p is the specific heat of the brick, ρ is its density, R is the ratio of the total volume of the bricks to their exposed surface, and k is the thermal conductivity. For most regenerator problems the third term of the denominator will be found negligible (although blast-furnace stoves represent an application in which the cycle of operation is too long to justify neglecting the brick action).

Coefficients of heat transmission suitable for use in regenerator design are available in the reference cited.

The pressure drops through such checkwork or flues can be estimated in the usual way (pages 77–97). In this country the velocities employed are very low (5 to 10 lin. ft. per sec.) because dependence is usually upon stack draft. As the cost of fuel goes up, the necessity for heat recovery will increase, regenerators

[*] *Arch. Eisenhüttenw.*, **4**, 367 (1931).

will be built larger or else be operated at higher gas velocities, and the necessary pressure drop will be overcome by forced draft.

Air consists of 79 per cent by volume of nitrogen. Since the specific heat is nearly the same as that of oxygen, it may be seen that a great saving in heat could be effected if the oxygen content of the air used could be increased. For some purposes this will be accomplished with much profit in the near future. This possibility of saving is, however, a practical rather than a theoretical one, as it should be possible by the methods of recovery just described to preheat all the nitrogen entering the furnace with the sensible heat of that leaving it; the present preheaters required are large, expensive and relatively inefficient.

7. CALCULATIONS

The general methods of thermal calculation of furnace problems will be illustrated by the following computations on a gas-fired continuous preheating furnace.

TEST DATA

Duration of test..................................... 12 hr.
Stock fed, total...................................... 512,020 lb.
Average temperature of stock fed...................... 86°F.
Average temperature of stock discharged............... 1167°C.
Average specific heat of stock........................ 0.153
Fuel gas consumption, saturated with water vapor at 86°F.
    and 29.5 in. barometer............................ 1,301,000 cu. ft.
B.t.u. per cu. ft. of gas (water condensed) saturated at
    86°F. and 29.9 in. barometer...................... 517
Average fuel gas temperature (100 per cent relative humidity... 86°F.
Average air temperature............................... 86°F.
Average air relative humidity......................... 53 per cent
Average gas temperature entering stack................ 843°F.
Average gas analyses:

	Leaving Furnace	Entering Stack
CO_2..................................	8.24	4.51
O_2.....................................	1.15	12.05
CO......................................	5.34	0.12
N_2.....................................	85.27	83.32
Total (dry basis).................	100.00	100.00

FUEL GAS (DRY BASIS)

	Per cent
CO_2	2.3
Illuminants	3.3
O_2	0.4
CO	7.0
H_2	53.0
CH_4	29.0
N_2	5.0

Preliminary Calculations

1. *Basis*: 100 *mols of dry fuel gas*:

Gas	Mols	Atoms C	Mols H_2	Mols O_2
CO_2	2.3	2.3	....	2.3
Ill.*	3.3	9.9	9.9	....
O_2	0.4	....	....	0.4
CO	7.0	7.0	....	3.5
H_2	53.0	....	53.0	
CH_4	29.0	29.0	58.0	
N_2	5.0			
Totals	100.0	48.2	120.9	6.2

* Taken as equivalent to C_3H_6.

2. *Basis*: 100 *mols dry flue gas at furnace.*

Gas	Mols	Atoms C	Mols H_2	Mols O_2
CO_2	8.24	8.24	....	8.24
O_2	1.15	....	....	1.15
CO	5.34	5.34	....	2.67
N_2	85.27			
Totals	100.00	13.58	....	12.06

3. *Basis*: 100 *mols dry flue gas at stack.*

Gas	Mols	Atoms C	Mols H_2	Mols O_2
CO_2	4.51	4.51	....	4.51
O_2	12.05	....	....	12.05
CO	0.12	0.12	....	0.06
N_2	83.32			
Totals	100.00	4.63	....	16.62

Ratio of air to fuel gas. Basis: 100 mols dry fuel gas.

1. *At furnace.*

By *carbon* balance.

$48.2 = 0.1358y$; whence $y = 355$ mols dry flue gas.

By *nitrogen* balance.

$0.79x + 5.0 = 0.8527$ (355); whence $x = 376$ mols dry air
$376/100 = 3.76$ mols dry air per mol of dry fuel gas.

2. *At stack.*

$48.2 = 0.0463y$; $y = 1040$ mols dry flue gas,
$0.79x + 5.0 = 0.8332$ (1040); $x = 1090$ mols dry air,
$1090/100 = 10.90$ mols dry air per mol of dry fuel gas.

3. *Flue leakage.*—The increase in air from furnace to stack is obviously leakage. Since the basis is fuel gas, air quantities may be subtracted directly, *i.e.*, the in-leak of dry air is $10.90 - 3.76 = 7.14$ mols/mol of dry fuel gas.

Mols O_2 theoretically required for fuel $= 48.2$ (for carbon) $+ \dfrac{120.9}{2}$ (for H_2)

$= 108.65$. Since the fuel contains 6.2, the difference, 102.45 mols O_2, requires $102.45/0.210 = 488$ mols of dry air.
Mols dry air in flue gas per mol of dry air theoretically required.

Leaving furnace.

$376/488 = 0.771$; excess air $= -22.9$ per cent.

Entering stack.

$1090/488 = 2.23$; excess air $= +123$ per cent.

Overall heat balance. Basis: 12 hr.

$1,301,000 \dfrac{(29.5 - 1.248)}{(29.9 - 1.248)} = 1,285,000$ cu. ft. saturated fuel gas at 86°F. and 1 atmosphere, since pressure of water vapor at 86°F. $= 1.248$ in. mercury.
Input (in fuel gas).

$(1,285,000)$ $(517) = 664,000,000$ B.t.u.

$1,285,000 \dfrac{(492)}{(546)(359)} = 3220$ mols saturated fuel gas,

$3220 \dfrac{1.248}{29.5} = 136.5$ mols *moisture* in fuel,

$3220 - 136 = 3084$ mols dry fuel.
(100) $(136.5)/3084 = 4.42$ mols moisture/100 mols dry fuel.

Mols water from *burning* 100 mols dry fuel = 120.9.
Total from 100 dry fuel = 120.9 + 4.42 = 125.3.
Partial pressure of water in air = (0.53) (1.248) = 0.662 in. of mercury.
Partial pressure of air = 29.5 − 0.66 = 28.84 in. of mercury.

$$\text{Moisture from air} = \frac{(1090)(0.662)}{28.84} = 25.0 \text{ mols.}$$

Mols moisture in stack gas.

$$
\begin{array}{ll}
\text{From fuel} = & 125.3 \\
\text{From air} \ = & 25.0 \\
\hline
\text{Total} & 150.3
\end{array}
$$

Latent heat up stack. Basis: 12 hr.

$$\frac{3084}{100}(150.3)(18)(1044) = 87,400,000 \text{ B.t.u.}$$

Potential heat up stack. Basis: 12 hr.

$$\frac{(3084)(1040)(0.0012)(67,650)*(1.8)}{100} = 4,700,000 \text{ B.t.u.}$$

SENSIBLE HEAT* UP STACK ABOVE 86°F., PER 100 MOLS DRY STACK GAS

Gas	Pound mols	At 843°F. B.t.u. above 60°F.	At 86°F. B.t.u. above 60°F.	Difference	B.t.u. loss
CO₂...........	4.51	8,340	231	8,109	36,600
CO...........	0.12	5,610	181	5,429	700
O₂............	12.05	5,850	182	5,668	68,400
N₂............	83.32	5,560	181	5,379	448,000
H₂O..........	14.44†	6,610	210	6,400	92,500
Total.......	.....	.....	...	.....	646,200

*Based on Fig. 1, page 10.
† 150.3/10.4 = 14.44 mols total H_2O vapor per 100 mols stack gas.

Total sensible heat up stack above 86°F. Basis: 12 hr.

$$(3084)(10.4)\frac{646,200}{100} = 207,500,000 \text{ B.t.u.}$$

Heat into charge. Basis: 12 hr.

$$(542,020)\ (0.153)\ (2135 - 86) = 170,000,000 \text{ B.t.u.}$$

* 67,650 gm. cal. evolved by burning 1 gm. mol. of CO to CO_2.

Distribution of Heat

	B.t.u./12 hr.	Input, per cent
Input (in fuel)............................	664,000,000	100.0
Output:		
Into charge...........................	170,000,000	25.6
Stack losses:		
Potential...........................	4,700,000	0.7⎫
Latent.............................	87,400,000	13.2⎬ 45.1
Sensible............................	207,500,000	31.2⎭
Unaccounted (radiation, cooling water, etc.)	194,400,000	29.3
Total..............................	664,000,000	100.0

CHAPTER VIII

GAS PRODUCERS

As pointed out on page 182, producer gas, the product of controlled primary combustion of coal with a thick fuel bed and with steam mixed with the primary air, is of increasing importance in industrial furnaces. Producer gas is the logical development of the "long-flame" combustion of fuels with suppression of primary combustion and increase of secondary. As in the case of coal-fired furnaces, the steam is used to make possible the utilization of low-volatile fuels and the gasification of all the combustible matter of the fuel and not merely of the volatile combustible. The gas producer represents the isolation of primary combustion under conditions of exact control, thus rendering it unnecessary to compromise in design and operation between the demands of the gas-producing apparatus and those of the furnace itself. Each may be constructed and run to the best possible advantage for its own purpose irrespective of the other. Consequently modern construction is to an ever-increasing extent discarding the direct use of coal in the furnace. For example, lime kilns fired with producer gas have been installed and are proving successful.

From the discussion on page 181, it is obvious that a gas producer must operate with a thick fuel bed. The oxygen of the air burns to CO_2 extremely rapidly, raising the bottom of the fuel bed to a very high temperature. This temperature is lowered by the presence of the steam, largely due to its diluent effect, since the rate of interaction of steam with carbon is slow compared with that of oxygen and also since any hydrogen formed would be largely reoxidized as long as oxygen is present, because of the high rate of this last reaction. As soon as the oxygen has disappeared, however, carbon begins to reduce both steam and CO_2 as indicated on page 174. Because all these reduction reactions absorb heat, the fuel bed is chilled thereby. There is therefore a sharp temperature gradient in the fuel bed, heat flowing rapidly by both radiation and conduction from the lower layer of the bed (the oxidizing layer of CO_2 formation) up to this reduction zone. This tends to keep down the temperature of the oxidation zone, but that temperature will rise rapidly with increase of combustion rate, because the heat evolution due to increased CO_2 formation will be greater than can be dissipated to the reduction zone. Since, as will appear later, one of the most serious difficulties in gas producers comes from fusion of the ash, it is necessary to have the steam quantity high and the combustion rate low in order to keep down the temperature in the oxidation zone because this is the very point where the ash is being deposited. It is on this account that gas producers cannot, in general, be forced above a combustion rate of 40 lb. of coal per sq. ft. of 'cross section of fuel bed per hr., while, with some coals with low-fusing ash, rates of 10 to 15 lb. cannot be exceeded with safety.

Where the hot gas rises through the cold fuel, the latter is distilled in the entire absence of air. If the temperature of this distillation is low, as is usually the case, large quantities of tar are formed, the removal of which is one of the serious problems of gas-producer operation. Where the temperature is higher, these hydrocarbons are cracked with formation of soot, almost equally obnoxious. Where the hot gas can be led directly from the producer to the furnace (raw producer gas), these impurities may not be a serious problem. The formation of this tar and soot can be eliminated by passing the air down through the fuel bed but the mechanical difficulties encountered have in the past proved sufficiently serious so that this type of producer is not widely used.

The methane and traces of illuminants in producer gas come mainly from distillation of the fuel and are therefore highest in high-volatile high-B.t.u. coals.

From the discussion on page 174, it is clear that a producer operated at low temperature will give relatively large quantities of CO_2 and less CO and hydrogen, in other words, a low-B.t.u. gas. The higher the temperature, the greater the capacity of the producer and the higher the heating value of the product. Since the temperature of operation is limited by the temperature of fusion of the ash, the value of a coal for gas producer operation depends largely thereon.

Where producer gas is cleaned or piped any great distance, it is cooled and the sensible heat of the gas is lost, while raw gas is used directly and this heat is conserved. The efficiency of conversion of the energy of the coal into heating value in the gas is therefore reported sometimes on a "cold," sometimes on a "hot," basis. It is convenient to use the cold basis as a standard for comparisons, even though, where conditions warrant, the additional sensible heat is recoverable.

Were no steam used in a coke-fired producer but the CO_2 completely reduced to CO, the efficiency (cold) would obviously be 135,300/2(97,000) or 70 per cent (see page 173). Were heat loss eliminated, the remaining 30 per cent would be the sensible heat in the gas. While steam absorbs part of this sensible heat and converts it into chemical energy in the formation of hydrogen and CO, the facts that the undecomposed steam carries away sensible heat and that the decomposition of steam tends to suppress the reduction of CO_2 partially offset the advantages gained. Incomplete reduction of CO_2 reduces the efficiency of a producer. Volatile combustible matter in the coal greatly increases efficiency since it can be distilled at the expense of the sensible heat in the spent gases but increases trouble with tar. As a result of all these factors, the cold efficiency of commercial producers is from 65 to 85 per cent, 70 per cent representing average practice.

The effect of steam on the efficiency has been determined experimentally;[*] although the data are not conclusive, it is definitely shown that the efficiency is affected but little with steam injections of from 0 to 0.4 lb. per lb. of coal fired, but that efficiency rapidly decreases as the steam quantity is increased above this value. It is therefore desirable to keep the steam consumption down to the lowest point compatible with prevention of fusion of the ash and maintenance of a reasonable rate of combustion in the producer.

It must be kept in mind that the fuel bed of a producer consists of four zones: the bottom layer of ashes, the function of which is to support and insulate the incandescent fuel; the oxidation zone where the temperature is very high owing to CO_2 formation; the reduction zone where the temperature is low owing to the heat absorption resulting from decomposition of water and CO_2; and the preheating and distillation zone where the cold fuel is coked

---

* BONE and WHEELER, *J. Iron Steel Inst. (London)*, **76**, 126 (1907); CLEMENTS, *J. Iron Steel Inst. (London)*, **107**, 97 (1923).

by the sensible heat of the gases from the reduction zone. It is obviously desirable to have the time of contact of the CO_2 and steam with the incandescent coke as great and to have the temperature of this reduction zone as high as possible in order to get high percentage decomposition into combustible gases.

The reduction zone gets its heat exclusively from the oxidation zone, and consequently the top part of the reduction zone is at a temperature so low that the rate of the reduction reactions is very slight. Hence it is unsatisfactory to try to secure time of contact by greatly increasing the depth of the fuel bed. It must be realized by increasing the cross section of the producer, *i.e.*, by cutting down the velocity of the gases through the fuel bed and reducing the combustion rate. This reduces the distance between the oxidation zone where the heat is generated and the reduction zone where it is consumed, and therefore facilitates the flow of heat from the first to the second. This increases the reduction of CO_2 and steam, because of the increase in both time of contact and temperature of the reduction zone. In this way it is possible to increase the heating value of the gas produced by 20 per cent and to increase the efficiency of the equipment by a corresponding though smaller amount.

It must not be concluded from the preceding paragraph that a gas producer should be operated with a thin fuel bed. The thicker the fuel bed, *other things equal*, the better the results because the greater the action in the reduction zone and the more complete the recovery of sensible heat in the distillation zone. The point is that increase in time of contact, obtained by increase in cross section of the fuel bed, is far more effective in increasing the efficiency of the reduction zone than a corresponding increase secured by greater depth.

The maximum temperature allowable in the oxidation zone of a producer is from 50 to 200°F. below the fusion temperature of the ash. The producer must be fired at a rate sufficiently low and with a steam-to-air ratio sufficiently high to keep the temperature down to this point. If the ash fuses at 2000°F., the combustion rate cannot exceed 5 to 6 lb. of coal per sq. ft. of cross section of the fuel bed per hr. without the use of an excessive amount of steam, which will result in a low efficiency and a low-B.t.u. gas, rich in CO_2. A fusion point of 3000° makes it possible to more than double these combustion rates, reduce the steam-air ratio and increase the reduction, thereby increasing the efficiency. Therefore, while it is possible to make producer gas with fuels having low-fusing ash, the overhead expense of gas production is nearly double and the quality of the resulting gas is lower, in comparison with a coal of high-melting ash. Where the wear and tear on the lining is the limiting factor (see page 229), a very high-melting ash makes it possible to carry a heavy emergency overload for a short time, though at the expense of depreciation of the lining.

The great disadvantage of producer gas is its low heating value due to the large amount of diluent nitrogen and undecomposed CO_2. Gas with a heating value less than 90 to 95 B.t.u. per cu.ft. will not support its own combustion without preheating, and such gas may all too easily be obtained from a producer because of difficulties that will be discussed under operation. An anthracite coal should give a gas of 130 to 135 B.t.u. and a good bituminous coal will easily produce 150 to 160 B.t.u. The highest grade bituminous coal in well-designed producers operated at reasonable combustion rates will give 180 B.t.u. continuously and has been known to yield 215 B.t.u. under special conditions. These excellent results can be realized, however, only where very complete decomposition of the CO_2 and steam is obtained, the CO_2 in the resulting gas being brought well below 5 per cent.

TYPES OF PRODUCERS

One of the major advantages of the gas producer lies in the fact that it can be designed and operated so as to handle low-grade fuels, either those with excessive ash (if nonfusing) or of low heating value (brown coals, lignites, etc.). In the latter case the heating value of the gas is lower. It is unfortunate that the combined water of these low-grade fuels is driven off in the distillation zone and cannot be utilized as the source of steam for the production of the gas in up-draft producers. This disadvantage is overcome in some large units into which pulverized low-grade coals are fed at the bottom of the fuel bed; this type of producer is now being developed in Europe. Likewise, the development of thoroughly successful down-draft producers would greatly increase the efficiency of decomposition of such low-grade fuels.

The apparatus for making industrial gas by these reactions is called a **producer,** and consists essentially of:

1. A container or reaction vessel.
2. Provision for supplying fuel.
3. Provision for supplying air and steam.
4. Provision for removing ash.
5. Provision for removing gases formed.
6. Provision for removing flue dust and tar.

1. The Container.—The container is usually a steel cylindrical shell lined with fire brick. It may be one stationary piece, or one piece rotating on a central axis, or in two parts, either or both of which may rotate. The top and other vulnerable points are generally water cooled. The size varies from 5 ft. diameter to dimensions of 10 and 12 ft., and the capacity is from 500 to 3500 lb. of coal per hr. The bottom may be a special shaking grate, but more frequently the fire bed rests upon a mass of ashes which is supported by a pan filled with water.

It is a well-known fact that steam has at high temperatures a selective disintegrating action on fire brick that is very serious. Also in a producer the fuel bed is continuously working downward and thereby abrades the lining. Furthermore the ash may exert a fluxing action on the lining even below its melting point (just as salt will melt ice below 0°C.) Consequently a producer lining operates under exceptionally severe conditions and the temperature of the oxidation zone must be held down to keep the deterioration within reasonable limits. The development of a special refractory to resist these conditions would make it possible to increase the efficiency and capacity of producers when using coals of high-fusing ash.

2. Fuel Supply.—The supply of fuel may be intermittent or continuous; an intermittent feed is simpler from a mechanical point of view, but the spasmodic addition of large quantities of green coal leads to an irregular production of distillation gas and tar. It is all-important that the top of the fuel bed be kept level and the mass of fuel uniformly distributed. There is a tendency for the larger pieces of the fuel to pass to the outside edge of the charge, thus creating here a path of smaller resistance than through the center and causing irregularity of combustion. The blast of air and steam naturally takes the path of least resistance, and, when a channel or "chimney" is once formed in the fuel bed, it rapidly increases in size owing to the localized combustion. This is fatal to good operation; first, the intense heat thus set free fuses the ash into masses of clinker very difficult to manage; second, much steam passes through so rapidly that it does not react with the carbon and, leaving the producer at a high temperature, carries with it large quantities of sensible heat; third, uncombined air passes through these channels or blowholes and burns at the top of the fuel bed, causing high CO_2 content and low calorific value in the gas. Provision for maintaining a bed of reacting fuel of uniform density free from such openings is a matter of importance and is accomplished more or less successfully in a number of ways which will be discussed later.

Coal broken to a uniform size of from 1 to 2 in. and freed from dust is the most desirable size of fuel, although "run of mine" when crushed to pass a 4-in. mesh or ring is the most common in use. It seldom, if ever, pays to use strictly slack coal even though the first cost is very low. The capacity of the apparatus is cut down by the choking of the blast, which must be driven at a higher pressure to force it through the fire. Blowholes are on this account more readily formed and a hot gas of low calorific value is produced. Suction producers are generally fed with anthracite coal, for, although a great deal of work has been done toward utilizing soft coal, the high ash, sulfur and coking characteristics have until recently prevented its successful use. Western lignites in large sizes and German brown-coal briquettes give very good results. Bituminous coals work well in pressure producers and consequently anthracite is burned only in comparatively small plants of this class.

3. Supply of Air and Water Vapor.—Gas producers may be divided into two types according to the method of supplying air and steam; in the first they are drawn through by means of an exhauster or other form of suction, and in the second they are forced through by pressure from a blower or injector. The former is used chiefly to supply internal-combustion engines where the vacuum of the cylinder is directly communicated to the producer. In such cases provision is made for saturating the air with moisture in an independent apparatus.

In pressure producers the steam supply is usually under high pressure and is often used to inject the necessary volume of air into the fuel bed. It is desirable to be able to control the air fed to the producer and the ratio of steam to air independently of each other, since the first controls the combustion rate in the producer, while the second should be kept substantially constant for a given fuel but be capable of adjustment if the fuel changes. With a steam injector this control is impossible. The steam-air ratio can be maintained constant either by a thermostatic control inserted in the mixture and by operating the steam valve, or by humidifying the air with hot water up to a thermostatically controlled temperature. The steam for direct injection or for heating the water can be obtained advantageously from the exhaust of the steam-driven air blower. Proper design of the distributing head is important inasmuch as an even distribution of the air and steam supply is highly desirable in the operation of the producer. In those types in which the fuel rests upon a bed of ashes in a water-cooled pan, the distributing injector is placed in the center just below the zone of active combustion. Obviously suction producers must employ some form of grate so designed that the even distribution of the supply gases is insured. The avoidance of large clinkers is directly dependent upon the even distribution of this blast. Localized high temperature incident to blowholes and "chimneys" produces clinkers difficult to remove from the ash bed. When this occurs on the edge of the fuel bed, they stick to the wall and may cause the fuel to arch across or "hang," thus greatly interfering with regular operation.

4. Removal of Ash.—In *suction* gas producers and others employing grates, the ash is removed by a movement of the grate bars. In order to compensate for the more easy passage of the supply gases at the area of contact between the fuel bed and the lining of the shell, the ashes must be somewhat more completely removed at the center of the mass than around the edge. In the various types of *pressure* producers the evolution from a stationary grate, through the rotating or otherwise movable exposed grate to grates submerged in water, and finally to the grateless bottom in which the ash stands in a pan of water accessible from every point of its circumference, has been slow but continuous. The periodical removal of the ash and clinker of necessity disturbs the fire zone and interrupts the production of a uniform gas. Hence most modern producers provide for either a large storage space for ashes, so as to render removal necessary only at long intervals, or for a continuous removal by working the bottom toward the outside edge and periodically lifting out the exuded portion by means of a plow.

5. Removal of Gas Formed.—The gas is generally removed through an outlet in the side of the top of the producer, whence it passes to the coolers and scrubbers, usually through a water seal. Attempts have been made to withdraw the gas from the center of the producer below the upper level of the fuel bed in order to decompose the tar by cracking, but the mechanical difficulties encountered have resulted in the abandonment of this type.

6. Removal of Flue Dust, Soot and Tar.—Where the gas is to be used for operating an internal-combustion engine, it must be cooled and purified from the dust of the ash and the soot and tar that always accompany the decomposition of soft coal. Until very recent times coal tar of any description has not had ready sale except from large installations, and the logical method of disposition was to return it to the body of the producer for further action, despite the fact that for many heating purposes highly carbonaceous material is particularly advantageous on account of the luminous flame produced and the radiant energy set free. The principles of removal of liquids and solids from gases are taken up in the chapter on Separation and their application here is obvious. The distribution of clean cold gas over wide areas can be done under low pressure (1 to 5 lb.) and does not present difficulties of leaks or heat insulation. Condensation of tar is usually encountered on account of its incomplete removal. It is important to provide suitably located traps for it.

The application of the above general considerations in the design and operation of modern gas producers will be illustrated by a few of the large number of machines now available.

The Morgan producer consists of a stationary water-cooled top equipped with an automatic intermittent fuel door and an outlet for the gas. The shell is partly water cooled and rests upon a base with which it rotates, while the fuel bed is supported by a layer of ashes held in a water-cooled pan. A spiral-shaped bar on the bottom causes the ash to travel to the outside rim where it is continuously removed by a plow. The fuel bed is kept level and compact by a heavy bar which floats on top of it and accommodates itself to any height, distributing the fresh fuel evenly and closing up blowholes. The blast is forced up under a central hood with cowl located in the ash bin. The working capacity of the unit is about 2000 lb. of coal per hr.

The Chapman producer uses a stationary shell located above a pan of water which serves as a water seal and which is so shaped that the ashes can be hoed out of it without difficulty. It is fed continuously with a ratchet-operated gear-tooth feed. The fuel bed is kept even and blowholes are closed up by a water-cooled rake, the prongs of which project into the fuel bed so that, unlike

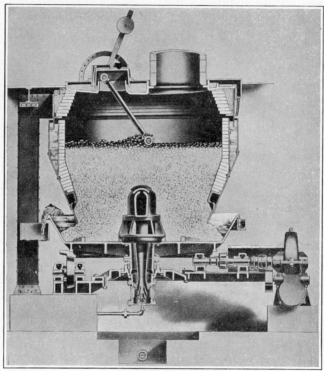

Fig. 79.—Morgan gas producer. (*Courtesy of Morgan Construction Co., Worcester, Mass.*)

the Morgan producer, holes are closed up by sidewise pressure rather than by having green coal raked into them.

The Smith producer consists of a series of rectangular sections side by side, each of which has its own grate and air supply. The grates slope backward at an angle of 35 deg. and mechanical stokers charge coal through the front wall, building up a single fuel bed for the series of sections. Air, saturated with water vapor at a definite temperature, is drawn up through this bed by suction and the gas comes off through a central outlet and is cooled and cleaned before distribution.

The Hughes producer consists of a revolving brick-lined shell with a stationary water-cooled top carrying the charging doors and the exit for the gas, and an ash pan revolving with the shell. The fuel is leveled and the reaction mass is kept free from channels

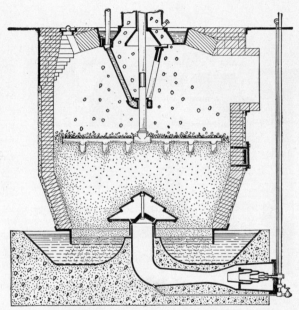

FIG. 80.—Chapman gas producer.

by a vibrating water-cooled poker depending from the stationary top and reaching well into the incandescent zone. This poker swings backward and forward, and as the shell revolves it takes as a path a series of ellipses moving in an arc between the center and a few inches from the shell lining. The blast is introduced at the center through a bell-shaped distributing head. The capacity is about 2000 lb. of coal per hr.

GAS PRODUCER COMPUTATIONS

Exactly as in the case of furnaces, the performance of a gas producer is most easily controlled by gas analysis. A complete test on a producer set is time consuming and usually the equipment is so arranged as to make it difficult or impossible to secure all the data needed. It is therefore fortunate that the gas analysis can be made to give so much information.

It is often difficult to measure the amount of gas produced because the quantity is large and meters of sufficient capacity are not usually available and more particularly because the rate of gas production is liable to wide fluctuation. From the amount of fuel used, which can be determined readily and accurately, and a knowledge of the carbon content of the fuel, a carbon balance will immediately give the gas production, provided correction is made for the tar and soot formed and for any unburned combustible in the ash. The latter is obtained from analysis of the ash but data on the former are difficult to secure accurately in a short test. Where a given fuel is used over a long period of time under reasonably constant conditions of producer operation, the tar and soot formed can be obtained directly from the plant records; the result can be expressed as percentage on the fuel, or better still as percentage on the total combustible matter fired. For coal from a given mine this figure will be quite constant; indeed for a given coal it will not change greatly even with wide variations in operating conditions.

Calculation of Gas Production.—The following illustration indicates the general method of computation of producer-gas data. In the test chosen the gas production was measured directly and can therefore be compared with the computed result. In most industrial installations the gas cannot be measured with accuracy without undue trouble and expense, but the data used below can all be obtained without difficulty. Since the ultimate analysis of the coal was not available (as is usually the case), it was necessary to estimate its carbon content from its heating value (see page 169).

Test 105, U. S. Bureau of Mines Bull. 13

FUEL ANALYSIS

Ash	11.41 per cent
B.t.u. (as fired)	10,528
Sulfur	1.33 per cent
Pounds fuel per hour	370.7
Pounds tar per ton fuel	144

GAS ANALYSIS

Gas	Per cent
CO_2	9.2
C_2H_4	0.4
CO	20.9
H_2	15.6
CH_4	1.9

CALCULATIONS

		C	H_2	O_2
CO_2	9.2	9.2	....	9.2
C_2H_4	0.4	0.8	0.8	....
CO	20.9	20.9	....	10.45
H_2	15.6	....	15.6	....
CH_4	1.9	1.9	3.8	....
N_2	52.0	....	....	....
		32.8	20.2	19.65

O_2 from air $= 52(0.21/0.79)$ =   13.82

O_2 from steam =   5.83

H_2 from steam $= 2(5.83)$ =   11.66

H_2 from net H_2 in coal =   8.54

Weight per cent of carbon in the coal which goes into the gas $= x$.
Weight per cent of oxygen in the coal (total, except ash) $= y$.
Weight per cent of net hydrogen $= z$.
Assume tar to be $(CH_2)_n$, or 20.7 lb. H and 123.3 lb. C per ton of coal or 1.035 per cent H and 6.165 per cent C on the fuel as fired.

From the fact that $\dfrac{\text{carbon}}{\text{oxygen plus ash}}$ is $\dfrac{17,230}{16,750 - \text{B.t.u.}} - 0.98$,

$$(x + 6.165)/(y + 11.41) = 1.79.$$

The ratio of carbon to net hydrogen in the gas, in mols, can be equated to the same ratio calculated from the coal:

$$\frac{32.8}{8.54} = 3.841 = \frac{x/12}{(z - 1.035)/2.016}.$$

Also, assuming 1.2 per cent N in the coal,

$$x + 6.165 + z + \frac{18.02}{16}\,y + 1.2 + 1.33 + 11.41 = 100.$$

From these three equations, $x = 52.4$ per cent carbon in the coal which goes into the gas. Hence the gas per hour is:

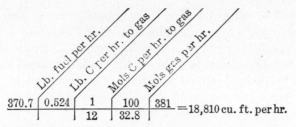

$$\frac{370.7 \left| 0.524 \right| \quad 1 \quad \left| 100 \right| 381}{\left| 12 \right| 32.8 \left|} = 18,810 \text{ cu. ft. per hr.}$$

The actual gas production per hr. as metered was 18,170 cu. ft.

Estimation of Steam Consumption and Decomposition.—Perhaps even more important than knowledge of the gas production is the determination of the steam consumption and of the extent of its decomposition in the producer. Under normal plant conditions the direct measurement of the steam used is almost as difficult as that of the gas produced, because the essential thing is the ratio of steam to gas and both these quantities are subject to wide fluctuation. Where a plant happens to be so equipped that the steam for a given unit can be fed to that unit as water, the measurement of the total amount of this water over a given period of time is easy. Where, however, resort must be had to steam meters of either the orifice, Venturi or Pitot-tube type, these, even when of the integrating type, lose somewhat in dependability owing to the excessive variations in operating conditions. It is sometimes possible to cool the gas below its dew point under such conditions as to measure the condensed water, although condensing tar makes this difficult. From this, correcting for the residual vapor in the saturated gas, one obtains the water vapor in the gas leaving the producer. This figure includes, however, all the water, both free and combined, in the fuel used, and very little of this is decomposed in the producer.

The reaction-rate equations developed on page 184 can be used for estimation of the steam consumption and its percentage decomposition. It must be remembered that in the oxidation zone of the producer the oxygen goes almost quantitatively to CO_2 while the water vapor will be little reduced because any hydrogen formed would immediately be reoxidized. In the reduction zone this CO_2 and water vapor interact with the carbon in the way described on page 224, the only differences being the presence of the diluent nitrogen and the fact that the initial CO_2 is high, while in the production of water gas it is zero.

It is well to remember that these equations mean simply this: that, if steam is being reduced by carbon, any CO_2 mixed with the steam is also being reduced, and that, therefore, the ratio of reduction of the two depends only on their relative concentrations, and not on time of contact and temperature (except to a minor degree), since any change in these last two variables will have a similar effect on the reduction of both.

For computation it is best to use 100 parts of nitrogen as the basis because this gives an unchanging standard. On this basis call the parts of CO_2 v and of water vapor x as before, but remembering that the basis has changed. It will be seen that the differential equations are absolutely identical with those for the case of water gas, *i.e.*,

$$dv/d\theta = k_7 x - k_2 v \quad \text{and} \quad dx/d\theta = -(k_6 + 2k_7)x,$$

whence

$$\frac{dv}{dx} = \frac{\beta v - x}{\alpha x},$$

where

$$\beta = k_2/k_7 \quad \text{and} \quad \alpha = 2 + (k_6/k_7),$$

which integrates into

$$(\beta - \alpha)v = x + [(\beta - \alpha)v_0 - x_0]\left(\frac{x}{x_0}\right)^{\beta/\alpha}.$$

For simplification assume that all the oxygen has gone to CO_2 at the top of the oxidation zone. Since air consists of 21 per cent oxygen and 79 per cent nitrogen, this means that the CO_2 at the start of the reduction zone is 26.6 per cent on the basis of $100 N_2$. Call the injected steam per 100 parts of nitrogen x_0. Inserting these values and remembering that the values of β and α should be the same as before, the following equation should represent the relation between the CO_2 content of the producer gas, steam used and the steam remaining undecomposed:

$$(1.01)v = x + (26.9 - x_0)(x/x_0)^{1.319}.$$

If this equation is used to compute the CO_2 content of the gas by inserting into it experimentally determined values of the steam utilization and decomposition from gas-producer tests, it is normally found that the calculated CO_2 value is lower than the observed one. There is general agreement that at the temperatures prevailing in the top of the fuel bed of a coal-fired gas producer, particularly because of the catalytic action of the hot coal particles, the reaction,

$$CO + H_2O = CO_2 + H_2 \tag{1}$$

goes extremely rapidly in comparison with the reduction reactions discussed on pages 180 to 185. Furthermore, at these temperatures the equilibrium of this reaction lies toward the CO_2 side. In other words, this reaction causes the conversion of CO to CO_2, without, however, changing the total amount of reducing gas in the mixture. This increase of CO_2 at the expense of CO, not only in the upper zones of the fuel bed but in the gaseous space above it, has long been recognized. That part of it which occurs in the gaseous space above the fuel bed is called the **Neumann reversion.** The differential equations used above take no cognizance of this reaction and therefore give too low a value for the CO_2 content of the gas. Study of the results of a large number of producer-gas tests indicate that, for coke-fired producers, the CO_2 in the gas corresponds to the values given by this equation, whereas, with coal as a fuel, the actual CO_2 percentage averages about 3.6 units above the predicted value. Hence, the equation will give the relation between steam decomposition and the gas analysis if it is written in the following modified forms:

$$\frac{101(CO_2 - b)}{N_2} = x + (26.9 - x_0)\left(\frac{x}{x_0}\right)^{1.319} \tag{2}$$

or

$$1.01\left(\frac{CO_2 - b}{H_2'}\right)(1 - \phi) = \phi + 0.269(1 - \phi)\left(\frac{N_2}{H_2'} - 1\right)\phi^{1.319} \tag{2a}$$

where b is either 3.6 or 0 as pointed out above, ϕ is x/x_0 and H_2' is the hydrogen from the decomposition of steam which is equal to $2CO_2 + 2O_2 + CO - 0.528N_2$, where CO_2, CO, O_2 and N_2 represent the molal percentages of the respective constituents in the gas. The latter form of the equation is shown plotted in Fig. 81.

It should be pointed out that an equation of different form which yields almost identical results can be obtained by assuming that the composition of the gases leaving the reduction zone corresponds to equilibrium of reaction (8)* at a temperature of approximately 2000°F. Stoichiometric substitution into the equilibrium constant, $K_p = (CO)(H_2O)/(CO_2)(H_2') = 2$ at 2000°F. (see Fig. 66, page 175) gives

$$\frac{1}{(1-\phi)} = \frac{1+2(CO_2/H_2')}{1+2\{0.269(N_2/H_2') - [(CO_2-b)/H_2']\}}.$$

A plot of the values given by this equation can be superimposed on Fig. 81,

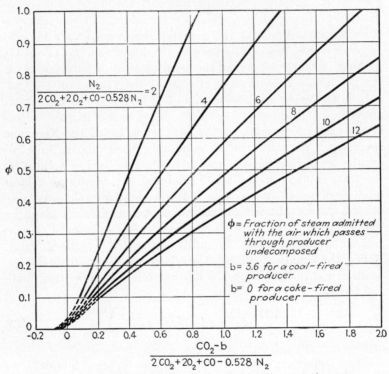

FIG. 81.—Estimation of steam decomposition in gas producers.

the differences between corresponding curves being within the experimental error of the data upon which this plot is based.

Figure 81 offers a convenient solution of the important problem of determining the steam consumption of a gas producer from analysis of the gaseous product without the necessity of further data. The technique of using it will be made clear by a study of the accompanying table. The first seven columns give the experimental results of the producer-gas tests in question. The

* P. 173.

first six are the gas analyses and the seventh is the per cent steam decomposition as reported by the investigators. The remaining columns of the table represent the steps in the computations. Of the three runs reported, two are taken from Bone and Wheeler* and the last from Haslam, Mackie, and Reed.† The former used a high-volatile coal and the latter anthracite.

	1	2	3	4	5	6	7	8	9	10	11
Run No.	Dry gas composition, per cent						Per cent steam decomposed reported	$\dfrac{CO_2-b}{2CO_2+2O_2+CO-0.528N_2}$	$\dfrac{N_2}{2CO_2+2O_2+CO-0.528N_2}$	ϕ, fraction steam undecomposed	Per cent steam decomposed
	CO_2	CO	H_2	CH_4	N_2	O_2					
1	5.25	27.3	16.6	3.25	47.50	....	87.4	0.13	3.74	0.123	87.7
5	13.25	16.05	22.65	3.50	44.55	....	42.0	0.508	2.35	0.568	43.2
103	11.03	20.35	15.63	0.11	52.13	0.75	59.1	0.455	3.20	0.434	56.6

Column 8 gives the ratio $(CO_2-b)/(2CO_2+2O_2+CO-0.528N_2)$ and column 9 the ratio $(N_2)/(2CO_2+2O_2+CO-0.528N_2)$, which are the two values necessary to determine a point on Fig. 81. The fraction of steam undecomposed, ϕ, as read from the figure, is given in column 10. The last column contains the calculated percentages of steam decomposed, $100(1-\phi)$, which may be compared with the results obtained by the investigators. It will be noted that the agreement is excellent.

Column 9 of the above table represents the ratio of the mols of nitrogen per mol of hydrogen from decomposed steam in the producer gas. The reciprocal of this value multiplied by 100 gives the mols of hydrogen formed from steam per 100 mols of nitrogen. Dividing this value by $1-\phi$, where ϕ is the fraction steam undecomposed from column 10, gives the mols of steam injected per 100 mols of nitrogen; since 26.6 mols of oxygen enters with this nitrogen, the molal ratio of injected steam

* *J. Iron Steel Inst. (London)*, 126 (1907).

† *Ind. Eng. Chem.*, **19**, 119 (1927).

to air is found by dividing the mols of steam injected per 100 mols of nitrogen by 126.6. If one knows the carbon content of the coal employed and the per cent gasification of this carbon, these figures can readily be converted into pounds of steam injected per pound of coal fired, a form more frequently employed in producer practice. Thus, if the molal ratio of injected steam to nitrogen is multiplied by the ratio of nitrogen to total carbon as shown by the gas analysis, it is converted into the ratio of mols of steam injected per atom of carbon gasified. Multiplying in turn by the ratio of the molecular weight of steam to the atomic weight of carbon gives the pounds of steam per pound of carbon gasified and multiplying by the pounds of carbon gasified per pound of coal gives the required figure. The last run shown in the table was made with an anthracite containing 78.84 per cent carbon and, because of the character of the coal, its gasification was substantially complete. Hence, for this case the conversion becomes

$$\left(\frac{55}{100}\right)\left(\frac{52.13}{31.49}\right)\left(\frac{18.02}{12}\right)0.7884 = 1.08.$$

The investigators report a steam consumption per pound of coal of 1.03.

Equation 2, which is the basis for Fig. 81, indicates that, as one increases the steam fed to a gas producer, the percentage decomposition of steam of necessity drops off and at the same time the CO_2 increases while the ratio of CO to H_2 decreases, and the changes in these quantities make it possible to compute the corresponding change in steam injection. Hence, the changing composition of a producer gas with increasing steam would follow a path upward and to the right on Fig. 81. Furthermore, as the point representing the gas analysis moves upward, a decrease in efficiency is indicated because of the increasing amounts of steam fed, although this steam increase may be necessary in order to prevent clinkering troubles. As the point moves to the right, thinning or channeling of the fuel bed or excessive firing rates are indicated. In general, then, it may be said that points far to the right on Fig. 81 indicate poor fuel-bed conditions or excessive firing rates, while points high on the plot indicate excessive use of steam. The nearer to the origin a point falls, the lower the CO_2/H_2' ratio, the better the steam decomposition and hence the greater the efficiency of producer operations.

The quantitative relationship in a producer between the steam consumption, the rate of firing and the depth of the fuel bed has never been determined. From the explanations already given it is obvious that both an increase in the rate of firing and a decrease in the steam-air ratio run up the temperature in the oxidation zone. Since this temperature must be kept below the fusing point of the ash, a knowledge of the relation is important.

One can set up a heat balance on the producer from the bottom up to any particular section of the reducing zone. Consider 100 mols of entering nitrogen, corresponding to 26.6 mols of oxygen. At the oxidation zone, where this air first hits the hot coke, it will burn to CO_2. Call t the temperature at the section in question in the reducing zone. If the fuel bed is of adequate depth, the counterflow of the hot gases rising above this section will preheat the coke flowing down to it substantially to the temperature t. The heat generated by combustion is partly consumed below this section in the reduction of CO_2 and water vapor, while the rest of it rises from the section into the upper part of the producer, partly as heat carried up by conduction and radiation through the incandescent fuel bed due to the temperature gradient through it, and partly as sensible heat in the gases. The heat flowing up through the section by conduction and radiation may be calculated by subtracting from the total heat available from combustion above the temperature level t the heat consumed by the reduction reactions taking place below that section, computed, however, on the assumption that they take place at the temperature t. This is allowable, since, although the reaction mechanism is entirely different, the net overall result is the same.

The heat of combustion of 26.6 mols of oxygen to CO_2 is 26.6 (97,000) = 2,580,000 P.c.u. or 4,640,000 B.t.u. To this must, however, be added the sensible heat content of the coke up to the temperature t, since the coke enters that part of the producer under consideration at this temperature level. The temperature in the active part of the reduction zone averages about 1700°F., and the average heat capacity of carbon up to this temperature is approximately 4.7 B.t.u. per lb. mol. Taking the temperature t_a at which the reacting materials enter the producer as the base line, the heat brought in by the hot carbon consumed in the oxidation zone is 4.7 (26.6) $(t-t_a)=125$ $(t-t_a)$. The total heat available above the temperature level t is equal to the sum of the preceding quantities less the heat content of the primary combustion products at this temperature. There are 100 mols of nitrogen with an average heat capacity (see page 10) of about 7.4, corresponding to 740 $(t-t_a)$ heat units and 26.6 mols of CO_2 with a heat capacity of about 11.5, corresponding to 305 $(t-t_a)$ heat units. There are also x_0 mols of steam which entered with the air; its heat capacity averages 9 (see page 10) and its heat content $9 x_0(t-t_a)$. The algebraic sum of these quantities is $2,580,000-(920+9 x_0)(t-t_a)$. The heat consumed by reduction with carbon is due partly to reaction of CO_2 and partly to steam. Per mol of gas reduced, the former consumes about 38,000 P.c.u. *at the temperatures of the reduction zone* (somewhat less than at room temperature) and the latter about 30,000. The relative reduction of the two obviously varies from case to case, but, if one will employ an average heat of reduction of 34,000 P.c.u., one can, without serious error, speak of the total reduction of the two gases combined.* Designating the initial CO_2 plus steam as z_0 and the sum of unreduced CO_2 and steam at the section in question as z, the total reduction is obviously z_0-z. Furthermore, $z_0=26.6+x_0$. The heat consumption of these reduction reactions is therefore 34,000 (z_0-z). Consequently, per 100 mols of nitrogen entering the bottom of the producer, the residual heat flowing up by conduction and radiation through the section under consideration is $2,580,000-(920+9x_0)$ $(t-t_a)-34,000$ (z_0-z) P.c.u. Calling r the amount of nitrogen rising per hour per square foot of cross-sectional area of the producer, expressed as hundreds of mols, the conduction heat current flowing upward through the section involved is

$$\frac{Q}{A\theta}=r[2,580,000-(920+9x_0)\ (t-t_a)-34,000(z_0-z)], \text{ in P.c.u.}$$

$$=r[4,640,000-(920+9x_0)\ (t-t_a)-61,200(z_0-z)], \text{ in B.t.u. (3)}$$

where in the first expression degrees centigrade are employed and in the second degrees Fahrenheit.

* This is satisfactory provided the CO in the resulting gas exceeds the H_2 from decomposition of steam. This is always the case unless excessive quantities of steam are used.

The equation is on a basis of 1 sq. ft. of cross section of the producer and 1 hr. This heat current may be equated to the thermal conductivity of the fuel bed times the temperature gradient, *i.e.*,

$$Q/A\theta = -adt/dL. \tag{3a}$$

This is allowable, despite the fact that much of the heat flows by radiation, if the coefficient a is empirically chosen for the temperature range in question (see pages 160–161). Furthermore, since the reduction rates of the two gases are roughly the same but since the reaction rate increases in the usual way, geometrically with increase in temperature, one may set up the reaction-rate expression

$$rdz/dL = -kze^{bt}. \tag{4}$$

The exact solution of these equations, even if possible, would be complicated. For an approximate solution it is perhaps allowable to give an average value in each specific case to t in Eq. 3, *i.e.*, to write

$$B = 2{,}580{,}000 - (920 + 9x_0)\left(\frac{t_0 + t_1}{2} - t_a\right) - 34{,}000z_0. \tag{3b}*$$

With this approximation the solution is as follows:

$$e^{bt_0} - e^{bt_1} = \frac{br^2}{ak}\left[B \ln \frac{z_0}{z_1} + 34{,}000(z_0 - z_1)\right] \tag{5}$$

where the subscript 0 indicates conditions at the border line between oxidizing and reducing zones and 1 corresponds to the end of the reducing and beginning of the distillation zone.

For normal conditions of producer operation with adequate depth of fuel bed, the second term on the left-hand side of Eq. 5 is negligible in comparison with the first, rarely amounting to 5 per cent of it. It is therefore advisable to drop it and rewrite the equation as

* This expression assumes temperatures in degrees centigrade; if degrees Fahrenheit is used, it is necessary to multiply the first and last terms on the right-hand side by 1.8.

$$e^{bt_0} = Kr^2 \left[B \ln \frac{z_0}{z_1} + 34,000(z_0 - z_1) \right]. \tag{5a}$$

The constant b is approximately 0.006 to 0.007 (see below); K is best determined from data on the coal in question, or at least on a coal of similar type as to coking quality and texture of the ash.

The qualitative interpretation of this equation is instructive. The left-hand side rises rapidly with temperature, but the rate appears on the right-hand side as a square term. Consequently, while the working rate (*i.e.*, capacity) of a producer increases with the temperature, its increase is less rapid than the ordinary increase of reaction rate for a given increase in temperature of the oxidation zone. This is because the average temperature of the reducing zone is far below that of the oxidizing zone and rises less rapidly than it. Furthermore, for a given increase in temperature, *i.e.*, for a given increase in the left-hand side of this equation, one gains a double advantage, namely, improvement in both capacity and amount of decomposition of the steam and CO_2. Within certain limits one can, by changing the steam-air ratio, use this advantage for either purpose. Since the rate term appears as a square while the decomposition term is the first power, it is obvious that increase in temperature is more effective in securing complete decomposition than greater capacity. Producer experience bears out this conclusion.

The useful work done in the reduction zone of a gas producer is the reduction of $z_0 - z_1$ mols of CO_2 and water vapor to combustible gas. The numerical value of this expression is obviously the sum of the mols of CO plus the mols of hydrogen from steam decomposition per 100 mols of nitrogen [from the table on page 241; equals $100 \left(\dfrac{\text{column } 2}{\text{column } 5} + \dfrac{1}{\text{column } 9} \right)$]. Under comparable conditions of operation it is surprising how constant this quantity is. When a cold air-steam mixture is used, it averages around 30, seldom deviating more than 10 per cent from this figure. The data indicate that, as one would expect, the reduction falls off slightly with increasing steam-air ratio. Preheating of the air greatly increases $z_0 - z_1$. Thus, Bone and Wheeler, using about 30 mols of steam per 100 of nitrogen with air preheated to about 250°C., obtained values of $z_0 - z_1$ of 42, whereas Haslam, under comparable conditions, without preheat other than that due to the steam, realized only 31. His steam-air mixture entered at about 80°C. Equation 3 can be used to estimate what the increase ought to be, since decrease in the temperature term secured by increasing t_a should give a corresponding increase in $z_0 - z_1$. In other words, calling the increment in $z_0 - z_1 = \Delta z$,

$$\Delta z = -\frac{920 + 9x_0}{34,000}\Delta(t_1 - t_a). \tag{6}$$

Bone and Wheeler used a much deeper fuel bed than Haslam and were thereby able to cool their gases approximately 100°C. lower. Their net temperature gain was, therefore, $250 + 100 - 80 = 270°$. Hence, from the above expression, Δz should be 9.5, as compared with the 11 actually realized. This emphasizes the great value of preheating the steam-air mixture in increasing the cold efficiency of the producer.

From a study of the data available, it seems that the reduction realizable in a producer may be estimated with reasonable precision by the following expression, temperatures being in Fahrenheit,

$$z_0 - z_1 = 54 - 0.04x_0 - 0.018 \ (t_1 - t_a). \tag{7}$$

It must, however, be kept in mind that this assumes a fuel bed of adequate depth, properly operated to maintain uniformity. Where one finds total reductions much lower than indicated by this expression, one is probably faced with poor fuel-bed conditions. In using Eq. 7, one must also remember that the deeper the fuel bed the lower t_1, although with reasonable depths the variation in t_1 is not great. It is seldom above 1500 or below 1100°F.

All these expressions are based upon a given amount of air entering the producer (126.6 mols, equivalent to 100 mols of N_2). The underlying reason for this basis is that the heat supply and hence the performance of the unit are determined by the rate of combustion, and this in turn is determined by the air supply. Firing rate need not be and in general is not constant; one need only make sure that there is never an inadequate amount of fuel on the hearth, although in the end this, of course, implies that average firing rate is approximately proportional to the average rate of air supply.

Considerable data on fuel-bed temperatures have been reported by Haslam and his associates.*   Analysis of these data indicates that, in the temperature range of the reducing zone, the constant b lies between 0.006 and 0.007.   Accurate measurement of temperature conditions in a producer bed is, however, very difficult.   While in a carefully operated producer conditions are reasonably uniform across any section taken near the top of the fuel bed, at the bottom, in the oxidation and hotter portions of the reduction zones, this is by no means the case.

In and just below the oxidation zone it is impossible to avoid localized packing of ash and partially burned-out fuel.   Consequently, the entering air rises rapidly through some portions of the bed and far more slowly through others.   The former are equivalent to little producers within the main unit operating at higher firing rates and hence at far higher temperatures.   Because of this, there are wide temperature fluctuations at any given level of the lower portions of the bed.   Thus, at a given level, just above the oxidation zone, where the air rate is low, one will find a low temperature, whereas at a point a little to one side one may find a much higher temperature farther up in the producer. Differences in gas composition at a given level will, however, be far less than differences in temperature.   The hot chimneys are still functioning as gas producers, although at operating rates far higher than the average.   Now t_0 in Eq. 5 is the temperature of the oxidation zone, *i.e.*, the maximum temperature existing in the fuel bed.   It is vitally important, because it determines the capacity limit of the producer without developing clinker trouble, but in measuring it directly one must remember that the point of maximum temperature may be found first at one level in the producer bed and later at another.

The utility of Eq. 5 may best be illustrated by applying it to certain of Haslam's data.   He reports a run with a coal containing 78.84 per cent carbon, using 0.413 lb. of steam/lb. of coal, firing at the rate of 9.72 lb. of coal/(sq. ft. of grate area)(hr.), yielding a gas containing 7.88 per cent CO_2, 0.10 per cent O_2, 23.4 per cent CO, 8.72 per cent H_2 and 59.9 per cent N.   In this operation he found a maximum fuel-bed temperature of 1900°F.   His entering air-steam mixture may be assumed 100°F. and the top of his fuel bed 1200°.   Using $b = 0.007$, compute the value of K for this coal.   The following tabulation will be self-explanatory.

* HASLAM, MACKIE and REED, *J. Ind. Eng. Chem.*, **19**, 119 (1927); HASLAM, WARD and MACKIE, *J. Ind. Eng. Chem.*, **19**, 141 (1927).

		C	O_2
CO_2........	7.88	7.88	7.88
O_2........	0.10	.....	0.10
CO........	23.40	23.40	11.70
H_2........	8.72		
N_2........	59.90		
	100.00	31.28	19.68
O_2 from air $=59.9\frac{21}{79}=$			15.93
O_2 from steam, difference $=$			3.75
H_2 from steam $=$			7.50

$$\frac{\text{Lb. steam/lb. C}}{\dfrac{0.413}{0.7884}} \left| \frac{\text{mol. steam/atom. C}}{\dfrac{12}{18.02}} \right| \frac{31.28}{0.599}=18.24 \text{ mols steam/100N}_2=x_0$$

$$\frac{\text{Atoms C/(hr.) (sq. ft.)}}{\dfrac{9.72\,(0.7884)}{12}} \left| \frac{0.599}{31.28}=0.0122=r=\frac{N_2/\text{hr.}}{100}.\right.$$

$$\frac{100CO_2}{N_2}=7.88\left(\frac{100}{59.9}\right)=13.15.$$

$$x_0-x_1=7.50\left(\frac{100}{59.9}\right)=12.52.$$

x_1, by difference $=5.72$.

$z_0=26.6+18.24=44.84$.

$z_1=13.15+5.72=18.87$.

$z_0-z_1=\qquad 25.97$.

$$B=4,640,000-\left(920+9\,(18.24)\right)\left(\frac{1900+1200}{2}-100\right)-61,200\,(44.84)$$

$$=332,000.$$

Inserting these values in Eq. 5a, $K=2100$.

Let it be required to increase the firing rate of this producer by blowing with air 9.7 times as fast as at present, using, however, a steam-air ratio only 90 per cent as great. (These figures are chosen because Haslam actually conducted such an operation.) What maximum temperature would one anticipate in the fuel bed under these new and more drastic conditions?

The reduction z_0-z_1, obtainable is computed by the use of Eq. 7 on page 247. Otherwise, the tabulation below should be self-explanatory.

$r=9.7(0.0122)=0.118$.

$x_0=0.90(18.24)=16.4$.

$z_0=26.6+16.4=43.0$.

$z_0 - z_1 = 54 - 0.04(16.4) - 0.018(1200 - 100) = 33.7.$

$$B = 4,640,000 - \left(920 + 9 \ (16.4)\right)\left(\frac{2600 + 1200}{2} - 100\right) - 61,200 \ (43.0)$$
$$= 87,000.$$

The term $t_0 = 2600$ in B is estimated. Inserting the values in Eq. 5a, one obtains $t_0 = 2570°F$. Haslam actually found a temperature of 2600°.

To emphasize the effect of changing steam-air ratio, compute the maximum temperature of the fuel bed, first, for an air rate 3.9 times that of the original experiment, with a steam-nitrogen ratio of 0.175, the steam-air mixture entering at 150°F. and the gases at the top of the fuel bed being at 1450°, and second, for conditions the same except that 2.8 times as much steam is used and the top of the fuel bed is at 1300°. Under the first conditions, computed as before, $z_0 - z_1 = 29.9$, $z_1 = 14.2$, $B = 80,000$ (if t_1 is assumed 2300), whence, from Eq. 3, $t_0 = 2290°$. Haslam found 2400 under these conditions. Similarly, with 2.8 times the steam, $x_0 = 49$, $z_0 = 75.6$, $z_0 - z_1 = 31.3$, $z_1 = 44.3$, $B = -2,100,000$ (assuming $t_0 = 2150$), whence, from Eq. 3, $t_0 = 2170°$. The temperature as actually measured was 2200°F.

It will be noted that in each case in computing B one must estimate t_0. If the final value of t_0 thus computed does not check this estimate, the computation must be repeated. However, in the equation for B, a small error in t_0 makes little difference.

The figures emphasize the fact that oxidation-zone temperature comes down far more rapidly with drop in firing rate r than with increase in steam-air ratio x_0. Nonetheless, increasing steam is a potent means of increasing capacity without encountering clinkering troubles.

CHAPTER IX

CRUSHING AND GRINDING

OBJECTS OF CRUSHING AND GRINDING

When a solid body is subjected to chemical change from without, the action producing such change is confined to the surface of the solid, and the rate of the reaction is a function of the surface exposed. In order, therefore, to complete a reaction in a minimum time, the area per unit weight or volume must be made as large as possible. This object is accomplished by first crushing the solid to small pieces and then grinding these to a very fine powder. The relationship between the area exposed (as determined by the size of the particles) and the rate of reaction plays an important part in many industrial processes. Examples are seen in the solution of solids in liquids; in the interaction of two solids, as in the production of cement clinker; in reaction between solids and gases, as in the combustion of pulverized coal; and in the chemical reactions that result in the setting of Portland cement. The physical properties, also, of a material may be profoundly influenced by its state of division, for example, the covering power of pigments.

If, however, the solid is not homogeneous, a second object that may be attained in crushing is the detaching or cleaving of one mineral or constituent from another closely associated with it. In some cases a satisfactory breaking apart is accomplished by relatively coarse crushing, as, for example, the parting of coal from slate. On the other hand, many mineral ores require very fine grinding to effect a complete separation of one constituent from the others. The concentration of the valuable constituent of a raw material from the gangue or worthless portion by subdividing and separation is generally spoken of as "ore dressing" and forms a very important step in many industrial chemical processes.

Occasionally the primary object of a grinding operation is mixing, as in the grinding of certain pigments in oils.

PARTICLE-SIZE MEASUREMENT

Since the primary effect of crushing and grinding is a diminution of particle size, determination of the size of the product is necessary in order to evaluate the results of a given operation. Large pieces of material are customarily defined by their dimensions expressed in inches. Smaller pieces are defined by their ability to pass through or be retained upon a screen of a given mesh. For a more complete discussion of screen mesh refer to page 289. With the advent of improved methods of grinding which yield particles so small that screens cannot be made fine enough for mesh analysis, other methods of determining particle size have been developed. Occasionally the results of measurement by other methods are expressed in terms of theoretical screen mesh. For instance, a product may be as fine as 80 per cent through 625 mesh (625 openings per linear inch), although a 625-mesh screen has not been made or used in the analysis.

Since the object of grinding is frequently the formation of new surface area, certain industries (notably the cement industry) express the fineness of material in terms of area per unit weight, with dimensions of square centimeters per gram. This measurement is almost invariably determined from the rate of settling of the particles in a suspension. The simplest method is to determine the rate of sedimentation by successive gravimetric analyses of the suspension at a given location below the surface. Another method depends upon the changing difference in specific gravity of the suspension and the pure liquid as settling proceeds. Probably the most generally used apparatus is the turbidimeter, which determines the transmission of light from a standard source by the suspension. The superiority of turbidimeters lies in the rapidity with which samples may be analyzed, although the analyses depend upon arbitrary determinations of the reflectivity of the surface of the material and consequently are not well adapted to mixtures. Moreover, fictitious observations may result when particle dimensions approach the wavelength of visible light, when the solid material is quite transparent, when agglomeration of small particles occurs in the suspension or when different particle shapes are encountered. The Wagner turbidimeter takes measurements at different time intervals at different depths, obtaining curves of particle-size distribution

The Klein turbidimeter is applicable for the determination of surface areas where particle size is fairly uniform. A more complete treatment of settling is presented in the succeeding chapter (Chap. X).

When extremely small particles are encountered, microscopic examination is made and the average particle diameter is expressed in microns. One micron (μ) is one one-thousandth of a millimeter.

TOTAL SURFACE

Consider a mass of identical particles, having a characteristic dimension (diameter, side, etc.) L. Calling the total weight of all the particles ΔW, and their density ρ, the total surface ΔA is the number of particles, $\Delta W/\rho k L^3$, multiplied by the surface area of each, KL^2:

$$\Delta A = K \, \Delta W/k\rho L$$

the constants K and k depending on the shape of the particles.*

For any given material K/k often remains approximately constant over a wide range of sizes; hence K/k need not be known to compare the specific surface of different states of subdivision. Let ΔW be the weight of material passed by a sieve of mesh width L_1 and retained on a smaller sieve having mesh width L_2. If the ratio L_1/L_2 does not exceed 2, little error will be introduced by using the arithmetic mean, giving:

$$\Delta A = \frac{K \, \Delta W}{k\rho(L_1 + L_2)/2} = \frac{K \, \Delta W}{k\rho L_{av.}}$$

where ΔA is the surface of the fraction of weight ΔW. One should use a series of screens so that ΔW for each screen is only a small fraction of the original sample. The total surface is readily estimated by graphical integration, *i.e.*, by plotting $1/L_{av.}$ as ordinates versus W as abscissas; the area under the curve, multiplied by $K/k\rho$, is the total surface.†

* If the particles have the shape of a cube or a sphere, the shape factor K/k is 6. This value is frequently used for all shapes, but K/k is 7 to 8 for powdered coal. For flat particles of mica, basing L on the average diameter of the large face, K/k is 55.[1]

† If, however, a large fraction passes the finest sieve, the summation will be inaccurate since the specific surface varies rapidly with diameter at small diameters. Empirical relations between W and L have been suggested

The total surface A of two different grindings a and b will be

$$\frac{A_a}{A_b} = \frac{\Sigma[\Delta W_a/(L_a)_{\text{av.}}]}{\Sigma[\Delta W_b/(L_b)_{\text{av.}}]}.$$

ENERGY CONSUMPTION

Obviously a mass may be subdivided in either of two ways.

1. A force may be applied to it greater than its breaking strength, so that it is crushed and split, or

2. The mass may be cut or torn apart.

The final result in either case is an increase in the surface of the mass.

Rittinger's law assumes the mechanism of subdivision to be essentially that of shearing, and that the energy consumed is proportional to the fresh surface produced. Since the total surface per unit weight is inversely proportional to the size of particle, the work done in reducing a given amount of material, E, is

$$E = C\left(\frac{1}{L_2} - \frac{1}{L_1}\right)$$

where L_1 is the initial and L_2 is the final linear dimension of the individual particles; C depends on the characteristics of the material and on the type and method of operation of the apparatus. Thus, if 10 hp.-hr. is required to crush a given weight of a certain material from 2 in. to 1 in., the work (E_2) required to crush from 1 in. to $\frac{1}{2}$ in. may be calculated as follows:

$$\frac{E_2}{10} = \frac{C\left(\frac{1}{0.5} - \frac{1}{1}\right)}{C\left(\frac{1}{1} - \frac{1}{2}\right)}$$

whence $E_2 = 20$ hp.-hr.

Kick's law assumes the energy required for subdivision of a definite amount of a material to be the same for the same fractional reduction in average size of the individual particles. Thus, if 10 hp.-hr. is required to crush a given weight of a certain material from 1 in. to $\frac{1}{2}$ in., the energy required to reduce it

---

and for specific cases[2] permit prediction of the complete screen analysis from data obtained with the use of only a few sieves.

from $\frac{1}{2}$ in. to $\frac{1}{4}$ in. or from $\frac{1}{4}$ in. to $\frac{1}{8}$ in., etc., would be the same. Mathematically expressed, Kick's law becomes

$$E = b \, \log \frac{L_1}{L_2}$$

where b is an experimentally determined coefficient.

This coefficient depends on the type of crusher employed, as well as on the character of the material. This relationship can be derived if one assumes that each particle is crushed by direct pressure, that the crushing strength per unit area is constant and that a given particle, whatever its size, upon breaking forms a definite number of smaller particles of shape similar to the original.

Neither Rittinger's nor Kick's equation represents the facts accurately. In general, $dE = -C dL/L^n$. If $n = 1$, this gives Kick's law; if n equals 2, integration gives Rittinger's law; if n exceeds 1,

$$E = \frac{C}{n-1}\left(\frac{1}{L_2^{n-1}} - \frac{1}{L_1^{n-1}}\right).$$

When the product and feed vary widely in size, appropriate values of L for these equations are

$$\frac{1}{L_2^{n-1}} = \frac{\Sigma(\Delta W/L_2^{n-1})}{\Sigma \, \Delta W} \quad \text{and} \quad \frac{1}{L_1^{n-1}} = \frac{\Sigma(\Delta W/L_1^{n-1})}{\Sigma \, \Delta W}.$$

SELECTION OF MACHINES

The selection of machines for crushing and grinding usually depends on three factors:

1. Physical properties of the material to be ground.
2. The size of the feed and product.
3. The total tonnage to be ground and other local conditions.

1. Physical Properties of the Materials.—The selection of proper machines for crushing and grinding is greatly affected by

  a. The hardness of the material to be ground.

  b. Mechanical structure of the material, *i.e.*, whether brittle, or fibrous and tough, or soft, or whether it softens when warm, etc.

  c. The moisture content.

  a. Hardness.—The meanings of the words "hard" and "soft" are entirely relative, yet the materials that require subdivision in order to prepare them for further operations may be divided roughly into these two classes. The scale of hardness employed in mineralogy is utilized in this connection, and is as follows:

1. Talc, soapstone.
2. Rock salt, gypsum, pure graphite, soft coal, etc.
3. Calcite, burned lime, marble, soft grades of limestone, chalk, hydraulic limestone (common), cement, barytes, etc.
4. Fluorite, magnesite, soft phosphate, limestone, etc.
5. Apatite, hard phosphate, hard limestone, chromite, etc.
6. Orthoclase, feldspar, magnesite, hornblendes, etc.
7. Quartz, granite, ores, sandstone, etc.
8. Topaz, etc.
9. Sapphire, corundum, emery, etc.
10. Diamond.

Materials up to and including class 4 are designated as "soft," while those in the higher classes are termed "hard." A rapid method of approximating hardness is to cut the material under examination with a knife or to scratch ordinary window glass with it. If it can be whittled easily like chalk, it is "very soft." Marble and many hydraulic limestones can be cut quite easily and would be classified as soft. Magnesite and phosphate rock can be easily scratched but will not scratch glass and are termed medium. Beyond this line, little impression can be made with a knife and the materials may be classified as very hard.

Hardness not only affects the size and design of the machine in order that it may have sufficient strength to crush the material, but as the material increases in hardness its abrasive action increases and the machine must be designed so as to provide the fewest possible wearing parts. Furthermore, in grinding abrasive materials, a machine not only should have few bearings but these should be protected from dust in a proper manner. Also, in grinding abrasive material, low-speed machines require much less maintenance than do the high-speed machines. In general, low-speed grinding machines should be used when the amount of quartz in an ore is higher than 4 or 5 per cent.

b. Mechanical Structure.—If a material is of a fibrous nature, it cannot be crushed by pressure or shearing action, but must be torn apart. While both coal and wood are soft materials, they require radically different types of machines for disintegrating them, on account of the fact that the wood is of a fibrous nature and must be cut or torn apart. Machines for subdividing such fibrous materials as wood, bark, etc., are often called **disintegrators.**

c. Moisture.—Moisture plays an important part in the selection of crushing and grinding machinery. If the moisture content is more than 4 or 5 per cent, the material becomes sticky or pasty and under such circumstances it is extremely difficult to maintain free crushing.* On the other hand, after the moisture content exceeds about 50 per cent, the material is quite fluid and under such circumstances the water may actually be used to aid free crushing by washing and carrying away the finely ground product. It is apparent that moisture affects the pastiness of fine material more readily than it does coarse material. While some mills cannot handle material containing more than 3 or 4 per cent of moisture, others work best when the moisture content is over 55 or 60 per cent.

2. Fineness.—Fineness governs the selection of machines in two ways:

a. The size of feed.

b. The size of product.

Some machines from their very design can handle only coarse material, while others can handle only fine material. Some machines produce a very uniform product, *i.e.*, all the particles are close to a given size, whereas others, by virtue of their construction, produce a product with considerable variation in size. There is frequently a lower limit to the size of the particles desired in the product. Thus, in crushing pyrites for making sulfuric acid, very fine material is not desired. Also, in grinding malt or any substance to be leached, very fine subdivision is undesirable. In such cases machines must be selected which produce a minimum amount of fine material.

3. Tonnage and Other Local Conditions.—Tonnage is a vital factor in determining the economic balance between fixed charges (interest, depreciation and taxes) and operating costs (labor, power and maintenance). The greater the tonnage, the more money may be spent for the initial installation in order to cut down such operating costs as power and maintenance. Interest

* See p. 259.

and depreciation must be balanced against power, labor and maintenance, and the greater the tonnage the more necessary it is to use machines whose *operating* costs are low.

In addition to tonnage, there are always a number of local conditions that affect the selection of machines. For example, in certain mining fields only those machines which can be demounted and easily freighted by pack animals are purchased. Every situation has local peculiarities that must be given due weight.

CLASSIFICATION OF MACHINES

Machines may be classified in two ways, either by the size of feed or by the method of applying the breaking force. In considering the crushing and grinding machines, it is obvious that any one machine will operate efficiently only between certain size limits. One should not drive a tack with a sledge or a spike with a tack hammer. A single machine will not crush economically from a very large to a very small dimension, and hence crushing and grinding machinery is divided into the following classes:

1. **Preliminary breakers,** which crush pieces having a maximum dimension of 2 to 60 in.

2. **Secondary crushers,** which will take a feed of about $1\frac{1}{2}$ to 2 in. and produce a product that will pass through a 10-mesh screen.

3. **Fine pulverizers,** which will take a feed of from $\frac{1}{2}$ to $\frac{1}{4}$ in. and produce a product as fine as 200 mesh.

4. **Colloid mills,** etc., which will take a feed of about 80 mesh and produce a product as fine as 0.5μ.

In addition to the above four classes, there is a class known as **shredders** or **disintegrators,** designed to handle fibrous and brittle material.

It will be noted that in the above classification there is an overlapping in the range that these machines will handle, and it must be remembered that this classification is not rigid.

Crushing and grinding machines may also be classified into three principal groups according to the method of applying the breaking force:

1. Those which break from a continued pressure.

2. Those which break from impact or direct blow.

3. Those which break by abrasion or grinding through a shearing force.

In general, it may be said that the first is best adapted to coarse crushing, while the other two, either singly or combined, are employed for fine crushing and pulverizing.

Free Crushing.—Before discussing individual machines, it is necessary to call attention to a basic principle in all operations involving the reduction of size, and one which is of the utmost importance in the design and operation of crushing and grinding machinery, namely, that of "free crushing." In order that the breaking force, however applied, may be efficiently used, and in order that the maximum capacity of the mechanism employed may be obtained, it is essential that each particle be removed from between the crushing surfaces as soon as it has reached the dimension desired. Fine material, by remaining between the moving surfaces, cushions the material to be broken, absorbs a large portion of the energy expended, cuts down the output of the machine and increases the percentage of the so-called "fines," which is that portion smaller in diameter than the size desired. The opposite of "free crushing" is known as "choke feeding" or "choke crushing."* Particular attention, therefore, should be paid to the design of crushing and pulverizing machinery to insure a free discharge of the fine material and its complete removal from the zone of reduction.

The rapid removal of product to aid free crushing may be accomplished, in general, in three ways:

1. By the use of fluids, usually water, to wash out fine particles.

2. By the use of air to blow or suck them out.

3. By the use of centrifugal force, which may be applied in various ways, as will be noted under the discussion of the various types of machines.

Open- or Closed-circuit Operation.—There are two general methods of crushing and grinding, the "open-circuit" and the "closed-circuit" methods. In the open circuit, all the material discharged by a machine goes on through the system. In the closed-circuit method, as soon as any of the product reaches the desired size, it is screened and removed. The oversize particles are recirculated through the machine until they reach the desired

---

* In unusual cases choke feeding may be economically resorted to for increasing the production of fines from equipment at hand.

size and are then removed.   In the open-circuit method initial cost of installation is low, but the power cost per ton of output is high.   The closed-circuit system should be used on all large-scale installations on account of the uniformity of the output and the low cost of power.

For closed-circuit operation it is advisable to regulate each mill so that it delivers a product much of which is oversize.   If the scale of installation warrants, it may be advisable to use one size of machine for grinding the main output and another for regrinding the oversize particles or tails, since these average smaller than the original feed and therefore require a different mill setting for best results.

Since there are usually two or more machines in series and since each unit produces a certain amount of material finer than the normal product of the next unit in the series, capacity can be increased and power consumption reduced by screening out these fines and having them by-pass the next unit in the series.   As a result, the load on the mills is reduced, the cushioning effect of fines is diminished and the product is more uniform.

Grinding Aids.—It has been observed in certain types of grinding that the incorporation with the material to be ground of minute amounts of organic materials appreciably increases the grinding rate.   Materials that have been used vary from anthracite and bituminous coal, oleic acid or rosin to various complex organic materials.   The action of grinding aids is in the nature of a dispersing agent, preventing agglomeration and consequent regrinding of agglomerated fines.   Accordingly, the use of such grinding aids may result in an unusually finely divided product.

1. PRELIMINARY BREAKERS

There are two types of preliminary breakers which handle material from 2 to 60 in. in diameter, the first being jaw crushers, and the second gyratory crushers.   Both these machines break with a continuous pressure.   Jaw crushers employ a reciprocal motion and are intermittent in action, whereas in gyratory crushers this reciprocal motion is combined with a rotary motion and the action is continuous.

Jaw Crushers.—Jaw crushers, which break material by squeezing it between a fixed and a movable jaw, may be considered as of three types according to the movement of the jaw: first, those which have the movable jaw pivoted at the top and which therefore have the greatest movement at the point of *egress;* second, those pivoted at the bottom, which therefore have the greatest movement at the point of *entrance;* third, those which have a relatively uniform movement along the entire face of the jaw.

Construction of Jaw Crushers.—The jaw crusher was invented by Ely Whitney Blake in 1858 and was first used for crushing rock for road work. With the exception of the point at which the movable jaw is pivoted, the construction of all jaw crushers is similar. Figures 82 and 83 show views of typical jaw crushers.

In the crusher shown in Fig. 82, the reciprocating motion is given to the jaw by means of an elliptical cam. As the shaft revolves, a backward and forward motion is given to a rocker arm, which in turn communicates this motion to the jaw through a small breaker bar. This breaker bar is the weakest part of the crusher and protects the rest of the machine from breakage in case hard material, such as iron, falls in between the jaws.

Another common method of imparting a reciprocating motion to the movable jaw is by means of an eccentric and toggle joint. In this case a so-called "pitman" is mounted eccentrically on the rotating shaft, thus receiving a motion upward and downward in the vertical direction. The lower end of this pitman is connected to a toggle joint, one arm of the toggle being fixed to the rear frame of the crusher and the other arm being fixed to the movable jaw. This construction, being more powerful, is used on the large jaw crushers, particularly of the Blake type.

Jaw Crusher Control.—The size of the crushed material is governed in two ways: first, by changing the distance between the jaws at the point of discharge; second, by the length of stroke of the movable jaw. The distance between the jaws may be regulated by means of wedges so that the fixed jaw is moved forward or backward, thus decreasing or increasing the discharge opening. The length of stroke may be changed only with difficulty.

Blake Type of Jaw Crusher.—In the Blake crusher (Fig. 82), the material to be crushed enters the jaw at the top, is crushed by continuous pressure and by its own weight falls toward the bottom. As it falls, it is successively crushed finer and finer, and drops from between the jaws at the bottom. Because the greatest motion occurs at the point of egress, the Blake type of crusher eliminates the danger of choking and may therefore be used in the crushing of material that has a slight tendency to pack. This type of crusher can handle without difficulty most material containing 5 to 10 per cent of water. On account of the great range of motion between the jaws at the point of discharge, the Blake crusher delivers a product that is uneven in size, *i.e.*, there is considerable variation between

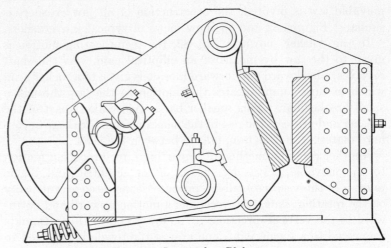

Fig. 82.—Jaw crusher, Blake type.

the large and the small lumps discharged from the machine.   In view of the fact that a jaw crusher very rarely delivers a finished product, this disadvantage is not serious.

The main wearing parts of jaw crushers are the crushing faces of the jaws, which are usually made of chrome (or manganese) steel or chilled iron and are so arranged as to be easily replaceable. Furthermore, the greatest wear is at the point of discharge of the jaws and the position of these plates may be reversed end for end, so that the top, which is worn but little, is placed at the bottom of the jaw.   In this way the life of the plates may be considerably prolonged.   In some crushers the crushing faces are curved in a manner that results in a more even distribution of the wear over the faces.

The advantages of the Blake type of jaw crusher lie in its large capacity, the low cost for repairs, low power consumption per unit of product and its freedom from choking. It has the disadvantage that the size of the product is quite variable and also the minor drawback that its action is intermittent instead of continuous; that is to say, crushing occurs only on the forward stroke of the jaw.

Dodge Type of Jaw Crusher.—In this crusher the movable jaw is pivoted at the bottom (see Fig. 83). Since the minimum movement of the face is at the point of egress of the stock, this

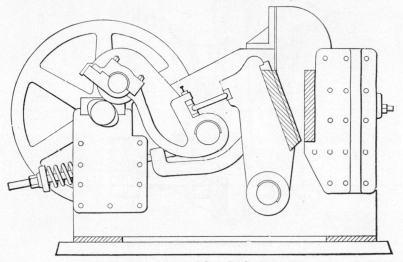

Fig. 83.—Jaw crusher, Dodge type.

crusher gives a more uniform product than the Blake but does not clear itself when choked.   In consequence it can be employed only for free-running material. The Dodge crusher, lacking the leverage of the Blake crusher at the feed end of the jaw, is not designed to handle such large-sized feed as the Blake.   The Dodge crusher is capable of unusually high reduction ratios and in consequence has found a special field in plants of low tonnage which desire to keep their crushing equipment as simplified as possible at the expense of efficiency, but the marked tendency to choke precludes the use of the Dodge crusher in the majority of installations.

Roll Jaw Crusher.—In the roll jaw crusher the face of the movable jaw is so shaped and the motion imparted is such that the face of the movable jaw rolls along the face of the fixed jaw plate. The movable jaw of this type of crusher is pivoted at the top, and the motion to the movable jaw is imparted at a point in between the top and bottom of the jaw and from a movable pivot situated well back from the discharge opening. The roll jaw crusher is a compromise between the Blake and the Dodge types

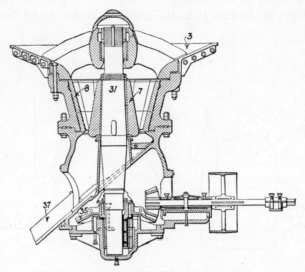

Fig. 84.—Gyratory crusher, Gates type.

of jaw crusher and as such it does not possess so prominently the advantages or the disadvantages of these machines. Thus, while it is not so liable to clog as the Dodge, it delivers a more uniform product than does the Blake. However, it does not have the capacity and low power cost of the Blake or the uniformity of the Dodge. Furthermore, it is more complicated in construction and the field of its use is limited.

Gyratory Crusher. *Gates Type.*—A sectional elevation of the Gates gyratory crusher is given in Fig. 84. The breaker crushes by rotating eccentrically a truncated conical head 7, which has its small end up, inside a truncated conical ring 8, which has its small end down. The truncated cone is mounted on a shaft 31, which is pivoted at the top in a semiuniversal joint. The lower end of the shaft is mounted eccentrically in the gear 35, so that, as this gear rotates, the shaft receives not only a rotary motion but also a gyratory motion, thus causing the inner inverted truncated cone alternately to advance toward and to recede from any given point on the truncated ring. It is further to be noticed that the greatest relative motion between the inner cone and the outer ring is at the lower end or the point of discharge, thus giving to this machine many of the advantages of the Blake type of crusher. Also, this machine is continuous in its action, and, the motion being rotary instead of reciprocating, the vibration is reduced to a minimum.

The material to be crushed is fed in through the hopper 3, is crushed between the inner cone and outer ring by continuous pressure through the successive advances of the inner cone and is discharged through the spout 37. The size of the particles being discharged from this machine is regulated by raising or lowering the shaft 31 to which the inverted truncated cone is fastened. This produces a smaller or larger opening in between the cone and the ring, but such regulation is difficult compared to the easy control of a Blake jaw crusher.

The Gates gyratory crusher will handle pieces of rock from 6 to 60 in. in diameter and will reduce them to pieces of $\frac{1}{4}$ to 4 in. in diameter. An advantage of the gyratory crusher is that it has a relatively large feed opening compared to a small discharge opening, and therefore the range of reduction in one pass through the machine is large. A gyratory crusher with a large feed opening has an extremely large capacity; consequently, these machines should be used only when such capacity can be utilized. In other words, if a small amount of very large pieces of rock is to be crushed, the Blake type of jaw crusher is more suitable than the gyratory crusher, owing to lower initial cost. However, if a large amount of large-size rock is to be crushed, then the gyratory crusher is the more suitable machine, because the power per ton of material is lower than in the case of jaw crushers. The original installation cost and the maintenance cost of a gyratory crusher are greater than those of the Blake jaw crusher so that the selection of a preliminary crusher involves balancing the costs of initial investment, maintenance, labor and power. The gyratory crusher also possesses the advantage of being able to handle material directly from the bin without a feeding attachment, and can therefore form the bottom hopper of a storage bin, taking the feed directly from such bin without clogging.

2. SECONDARY CRUSHERS

Cone Crushers.—Cone crushers are a prominent development of modern ore-crushing practice. A Symons cone crusher is illustrated in Fig. 85. These crushers have tended to replace

FIG. 85.—Symons cone crusher. (*Courtesy Nordberg Manufacturing Co.*)

many other types of intermediate crushers and are capable of such high reductions that they have sometimes been installed in place of gyratory crushers and crushing rolls, performing in one stage a reduction formerly performed in two or more stages.

The cone crusher is essentially a high-speed gyratory crusher whose crushing head rests in a bearing within the cone, eliminating the overhead spider and universal joint. As in the gyratory type, the greatest relative motion between the inner cone and the outer bowl is at the point of discharge. The point of pivot of the shaft is located near the feed entrance to the crushing surfaces. The crushing bowl is so shaped that the feed passes through a final zone where the sides of the bowl and the crushing head are substantially parallel, and the speed of gyration is sufficiently rapid (about 500 r.p.m.) so that each particle is crushed between the head and the bowl at least once while it is in this parallel zone. Consequently, the maximum size of the product is limited by the minimum clearance between the head and the bowl and an exceptionally uniform product is delivered. Cone crushers will take a feed from $1\frac{5}{8}$ to 14 in. in diameter and reduce it to $\frac{1}{8}$ to $2\frac{1}{2}$ in., handling from 14 to 900 tons per hr. The discharge opening of a cone crusher can be adjusted while the crusher is in operation.

Gyratory crushers also have been designed for this field. Such crushers frequently have curved crushing surfaces (as mentioned under jaw crushers) which distribute the wear and aid free flow of material.

Symons Disk Crusher.—This crusher introduces a new principle in that centrifugal force throws the pieces out of the crushing zone as soon as they are sufficiently small to escape through the opening between the faces. The crushing force is applied by two saucer-shaped disks which rotate in the same direction at the same speed. The shaft for one of the disks is supported in an eccentric bearing which causes that disk to be always at an angle to the other disk. The feed is introduced axially between the disks, is thrown to the outside and caught by the disks at the point of widest opening, and is crushed by direct continuous pressure as the rims of the disks approach each other owing to the eccentricity of their shafts.

Hammer Mills.—The principle involved in this type of machine is that of striking a blow while the material is suspended in air, as when a baseball is struck with a bat. The particle is hit with a force sufficient to crush or tear it, and with a velocity such that it does not adhere to the moving part. These mills are used on brittle material, preferably not too abrasive. They also possess special uses as disintegrators when it is necessary to crush material of a fibrous nature by imparting a tearing action. Another specialized use is the breaking of a brittle material which softens easily with heat.

A mill illustrating this principle is shown in Fig. 86. Hammers are fastened flexibly to an inner shaft or disk and the latter rotated at high speed. Except when retarded by the material that is fed to the mill, these hammers, owing to centrifugal force, extend radially from the center shaft. The material, after it enters the beater box, remains there until pounded to a sufficiently fine state of subdivision to pass between the wedge-shaped grate bars covering the bottom of this box. Such mills may be used to crush wood chips, barks and material of a fibrous nature, as well as shale, clay, bone, shells, etc. The mill is

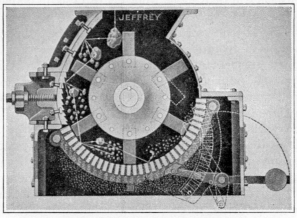

FIG. 86.—Hammer-bar mill.

extensively used in the cement industry to handle the discharge from gyratory crushers.

Squirrel Cage Mill.—This mill is similar in operation to the hammer mill but is used more exclusively for purposes of disintegration. The mill consists of "cages" built up of bars arranged in a circle, rotating at high speed. Often one such cage is placed concentrically between two others, the first rotating in the opposite direction from the other two. The material is fed into the center of the cages, is thrown out by centrifugal force and is broken up by impact. These mills are excellent for materials which are not too strong mechanically and which may be too damp and sticky to be handled in other types of apparatus.

Crushing Rolls.—In the gyratory crusher, the crushing head was made to roll upon the inner surface of the conical ring while traveling on the circle within it, and for coarse crushing this principle works satisfactorily; but for fine crushing such application of the roll principle would be impracticable owing to the lack of constancy of the distances between the two crushing surfaces. However, the rolling principle is utilized by providing two cylinders mounted upon horizontal shafts which revolve toward each other. The rotating surfaces nip the lump of material and gradually draw it in between them and crush it to a size determined by the distance separating the faces at their nearest point. A typical machine is shown in cross section in Fig. 87. The diameter of the crushing rolls is greater than the width, and, while both dimensions vary considerably from machine to

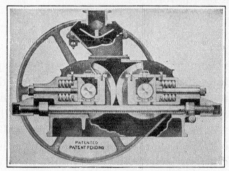

Fig. 87.—Sturtevant crushing rolls.

machine, these rolls average 14 in. in width and 36 in. in diameter. They consist of a central permanent core of soft iron forced upon movable shafts and are fitted with a replaceable wearing surface of hardened steel. They are maintained a constant distance apart by blocks and are held in place by powerful springs which give way when noncrushable material is accidentally introduced. These springs retreat slightly as the regular product passes through the rolls, so that, in general, the ratio between the size of opening and the size of product is 0.8, *i.e.*, rolls which have a ½-in. opening will product a material that is ⅝ in. and under. It is vital to have an even distribution of feed across the faces of the rolls; otherwise they will groove and deliver a product containing much oversize material. This not only causes unsatisfactory operation of the rolls, but also increases maintenance, decreases the volume of output and increases the power consumed. Therefore, such crushing rolls should be fed with an automatic device that will spread the material uniformly along the faces.

In the machine shown in Fig. 87, the material being crushed is fed through the automatic reciprocating feeder of a satisfactory type, falls between the faces of the two crushing rolls and is gradually drawn in between them. The angle, made by the tangents at the point where the largest piece the roll will "bite" meets the roll faces, is called "maximum angle of nip," and is equal to twice the angle of kinetic friction between the material and the surface of the roll. The relation between the size of feed, space between the rolls, the radius of the rolls and the angle of nip is given by the formula

$$\frac{r+a}{r+b} = \text{cosine } \frac{N}{2}$$

where r is the radius of the rolls, a is one-half the space between the rolls, b is the radius of the particles to be crushed and N is the angle of nip, in degrees. The maximum angle of nip is given by the above formula when b is taken as the radius of the largest particle that will be crushed by rolls of radius r and clearance $2a$.

Crushing rolls are advantageously used when the material is brittle and if crushing is desired with a minimum of dust. Materials fed to such rolls rarely exceed $1\frac{1}{2}$ in., and for the minimum power consumption and the maximum production the ratio of reduction in size per pass should not be greater than 4 to 1, especially if the formation of fines is to be avoided. Crushing rolls may be used for grinding material down to a fineness of 10 to 15 mesh, and in some cases a little finer, but in general it is more satisfactory to use ball mills when the size desired is finer than 10 mesh (Tyler standard screen). If the material is not to be ground below 10 or 15 mesh, there are no better machines made for the work, and, on account of their relatively large capacity and freedom from dust, together with their simple construction, such rolls are used extensively. Wet materials may, if desired, be crushed to 20 mesh.

As mentioned above, the size of the material discharged from the crushing rolls is determined by the distance between their faces at the nearest point. Therefore, in selecting crushing rolls it is highly desirable to be able to adjust easily the opening between the rolls to the proper distance, especially when a minimum of fines or dust is desired, because easy adjustment facilitates maintenance of good operation. Arrangements should also be provided so that the rolls may be set up more closely as wear takes place. Some rolls are adjusted by means of shims placed between the journal boxes of the rolls and fixed supports on the crusher frame. In other makes, the distance between the roll faces is adjusted by worm gears moving the journal boxes backward or forward. This latter method is simple and capable of quicker control.

The strong points of crushing rolls are simplicity and ruggedness and the small amount of fines or dust produced when operated under proper conditions, namely, an even feed and the ratio of reduction not over 4 to 1. They are unsurpassed in producing a coarse granular product, and they show up to disadvantage only when used in fields for which they are not suited, such, for example, as producing fine material by means of choke feeding.

FIG. 88.—Sturtevant rotary crusher.

There are many special designs of crushing rolls for handling special products. For example, one type crushes the material against a fixed plate by a single roll whose rotating face is studded. Such a crusher is used for material containing cleavage planes, such as coal, etc. Other rolls have circular rows of saw teeth and are used as disintegrators.

Rotary Crushers.—The rotary crusher is a disintegrator suitable for handling soft friable material, such as coal, coke, tanbark, etc., if the material fed to the crusher is not over 3 to 6 in. in size. Under such conditions the rotary crusher will produce a product whose diameter is $\frac{1}{4}$ to $\frac{3}{4}$ in. in length and under. Such crushers are sometimes known as "coffee mills."

In Fig. 88, it is seen that the crushing action takes place between an inner rotating grooved cone and an outer grooved ring. The adjustment of this machine to produce finer or coarser material is by means of a small handwheel (shown in the lower right-hand corner), which raises or lowers the step bearing on which the rotating grooved cone is mounted.

Stamps.—Gravity stamps, or mills, may be used to crush material from a maximum diameter of $1\frac{1}{2}$ in. down to a minimum diameter of 40 mesh (Tyler standard). The material to be crushed is fed into boxes or mortars and subdivided by blows from stamps or hammers weighing about 1000 lb. These hammers are raised by means of cams and are allowed to fall on the material to be crushed, thereby reducing it by blow or impact. Stamps are largely used in wet crushing (water 50 per cent or over) but their present-day field is almost wholly confined to the gold-mining industry, where crushing and grinding take place simultaneously with cyaniding or amalgamation.

The fineness to which the material is ground is regulated by the size of screen that surrounds the mortar boxes, by the weight of the stamps and by the rate of feed of water and ore.

Outside of the field mentioned above, stamps are not used on account of their high power cost and large initial cost per ton of output. It is obvious that the power required is not proportional to the work done, since the power consumption stays constant whether there is any material in the mortar boxes or not. Furthermore, stamps produce more fines or dust than is usually desired.

Chilean Mill (Pan Rolls).—Most of the machines so far considered crush by means of a compressive force. It is possible to use also a shearing force and produce the action familiar to us when a nut is crushed by stepping on it and turning around at the same time. This is in principle a grinding and crushing force combined and has been utilized for many years in the machine known as the Chilean mill, edge runner or chaser. It consists of one or more heavy steel rolls (formerly of stone) fixed on a horizontal shaft and caused to rotate over a bed or track. Since the outside of the roll must travel over a greater distance than the inside, there is a constant slip or shear. The feed is continually carried under the rolls by the plows, and when the operation is finished the product may be discharged by dropping a plate supporting a grid in the roll track. These machines are used when tough or plastic masses, such as clay for ceramics and black gunpowder, must be ground or mixed. Formerly they were largely used in the mining field, but here they have been replaced quite generally by ball mills.

3. FINE PULVERIZERS

Ball Mills.—In all the mechanisms so far considered the crushing elements have been mechanically guided and the feed introduced between the moving parts. It is possible, however, to effect crushing by allowing balls of chrome or manganese steel to fall and revolve upon each other when held in a large rotating drum or steel-lined cylinder containing the material to be ground. This constitutes the ball mill, which has become popular on account of its simplicity of construction, ease of operation, absence of delicate parts and low cost of maintenance. Ball mills are usually short in length and relatively large in diameter. They are generally supported and rotated on hollow axial trunnions, through which the material is fed to the cylinder and from which the finished product is discharged, although they may also be used in batch operation. Figure 89 shows the standard mill, while Fig. 90 shows a Hardinge conical ball mill. A standard mill is characterized by the fact that it is very short in comparison with its diameter. For example, in one large mill of this make, the diameter is approximately $10\frac{1}{2}$ ft., whereas the working length is only 6 ft. This mill is generally used in wet grinding and the entire discharge end is fitted with a grate. Between this grate and the end of the mill there are lifters which elevate the product so that it will be discharged through the trunnion of the mill. For example, pulp or material to be ground is mixed with water and put in through a hollow trunnion on the feed side of the mill (right-hand side of the mill shown in Fig. 89) and flows across and down through the body of the mill in which the balls are tumbling, and then passes out through the discharge grating. Here the wet pulp is elevated by the lifters, and is ejected through the trunnion on the discharge side of the mill. There is a difference in elevation between the feed as it enters the mill and the point of discharge through the grate. This causes the water to have a sluicing action, which carries the fine material through the grate and out through the trunnion at the discharge end of the mill. This relieves the mill of the mass of pulp and causes the fines to migrate faster than the coarse particles. Tests seem to show that this difference in head through the mill gives better operation than the so-called "overflow" types of mill, where the material to be ground flows in the feed trunnion through a cylindrical mill and directly out through the discharge trunnion.

The balls are introduced full size, and wear away gradually, finally disappearing in the product, new ones being added from time to time to keep up the proper number in the mill. Therefore, after a mill has been in operation for some time, there will be found in it an assortment of sizes of balls, from freshly added ones down. New balls must be large enough to crush the largest particles in the feed, but are too large to handle the fine particles

Fig. 89.—Typical ball mill. (*Courtesy Allis-Chalmers.*)

of the product efficiently. This, together with the cushioning action of the fines upon the coarser particles, causes waste of power.

The unique feature of the Hardinge conical ball mill, shown in Fig. 90, is the action brought about by the shape of the rotating shell in classifying the crushing balls. This classifying action causes the larger balls to assume a position at the large diameter of the mill. Toward the discharge end of the mill its diameter gets smaller and at these smaller diameters will be found the smaller or worn balls. The material, fed in through a scoop at the feed end of the mill (left side of mill shown in Fig. 90), is first crushed by the large balls. As it works its way along the cone,

it is crushed by continuously smaller balls until it is finally discharged in a finely ground condition through a trunnion at the
opposite end of the mill.

Ball mills will handle a feed containing lumps as large as 1½
to 2 in. in diameter. These mills may be used for either wet or
dry grinding, although the former method usually results in
decreased power consumption and increased capacity, as long
as the moisture content is sufficiently high to prevent caking.
Wet grinding is extensively used for ores because of the opportunity to use cheap classifiers, the elimination of dust nuisances,
the convenient use of water as a conveyor and the need of sus-

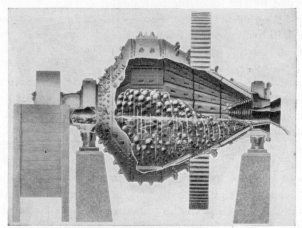

Fig. 90.—Hardinge conical ball mill.

pending the product in water prior to flotation. Wet grinding,
moreover, frequently results in simplified mixing of materials
at a subsequent stage in a process and, as mentioned above,
reduced power consumption, although these advantages may be
offset by costs of subsequent water removal. Wet grinding,
of course, cannot be used for grinding water-soluble material,
the grinding of grain, etc., and is consequently less frequently
encountered in the chemical industries. Even when grinding
abrasive material, the ball consumption does not amount to
over 0.7 lb. of iron per ton of material ground in the dry process,
or 2 to 3 lb. of iron per ton of material ground wet. However,
for most materials, the ball consumption will not amount to one-
half this figure providing the mill is fed with sufficient material

to prevent one ball from falling or pounding on another. The material being ground should always cushion the fall of these balls as they rotate in the mill, and the sound coming from the mill should be a dull rumble, indicating an absence of metal-to-metal contact.

In the case of ball mills, the crushing action is by impact or blow of one ball falling upon another ball with the material in between. There is a certain amount of grinding or shearing action taking place in the mill, owing to rolling of the balls; this becomes important in fine grinding.

The fineness of the discharged product from a ball mill may be governed by the following methods:

1. *By Changing the Rate of Feed.*—Increasing the rate of feed in a ball mill decreases the fineness, since the material remains in the mill a shorter time, being crowded out by the incoming feed.

2. *By Changing the Diameter of Feed.*—It is obvious that increasing the diameter of the particles fed to a ball mill will decrease the fineness of the discharged material if the *rate* of feed is maintained constant.

3. *By Increasing the Total Weight of Balls.*—Increasing the total weight of balls of a given size increases the fineness of the discharged product, providing the rate of feed is kept constant. This increase in weight of balls may be brought about either by adding additional balls to the mill up to the capacity that can be handled (roughly 50 per cent of the cubic contents of the mill) or by increasing the specific gravity of the balls. For example, either the capacity of the mill or the fineness of the discharged product may be increased by changing from flint to iron balls as grinding media.

4. *By Changing the Diameter of the Balls.*—When a mill is charged with balls of a given diameter, the reduction of the feed proceeds to a certain limiting particle size beyond which further size reduction is so slow as to be quite impracticable. This practical limit to grinding is known as the "free grinding limit" and is a function of ball diameter and the material being ground. The use of smaller balls results in slower grinding during the initial reductions but shifts the free grinding limit so that a finer product may be obtained. Consequently, an assortment of 3-, 4- and 5-in. balls would be used for coarse grinding, while

an assortment of ½- to 1½- or 2-in. balls would be preferable for fine grinding.

5. *By Changing the Slope of the Mill.*—Increasing the slope of the mill or lowering the discharge opening decreases the fineness of the product. Such a procedure also increases the capacity of the mill.

6. *By Increasing the Freedom of Discharge.*—In ball mills having the discharge grating, the fineness of the material may be decreased by increasing the size and number of openings in the discharge grating or plate. This also increases the capacity of the mill.

7. *By Changing the Speed of Rotation.*—At low speeds the ball action is largely the rolling of one ball over another and frequent impacts between balls after a drop of one or two ball diameters. This action is desirable for breaking up small particles of feed, and the intensity of this action increases with mill speed until the balls begin to fly short distances through space as they leave their position near the shell of the mill. At this stage larger particles of feed can be broken up and the rolling action becomes small compared to the more violent (though less frequent) impacts between the balls. The force of the impacts is increased with mill speed until the balls begin to fly clear across the mill, striking against the shell lining on the opposite side. At this stage grinding is done at the expense of extreme wear on the lining. At higher speeds the balls are held against the shell by centrifugal force during the entire revolution and no grinding is done. It is seen that the mill speed must be adjusted to the size and physical properties of the material in the mill.

Maintenance of a ball mill is extremely low, inasmuch as there are only two or three bearings and these are so located that they may be enclosed in dustproof journals. Furthermore, the mill is a low-speed machine, usually operating at from 22 to 30 r.p.m. Practically all the wear and tear occurs in the liners of the mill and the balls and liners must be replaced at infrequent intervals, depending largely upon the tonnage and abrasiveness of the material ground. The liners are sometimes fitted with lifter bars which minimize slipping of the balls over the surface of the liner. Hard rubber liners have also been used. Most of the wear inside the mill occurs on the balls, and additional balls are thrown in the mill daily, weekly or at other intervals, depending upon the tonnage ground. This extremely low maintenance is one reason for their popularity. Furthermore, they are simple to operate, and cost of installation and power consumption are extremely low. The product is not, however, at all uniform in size, and, as previously mentioned, rolls are more satisfactory if the product is to be coarser than 8 or 10 mesh. Also, rolls are better if the material is moist, because ball mills can handle only material either relatively dry (under 3 or 4 per cent water), or else very wet (over 50 per cent water), as moist material packs around the balls and cushions them.

When the production of extreme fines is objectionable and the grinding is done wet, efficient work is accomplished by closed-circuit grinding, *i.e.*, by passing the charge through the mill with relative rapidity and immediately into some sort of a hydraulic classifier. The overflow is taken off as finished product, while the oversize is returned to the mill or is fed to a second mill with smaller balls. Closed-circuit grinding is essential when it is desired to obtain a very fine product (325 mesh) with practically no oversize.

Ball mills of the cylindrical and conical types will grind ore from a gyratory or disk crusher so that only 2 per cent will be on a 48-mesh screen and 60 per cent will pass a 200-mesh screen with a power consumption of only 10 to 12 kw.-hr. per ton.

Pebble Mills.—These are merely ball mills whose ball charge has been replaced with flint rock or pebbles. Since pebble mills are used principally where contamination of the product with iron is to be avoided, the shell is usually lined with porcelain, flint or burrstone and lifter bars are not present. Pebble mills are used in batch operation very extensively for grinding to a finer and more uniform product than the usual ball-mill output. Pebble mills are used in the manufacture of talc, plate-glass sand, ground feldspar for porcelain, etc.

Tube Mills.—There is relatively little difference between tube mills and ball mills. In general, a tube mill (Fig. 91) may be considered as an elongated ball mill, that is to say, a mill that is relatively long in comparison with the diameter, in contrast to a ball mill that is relatively short in comparison with the diameter. The construction, the method of adjustment and the control are the same as for ball mills. The difference between the two machines lies in their different spheres of usefulness, the ball mill being suited to fine crushing, granulating and comparatively coarse pulverizing (so that 95 to 98 per cent passes through 50 or 60 mesh), whereas tube mills are used for still finer pulverizing. The tube mill is important in the cement industry, where a large quantity of material must be ground to a fine state of subdivision in equipment that is as simple as possible in design. Tube mills vary in size from 10 to 30 ft. in length and from 3 to 8 ft. in diameter. A 5- by 26-ft. mill will grind from 75 to 95 tons of medium hard material from 20 mesh to 150 mesh per 24 hr.

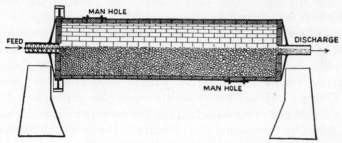

FIG. 91.—Tube mill.

Compartment Mills.—This mill combines the ball and tube mills into one unit, with the objects of simplifying the grinding process, saving floor space and reducing installation, operating and maintenance costs. The tube-mill section is frequently divided by grids into additional compartments, each compartment containing balls of a size smaller than those in the preceding section. Such mills act as a group of ball mills in series. Some mills are capable of receiving and discharging material between the compartments, enabling individual compartments to be operated in closed circuit.

Rod Mills.—These differ from ball or tube mills in the use of high-carbon steel rods as a grinding medium. The length of a rod mill must be about twice the diameter to counteract a tendency of the rods to cross and become twisted. The rods are usually 2 or 3 in. in diameter. To a greater extent than in ball mills, the grinding action consists of a rolling action, relatively little grinding occurring from impact of one rod upon another. In consequence, the rod mill is inferior to the ball mill for grinding hard or tough materials. The advantages of a rod mill lie in a very uniform product, decreased power consumption, decreased wear and tear on grinding medium and liners and the cheaper cost of rods as compared to balls. The larger pieces of feed keep the rods apart so that the amount of fines is minimized and the grinding action is concentrated on the larger particles. On the other hand, rod mills are quite limited in application for they can grind only friable solids and the maximum particle size of the feed generally does not exceed 1 in. Rod mills not only have comparatively small reduction ratios but are not suitable for very fine grinding. Rod mills are valuable for the mixing of a sticky mass because the weight of the rods is sufficient to tear them out of suspension.

Centrifugal Roll Mills.—The principle of rolling one element upon another has been widely used at all times in the design of crushing and grinding machinery. It has been seen that the gyratory crusher uses it to some extent, while crushing rolls and the Chilean mill are based wholly upon this principle. There are a number of other mills that use the same principle in a modified form, by developing the pressure between one element and the other by the use of centrifugal force. Most of these mills have been designed to meet the necessity that has arisen in certain specific fields, and they are difficult of classification from the standpoint of the size of product handled on account of serious overlapping. In general, they not only crush the material by direct pressure but they also grind by attrition (shear). Some roll mills, although not dependent on centrifugal force to develop pressure, are so similar in design to centrifugal roll mills that they are included in this section.

Sturtevant Ring Roll.—As mentioned previously, when material is to be finely crushed or pulverized, small rolls set close together are not economical. To meet this situation, rolls have been designed which travel rapidly around the interior surface of a ring in a manner somewhat similar to that of the gyratory crusher, or, conversely, the rolls may be in a fixed position and the outer crushing surface rotated. One machine of this latter type is the Sturtevant ring-roll mill. The ring has a concave inner face which is rotated at a relatively high speed, and the material to be crushed is fed between the ring and one of the rolls. This roll has a convex surface and is pressed against the outer ring by powerful springs. The material is crushed as it passes between the roll and the ring, and some of the finer material is thrown off through the discharge. Centrifugal force holds a large amount of the material on the ring. In this way, the material is carried around under successive rolls until it finally works its way out of the mill, being crowded out by incoming feed. Oversize material is screened in an outside separating machine and returned to the mill for further grinding.

Fuller-Lehigh Mill.—The Fuller-Lehigh mill may be designated as a centrifugal roll mill in which the roll is replaced by balls held in sockets. It has a number of heavy steel balls which are rolled at high speed around the inside surface of a grinding ring. The material to be ground is fed through a hopper to a screw conveyor at the top of the mill, is dumped into a center cage, and is then thrown against the ring by the motion of the balls and pushers. Attached to the rotating cage is a series of fan blades which elevate the finely crushed material and force it against the screen directly above the blades. Material that is sufficiently fine passes through the screen, whereas the material that is too coarse falls back into the crushing zone and is again thrown between the balls and rings. The fineness of material from this mill is largely governed by the rate of feed and the screen size. When properly adjusted it may be used for very fine grinding and is widely used for grinding coal for powdered-coal burners and for the grinding of cement.

Raymond Mill.—The Raymond roller mill shown in Fig. 92 has been successful very largely because of the fact that the mechanical details are well worked out, because it is a complete grinding unit and because of the success of its air separator. The material is fed in through spout S (Fig. 92) and is delivered to the mill at a uniform rate by the feeder F. It is ground between the rollers R and the annular grinding ring B. The rolls R are attached to a spider, which is rotated by a shaft driven from beneath by bevel gears, and centrifugal force causes the rolls to fly outward and crush the material against the stationary annular ring B. These mills are made with two to five rolls, depending upon the capacity of mill desired. The material that falls from between the roll and the ring is picked up by plow P and again driven back into the sphere of crushing action. Air is led in through the passages G and picks up the finely ground material and carries it up through the slightly conical dome which

encloses the rolls and their shafts.   Here the velocity of the air
is somewhat decreased, allowing the coarser material again to
drop back between the crushing rolls and the rings, while the fine
material is carried up through a fan and tangentially into the
top of a collector.   The tangential motion, together with the
decrease in velocity, due to the increase in cross section, throws
out the finely ground material, which drops through a slide at the

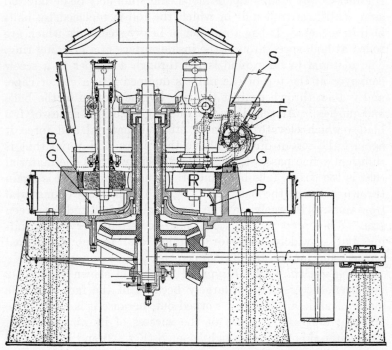

FIG. 92.—Raymond mill (see also page 302).

bottom of the collector.   The air, thus freed of dust, is returned
to the base of the mill, where it again picks up the finely ground
material, and the cycle is repeated.

There are two types of Raymond roller mills, one known as
the "low side" and the other as the "high side," the low side
mill being the one just discussed.   The high side mill differs
from the low side mill in that it has a separator (Fig. 93), placed
on the mill between the rolls and the fan.   The air, laden with
material that has been ground, passes up between the inner and

outer cones in this separator, through gates set at the periphery of the base of the inner cone and into the inner cone. These gates may be set at varying angles so that the swirling tangential motion imparted to the air may be varied at will. In this inner cone there is a separating action similar to that already described for the collector. The more tangentially the air is sent to the separator, the finer will be the product carried by the air to the collector. The coarse material settles to the bottom of this inner cone and is again fed to the mill through the two spouts at the bottom of the inner cone. The air, bearing only the finest material, is carried through the fan and over to a large collector, where the finely ground material is settled out.

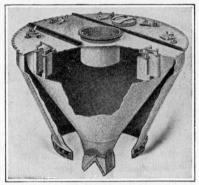

It is thus seen that the air in a Raymond roller mill is used over and over again. However, there is always a small amount of air that is unavoidably admitted with the feed, and this is withdrawn from the system through a small pipe leading from the return air pipe.

FIG. 93.—Raymond separator.

The dust in this excess air is removed by means of bag filters or water sprays.

The feeder of the Raymond roller mill shown in Fig. 92, page 282, consists of a hopper under which passes a corrugated roll. The speed of this corrugated roll may be changed gradually over a wide range by a series of pawls operating ratchets. The operation of the mill is effectively controlled by regulation of this feed device and of the separator gates.

Being a high-speed machine, this mill is not suited for grinding hard, abrasive material, but for many materials, such as lithopone, phosphate rock, barytes, limestone, etc., it is extremely well suited. It will not handle moist materials or those that soften on heating. For example, asphalt or hard pitch cannot be ground in this mill *without* foregoing recirculation of the air and sending all the air to the bag dust filters. It is one of the best fine-grinding pulverizers made, and will handle material ranging from ¼ in. in diameter down to material that will all pass a 200-mesh screen. A five-roller mill, which requires 50 hp. to drive the mill and 40 hp. to operate the fan, will produce about 5 tons per hr. of material ground so that 90 per cent will pass a 200-mesh screen.

Unless the material being ground is abrasive, maintenance cost on these mills is low, although they are run at high speed and are used for fine grinding; furthermore, power cost is relatively low considering the range of fineness over which they operate.

Other Types.—There are a number of roller mills somewhat similar in operation to the Raymond, such as the Bradley, the Griffin and the Huntington mills. The Griffin mill has only one swinging roll operating against the inner face of the crushing ring.

The Raymond bowl mill is similar to the Sturtevant ring-roll mill except that the plane of rotation is horizontal and the charge moves up the sloping sides of the outer crushing surface by centrifugal force.

High Speed Hammer Mills.—In recent years there have been developed commercially hammer mills which operate as fine pulverizers. As an example, the Mikro-Pulverizer operates at speeds as high as 4600 r.p.m.; is characterized by simple installation, open-circuit operation, easy cleaning, close particle-size control and efficient operation in either wet or dry grinding; and is capable of extremely fine pulverization. Like other high-speed machines, these mills cannot be used to grind abrasive materials.

Attrition Mills.—One of the oldest forms of grinding machines is the burrstone mill, consisting of two flat stones, one rotating on the other. The center part of each of the flat faces is slightly dished, whereas the outer rim portion is flat. This outer rim is known as the "face," and it is on this face that the grinding is accomplished. In order to facilitate grinding action, radial grooves are cut from near the center axis of the stone to the outer edge, and from these shallower grooves fan out across the face. The depth of these grooves is governed by the fineness desired. Material is fed down through a hole in the center of the top stone and is carried outward by centrifugal force and by the grooves. As it passes from the center to the outside edge, the rubbing action of the stones wears the particles to be crushed by attrition. These mills find considerable use in the paint industry, where it is desired to grind to a very fine state of sub-division and combine at the same time a mixing or rubbing action. The fineness of the product from such mills is controlled by the rate of feed, by the dressing of the faces (depth of groove, etc.) and by the distance between the two grinding stones. When abrasive material is to be handled in such mills, the burrstones are replaced by rock emery. Such mills have a relatively low capacity and high power consumption per ton output.

Other types of attrition mills may use steel surfaces in place of stone or conical surfaces instead of flat disks, or may rotate about a horizontal axis.

THE MICRONIZER, COLLOID MILLS, ETC.

Mills that reduce materials to particle sizes of a few microns have opened up new fields. There is some evidence to indicate that too fine grinding may occasionally be harmful; for instance, cement needs some particles of super-micron size to give it the proper physical qualities. However, grinding to micron sizes has resulted in remarkable results in fields such as color dispersion and chemical reactivity.

Mills of this class are termed **colloid mills** when they are designed for wet grinding. As mentioned above, the classification of grinding equipment is not rigorous; mills of this class may be operated as fine pulverizers and a pebble mill may produce products of micron size.

The Micronizer.—This mill has no moving parts. Jets of air or high-pressure steam are directed into a short cylindrical chamber into which dry feed is introduced. The jets are directed in a manner that applies tangential and inwardly directed forces to the feed. The tangential motion keeps the feed whirling around the circumference of the cylinder, except for particles whose size is so small that the inward force overcomes the centrifugal force of the particle. When the jet of air strikes this whirling suspended mass of feed, the resulting turbulence causes the particles to shatter one another, relatively little grinding being done against the walls of the cylinder. Small particles that are swept to the center of the cylinder already have a whirling motion, which is utilized by sending them to an attached air separator before this motion is dissipated.   The mill takes a feed preferably less than 50 mesh.   Wear seems to be more seriously affected by the size of the feed particles than by the abrasiveness of the material.

The Myer Impact Pulverizer.—This mill is used largely in ore grinding to prepare a feed for colloid mills prior to amalgamation.   The material is blown by an air jet against anvils.   The mill operates in open circuit and is simple to install.   Most of the wear occurs on the anvils, which are replaceable.

Colloid Mills.—These mills serve two purposes: (1) the grinding of solid materials to a high degree of dispersion, and (2) the "homogeneization"* of materials existing as two separate phases to form colloidal emulsions and suspensions.   The operation of a colloid mill depends upon the enormous shearing forces set up in a liquid film between two surfaces moving relative to one another.   Such surfaces may consist of disks, cylinders or truncated cones and either the two surfaces may rotate in opposite directions or one of the surfaces may be stationary. Frequently grooves are cut into the surfaces in order that the consequent turbulence set up in the liquid film may further aid dispersion of the feed.   In some mills the surfaces may rotate as fast as 20,000 r.p.m.; with grooved surfaces such high velocities are not necessary since the liquid turbulence supplements the hydraulic shear.   Other types of colloid mills involve beater arms which impinge on a liquid surface and intermeshing gears between which the feed is passed.

Hard solids cannot be ground to a high degree of dispersion except at a prohibitive cost in power and wear on the apparatus. Consequently, colloid mills as grinding agents are used almost exclusively for the disintegration of soft solids or the breaking down of aggregates of particles of harder solids.   The feed usually comes to the mill under pressure and consists of a more or less coarse suspension of the solid in a liquid, with the general addition of a "dispersing agent."   The agent is a substance,

---

* This second purpose is frequently accomplished in "homogenizers." In an homogenizer immiscible liquids are passed simultaneously at high pressures through specially designed valves; the emulsification is mechanical but there are no moving parts and no grinding surfaces.   However, colloid mills which are designed expressly for homogeneization to the exclusion of grinding are also frequently called homogenizers.

selected according to the nature of the material being ground, which prevents the formation (or reformation) of aggregates.

Examples of the use of colloid mills include incorporation of pigments and filler in paints and enamels; compounding ingredients for mixing with rubber latex; the manufacture of pharmaceutical mixtures and ointments, printing inks, tooth paste, cosmetics, etc.; and the minute dispersion of solids in liquids to speed up chemical reactions.

GENERAL CONSIDERATIONS IN THE SELECTION AND LAYOUT OF EQUIPMENT

It is worth while to bring together the more important points that should be observed in the selection and layout of grinding equipment. These often prove helpful in reducing maintenance and in keeping production continuous and the quality of the product uniform. One must not, however, overlook those special local conditions which are often controlling in the treatment of the individual problem.

1. Control.—The apparatus should be so adjustable that the size of the product delivered can be changed easily over a reasonable range and so that, once the desired fineness is secured, the product will be delivered uniformly and continuously.

2. Automatic Feed.—The rate of feed is most easily kept uniform by having it automatic, and this results in two advantages: first, it helps maintain uniformity in size of product, and, second, it keeps the mill running continuously at maximum capacity. The feeding device should be supplied from a large hopper or bin which acts as a reservoir to take up fluctuations in operation. It is usually advisable to have each unit in a series of machines equipped with individual feed and storage.

3. Size Reduction by Steps.—In laying out a department for crushing and grinding, it is best to operate in successive steps, without making the size reduction between the steps too great.

4. Closed-circuit Operating and By-passing.—The importance of these methods of operation must not be underestimated.

5. Auxiliary Apparatus.—It is always advisable to have the auxiliary apparatus, such as elevators, conveyors, screens, etc., oversize in capacity. In many crushing and grinding installations the output is not limited so much by the grinding mill itself as by some elevator, conveyor or screen. Often, in closed circuit grinding, the amount of oversize material that has to be rehandled is underestimated in installing this auxiliary equipment. In general, when grinding in closed circuit, it is advisable to have such apparatus possess a capacity of about five times the output of the system.

Bibliography

1. HEYWOOD, H., *Proc. Inst. Mech. Eng.*, **125,** 383 (1933).
2. ROSIN, P., and E. RAMMLER, *J. Inst. Fuel*, **7,** 29 (October, 1933); J. G. BENNETT, *ibid.*, **10,** 22 (October, 1936).

CHAPTER X

MECHANICAL SEPARATION

PART I. SOLIDS FROM SOLIDS

The necessity for separating one solid from another may arise from a desire to accomplish either of two results: first, to subdivide a mass of relatively homogeneous material, existing in pieces or particles of different size, into fractions, in each of which all individual particles are of approximately the same size; and second, to divide a mass composed of two or more individual substances into fractions so that each fraction will consist so far as possible of but one of the substances. It is seldom that both the above purposes can be attained in one operation.

Obviously, in order to effect a separation of any two materials of any sort whatever, there must be found or produced in the individual units making up the mass some inherent property in relation to which these individual units differ. The fundamental properties or conditions most commonly utilized in processes of separation are:

A. Dimensions of units as affecting
    1. Ability to pass through a given opening.
    2. Friction manifested when falling through a resisting
       medium.
B. Density, which may be either
    1. True specific gravity.
    2. Apparent specific gravity maintained for a short
       time.
C. Other properties:
    1. Magnetism.
    2. Electrical Conductivity.

SIEVES AND SCREENS

Introduction.—Separation according to the first subdivision is accomplished by giving the material opportunity either to pass through or to be refused by an opening of definite dimensions. If the openings exceed $\frac{1}{3}$ in. in size, they are generally expressed in terms of the linear dimensions of the largest particle that can pass through when the screen is in a horizontal position. When dealing with crushed rock for road building and concrete work, it is common practice to describe the size of unit pieces as those which will pass through a ring of given diameter. When the openings are smaller than $\frac{1}{3}$ in., it has in the past been a general practice to speak of the size in terms of the number of square openings or meshes per linear inch. The latter is manifestly very inaccurate, for in a structure having any definite number of openings per linear inch the actual size of the opening will depend upon the proportion of the inch that is taken up by the supports. Owing to the confusion that has existed in this matter for many years, the United States Bureau of Standards, in cooperation with certain enterprising users and makers of screens, has adopted as a basis for sieve construction a wire having a diameter of 0.0021 in. When woven into cloth having 200 openings per lin. in., the dimension of each mesh produced is 0.0029 in. (0.0737 mm.). The ratio of the dimensions of the other sieves making a series is, of course, a matter of choice. A very rational basis for a screen scale is that proposed years ago by Rittinger, namely, that each opening shall be just twice that of the next smaller. The ratio of linear dimensions to produce this ratio of areas is, therefore, $\sqrt{2}$ or 1.414. A very complete set of sieves has been produced in accordance with this plan by the W. S. Tyler Co. The size of the wire for the sieve cloth is so chosen that the ratio of opening above noted produces a relatively uniform series of sieves. When it is necessary to obtain a closer analysis for the finer sizes than is thus provided, it has been proposed to use for sieves having more than 65 meshes per in. a ratio of areas of $\sqrt{2}$, or a ratio of linear dimensions of $\sqrt[4]{2}$.

The separation of particles of different size by means of a screen or sieve is rendered difficult by two factors, both of which increase as the particles become smaller. The first of these is the *cohesion* of the individuals, which tends both to carry very fine material along with the coarse and to make a number of small units function as one large one, thus preventing separation. The second is the *adhesion* of the particles to the structure of the screening surface, tending to make the openings smaller, or even closing them. An efficient screening system, therefore, provides, so far as possible, against the presence of these conditions. Since both cohesion and adhesion in a pulverized material are functions of the moisture content, it is apparent that, to screen easily, the mass must be either very dry or mixed with excess water. A further difficulty encountered in very accurate separation is a tendency for the wires to spread, thus enlarging some openings and closing others. This error is largely eliminated by proper screen construction and by using a secondary protective screen above the fine one to prevent the pounding effect of the larger pieces. It is obvious that the material to be screened must be kept in constant motion; only by giving the particles opportunity to take different paths can a separation be effected. Care must be exercised that in producing this motion the smaller particles are directed toward the openings through which they are to pass and not away from them. The violation of this principle renders some well-known types of apparatus for separation very inefficient.

Grizzly.—The simplest device for effecting separation is to provide a grating or perforated plate inclined at an angle greater than the angle of repose of the material to be separated. Across this surface the material is made to pass by the force of gravity, the smaller particles falling through while the larger pass over. Such an apparatus may be easily made from heavy wedge-shaped iron bars held apart by distance blocks and bolted together, thus forming a frame generally known as a **grizzly.** By placing the small edge of the wedged-shaped bar downward, the narrow part of the slit is on top and clogging is avoided. Such a frame is used in screening coal and crushed rock, and, when made from heavy wire, is employed for hand-separating sand and gravel. These types are to be recommended when accurate separation is not required and when cheapness of construction and maintenance is a necessity. As will be explained later, the angle at which a screen of this type is set is an important factor in determining the size of the particles passing through it.

When it is necessary to effect more complete separation by such an apparatus, the inclination of the screen is made less than the angle of repose and the material to be screened is propelled along the surface by a motion imparted to the screen. This motion may be

1. Rotating.
2. Gyratory.
3. Reciprocating (bumping).

Rotating Screens.—In a rotating screen, frequently called a **trommel** (Fig. 94), the screening surface may consist of wire cloth, perforated metal or iron bars and is formed into a long cylinder carried by an axial shaft and radiating arms, or frequently supported by circular rings running on friction rollers. The openings in the cylinder walls may be graded in size, or the cylinder may be made in sections, each section having openings of a definite size, so that the screened material may be drawn off in a number of fractions. The speed of rotation and the angle of inclination are so chosen that the material is carried uniformly

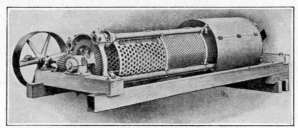

FIG. 94.—Rotary screen.   (*Courtesy of Colorado Iron Works Co.*)

forward from the feed to the exhaust end. The efficiency of such an apparatus is limited by a number of conditions. *First,* the large pieces at the entrance or fine end of the screen tend to spread the meshes and to drive the oversize through the small openings. *Second,* subjecting the fine screen to the impact of the heavy pieces greatly decreases its life. *Third,* the rotation of the charge tends to throw the larger pieces to the bottom of the layer; and this, it will be noted, is contrary to the relative position necessary for insuring the passage of the fine particles through the openings. *Fourth,* a very large percentage (90 per cent) of the area of the screen is not in action while the screen is in use. *Fifth,* since the operation depends upon the weight of the particles to overcome surface adhesion and to clear the screen when inverted, the machine is unsatisfactory for screening small particles. The first two objections are met by arranging a number of cylinders, each made of an increasing fineness, in series, so that the coarse screen comes first. The undersize of the first cylinder forms the feed for the second, while the oversize from the first is shunted off to its respective bin. Space may be economized by placing one screen within the others in a series of concentric drums. In this arrangement the coarse screen is at the center and each succeeding screen passes a finer material. If it is desired to operate the screens wet, or to wash the coarse material, as in the mining of phosphate rock, water may be introduced from orifices in the hollow shaft. In order to eliminate the end thrust on the bearings, rotating screens are frequently set with the axis horizontal, and the screening surface is made conical or pyramidal instead of cylindrical.

Vibrating Screens.—A large number of so-called "shaking" or "vibrating" screens, using both a reciprocating and a gyratory motion to keep the openings free and to propel the charge, are available, but it will be possible to mention only a few of the types. The success of any vibrating screen depends upon maintaining clear, free openings. This may be done better by sharp rapid vibration than by any method of simply shaking the charge on the screening surface. In screens of this type the screen frame should be inclined at an angle less than the angle of repose of the material operated upon, in order that an undue proportion of fines may not be carried over with the tailings. As the slope of the screen is decreased, sharper separation is obtained at the expense of capacity, and such flexibility of operation is frequently incorporated in these screens. In many cases several screens are used, thus multiplying the number of products. Fine screens may be shielded by a coarse protecting screen to carry the heavy particles present in the charge; this heavy screen is called a **scalper** and greatly prolongs the life of the working screen by preventing both abrasion and the spreading of the wires.

The Colorado impact screen (Fig. 95) consists of a main frame on which is mounted the screening surface held in a vibrating frame of wood. This is flexibly supported by a pair of elliptical springs which force it upward against four adjustable stops. In recent machines a pair of steel cables stretched between the ends of the stationary frame are used instead of elliptical springs. To this vibrating frame, motion is imparted by two ratchets operating as multiple cams keyed to a revolving shaft. The effect of the cams is to depress the vibrating frame, which snaps sharply upward against the stops when the cams release the frame. The meshes of the screen are thus kept

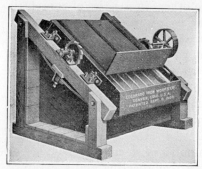

FIG. 95.—Impact screen.

free, and the charge is driven forward. The length of stroke and inclination of frame are adjustable, and the apparatus as a whole may be easily adapted to wet screening. A motion at right angles to the face of the screening frame has a great advantage in that the heavier particles of the charge are thrown to the top, thus allowing the fine particles to come into immediate contact with the openings through which they are intended to pass.

In the Hum-mer electric screen (Fig. 96), the wire cloth is given a positive and rapid vibration by connecting it rigidly to an

FIG. 96.—Hum-mer electrically vibrated screen.   (*Courtesy of W. S. Tyler Co.*)

armature which is lifted by an electromagnet and repelled by a set of springs. The intensity of the vibration is regulated by adjusting the springs controlling the recoil of the armature. Rapid and efficient separation is thus effected.

The Moto-Vibro screen is an inclined vibrating screen, built with a rigid steel frame on which the screen surface is held taut. A sharp rapid vibration of the wire cloth is obtained by tapping the screen surface from below with light hammer blows transmitted by a high-speed short-stroke eccentric.

Swinging Screens.—It was noted above (page 293) that material to be screened must be kept in constant motion and that the small particles should be directed toward the openings through which they are to pass. This effect is obtained by mounting a screen in an essentially horizontal position and

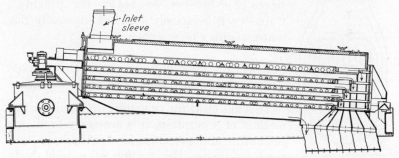

Fig. 97.—Rotex vibrating screen. (*Courtesy of Orville Simpson Co.*)

swinging or gyrating the screen; the fine material settles next to the sieve while the coarse material "floats" on top. Swinging screens may in addition employ vibration to keep the screen clear.

The Rotex (Fig. 97) and Gyro-Sifter screens involve a unique method of vibrating the screens. The frame, containing one to five screens, is gyrated by a rotating wheel to which one end of the frame is attached. The screens rest in an almost level position and the gyratory motion of one end of the frame imparts a reciprocating motion to the other end. Below each working screen is a coarse wire screen, and the space between these two screens is divided into a number of compartments, each containing several resilient rubber balls. The semigyratory motion of the frame causes these balls, whose size depends upon the material being screened, to be deflected upward either by the beveled walls of the compartment or by deflecting rods mounted on the coarse supporting screen. The feed enters through a flexible spout at the gyrating end. The screening surfaces are arranged with the finest screens at the bottom, and the impact of the rubber balls provides vibration to keep the screens clear. The coarse screens on the bottom of the ball compartments serve only to support the balls; material that passes through one working screen falls through the supporting screen onto the next working surface.

In other types the screens are suspended horizontally and are swung in full gyration by eccentric weights revolving about a vertical shaft fastened to the screen box. The material is pushed along the surfaces of the sieves by brushes or heavy tin "flights." Capacity is relatively low but unusually fine materials may be screened.

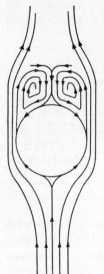

Fig. 98.—Sphere falling through a fluid; note eddies above sphere.

Separation Depending on the Difference in Frictional Resistance of Particles

To make clear the principles that underlie this method of separation, it is necessary to discuss the nature and governing laws of the forces that tend to oppose the motion of a solid body through a fluid.

Laws of Fluid Motion.—When a small solid body moves through a fluid so slowly that the latter flows past it in smooth streamlines, without forming eddies, it is subject to a retarding force R proportional to the relative velocity V between the body and the fluid, and to the absolute viscosity μ of the fluid. For a smooth sphere of diameter D this force is given by Stokes's law:[1]

$$R = 3\pi\mu\, DV \qquad (1)$$

As the size of the body and its relative velocity increase, eddies form, particularly at the sides and in the rear, as shown diagrammatically in Fig. 98. In consequence, the resistance due to inertia forces becomes large in comparison to the viscous drag, and the relation is given by Newton's law:[2,3]

$$R = kA\rho V^2/2 \qquad (2)$$

where A is the projected or frontal area of the body, ρ is the density of the fluid and k is a dimensionless factor to be determined by experiment.*

For particles having diameters intermediate between "large" and "small," neither Newton's nor Stokes's law holds. The situation is handled in a matter analogous to that used for fluid flow in pipes, *i.e.*, by defining a dimensionless friction factor f by the following rearranged form of the Fanning equation (page 77):

$$f=\frac{2R}{A\rho V^2} \tag{3}$$

Upon comparing Eqs. 1, 2 and 3, it is seen that in the zone of eddy resistance f equals k, while for streamline flow f equals $24\mu/DV\rho$ $=24/Re$, where Re is the Reynolds number. A plot of f vs. Re on logarithmic paper gives a curve having a slope of -1 in the range where Stokes's law holds and a curve of zero slope where Newton's law holds. A mass of experimental data obtained for the flow of gases or liquids past spheres of various diameters and densities is correlated by the curve $ABCD$ of Fig. 99.[4,5] At very small values of Re, where the particle diameter approaches the order of magnitude of the mean free path of the molecules of the fluid, deviations develop.† At higher values of Re, ranging from 0.0001 to 0.4, the data are in good agreement with Stokes's law, but at values of Re above 0.4 the measured values of f are higher than given by $f=24/Re$,‡ as shown by the curve BC. When Re reaches 1000, the values of f are substantially constant at approximately 0.44 until Re of 100,000 is reached; beyond Re of 200,000 the values of f are somewhat erratic, but are less than in the range CD.

Consider now a solid particle in a fluid medium. If at any instant the force tending to move the particle exceeds the frictional resistance, the unbalanced part of this force will accelerate the particle (according to the law: unbalanced or resultant force $=$ mass $\times$ acceleration) until it reaches a uniform velocity where the frictional resistance just balances the impelling force. If, on the other hand, the frictional resistance is greater than the impelling force, the particle will be given a negative accelera-

* Newton originally proposed a value of k of 0.43.

† Corrections to Stokes's law have been proposed[6,7] for this range.

‡ Thus at Re of 1000, f is 0.40 instead of 0.024.

tion.   In any case, then, a particle of given size and weight falling freely through a fluid quickly assumes a constant "free-settling" velocity, the magnitude of which is of great importance.   It may readily be found by equating the frictional and other forces

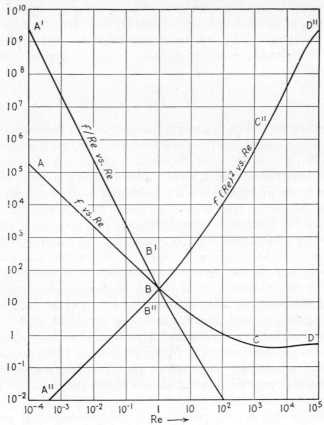

Fig. 99.—Free settling of spheres in liquids.
Curve $ABCD$: $f = 4gD(\rho_s - \rho)/3\rho V^2$ vs. $Re = DV\rho/\mu$.
Curve $A'B'$: $4g\mu(\rho_s - \rho)/3\rho^2 V^3$ vs. $DV\rho/\mu$, for obtaining D.
Curve $A''B''C''D''$: $4gD^3\rho(\rho_s - \rho)/3\mu^2$ vs. $DV\rho/\mu$, for obtaining V.

that are acting on the body, since these must be balanced to give uniform motion.

Gravity is, of course, the impelling force acting on a freely falling body.   Using the previous notation, for a spherical particle,

$$F_g = \pi D^3 \rho_s g/6$$

where ρ_s is the density of the solid.

In any fluid medium, however, the solid body is buoyed up by a force equal to the weight of fluid displaced:

$$F_b = \pi D^3 \rho g / 6$$

where ρ is the density of the fluid.

The resultant force or "residual gravity" is then the difference of these two

$$F_r = \pi D^3 (\rho_s - \rho) g / 6.$$

Equating F_r to R of Eq. 3, noting that the projected area of a sphere is $\pi D^2/4$, gives

$$f = \frac{4gD(\rho_s - \rho)}{3\rho V^2}. \tag{3a}$$

To avoid trial calculations in using Fig. 99, the curve $ABCD$ of f vs. Re can be replotted. Thus, for determining D from the measured rate of settling, one uses the curve $A'B'$ involving the new ordinate f/Re, which equals

$$\frac{4g\mu(\rho_s - \rho)}{3\rho^2 V^3}$$

and from the corresponding abscissa D is readily determined. Similarly, for calculating the free-settling velocities attained by particles of known diameter, curve $A''B''C''D''$ is used, where the ordinates are $f(Re)^2$ or $4gD^3\rho(\rho_s - \rho)/3\mu^2$. Since all these relations are dimensionless, any self-consistent units may be employed. Values of the absolute viscosities of various liquids and gases are tabulated on pages 687 to 690.

Illustration.—Assume that spheres having diameters of 0.05 cm. and a density of 2.65 gm./c.c. are settling in water ($\mu = 0.01$ poises) under free-settling conditions where the particles do not interfere with each other. What would be the free-settling velocity?

The ordinates of the curve $A''B''C''D''$ are

$$\frac{4gD^3\rho(\rho_s - \rho)}{3\mu^2} = \frac{4(981)(0.05)^3(1)(1.65)}{3(0.01)^2} = 2700$$

and the corresponding abscissa is $40 = (0.05)(V)(1)/(0.01)$, whence V equals 8.0 cm./sec.

If the same particles settled in air ($\rho = 0.00121$ gm./c.c., $\mu = 0.00018$ poises), the ordinate is 16,200, Re is 108 and V equals 322 cm./sec.

For approximate calculations the curve $ABCD$ may be replaced by three equations:[8]

From Re of 0.0001 to 2: $f = 24/Re$.   (4)
From Re of 2 to 500: $f = 18.5/Re^{0.6}$.   (4a)
From Re of 500 to 200,000: $f = 0.44$.   (4b)

where in all cases f equals $4gD(\rho_s - \rho)/3\rho V^2$.

Data are also available for the fall of disks, cylinders and particles of irregular shapes; the relations are similar to those for spheres but the constants depend on the shape of the bodies. In the region of eddy resistance

$$V = K_E \sqrt{\frac{gD(\rho_s - \rho)}{\rho}} \tag{5}$$

where D is the average diameter of the particle and K_E is a constant dependent on the shape of the body but independent of the viscosity of the fluid. Upon comparing Eq. 3a for a sphere with Eq. 5, K_E is found to equal $\sqrt{4/3f} = \sqrt{4/(3)(0.44)} = 1.74$. For a disk falling with its large face in the horizontal plane, K_E equals $1.35\sqrt{t/D}$, but, when the disk falls edgewise, $K_E = 18\sqrt{t/D}$, where t is the thickness. Similarly, in the streamline region

$$V = K_s gD^2(\rho_s - \rho)/\mu \tag{6}$$

where K_s is $\frac{1}{18}$ for a sphere, $3\pi t/64D$ for a thin disk when vertical and $2\pi t/64D$ for a thin disk when horizontal.

In the intermediate range neither Eq. 5 nor Eq. 6 applies, and one should use an experimentally determined curve similar to Fig. 99.

Applications.—To make use of these relations in separating particles of a given density into a number of different sizes, one may arrange a system like that shown in Fig. 100. The stream of water brings in pulverized material through a shallow trough which empties into a comparatively deep box. The box is so designed that the water has a fairly uniform horizontal velocity throughout. The larger particles fall rapidly into the first compartment in the bottom, while successively smaller particles are carried farther and farther horizontally into different compartments before they finally reach the bottom. The finest particles are carried over the edge of the box before they have time to settle.

To make a reasonably sharp separation, several points must be observed: the distance *b* must be large compared with *a*, otherwise particles coming in at the top of the stream would go into a more distant compartment than those of the same size entering at the bottom; the feed should enter smoothly at a uniform low velocity; the

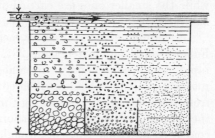

FIG. 100.—Settling box.

horizontal current in the box should be steady and fairly uniform.

Very frequently this method, using either air or water as the fluid, is used to divide the pulverized solids into but two classes, the finer of which is carried over the side, while the coarser remains in the box. Another way to accomplish the same separation is to employ a rising current of fluid with a velocity just greater than the free-falling velocity of the largest particles that it is desired to remove. These particles and smaller ones will then be carried up and out, while the larger ones settle slowly.

Probably the greatest use for this method of separation into two parts is in connection with the operations of crushing and grinding. As was pointed out under the discussion of the factors controlling the efficiency of fine grinding, it is essential for the best results that each particle be removed from contact with the grinding surfaces and be carried out of the machine as soon as it has become sufficiently small. In many stamp and pebble mills this is accomplished by passing a stream of water through the mill to carry away the fines in accordance with the principles above enunciated. Screens are usually employed to prevent the removal of particles not yet ground fine enough. Sharp separation by settling alone is impossible on account of the variations in velocity caused by irregular cross section and the motion of the grinding mechanism.

A stream of air is also used to effect the same sort of separation in various types of pulverizers. Screens are sometimes used here also, but they tend to clog, and it is often found better to remove the oversize particles by enlarging the cross section of the air duct, in this way reducing the velocity sufficiently for the large particles to settle and be returned to the mill, while the smaller ones are carried on to larger settling chambers, bag filters, etc.

An example of separation by means of screens is found in the Fuller-Lehigh pulverizer, page 281. In machines of this class a rapid circulation of air is obtained by attaching to the main rotating shaft four blades which constantly lift the fine particles from the zone of active crushing through a fine screen set around the upper or "separator" portion of the mill. Particles too coarse to be easily carried through this screen are returned by gravity to the further action of the crushing rolls.

The Raymond roller mill (Fig. 92) illustrates the utilization of air separation of the fine particles as soon as formed as a means of increasing the efficiency of grinding. A continuous current of air is drawn up between the crushing surfaces into a separator placed immediately over the mill. The diameter of the separator increases rapidly as it rises so that the velocity of the air current decreases and allows the larger pieces to fall back into the grinding zone directly. At the top of the separator the air current is deflected into an interior cone where further separation takes place; that which fails to stay in suspension falls again into the mill proper. Such a grinding device requires a very effective separator to arrest the product in the receiving chamber; mechanism for this purpose will be described on page 314.

There are a number of machines now on the market, built independently of any grinding apparatus, based upon this principle of air separation. The material passes first into a constricted area in order that a high initial velocity may be imparted to it. The cross-sectional area of the separator must then rapidly increase, allowing the air velocity to fall. Only those particles which at the lowest velocity maintain a frictional resistance greater than the force due to gravity are carried out of the separator into the final collector. These air separators are generally designed for materials finer than 40 mesh.

Separation Due to Difference in Specific Gravity

The separation of material that is composed of substances having different specific gravities presents a problem that has been worked out in much detail in the broad and important field of metallurgy. As a rule, the ore or valuable part of a mineral deposit possesses a specific gravity different from the worthless part or gangue, and it would seem a relatively simple task to effect a separation by making use of the difference in the velocity of fall through a resisting medium. Three important difficulties, however, are met. *First,* the dimensions D for all particles in the lot to be separated must be very nearly the same, and the close screening of the raw material required to accomplish this result is relatively expensive. *Second,* some of the grains consist of both mineral and gangue and therefore have a specific gravity between that of the pure constituents. *Third,* some of the particles are so small that they no longer obey Newton's law of settling, Eq. 5.

Free Settling.—From the relationships between linear dimensions and density already noted, it follows that two bodies of different dimensions D_1 and D_2 and of different densities ρ_1 and ρ_2, when falling through a medium of density ρ, will attain equal velocities when the inverse ratio

$$\frac{D_1}{D_2} = \left(\frac{\rho_2 - \rho}{\rho_1 - \rho}\right)^n \tag{7}$$

is satisfied. From Eqs. 5 and 6 it is seen that n will be 1 in the eddy-resistance zone and $\frac{1}{2}$ in the range of streamline fall. Since better results are obtained with the larger value of n, it is preferable to operate in the zone of eddy resistance.

The dimensions given by Eq. 7 are the limiting values which particles of two substances with densities ρ_1 and ρ_2 can have if separation by falling through the medium is to be carried out. So long as the diameter ratio is *less* than this, the smallest particle of the heavier substance will attain a final velocity greater than the largest particle of the lighter substance, and separation is possible. Hence, if a pulverized mass is sized by passing through a set of screens, the fraction on any one screen can be separated into its own components by settling, if the ratio of the largest particle to the smallest is not greater than is indicated by Eq. 7. Obviously, however, the more nearly these particles are of the same dimensions, the more nearly equal will be the frictional resistance of falling, and hence the greater will be the difference in the rates of fall. The ratio of the size of opening or mesh in the larger screen to the next smaller is called the *sieve scale* and has already been discussed on page 289. It is clear that the selection of those screens which must be employed will differ for each set of substances and is determined by Eq. (7). For practical purposes, when water is the fluid medium, this may be written $D_1/D_2 = (S_2-1)/(S_1-1)$, and, when air is used, $D_1/D_2 = S_2/S_1$, where S is the specific gravity of the solid. It is evident, therefore, that, when the specific gravities are not widely different, the sieve scale must be considerably smaller for separation in air than for separation in water. The ratio of the diameters of grains of a number of minerals having equal free-settling velocities has been determined by Richards.[9] From a number of analyses of quartz and galena ranging from grains having diameters from 2 to 0.5 mm., this ratio of diameters was found to be from 3 to 3.7. That calculated from Eq. 7 is in this case about 4, the specific gravities being 2.65 and 7.5, respectively. It is sometimes expedient to suspend in the water a material so fine that the mixture behaves as a liquid with a density materially greater than water. This principle seems not to have been sufficiently applied to determine its real value.

Since quartz and galena differ more in specific gravity than the majority of ores, in general, excessively close screening would be necessary in order to make possible a satisfactory separation by free settling. Another objection to this method lies in the fact that, if "free-settling conditions" (*i.e.*, conditions such that there is practically no interference between the falling particles) are to be maintained in any apparatus, the capacity of a given separating system for solids must be rather small compared to its volume. For these reasons a modified system of separation, known as **hindered settling,** is very much used in metallurgical work.

Hindered Settling.—There are a number of methods of separation which, while markedly different in apparatus and details of operation, nevertheless involve the same basic principles of hindered settling. This may be defined as settling under conditions designed to crowd the particles close together and cause interference between them.

Two principal advantages are found common to almost all the variations of this method:

First, it greatly increases the capacity of any separating system.

Second, it sets up a scale of "equal hindered settling particles" where the ratio of the diameters of the light and heavy particles which settle at the same rate is often nearly twice as great as before. This renders possible either a much more perfect separation for a given set of conditions or a satisfactory separation with a wider range of sizes. In this connection it is evident that the continual interference and agitation to which the grains are subjected in hindered settling prevent the formation of agglomerates by the small particles which would then be classified with the larger sizes.

Hydraulic Jig.—The increased ease of separation obtained with hindered settling is due to several causes which may well be considered in the operation of a *jig*, one of the simplest and most widely used of all hydraulic separators. Figure 101, page 306, shows side and end sections of a single compartment in a series of wooden jigs. The plunger has a fairly rapid reciprocating motion which keeps the water going up and down through the sieve. Assume that the feed contains particles of galena (sp. gr. 7.5) and quartz (sp. gr. 2.65) which separate into four groups.

1. *The tailings*—medium and fine particles of quartz and very fine particles of galena, which pass out with the effluent water to the next compartment.

2. *The middlings*—large particles of quartz which form the top layer of the bed of ore on the sieve, mixed with some medium-sized galena which has not yet worked its way through to the bottom. Middlings are raked off intermittently and sent back to the crusher.

3. *The coarse concentrate*—galena particles which are too large to pass through the sieve and which form a layer just above it. They may be removed automatically or raked off after the middlings. A few pieces are always left to form a bed for the next run.

4. *The fine concentrate*—small particles of galena which have passed the sieve and collected in the hopper. This is the chief product of the jig and is taken out through a gate in the side of the hopper.

It is evident that the bed of middlings, which is kept in a state of agitation or "teetering," operates somewhat as a screen,

allowing small galena particles to slip down through the channels but refusing the larger quartz, which has, however, the same
free-settling velocity.

Another effect is added to this screening when the upward
rush of water lifts the mass of particles off the screen. The
heavier particles then drop through the fluid, and under such
conditions of "teetering" the specific gravity of the mixture of
water and sand is greater than that of water alone.   This average

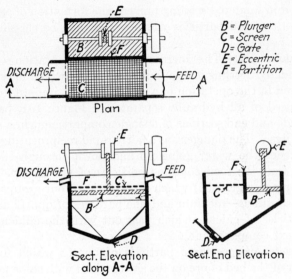

Fig. 101.—Hydraulic jig.

specific gravity would be recorded by a hydrometer placed in
the suspension, since a mixture of water and sand would be displaced, but it must be realized that to obtain an average specific
gravity greater than unity the particles must be heavier than
water and must be suspended in water, not at rest on the screen.
As a corollary to this it follows that the particles must have a
downward velocity relative to the water.   This greater specific
gravity increases the ratio of diameters of equal settling particles
so that much better separation is possible.   Richards calculates
hindered settling ratios for quartz and galena by using the
average specific gravity of the sorting bed, which is 1.5.   Under
these conditions

$$\frac{D_1}{D_2} = \frac{7.5 - 1.5}{2.65 - 1.5} = 5.2,$$

which checks fairly well with the results of his experiments.

The function of the pulsating or upward-moving current is not to separate the particles by any difference in the acceleration given to the different-sized particles (as sometimes stated) but solely to keep the particles in suspension and thus increase the apparent density of the separating medium.

Jigs are used extensively on relatively coarse materials and to some extent on finer products.

Wilfley Table.—Various types of riffles are employed for the separation of fine sands, the simplest type being constructed of blocks or bars across the bottom of a sluiceway. The Wilfley table usually consists of a nearly horizontal table with parallel cleats or riffles along its surfaces, equipped with an eccentric and springs or similar devices at one end to give a longitudinal jerking motion to the whole. The ore is fed at the highest corner and water from a pipe along the upper side floats the lighter particles with it across the table while the heavier mineral is caught by the riffles and carried down the length of the table by the jerking motion imparted to it.

The Vanner, which is used for sands and slimes, consists of an endless belt running up a slight incline which is given a shaking motion in the plane of the belt. Water flowing down the belt removes the lighter mineral while the heavier is carried to the upper end and discharged.

Hydraulic Classification and Hydraulic Separation

From the preceding discussion of free and hindered settling it should be clear that, to effect the separation of two admixed solid materials of differing specific gravity, it is necessary that the ratio of diameter of the largest particles of light material to that of the smallest particles of heavy materials shall not exceed a definite value, a value that is greater in the case of hindered settling than in the case of free settling, but still definite and not very large. It is, therefore, imperative that hydraulic separation be preceded by some sort of sizing operation and obviously screening is the sizing method that first suggests itself. It has already been pointed out that screening is an expensive operation and one in which the exact control of sizing of particles is difficult to obtain. Expense and difficulty of sharp separation in screening increase very greatly as the particles to be separated decrease in size. Thus, for other than reasonably costly finished products, screening operations below 20 mesh become impracticable on a commercial scale. It is, therefore, necessary to substitute for screening some cheaper method of sizing.

Hydraulic Classification.—The method employed to avoid the difficulties of exact sizing by screening of fine materials in large quantities is to subject the materials first to a separation by *free settling*, the fractions obtained by this method being then subsequently separated into the component materials by hindered settling. If a mass of two materials, the particles of which vary in size between definite but widely separated limits, is subjected to free settling, the materials can be divided into fractions; the fraction containing the largest particles can be made to consist of the heavy material only; the fraction containing the smallest particles can be made to consist of the light material only; but in all intermediate fractions the largest particles will consist of light material only and the smallest particles of heavy material only, while the intermediate sizes will consist of particles of both materials.

If, now, each fraction obtained by free settling has been so controlled that the ratio of diameters of the largest particles in that fraction to the smallest does not exceed the hindered settling ratio for the two materials, these fractions obtained by free settling may be subjected to hindered settling, thereby securing complete separation of the material.

Preliminary free settling, utilized as above outlined to secure the sizing of the particles to be separated preliminary to the final separation, is spoken of as **hydraulic classification.** The subsequent separation by hindered settling is described as **hydraulic separation.**

Hydraulic *classification* is less efficient than screening in that in each fraction the particles of both materials are not uniformly graded from the smallest sizes to the largest, but, as stated above, the largest sized particles are of light material only. The amount of heavy mineral obtained by subsequent hydraulic *separation* is, therefore, less in the former case than would be obtained by treating the screened fractions. On the other hand, the avoidance of the difficulties of screening operations, especially for fine fractions, so far outweighs this disadvantage that hydraulic classification as a means of sizing preliminary to hydraulic separation is very widely used in mining practice.

Spitzkasten.—Possibly the oldest classifying device, and one yet much in vogue, is called a *spitzkasten*. In its simplest form it consists of a series of inverted pyramidal or conical boxes, each succeeding box being both larger and deeper than the first (Fig. 102). The "pulp" (as the mixture of fine raw ore and water

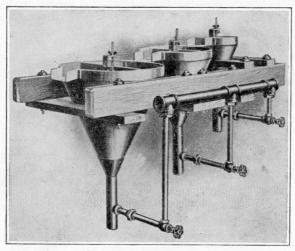

Fig. 102.—Spitzkastens.

is called) is allowed to flow in at one edge of each box and across to the opposite side and into the next box. The increasing cross section and depth produce a decrease in the rate of flow as the mass passes from the narrow to the broad end, and thus a more or less complete separation is effected. The classified ore is drawn off at the apex of each box, while the very fine, almost colloidal particles or "slimes" flow from the top of the last box to suitable collectors. Most modern classifiers introduce at the apex of each box an additional stream of water known as *hydraulic water*. By this means not only is a sharper classification obtained, but a considerable measure of concentration, *i.e.*, separation of the heavier mineral from the lighter gangue, is effected. Obviously a great number of variations and modifications can be introduced into such a type of apparatus; but if the principle is understood, the different factors may be changed to suit the conditions at hand.   Coal-washing machines operate on this principle, but in this case it is the valuable part that floats off, while the slate and pyrites settle out first; moreover, the coal has already been screened and in this case the apparatus operates as a separator.

Dorr Classifier.—When it is necessary to separate a relatively large amount of fine material from coarse, as in classifying the product of a tube mill grinding in water, involving, however, no separation of materials, machines of special design are available. The Dorr classifier (Fig. 103) can be noted as an example.   This machine consists of an inclined settling box in which the heavy

Fig. 103.—Dorr classifier.

material, which a predetermined current of water fails to carry over the discharge end, is continually removed by the action of mechanically operated rakes which push it up the incline. Other types of classifiers use a revolving helix or spiral in place of rakes.   The heavy material goes again to the pulverizers, while the slime is ready for treatment.

An important use of the Dorr classifier in the chemical field is for the countercurrent extraction of solids by liquids.

SEPARATION DUE TO TEMPORARY CHANGE IN SPECIFIC GRAVITY; FLOTATION PROCESS

The apparent specific gravity of a material of porous structure (such as crushed coke) is much less than the real specific gravity of the solid, owing to air that is entrapped in and around the particle, and frequently a relatively heavy material, even though coarse, may be made to float on water. Some substances, notably the metallic sulfides, possess the peculiar property of assuming a false specific gravity due, apparently, to their lack of adhesion to water and their ability to cling to a film of air or other gas. If properly introduced onto a moving stream of water, the valuable sulfide may be floated away from the much heavier gangue. This ability possessed by the metallic sulfides to cling to an air bubble and to be in this way transported to the top of the stream and thus separated forms the basis of a most important method of mineral concentration known as **flotation.** The selectivity or "preferential affinity" of the mineral for the air bubble, as compared to that of the particles of gangue, can be greatly increased by the addition to the admixture of crushed ore and water (pulp) of a very small amount of a large variety of substances, mostly organic in nature. Thus as little as 0.1 lb. of such widely differing compounds as the insoluble diazo-amino-benzene or the very soluble sodium-ethyl-xanthate to 1 ton of ore suspended in 5 tons of water effects a recovery of 93 per cent of the copper sulfides when contained in an ore carrying as little as 1 per cent of these minerals. In order to form bubbles of sufficient permanency to hold the sulfides until the mineral-bearing froth can be removed, a very small amount (0.2 or 0.3 lb. per ton) of certain oils, for example, steam-distilled pine oil, is also added to the ore-water mixture.

The air bubbles used to transport the mineral to the top of the containing vessels are produced within the pulp either by beating in air through violent agitation or by forcing air into the pulp from below through a porous membrane; sometimes a combination of both methods is employed.

The device used to effect separation in this way is generally a series of compartments of the spitzkasten type in which the gangue sinks to the bottom and eventually is discarded while the valuable mineral is drawn off into separate channels and is finally recovered by use of a continuous vacuum filter. This method of concentration has proved to be a most valuable one for sulfide ores of quite diverse character. There obviously exists the possibility of converting oxides or carbonates, which in themselves refuse separation, into the corresponding sulfides and subsequently separating by this flotation principle.

A number of different flotation processes are in successful operation, but none of the many theories advanced to explain the observed phenomena has yet been generally accepted as applicable to all cases.

OTHER METHODS

1. Separation Due to Magnetism.—The attraction that an electromagnet has for many metallic bodies has long formed the basis of a method for removing such substances from comminuted or ground material. Thus rags before being fed to a pulp digestor, or grain before milling, can be freed from adventitious particles of iron by passing the stock in a thin stream over a rotating magnet. The same principle may be employed in separating finely ground minerals which are more or less magnetic from the gangue which is nonmagnetic. Separation may be effected by subjecting the pulverized material to the influence of the magnet in four ways.

1. Separation by deflection while falling through air.

2. Separation by deflection from a moving belt.

3. Separation by adhesion to the moving magnet.

4. Separation while suspended in water.

Machines are available constructed on each of these four plans.

2. Separation Based upon Electrical Conductivity.—When a particle, itself an electrical conductor, comes into contact with a highly charged surface, it instantly assumes a charge of the same sign and is strongly repelled from the surface. If it is a nonconductor of electricity, the particle remains on the surface until it is removed, either mechanically or by the withdrawal of the support. Although theory requires only that one substance be a better conductor than the other to make separation possible, practically this difference must be quite appreciable. If, however, the mass is charged to a high potential of the sign opposite to that of the separator surface, the better conductor is more quickly discharged and again charged with the sign of the surface and repelled, while the poorer conductor adheres to the surface for some longer interval of time, and thus a sharper separation is made possible. The Huff electrostatic separator is a good example of this type of apparatus; its principle is shown in Fig. 104.

Huff Separator.—The fine mix feeds from a hopper *H* onto a metal plate *M* which is grounded. A copper wire at high potential inside the wooden electrode *E* gives a strong silent discharge between *E* and *M*. The better conducting particles *A* are more influenced by this discharge and are drawn out farther toward *E* while the poor conductors *C* drop directly. A mixture of *A* and *C* is collected in compartment *B*.

Electrostatic separation is a process that would seem to have an unique principle not yet fully developed.

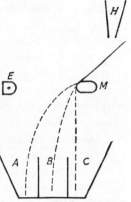

Fig. 104.—Huff separator.

PART II. SOLIDS FROM GASES

Settling Chambers.—Owing to the relatively slight resistance offered to the fall of a solid body by gas, difficulty in separation of the two is encountered only when the solid is so finely divided that the area of each particle is very large compared to its mass. For a great many years a simple settling chamber was all that was employed for most cases. Such an apparatus is generally a rectangular box of dimensions such that the volume of gas may pass through at a relatively low velocity. Obviously the rate of passage must be sufficiently slow to allow time for the smallest particle of solid which is to be removed to fall from the top of the chamber to the bottom; if it does not reach a support before it arrives at the end of the chamber, it is again caught up in the gas current and swept out of the chamber. But such a simply constructed chamber is generally fatal to efficient separation if the volume of the gas to be handled is large. It can be seen, however, that it is necessary only to shorten the path through which each particle must fall in order to reach a lodging place, in order to increase the capacity and efficiency of such an apparatus. This can be done by providing the chamber with a series of parallel shelves running lengthwise. Little resistance to the flow of gas is thus introduced,* while the lodgment of each particle of solid of a given size is assured before the exit end of the chamber is

---

* This is true, despite the great decrease in hydraulic radius, since in any case the gas velocity is very small.

reached.   It is necessary to pass substantially an equal volume of gas between each of the shelves in order that the apparatus may be operated at its maximum capacity.   The Howard dust collector embodies the above principle and insures an even distribution of gas automatically in this ingenious way.   Such separators are admirably adapted for burner and roaster gases and are quite extensively employed.

Centrifugal Separators.—Instead of gravitation, centrifugal force may be used to separate the solid particles from the gas current.   While the force tending to throw the particles away from the center may be made very great by maintaining a high peripheral velocity, provision must be made for withdrawing the separated dust from the sides of the container without allowing it to be again caught by the incoming gas.

A common centrifugal separator is the cyclone dust collector. It consists of a vertical cylinder provided with a bottom cone for receiving the product and a pipe at the top which projects inside for the length of the cylinder.   Dust-laden gas enters tangentially at the top of the cylinder and spirals down to the end of the pipe. The solid particles are thrown against the walls of the cylinder and drop by gravity into the cone, while the dust-free air passes up the pipe to the fan.   By removing the solid particles before the gas current reaches the fan, deterioration of the latter due to abrasion is practically eliminated, depending, of course, on the completeness of the separation.   One of a variety of more complex separators has been discussed on page 282.

Bag Filters.—The fact that solids as small as ordinary bacteria may be separated from air by passing it through a layer of cotton wool or heavy loosely woven cotton cloth indicates the efficiency of a filter medium of this kind.   Doubtless the removal of the bacteria is due more to their impact and subsequent adherence to the fiber than to a screening action; but this principle may be used both when a large amount of very fine particles is to be removed from a limited amount of gas, as in the manufacture of zinc oxide, and when a very little solid is taken from a large volume of gas, as in the filtration of air.   Bag filters are simple of construction and find considerable use in the zinc industry and in other cases when the particles are very fine and centrifugal separation is not applicable.

Separation by Impact with Water.—Separation occasioned by letting the gas and solid particles come in contact with a wet surface on which the particles will cling may be made very effective. By having the liquid actually flow over the impact surface, the solids are not only removed from the gas, but are continually carried away. An important element in design in any gas-cleaning device of this kind is to provide for a constant deformation of the gas volume as it passes through the apparatus. Thus a gas bubble may carry in suspension fine particles of a soluble salt and yet pass through water with the loss of only the relatively small portion of the solid which is near the surface of the bubble. It is only when the bubble is split up or deformed that the portion originally at the center can be brought in contact with the dissolving or adhering medium and a cleansing of the gas can be effected. The gas washers in steel mills illustrate this principle.

Instead of having the gas impinge upon a wet surface, the action can be reversed and drops of a liquid may be moved through the gas. Thus very effective cleansing can be obtained if a fine spray of water is forced through a current of gas moving in an opposite direction. If the dust is very fine, however, much will pass any of these washers when the velocity is high. The fact that upon condensation a vapor will deposit first upon dust particles as nuclei may be utilized in depriving a gas of all its dust. By saturating air with water vapor and then condensing out a portion, the dust particles are carried down.

Cottrell Separators.—An effective method for separating very fine particles of solids or liquids from a gas has been developed by Cottrell. Gas molecules can be ionized by α, β and γ rays and the brush and corona discharges from high potential electrodes. The gas is thus ionized in Cottrell's apparatus by passing it between a series of electrodes which maintain a silent or glow discharge. The very small dust particles are given an electrical charge by contact with the ionized gas and collect together. As the gas and dust pass farther along, they come under the influence of a second series of electrodes with rectified high-voltage discharge. The dust aggregations are attracted to one of these electrodes and deposited there.

PART III. LIQUIDS FROM LIQUIDS

Decantation.—The means employed for separating one liquid from another depends upon whether or not the two liquids are miscible. If they are not, and do not form an emulsion, it is necessary only to provide an opportunity for the two to separate into layers, according to their specific gravities, and to draw these two layers off from different levels. For intermittent separation a discharge pipe set in a swivel joint inside the tank is very convenient. The end of this pipe either may be attached to a float, which insures the inlet end of the pipe being always just a little below the surface of the liquid, or may be lowered by a chain. Alternatively, a flexible tube attached to the exit pipe may be employed.

If the two liquids are so nearly the same in density that they do not easily separate, it is sometimes expedient to add a substance soluble in but one in order that it may acquire a specific gravity materially greater than the other.

Centrifugal Force.—If the force of gravity alone is not sufficient to separate two liquids, as is the case in many emulsions, or if separation by gravity is too slow, centrifugal force may be employed. When the mixture is fed into a container that is rotating at a high rate of speed, the heavier liquid is thrown to the outside of the vessel, while the lighter remains in the center. The two vertical layers will rise to the top of the rotating vessel as the operation continues and, by suspending a diaphragm into the dividing lines, the two may be drawn off from separate exit spouts. The DeLaval cream separator was the first apparatus designed for this purpose and its extensive introduction has revolutionized the milk industry.

When the liquids are miscible, separation as a rule depends upon a difference in the vapor pressure of the constituents. The utilization of this property is the basis of the operation known as *distillation*, which is so important as to require for its treatment a separate chapter.

Other Methods.—Sometimes the solvent power of one liquid for another can be so changed by the addition of a third body as to make separation possible. Examples of this are the separation of ether and water and of methyl alcohol and acetone by the addition of a material that will depress the solubility of one liquid in the other.

PART IV. LIQUIDS FROM GASES

Entrainment.—When liquids are carried in suspension by gases, the phenomenon is generally spoken of as **entrainment**

and usually occurs as one of the factors in a more general problem. When a gas is formed from a boiling or decomposing liquid, it is not uncommon to have some of the liquid carried out of the container by the gas in the form of a fine spray from the bursting bubbles. Thus in steam boilers finely divided liquid water is sometimes carried with the water vapor; also, in the destructive distillation of substances such as soft coal, the coal gas will carry with great tenacity a small portion of liquid tar. Separation in these cases depends largely upon the principle of having the drop of liquid hit and adhere to a solid surface or baffle plate. This may or may not be wet and self-cleansing as in the apparatus already described for separating solids from gases.

Dissolved Gases.—From a practical standpoint, gases are carried by liquids only when in solution and are separated either by

1. Chemical combination and precipitation, or
2. Inducing the gaseous constituent to assume the vapor phase.

The means of accomplishing separation according to the first method are so simple and so closely allied to separation of solids from liquids as to need little treatment here. Thus hydrogen sulfide is removed from water by adding a little ferrous sulfate, and carbon dioxide by a slight excess of calcium hydrate.

The second method requires a disturbing of the equilibrium existing between the gas and the liquid. This may be done by heating the liquid, thus lowering the solubility, or by passing an insoluble gas through the liquid, thus sweeping out the gas, or by placing the liquid under a vacuum.*

PART V.   GASES FROM GASES

A mixture of gases may be more or less completely separated by three methods:

1. Rate of diffusion through a membrane.
2. Selective absorption and adsorption.
3. Fractional condensation.

Diffusion.—According to Graham's law, for a given membrane, the linear velocity of the diffusing gas is directly proportional to the difference in partial pressure of the gas in question between the two sides of the membrane and to the square root of

* See Chaps. XIV, XV and XVI.

the absolute temperature of the gas, and inversely proportional to the thickness of the membrane and the square root of the molecular weight of the diffusing gas. The coefficient of proportionality is determined experimentally for each material, and is doubtless a function of the percentage of voids in the membrane. Although it is easy to carry out such separation experimentally, no technical method of importance has as yet been introduced. It would seem that a valuable field of work lies here untilled.

Selective Absorption and Adsorption.—The separation of gases through the principle of selective *absorption* is well illustrated in the modern methods of gas analysis, and is of wide application. The most important factor in the design of the apparatus for this purpose is that which provides for the intimate contact of the absorbing liquid and the gas.

The principles of operation here are essentially those of the absorption of gases, which are taken up elsewhere.

The use of solids in the selective adsorption of gases is illustrated by the army gas mask.

Fractional Condensation.—While theoretically it may be possible to separate two gases by applying such a pressure and temperature that one will condense to a liquid, and not the other, it is found in practice easier to condense the gaseous mixture as a whole, and subsequently to separate by fractional distillation. The treatment of this method of separation will be found under Distillation.   Examples of this method are seen in the recovery of oxygen and nitrogen from the atmosphere, or of helium from natural gas.

PART VI. SOLIDS FROM LIQUIDS

The many important devices that are in use for separating suspended solids from liquids may be studied under two general heads: first, those in which the liquid is still and the solids move through it and settle to the bottom of the container owing to the force of gravity; second, those in which the liquid passes through a porous membrane of such character that the solid is retained.   The membrane may be of the most diverse character and varies from a tower filled with coarse charcoal to a plate of unglazed porcelain with almost microscopic openings.   A further classification may be made according to the character of the force that drives the liquid through the membrane.

1. Sedimentation.—As has been shown, the factors that control the movement of a solid body through a resisting medium are the size and specific gravity of the particle and the density and viscosity of the medium.

The viscosity of the medium may be greatly changed by a change in its temperature, and the rate of sedimentation thus modified. Manifestly, if the individual particle could be made larger, the frictional resistance would be decreased and sedimentation would follow. This may be accomplished in two ways. First, the large particles may be induced to increase in size at the expense of the smaller ones by agitation. Since a small particle has a greater solubility than a large one, the solution acts as a medium by which the material composing the small one is transferred to the large one.* Second, an aggregation of the fine particles into larger units may be brought about through the addition of an electrolyte which will destroy the colloidal condition or some substance capable of forming a voluminous precipitate which will entrap and drag down with it the very fine particles. The size of particle varies considerably in a suspension, but the rate at which the upper surface of the suspension settles is determined by the size of the smallest particle in it. If the range of particle size is not too great, the line of demarcation between sediment and supernatant liquid will, in general, be clear, becoming indistinct, however, if the percentage of the smaller particles is low.

The general laws according to which sedimentation takes place, a knowledge of which is necessary in order to design apparatus that will operate most efficiently as to time and material, have been investigated.[10]

It has been found that the settling of a solid through a fluid takes place in three stages—the first stage being known as *free settling*, the second as a *transition period* and the final stage as *impeded settling*. The rate of settling during the first stage is constant, *i.e.*, if the top of the sludge drops 1 ft. in one 20-min. period, it will drop the same distance in the next 20 min. When

---

* Since solubility usually increases with temperature, heating hastens the coagulation of a precipitate and hence its sedimentation. It also helps by decreasing viscosity.

the particles of the sludge have settled to such a point that they begin to interfere with each other's motion, the rate of settling decreases. This condition is reached when h/h_∞ reaches a certain value determined by the character of the suspended solid, where h is the height of the sludge at the time the rate is measured and h_∞ is the final height to which the sludge will settle after a very long time has elapsed. The rate during this transition stage gradually falls until a point is reached where h/h_∞ equals a second constant. Then impeded settling begins and the rate may be calculated from the expression, $-dh/d\theta = k(h-h_\infty)/h_\infty$. From this it follows that, during both free and impeded settling of a given suspension, the time necessary to drop between two fixed values of h/h_∞ is proportional to h_∞. During the transition period this relationship continues to hold, which in turn simplifies quantitative design. Thus, if in a tank 2 ft. deep the sludge settles to one-tenth of its original height in 1 hr., in a tank 10 ft. deep the sludge would settle to one-tenth of its original height in 5 hr.

In an intermittent sedimentation tank, the clear liquid must be drawn off as near the surface of the sludge as possible without disturbing it. This may be done by a series of drawoff cocks fitted down the side of the tank at different levels, or by the use of the "swing" described on page 316.

Dorr Thickener.—If the sedimentation tank is to be continuous in its action, provision must be made for allowing the liquid at some part of its path to come almost to rest in order that the solid may become attached to a support, or to allow the solid to drop from the moving part of the fluid into a portion which is still and from which it may further separate slowly. An example of this type of apparatus is the Dorr thickener (Fig. 105). This consists of a large, shallow, cylindrical tank into which the slurry is fed at the center. The solid material gradually settles to the bottom and the clear liquid overflows through openings in the periphery of the tank. The tank is fitted with rotating arms carrying plows which rake the settled material toward the center of the bottom, where it is discharged through an opening with the aid of an ejector or pump. Devices of this type find considerable use in the chemical industries.

In order that the time required for solid matter to settle out of a liquid may not be excessive, the path that the solid particle will travel before finding a lodging place must be short. The deposition of the sediment will, however, quickly interfere with the gentle flow of the liquid over the surface of a narrow channel, if some provision is not made for automatically removing the deposit. Apparatus of this type has found its greatest development in the art of water purification, especially the softening of boiler feed water. A good example of such structure is found

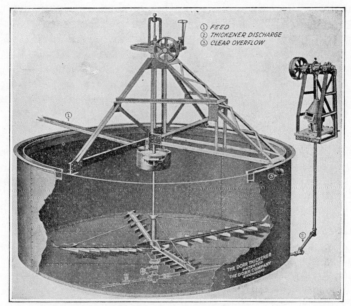

Fig. 105.—Dorr thickener.

in the Kennicott continuous water softener, where the boiler feed water, after having been mixed with lime and soda, is pumped into the bottom of the apparatus, which consists of several perforated cones placed one above the other in a cylindrical tower. The water containing the suspended solids passes through the perforations, the solid being deposited in the cones and settling down into the bottom of the tower.

When gravitation does not supply enough force to separate the solid from the liquid *by sedimentation,* recourse may be had to centrifugal force. Such devices are widely used for dewaxing lubricating oils and for separating acid sludges from oils.

Flotation.—Manifestly, when a suspended solid is lighter than the liquid, it can be collected at the top of the liquid and either skimmed or floated off. Frequently efficient and complete separation of fine particles requires the aid of a sort of bombarding effect of fine air bubbles ascending from the bottom. The particles are thus propelled upward and tend to coalesce with the mass at the top. This method frequently commends itself for handling greases, fats, gums and material of this kind—materials that do not lend themselves to other methods of separation.

2. Filtration.—This subject is of such importance that the succeeding chapter is devoted to it.

References

1. STOKES, G. G., *Cambridge Phil. Soc. Trans.*, **9**, (1851); H. LAMB, "Hydrodynamics," 5th ed., Cambridge University Press, Cambridge, 1924.

2. NEWTON, I., *Phil. nat. primo. math.*, **2**, Sec. 2, 7 (1910).

3. LUNNON, R. G., *Proc. Roy. Soc. (London)*, A118, 680–694 (1928).

4. CASTLEMAN, R. A., *Nat. Advisory Comm. Aeronautics, Tech. Note* 231, 1926; A. F. ZAHM, *Nat. Advisory Comm. Aeronautics, Rept.* 253 (1927); R. G. LUNNON, *Trans. Inst. Min. Eng.*, **77**, 65–73 (1928–1929).

5. SCHILLER, L., "Handbuch der Experimental-physik," IV, Part 2, pp. 337–387, Akad. Verlag, Leipzig, 1932.

6. CUNNINGHAM, E., *Proc. Roy. Soc. (London)*, A83, 357–365 (1910).

7. MILLIKAN, R., *Phys. Rev.*, **22**, 1–23 (1923).

8. SHEPHARD, C. B., personal communication, 1933.

9. RICHARDS, R. H., *Trans. Amer. Inst. Min. Eng.*, 409 (1894); **38**, 210–235 (1908).

10. ROLLASON, G. M., Undergraduate Thesis, Massachusetts Institute of Technology, 1913.

CHAPTER XI

FILTRATION

General Considerations.—Filtration is the process of separating suspended solid material from a liquid by forcing the latter through the voids of a porous mass called the **filtering medium.** The two important variables to be considered in the construction of a filter are therefore the material that forms the separating medium and the method used for forcing the liquid through this medium. It is obvious that the latter will be largely determined by the resistances to flow offered by the former. When this resistance is relatively small, the force of gravitation is all that is required, and such an apparatus is known as a **gravity filter.** If gravity is not sufficient, the pressure of the atmosphere may be allowed to act upon one side of the filtering medium, while it is withdrawn from the other side; such a device is called a **vacuum filter.** But a filter of this type is limited to 15 lb. pressure per sq. in.; therefore, if greater force is desired, a positive pressure in excess of the atmosphere is applied to the liquid mixture by means of a pump on the other side. This may be a heavy air pressure upon the supply reservoir, usually in the form of a **monte-jus,** or the liquid mixture may be forced directly by a pump against the filtering medium. This gives rise to the mechanism known as **filter press,** of which there are a number of types. Finally one may employ centrifugal force to drive the liquid through the filtering medium; machines so operated are known as **centrifugals** or **centrifuges.**

In a systematic treatment of filtration, however, it seems best to consider the different types of filters from the point of view of material making up the filtering medium, rather than from the point of view of the kind of force used in their operation. An efficient filtering medium may function in any, or all, of three ways: *First,* the size of the channels through it may be smaller than the size of the solid particles to be retained, and thus only the fluid can pass through. *Second,* the channels may be larger than the solid particles but may be of such a character that

323

the solids will adhere to their walls and only the clear liquid will pass through.   *Third*, the channels may at first be larger than the solid particles, but may be of such a size that they will fill up with the solids to an extent that the openings finally become smaller than the solid particles.   These solids may be the material itself or some "filter aid" such as kieselguhr, infusorial earth, fuller's earth, fine sand, wood pulp, calcium sulfate, calcium carbonate, etc.   In this last case, the first liquid to pass the filter may not be clear, and the active life of the filtering membrane may be short; but in practice it is generally better to employ a rather coarse material and to depend upon building up a desired filtering medium than to employ a very dense cloth.   The conditions that control the choice of a filtering membrane and the methods of forcing the liquid through it are so numerous that no general statement can be made.   The controlling factors will be discussed as they appear in treating the types of filters now available.

CLASSIFICATION OF FILTERS

To satisfy most commercial conditions, a filtering medium must be easily cleansed or cheaply renewed.   Hence the construction of the filter must provide either for removing the porous membrane for cleansing and replacing it as a separate element of the structure or for washing or re-forming the membrane within the apparatus.   This latter class is generally applicable only when the proportion of solids in the liquid is small and when it is not desired to recover the solids after their removal. Consequently filters may be classified according to their structure into:

1. Filters with a loose or granular membrane.
2. Filters with a felted or woven membrane.
3. Filters with a rigid porous membrane.
4. Filters with a semipermeable membrane.

1. Filters with a Granular Membrane

The simplest form of filter is a containing vessel with a false bottom filled with a granular material sufficiently fine to arrest the material in suspension.   The choice of substance must depend upon the character of the liquid to be filtered.   For example, a deep layer of coarsely crushed charcoal has been found most efficient for removing the heavy tar from pyroligneous acid, the product of destructive distillation of wood. In this treatment the purification probably is accomplished more by the ability of the charcoal to absorb and hold back the tarry matter than by the size of channels between the pieces of charcoal. For the removal of certain impurities in raw sugar syrup, a filter of this type is frequently employed, but the phenomenon is in this case one of adsorption.

Box filters consist of a box with a perforated bottom usually covered with successive layers of coarse gravel, fine pebbles and canvas or cloth, respectively. Although these filters are generally of the hydrostatic head type, suction may be used or a cover may be provided and positive pressure used in the filtration. An iron grating is generally placed over the canvas so that the sludge may be removed by means of shovels without injury to the filter.

For most salt solutions fine quartz sand is ordinarily adopted in this type of filter, as it is practically insoluble and quickly settles into a compact layer of uniform structure. For alkaline liquids, crushed marble or a pure limestone is a most serviceable material. Suspended matter is arrested by such a medium partly by its inability to pass through the minute channels between the grains of the filter bed and partly by adhesion to the grains. When cleansing is necessary, a current of water may be passed backward through the filter. This operation is efficient only insofar as the filtering medium is broken up and uniformly exposed to the reversed current. To avoid the formation of channels and to loosen the entire mass so that the grains may rub against each other and so be freed from the adhering sediment, a current of air may be forced up through the mass together with the water. Or if such agitation is not sufficient, the mass may be broken up by a mechanically driven stirrer. The slow rate of filtration through sand requires a large filtering area.

2. Filters with a Felted or Woven Membrane

When the amount of solid material in the liquid is large, or when it is desirable to recover the solid portion, a loose filtering medium becomes inadmissible and a felted or woven fabric of fibers is employed. This fabric may be made from vegetable fibers such as cotton, hemp or jute for weak alkalies;

of animal fibers, such as wool or horsehair for weak acids; or of mineral fibers, such as asbestos for strong acids; finally the membrane may be made from fine metal wire for very strong caustic, or where a high pressure is demanded. The use of wire filter cloth is developing rapidly.

The simplest form for such a filter is a circular or rectangular box or container to the lower edge of which is firmly bolted a perforated bottom. The filtering cloth or other fabric is laid on this false bottom and extends out between the walls of the container and the bottom, thus making a tight joint. By bolting to this false bottom an airtight shell, vacuum may be applied and the pressure of the atmosphere may be allowed to force the liquid through.

It is easily seen that, if a pressure of more than 15 lb. per sq. in. is desired, instead of attaching the shell to the false bottom, the container may be closed on top with a solid plate and the mixture to be filtered may be forced into this chamber from the side by a pump. Although this pressure is limited only by the strength of the apparatus and frequently rises to 100 or even 150 lb. per sq. in., the object of the operation may easily be defeated by using too great pressure, especially at the beginning. The size of the minute channels in the filtering cloth remains constant only when no part of the solid matter finds its way into these openings. If the precipitate to be filtered is crystalline and larger than the openings, a network soon forms on the surface of the cloth which protects the openings; but if the precipitate is gelatinous in nature, a large initial pressure can easily force enough of the solid matter into the channels to close them and render filtration impossible.

Development of Filter Press.—If in the pressure filter just described, instead of the airtight top, there is fastened to the container a second false bottom and filter cloth exactly like the first, and if the whole apparatus is placed on its edge, the liquid mixture to be filtered may be pumped into the container as before and the clear filtrate will flow from *both sides*. The active filtering area is thus doubled at very small cost. When the container has become entirely filled with the solid, the mass may be easily and efficiently washed by fastening a shell, with an opening at the bottom, to each of the filtering faces, filling one shell with water through its opening and forcing this wash water through the cake and out the other side. These shells will not interfere with the next operation of filtration, as the filtrate can discharge through the same openings that serve to introduce and discharge the wash water.

This pressure filter unit is now seen to consist of a chamber into which is pumped the mixture to be filtered, bounded on both sides by a filter cloth supported by a perforated structure or "false side." Next to each false side is a second chamber from which the filtrate passes from the filtering surfaces, and through one of which wash water may later be forced.

It is obvious that a number of these units may be placed side by side on a common support, may be filled from the same pressure supply pipe, and will discharge the filtrate into a common receiver. By placing these units close together, the space between the filtering faces will function as the shell above used for washing, so that, by forcing water into every other such chamber, one becomes a supply space and each alternate chamber a discharge space for wash water.

If, now, the end filter is placed against a solid rigid support, and provision is made for firmly pressing the other filters against it, the bolts can be omitted, the entire structure being held together by a heavy lateral pressure. In this way is built up an exceedingly important piece of apparatus known as the *filter press*.

It is apparent that an apparatus as above constructed may be much simplified. Instead of using a perforated plate as a support for the filter cloth, the plate may be solid, but supplied with checkered grooves or channels. The cloth is held against the face of this plate while the filtrate flows off through these channels. In another type the ridges radiate from the discharge opening, which may be located either in the corner or in the center of the plate.

Filter-press Plates; Flush and Recessed.—If the ribbed portion of such a plate is recessed, the cloth may be made to bulge into the hollow portion. When two plates of this type are placed together, a chamber for the solids is formed between the two filter cloths and the filter frame is eliminated. These are known as **recessed plates** and, when the amount of solids to be separated is small and difficult to filter, such plates are to be recommended, as the cake when formed is thin and easy to wash. When the amount of solids is large, however, the plate should be flush, and the distance frames already described should be employed, as too great a strain on the filter cloth shortens its life (see Fig. 108).

Instead of supplying these filter frames from a pipe on the outside of the structure, each frame and plate may have a hole

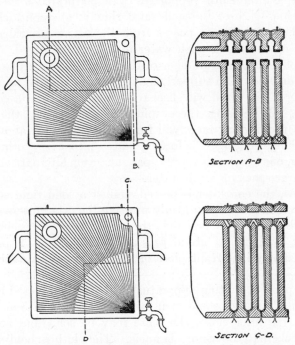

Fig. 106.—Diagram showing assembly of recessed plates.

in the corner, thus providing a channel from one end of the press to the other. This channel may connect with the interior of each frame by an opening in the corner and through this channel the entire press may be fed. Figure 106 shows the two types of recessed plates which fit on either side of such a frame, the reverse side in each being the same. The upper is known as a "one-button" plate and is provided with the discharge cock from the opening *B* to carry off the filtrate as it flows down the ribbed channels back of the filter cloth. The lower, called a "three-button" plate, has in addition, at the upper right-hand corner, an opening for the admission of wash water to the recessed

portion from the latter channel C. When the frame is full of
solids, the outlet cock of the "three-button" plate is closed, and
water is forced through this opening in behind the filter cloth.   It
spreads over the surface of this plate, passes through the cake
and is collected on the face of the "one-button" plate, and discharges through the outlet cock.

The two channels A and C must be provided with air-discharge
cocks; when the mixture is first forced through A, the air in the

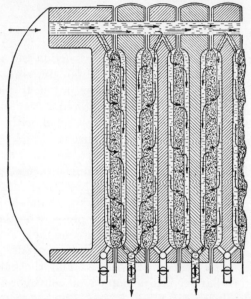

Fig. 107.—Washing of filter cakes in chamber press with recessed plates.

frames and plates can escape through C; when the wash water
is supplied through C, the air, which would otherwise be trapped,
escapes through A.*

Figure 107 shows the conditions during washing in a filter
press with recessed plates. The space between the filter cloth
and the plate is much exaggerated to show the course of the
wash water. Every alternate outlet cock is closed, the wash
water being diverted into a separate runoff trough by turning
the curved end on the outlet cock through 180 deg., or by means
of a short piece of rubber hose on the end of the outlet cock.

* For a general discussion of filter plates, see *Chem. Met. Eng.*, **22,** 493.

Obviously, the wash water must travel twice the distance through the press cake that the filtrate did.   The end plates, supporting frames and device for supplying the pressure to close the integral

Fig. 108.—Shriver plate and frame (chamber) filter press.

parts of the press must be of heavy construction and are generally of cast iron.   The frames may be of iron, tin, zinc, lead-coated iron, bronze or wood, according to the properties of the material to be filtered.

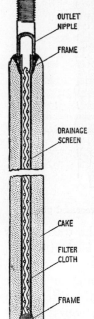

Fig. 109.—Moore filter leaf.

Presses may be constructed with channels in the frames and plates through which steam or cold brine can be circulated.   In this way one can at will maintain the filtering surface at either a high or low temperature.

In order to empty a chamber press, it is necessary to release the pressure on the plates and to separate the elements of the press by sliding each one along the supporting rods.   The cloths are cleaned or replaced and the cakes are discharged into a hopper or conveyor immediately below the press.

The filter press has a large area for its bulk, but washing, emptying and resetting are slow and labor charges are high when compared to those of a leaf press (see pages 358 to 364).

Leaf Filters.—Another method of supporting the filtering medium for either vacuum or positive pressure filtration is found in what is known as the "leaf" or the "submerged" filter.   The principle may be understood by considering the filtering mechanism shown in the diagram.   A frame is made of heavy screen suspended from an outlet nipple (see Fig. 109) and enclosed in heavy filter cloth.   When this leaf is submerged in the liquid magma and a vacuum is applied to the outlet pipe, the liquid is drawn through the cloth, while the solids adhere to the outside of the leaf. In addition to the diminished pressure maintained within the filter leaf, a positive pressure may be exerted upon the liquid mass in which the leaf is submerged. When a layer of sufficient thickness, which varies from ¼ to 1½ in., has been obtained, it

Fig. 110.—Kelly filter press.

may be washed in two ways. The loaded leaf with the vacuum still on may be transferred to a second vessel filled with water, and enough water may be drawn through to wash the precipitate, or the magma may be withdrawn from the first vessel and replaced with water without moving the leaf. The charge of solids adhering to the leaf may now be quickly discharged by forcing air or water through the leaf in the reverse direction; it is then again ready to be immersed in the filtration tank.

This idea has been utilized in a number of forms, the more important at present being that of the originator of the method, the Moore, and those for positive pressure, the Kelly and the Sweetland presses.

Moore.—The first of these is simple in construction, though it does not so easily admit of applying a positive pressure to the outside of the filtering leaf. The leaves are constructed in multiple in frames carrying 30 or more, and the whole is lifted and transported by a crane. In operation the frame is lowered into a tank containing the material to be filtered, kept continuously agitated. When suction is applied to the outlet pipe, the liquid passes through the cloth and the precipitate builds up an adhering cake. The cake is washed by bodily lifting the frame, suction being maintained, and immersing it in a tank of water or dilute wash water. It is dried more or less by suction and discharged by blowing water, air or steam back through the leaves.

Kelly.—The Kelly press consists in a heavy supporting frame upon which is mounted a pressure tank or press shell, which holds the material to be filtered when under pressure; a traveling filter carriage supporting the filter frames, each made up as already described of a frame and a filter-cloth covering, the whole telescoping into the tank; a closing device, forming the head of the pressure tank, by means of which the filter frame and leaves are tightly locked within the tank; and a series of automatic air and water valves.

Each leaf on the carriage is connected to a discharge cock in the head, and is proportioned in size to conform to the circular cross section of the pressure chamber into which it runs. The operation of the filter is as follows: the carriage is drawn into the chamber, locked, and the liquid mixture forced in. The air escapes through a valve and the clear filtrate flows from the cocks in the head to the discharge gutter. Should any leaf fail to give a satisfactory filtrate, it may be cut off by closing the cock as in the old type of filter press.

In case there is a tendency for the heavy particles to settle to the bottom of the tank before they become attached to a filter leaf, a circulation of the mass may be maintained by allowing some of the feed to flow back to the feed tank. The thickness of the cake is automatically determined by a telltale device.

As soon as cakes of sufficient thickness have been formed, the excess liquid is drained off, or forced out of the tank by means of compressed air, and wash water is forced in. When washing is completed, the head is unlocked and the carriage and loaded leaves run out of the tank by gravity. Compressed air, steam or water is now forced into the leaves and the adhering cakes are blown off; when the cakes are removed, the counterpoise weights draw the carriage back into the tank, and the cycle is repeated.

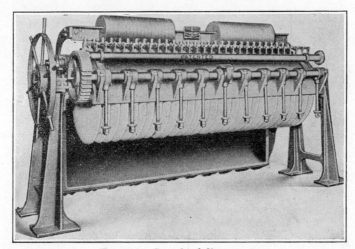

FIG. 111.—Sweetland filter press.

Sweetland.—The Sweetland press consists of two semicylindrical castings, the upper half being held rigid in its support and carrying circular filter leaves with suitable outlet connections. The lower half is hinged to the upper, and is capable of closing upon it, forming a tight pressure chamber, and later swinging open, exposing the leaves.

The operation of the press is in principle the same as the Kelly press, suitable provision being made for supplying and withdrawing the liquid magma and wash water and the compressed air for discharging the filter cake from the leaves. Some types provide for spraying the leaves with wash water while the shell is empty instead of entirely filling the shell with water, and for using a stronger spray, directed against the leaves, for sluicing out the sludge without the necessity of opening the press.

Continuous Rotary Filters.—The suction filters already described are stationary flat surfaces on which the precipitate is drawn by suction, and from which the accumulated sludge is periodically removed, either by scraping or by internal pressure. By making the filtering surface take the form of a rotating drum, from the hollow trunnions of which the filtrate is continuously removed, a type of filter is obtained, now much used for free-filtering solids, such as precipitated calcium carbonate.

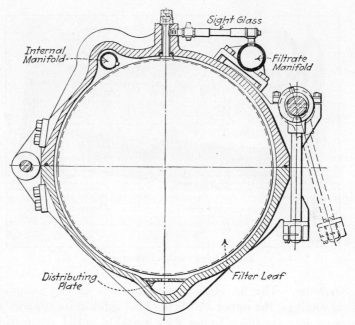

Fig. 112.—Cross section of Sweetland press.

The rotating element may be either a disk or a drum, the surface of which is made up of a number of shallow compartments over which is placed the filtering medium. If a disk, these compartments are segments of the circle forming the sides; if a drum, they are portions of the peripheral area. In either case these compartments are connected to the shaft by separate pipe systems leading to ports in the hub. The rotating portion is immersed in a tank of the material to be filtered. Those compartments which are submerged are at this time connected to the suction ports of the hub, the filtrate is drawn through the hollow trunnion and the sludge is deposited on the filter. When a compartment emerges from the liquid, the port connecting with the filtrate suction closes, and one connecting with the wash water

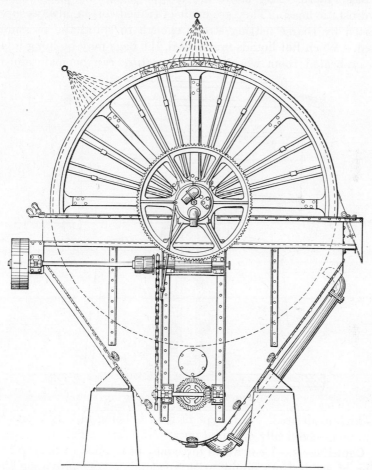

Fig. 113.—End view of Oliver continuous rotary filter.

suction opens. The necessary water for washing is sprayed upon the surface of the deposited sludge. When it is sucked reasonably dry, a third set of ports is reached, and compressed air, water or steam is blown through in a reverse direction and the filter cake is blown off into a suitable receptacle.

Filters of this type require little labor, and are adapted to free-filtering materials in solutions at a temperature such that vapor pressure does not defeat the action of the vacuum pump.

Bag Filters.—Bag filters are a type using the principle of hydrostatic head. They are made of twilled cotton, always supported by coarse netting strong enough to stand the pressure used. When hot liquids are filtered, the bags may be hung in a steam-heated room where the temperature can be maintained

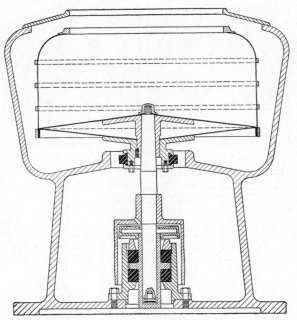

Fig. 114.—Hydroextractor.

as high as desired. This type of filter is being rapidly replaced by the mechanically operated ones.

Centrifugals.—Centrifugal force may be applied to the separation of solids from liquids with great advantage providing the nature of the solids is such that they do not under pressure form an impervious or impenetrable layer. Hence for the separation of liquid from cotton, wool or fibrous material of any kind or from granular or coarsely crystalline substances the so-called *hydroextractor* or centrifuge is extremely serviceable. Although there are a number of types of such machines, the principle of all is the same, namely, the rapid rotation of a perforated cage or basket in which the material is placed and which retains the solids while the liquid portion is pressed through into the outside casing. The revolving element must be free to assume as a center of gyration the center of gravity of the basket and its load. Therefore provision must be made for allowing the basket and supporting shaft upon starting to swing somewhat from the perpendicular.

Hydroextractors may be overdriven, *i.e.*, suspended and driven from a rigid support over the basket, or they may be underdriven as in Fig. 114. They are made of many materials such as steel, bronze, stoneware, etc., and the perforated basket is covered with such filtering medium as best serves the purpose at hand. For many materials the basket itself suffices.

In textile work hydroextractors are best discharged by lifting the load out through the top of the basket. For the chemical industries extractors may be built with a removable bottom which allows the charge to be dropped into a chute or conveyor.

When atmospheric or hydrostatic pressures are employed in filtration, suitable gauges are available for determining both the safe and efficient working conditions. There is, however, no ready means for finding the pressure being exerted upon the charge or the basket in a hydroextractor, so that recourse must be had to a calculation of the pressure due to the centrifugal force which obtains when the apparatus has reached its working speed. The formula for centrifugal force is

$$F = \frac{WV^2}{gR} = \frac{W(2\pi RN)^2}{gR3600} = 0.000341 WRN^2$$

where W is the weight in pounds, R the radius in feet and N the r.p.m. This is the radial component of force and therefore the measure of the tendency of the liquid to leave the solid.

Centrifugal filters are also made so that the cake can be continuously removed. One type of such a continuous filter has the basket rotating around a horizontal axis. Within the basket there is a large screw which is only a little smaller in diameter than the internal diameter of the basket. This screw rotates in the same direction as the basket but at a slightly lower velocity. This difference of velocity is not great enough to interfere with the filtration, but it does cause the portion of the cake thicker than the clearance between the basket and the rotating screw to be forced to one end of the centrifuge, from which it is continuously discharged.   In such an apparatus it is possible to replace the filtering membrane with a solid wall and carry out continuous sedimentations.

3. Filters with Rigid Porous Membrane

When ordinary brick or pottery clay is burned at a low temperature, a rigid material is produced which is filled with a large number of very small channels.   It is clear that the plastic mass may be given any desired shape before burning and that the porosity may be controlled by the density of the plastic structure. For some purposes such a material furnishes an excellent filtering medium.   A filter may be constructed by fitting tiles or blocks of this material as a lining to any convenient container and drawing away the filtrate from below.   A pressure filter, much like the leaf type in principle, may be made from a series of porous cylinders with one end closed and the other set in a headpiece, the whole being enclosed in a container that holds the liquor to be filtered.   Between the cylinders is placed a mass of coarse sand under which are ports for compressed air.   When the cylinders become clogged, air is blown up through these ports and the sharp sand effectively scours the filtering membrane and removes the accumulated sediment.   Filters of this type are efficient in removing exceedingly small particles and are much used in purifying water for domestic use.

In recent years a natural, porous, siliceous material (Filtros) has been introduced for such filter construction.   It can be cut into blocks and cemented into place.   It is acid resistant and has proved very successful for filters of this type.

4. Filters with a Semipermeable Membrane

The property possessed by some substances of passing in solution through a membrane such as animal bladder or parchmentized paper, which holds back other dissolved substances, furnishes a method of separation sometimes of great value.   This is known as **dialysis** and is extensively used in the beet-sugars industry.   The dialyzing apparatus for extracting the soluble "crystalloid" from the liquor is built up much like a filter press. The liquor and water are introduced slowly through two funnels and pass through alternate chambers which are separated by parchment.   The crystalloid diffuses through the membrane into the water and the two liquors are drawn off continuously through separate pipes.

SEPARATION IN HYDRAULIC OR SCREW PRESSES

When it is necessary to remove a small amount of liquid from a relatively large amount of solid, as, for example, the contained oil from seeds or the adhering oil from paraffin wax, a much greater pressure is required than can be exerted in the filter presses already considered, and a screw or hydraulic press is used. This is a very strongly built frame between the ends of which the mass, enclosed in properly designed receptacles, is placed and subjected to a great pressure either by a powerful screw acting through a toggle joint or by a hydraulic ram.

Pulpy materials, *e.g.*, apples for cider, are effectively handled in a press* consisting of a truncated conical shell built up of steel bars closely set together and fitted with a powerful internal screw. The stock is fed from a hopper at the larger end and forced through the shell parallel to its axis by the screw. The liquid exudes through the small cracks between the bars. The pressure is regulated by controlling the size of the outlet at the small end of the press and the time of exposure of the stock to pressure depends on the rate of rotation of the screw. The liquid must travel a relatively long distance through the stock and the pressure is not so high as in a hydraulic press but the capacity is very large and the labor costs are negligible; where applicable, this type is unexcelled.

NOTES ON OPERATION OF FILTERS

Back Pressure Operation.—In pressure filters with a closed delivery system, the drop in pressure from one side of the filtering medium sometimes results in conditions making continuous operation difficult. Thus, for example, hot liquors become supersaturated owing to the very rapid evaporation due to fall in pressure; the acid carbonates of calcium and magnesium lose their carbon dioxide and separate a crystalline deposit in the cloth. This trouble may frequently be eliminated by maintaining the discharge under a positive pressure until free from the press.

Choice of Pump.—For many years pressure filtration was limited to reciprocating pumps and compressed air in a monte-

---

* See Fig. 193, p. 616.

jus. The former is frequently objectionable on account of the pulsations of the stroke unduly compressing the cake and the tendency, even when supplied with ball valves, to fail to function owing to grit or other material wedging the valves. The montejus is ideal from many points of view, but is cumbersome and consumes much compressed air. Centrifugal pumps are efficient if the size is adapted to the discharge rate. If they are too large and if the rotor becomes an agitator, good filtration is sometimes made very difficult. The rotary displacement pumps are rightly becoming very popular because they combine positive action with an absence of valves and pulsations. Provision must be made for by-passing the discharge back to the supply tank when the working capacity of the press is exceeded.

Uniformity of Cake.—Where it is desired to wash a cake, especially in leaf filters, it is imperative to have it uniform in order to get equal distribution of wash water. If the sludge particles are nonhomogeneous in size and shape, *e.g.*, where "filter aid"* has been added, the slurry must be kept agitated during filtration. Otherwise the heavy particles will settle out and accumulate on the bottom of the leaf while the finer particles which filter less freely will be at the top. In such case the bottom will wash well and the top not so well.

When a sludge settles at an appreciable rate, decantation should precede filtration, even though it is necessary to pass the turbid liquid through the filter. This generally prevents the sludge from settling in the filter, although with nonhomogeneous sludges, or those containing filter aids, agitation may be necessary to insure an even filter cake.

Life of Filter Cloths.—If the liquids filtered are either acid or alkaline in reaction, it is very important to avoid concentration upon the filter cloths due to drying out of the cloth either during the dumping and cleaning period or while the press is not in use. Otherwise serious deterioration of the cloth will result. When not in use, the press should be kept filled with water not only to protect the cloths but also because any corrosion will form nonadherent oxide that can be readily removed prior to use.

Plugging of Cloths.—Especially in the case of fine slimy precipitates, the sludge is likely to force its way into the fabric and plug up the finer openings of the cloth, resulting in marked

* See p. 324.

increase in resistance. In many industries the commercial life of filter cloth is limited by this plugging effect rather than by weakening of the fabric. Sometimes the material can be removed by a suitable solvent, but often it is very refractory. Where allowable, it is desirable to minimize this effect by first charging the press with "filter aid" to form a removable filtering medium which will prevent the finer precipitate from reaching the cloth. Wire fabric has less tendency than cloth to plug up in this way and will stand more drastic treatment in cleaning.

Choice of Filters.—When a new problem in filtration comes up, it is impossible to predict with assurance what one of the many factors influencing the choice of filter equipment will be controlling in importance, but the following generalizations may be helpful.

The positive pressure type of leaf filter is used to handle sludges which filter with difficulty and therefore require pressure. With it the sludge may be subjected to a long, thorough washing. Furthermore, the solutions and wash water can be hot, even above the boiling point at atmospheric pressure, without evaporation or serious cooling during filtration. Since they are readily cleaned, they are especially adapted to the handling of extremely large quantities of sludge.

In the chamber press high pressure and temperature may also be used without difficulty. Washing, however, is less efficient than in leaf filters because reversal of flow through the half-cake opens up channels. The labor cost of dumping and reassembling is much greater than in the leaf press, but the initial cost per square foot of filtering area is less. Consequently the chamber press is superior to the leaf where the ratio of sludge to liquor handled is small and especially where it is unnecessary to clean the press frequently. For small-scale operation it usually is superior to other types. It can also be made to give a dry hard cake.

Free-filtering materials which can be filtered cold and which require no washing, or at most a short washing period, are best handled on the continuous rotary type of filter. For purely de-watering operations these are extremely successful. The scale of production must be reasonably large to justify their installation.

For the removal of very small amounts of precipitate from large volumes of water, sand filters are frequently employed. The removal in this case is to no small degree a matter of entanglement of the precipitate on the surface of the filtering medium. This type is extensively used in water purification. Box filters with cloth or other filtering medium are occasionally employed for small-scale work, especially for very free-filtering solids.

Acid liquors can be handled in plate and frame presses constructed of wood, on acidproof continuous rotaries or in open-tank vacuum-leaf filters of wood or lead. Alkaline liquors are successfully filtered upon a medium of woven wire cloth or screen.

De-watering of very free-filtering solids (crystals) is best carried out in centrifugals. In such apparatus the solution on the surface of crystals that are not too fine (30 or 40 mesh) can be reduced to below 5 per cent.

FILTER CALCULATIONS

A filter cake consists of a mass of small particles, irregular in shape, closely packed together. The liquid passing through the cake flows through the voids between these particles, and always follows streamline motion (p. 79). The cake may be considered as equivalent to a series of capillary tubes of definite average diameter. The flow through any one of these equivalent capillaries is given by Poiseuille's equation,

$$P = \frac{32\mu Lu}{gD^2},$$

where P is the pressure drop, μ the absolute viscosity of the liquid, L the length of tube, u the linear velocity of the liquid and D the diameter of the capillary. For a filter cake of thickness L and area A, with K capillaries per unit area,

$$\frac{dV}{d\theta} = K\frac{\pi D^4 PgA}{128\mu L},$$

$dV/d\theta$ being the rate of flow in volume per unit time.

This equation cannot be applied directly to the solution of filtration problems, but an understanding of it helps to explain the phenomena encountered and to develop a workable equation.

This equation indicates that for incompressible sludges, *i.e.*, those with constant size of voids, the filtration rate is proportional to the pressure, but that for compressible sludges the filtration rate will increase much less rapidly than in proportion to the pressure because the increased pressure decreases the size of opening. That the behavior of sludges under pressure will vary greatly with the character of the sludge may therefore be expected.

Since the rate of flow through capillary tubes is inversely proportional to the viscosity of the fluid, filtration is retarded by decreasing the temperature because of the increased viscosity of the liquid being filtered. The available data are insufficient to prove exactly what relationship exists. Where the physical character of the sludge does not change with temperature, it may be assumed that the rate of flow is inversely proportional to the viscosity, a relationship indicated by the experimental results on homogeneous incompressible sludges.

The equation also indicates that the filtration rate is directly proportional to the area of the filter and inversely proportional to the thickness of the cake.

DIFFERENTIAL EQUATIONS FOR FILTRATION

Since the pressure drop through a cake is proportional to the velocity of flow, it is most convenient to consider filtration rate as equal to the driving force, *i.e.*, the pressure, divided by the resistance. This resistance consists, however, of two parts: the resistance of the cake itself, R, and that of the press and filtering medium. The resistance of the filtering medium does not imply the resistance of this medium when no sludge is present, but is the resistance of the medium after plugging by the solid particles has taken place. For a given filtering membrane this resistance will therefore depend on the type of sludge being filtered, on the total filtration pressure and on the filtration rate. In a well-designed press the resistance of the main channels should be negligible, whence the press resistance will be inversely proportional to the filtering area. It is therefore assumed as such. It is convenient not to include the effect of the viscosity μ of the fluid in the resistances, but to include it as a separate variable. Hence

$$\frac{dV}{d\theta} = \frac{P}{\mu\left(R + \frac{\rho}{A}\right)} \tag{1}$$

The meaning of all symbols is given in the nomenclature table, page 364.

Most sludges are distinctly compressible. For example, very fine particles, such as barium sulfate, although undoubtedly granular, are capable of being packed more closely under high pressure and the increased velocity of flow around the particles which results therefrom. Hydrated sludges, such as the heavy metal hydrates, the calcium phosphate used for defecation of sugar sirups and the like, are highly compressible and the specific resistance increases enormously with increase of pressure.

While a great deal of experimental work has been done in this field, the theoretical solution of the problem is extremely difficult and has not been accomplished. In the first place, sludges that show the effect of compressibility to a high degree are hydrated precipitates; their degree of hydration and particle size are extremely sensitive to the conditions under which the precipitates are produced and change progressively with time. Consequently the production for experimental work of sludges of fixed characteristics is very difficult. Furthermore, the properties of these sludges are so exceedingly sensitive to temperature that slight temperature changes during filtration seriously affect results. Despite these experimental diffi-culties in checking quantitatively theoretical conclusions, it can be definitely stated that, for the practical problems of engineering design, it is sufficient to assume that the specific resistance r is a power function of the pressure, the exponent s being less than unity.

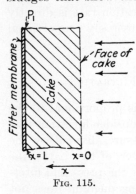

Fig. 115.

To visualize the compressive action, consider in Fig. 115[11] a single particle of sludge, suspended in the liquid, just approaching the face of the cake. It is under pressure of the liquid around it, but floats freely in the liquid stream. However, when it touches the face of the cake its motion is stopped, whereas the liquid flows on by it, producing a frictional drag which presses the particle down on the particle ahead of it. Every particle in the cake is subject to a similar frictional drag plus the cumula-tive pressure due to all particles behind it; i.e., as one goes deeper into the cake in the direction x, the liquid pressure P_x decreases, but the compressive effect p on the cake increases. That the cake is compact and dense near the cloth and open in structure at its opposite face is readily observable when it is removed from the press. The sum of the two pressures must at all points equal the total pressure P. That is, $p = P - P_x$, or $dp = -dP_x$. Assume that the specific resistance of the cake at a given point is some function $f(p)$ of the compression pressure p at that point. Since at a given instant the velocity at all points in the cake must be the same,

$$\frac{dV}{d\theta} = \text{const.} = \frac{P - P_1}{R} = \frac{A\,dp}{f(p)\,dx}.$$

Integrating from $x = 0$ to $x = L$ and correspondingly $p = 0$ to $p = P - P_1$,

$$R = \frac{L(P - P_1)}{A \int_0^{P - P_1} \frac{dp}{f(p)}}.$$

This means that the cake has an *average* specific resistance which, for a given sludge, is a unique function of the pressure drop through the cake, despite large variation of resistance through it. Assuming $f(p) = r'p^s$, this average specific resistance becomes $r'(1-s)(P-P_1)^s$, which may be written $r''(P-P_1)^s$. Since the volume of the cakes in the press is LA, equalling the sludge vV brought in by the liquid, one can eliminate L, obtaining

$$R = \frac{r''vV}{A^2}(P - P_1)^s.$$

It should be noted that the use of any other function of pressure would also give a definite average resistance for given pressure limits.

Data on the effect of pressure on the resistance of the filtering medium are very inconsistent. This is largely a result of the fact that this resistance is usually a small percentage of the total resistance, and its determination by the extrapolation of experimental data to zero thickness of cake leads to large errors. Measurements of the pressure drop through the filtering medium, without the cake present, are of little value because the resistance of the filtering medium and the flow conditions are modified by the presence of the cake. For practical purposes it is probably justifiable to take the resistance of the filtering medium as an exponential function of the difference between the total pressure and the fluid pressure at the face of the cloth, *i.e.*, $\rho = \rho'(P - P_1)^m$. Actually the pressure causing plugging would vary through the cloth and the pressure on the particles would not be the total pressure as soon as the boundary of the cloth was passed. However, a more complicated function is not justified on the basis of the data available at present.

Substituting these resistances in Eq. 1 gives

$$\frac{dV}{d\theta} = \frac{P}{\mu\left\{\frac{r''vV}{A^2}(1-P_1/P)^sP^s + \frac{\rho'}{A}(1-P_1/P)^mP^m\right\}} \tag{2a}$$

and for the case where P_1/P is small this reduces to

$$\frac{dV}{d\theta} = \frac{PA^2}{\mu(r''vP^sV + \rho'AP^m)}. \tag{2b}$$

In the following discussion Eq. 2b will be utilized, but in cases where P_1/P is not small Eq. 2a should be employed.

Incompressible Homogeneous Sludges.—Incompressible sludges are those for which an increase in the pressure on the press will not decrease the equivalent diameter of the voids between the particles. Actually it is doubtful if such sludges exist in commercial practice. It is possible to produce such a sludge artificially by taking a material, like kieselguhr, packing it into a press, subjecting it to high pressure and then operating at a pressure always lower than the maximum to which it has already been subjected. However, as an engineering approximation, sludges of sand, calcium carbonate, barium carbonate or other coarse, granular, strong particles may be assumed to be incompressible.

For this type of sludge s will be zero and Eq. 2b becomes

$$\frac{dV}{d\theta} = \frac{PA^2}{\mu(r''vV + \rho'AP^m)}, \tag{3}$$

which integrates for a constant-pressure filtration to give

$$\frac{P\theta}{(V/A)} = \frac{r''v\mu}{2}\left(\frac{V}{A}\right) + \rho'\mu P^m \tag{4}*$$

and for a constant-rate filtration

$$\frac{P\theta}{(V/A)} = r''v\mu\left(\frac{V}{A}\right) + \rho'\mu P^m. \tag{5}$$

* If during the constant-rate period of duration θ_r the filtrate volume V_r is obtained, for a subsequent constant-pressure period, Eq. 4 becomes

$$P(\theta - \theta_r) = \frac{\mu r''v(V^2 - V_r^2)}{2A^2} + \frac{\mu\rho'P^m(V - V_r)}{A}.$$

Compressible Homogeneous Sludges.—This type of sludge is typified by precipitates of the hydroxides of aluminum, iron and chromium but also includes most of the sludges met in industrial filtrations. For these sludges Eq. 2b integrated for a constant-pressure filtration gives

$$\frac{P\theta}{(V/A)} = \frac{r''v\mu}{2}P^s\left(\frac{V}{A}\right) + \rho'\mu P^m \tag{6}$$

and for a constant-rate filtration

$$\frac{P\theta}{(V/A)} = r''v\mu P^s\left(\frac{V}{A}\right) + \rho'\mu P^m. \tag{7}$$

Compressible Nonhomogeneous Sludges.—Since it is these slimy compressible precipitates that offer the greatest filtration resistance and are most difficult to handle, much effort has been expended in improving the methods of filtering them. One of the most successful devices developed is the addition to these precipitates of a certain amount of porous, granular material to open up the mass and make filtration easy. Of these so-called "filter aids" diatomaceous earth is one of the best. In the filtration of such sludges with the addition of filter aids, it is found that a *constant rate* of filtration with increasing pressure is on the average much more rapid than a constant-pressure filtration in which the pressure is maintained throughout the run at the maximum value realized at constant rate. The major reason for this is apparently as follows: If at the start of a filtration high pressure is used, the initial velocity is extremely high because the thickness of the cake, and therefore its resistance, is small. This high liquor velocity tears off the slime that is adhering to the particles of filter aid, *e.g.*, the diatomaceous earth, brings it again into suspension in the liquid and forces it forward through the cake. It finally reaches a crevice in the cake or filter membrane through which the precipitate cannot pass, but all such crevices are soon plugged up and there develops during the initial stages of filtration an excessively high "plugging" resistance in the cake and filtering membrane. Since this sludge first laid down remains throughout the filtration cycle, the average rate of filtration is correspondingly reduced. If, on the other hand, the filtration is started at a moderate rate which will not scour the slime off the filter aid, the resistance does not develop in this way and the effective filtering rate is increased. This phenomenon is encountered not only where filter aids are added but also in those cases where the precipitate itself consists of particles of diverse size, the larger lumps of which are granular and relatively strong, as in the case of filtering carbon from pitch and the like.

Apparently this phenomenon of **scouring** does not develop in homogeneous precipitates, however compressible. Homogeneous compressible precipitates will, however, under certain conditions filter faster on the average at constant rate than at constant pressure; but when this occurs, examination of the cake before filtration is completed will show evidence of sedimentation, *i.e.*, the filter has been used as an apparatus for decantation. In general, a sludge should be decanted as far as possible prior to filtration because construction and operation of decantation apparatus are cheaper than construction and operation of filters. In other words, where the filters are laid out and operated to the best advantage, decantation will not occur in the filter to an appreciable extent and Eq. 2*b* will apply.

In the case of the mixed precipitates, this scouring effect may be estimated by assuming the increase in coefficient of resistivity as proportional not only to P^s but also to a power function of the linear velocity of the filtrate through the cake, the exponent being t, *i.e.*, $r = r'' P^s \left(\dfrac{dV}{A d\theta} \right)^t$. The available laboratory data on the filtration of nonhomogeneous compressible sludges indicate that t is approximately zero and that Eqs. 6 and 7 apply to this type of sludge as well as to homogeneous sludges.

The increased average rate of flow during a constant-rate run might be due to a large value of the exponent m. In such case the resistance of the filtering membrane could increase faster than the pressure, which could cause decreased flow at high pressure.

Equations for Box Filters

Box filters are usually operated under static head only. Quantitative discussion therefore requires certain modifications of the general equations. Details of cases which frequently arise are given on page 349.

Special Case A. Very Slight Precipitate.—Filters used for the removal of small precipitates offer no resistance to filtration other than the resistance of the filtering medium itself. The filtering medium may be cloth, paper, sand, coke or gravel, and the rate of flow through the voids between the solid particles of the filter follows the laws of viscous motion (page 81). The cake obtained on filters of this type is negligible.

Assume the temperature of filtration constant and therefore the viscosity unchanged. The pressure is exerted by means of the hydrostatic head of liquid, H.

Therefore,

$$dV/d\theta = KHA, \tag{8}$$

or integrating, assuming H is maintained constant,

$$V = KHA\theta + \text{constant.} \tag{8a}$$

This constant of integration equals zero if time and volume of filtrate are taken as zero simultaneously.

If, however, the box filter is filled at the start and allowed to drain at constant temperature without the addition of any more liquid in the meantime, the rate of flow will at all times be proportional to the area of the box and the head prevailing at the time. Assuming that the box has straight sides and that therefore A is constant,

$$dV/d\theta = KAH,$$

or, substituting $-AdH$ for dV and integrating between the limits H_1 and H_2,

$$\ln \frac{H_1}{H_2} = K\theta.$$

The head H should be measured to the bottom of the bed. Since these equations are calculated for a constant thickness of filtering medium, they do not hold where the liquor level falls below the surface of the bed.

Special Case B. Granular Precipitates Which Settle Readily in Box Filter.—For granular precipitates, which may be considered incompressible, the rate of flow is directly proportional to the pressure. A highly granular precipitate will settle to the bottom of the box almost immediately and therefore, with a constant head, the thickness of the cake is directly proportional to the volume added to the filter plus the initial thickness, *i.e.*, the thickness of sludge that entered with the liquid necessary to fill the box, or

$$L = L_0 + \frac{\alpha V}{A}$$

where L_0 is the initial thickness of the sludge.

$$\frac{dV}{d\theta} = \frac{KHA}{L} = \frac{KHA}{L_0 + \dfrac{\alpha V}{A}}, \tag{9}$$

$$\frac{L_0 dV}{A} + \frac{\alpha V dV}{A^2} = KH d\theta, \tag{9a}$$

$$\frac{L_0 V}{A} + \frac{\alpha V^2}{2A^2} = KH\theta + \text{constant}. \tag{9b}$$

For varying heads, *i.e.*, in case the filter is filled and then allowed to drain without adding any further liquid, this case simplifies to the preceding one, and, as before,

$$\ln \frac{H_1}{H_2} = K\theta. \tag{9c}$$

This is because the precipitate settles at the start of the filtration, and, being incompressible, the sludge simply acts as a sand filter of type A.

Granular precipitates which settle easily but are compressible obey the same laws, because, if the head is constant, the precipitate is compressed equally throughout the filtration; if the head is allowed to fall, the greatest pressure is at the start and a precipitate, once compressed under not too high pressure, does not greatly alter in compactness with diminishing pressure. This compression can be allowed for in the equation, for, since

$$L = kH_1,$$
$$\frac{dV}{d\theta} = \frac{KHA}{kH_1}.$$

Then when the head falls and $dV = -AdH$,

$$\ln \frac{H_1}{H_2} = \frac{c\theta}{H_1}. \tag{9d}$$

NOTES ON USE AND INTERPRETATION OF EQUATIONS

The equations for filtration under constant pressure check the experimental data within its precision, *i.e.*, during a given run the ratio $(P\theta)/(V/A)$ is proportional to the total volume of filtrate per unit area and the proportionality constant varies from run to run as a power function of the pressure, the exponent being s.

Figure 116 shows the results of several investigators on constant-pressure filtration of both compressible and essentially incompressible sludges. The data conform to straight lines, which is in agreement with Eqs. 4 and 6. The slope of the line corresponds to $r''v\mu P^s/2$ and the intercept on the ordinate at $(V/A) = 0$ is $\rho'\mu P^m$. Essentially all the available experimental data give the same satisfactory correlation. Figure 117 is a similar type of plot for the compressible homogeneous sludge of chromium hydroxide. Both the slope and the intercept increase with increasing pressure, indicating positive values of

NOTE: V/A is expressed in pounds of filtrate per square inch on pages 351 to 354 and as cubic feet per square foot in Illustration 2, page 358.

both m and s. If the logarithms of these slopes are plotted *vs.* the logarithms of the pressures, the slope of the resulting line will be equal to s. Such a plot is given in Fig. 118 and the corresponding value of s is found to be 0.81. The value of m may be obtained in a similar way by plotting the logarithms of the intercepts *vs.* the logarithms of the pressures. The intercepts of Fig. 117 are plotted in Fig. 119, giving a value of m equal to

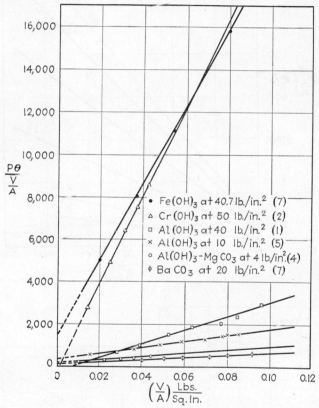

FIG. 116.—Constant-pressure filtration data.

0.52. The values of the slope $(r''v\mu P^s/2)$ and the intercepts for a number of different constant-pressure filtrations are given in Table I. This table also gives the values of the slope corrected approximately for variations in v by dividing these slopes by the pounds of solids per hundred pounds of filtrate.

The sludges of the hydroxides of aluminum, iron and chromium have resistances that are as much as a thousand-fold greater than the resistances of solids such as kieselguhr. The values of s for the results on the filtration of different com-

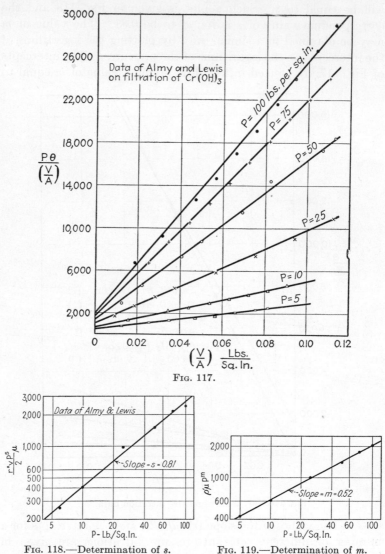

FIG. 117.

FIG. 118.—Determination of s.

FIG. 119.—Determination of m.

pressible sludges are summarized in Table II. These values are the greatest for the compressible hydroxide sludges, intermediate values being obtained for ferric oxide; a small but definite value of s is obtained for kieselguhr and calcium carbonate. The interpretation of the constant-rate data is more complicated owing to the fact that generally, when $(P\theta)/(V/A)$ is plotted vs. (V/A), both the slope $r''v\mu P^s$ and the intercept $\rho'\mu P^m$ vary

TABLE I

	P, lb./sq. in.	a, lb. solid/lb. filtrate $\times 100$	$t°C.$	$\dfrac{r''vP^s}{2}\mu$	$\mu\rho$	$\dfrac{r''vP^s}{2a}\mu$	Investigator
Kieselguhr...........	30	....	....	1,000	20	......	8
	16	1.23	23	1,550	90	1,260	6
	13	2.65	15.5	3,200	25	1,210	1
CaCO₃..............	15	4.11	28.8	2,900	140	705	7
	10	0.21	21	170	60	708	1
	20	0.21	19	120	50	570	1
	50	1.21	....	168	......	139	3
BaCO₃..............	38.7	2.19	....	6,300	60	2,880	7
70-mesh marble.......	5–20	0.48	70	120	70	250	1
100-mesh marble......	25	0.45	70	105	250	234	1
MgCO₃.............	30	0.22	23	2,500	360	11,400	1
PbCrO₄.............	20	1.48	30	390	35	260	7
Fe₂O₃..............	50	0.52	....	1,090	......	2,100	3
Al(OH)₃+kieselguhr...	15.5	....	25	18,000	650	......	6
	24.5	1.6	24	27,000	1,100	16,900	6
	33	....	27	54,000	900	......	6
Fe(OH)₃+Hyflow.....	15.5	{ 1.18 % Fe(OH)₃ 3.65 % Hyflow	21.8	4,500	90	930	7
ZnCrO₄.............	50	4	....	344,000	−500	86,000	4
Al(OH)₃+MgCO₃.....	4	2.4	....	7,500	110	3,100	4
Cr(OH)₃.............	5	....	....	26,000	400	......	2
	10	....	....	40,000	600	......	2
	25	....	....	96,000	1,000	......	2
	50	....	....	150,000	1,300	......	2
	75	....	....	210,000	1,700	......	2
	100	....	....	240,000	2,000	......	2
Al(OH)₃.............	15	0.46	23	17,300	350	37,600	6
	10	0.37	21	21,500	300	58,000	6
	22	0.4	25	19,000	200	47,500	1
	40	0.4	25	34,000	−300	85,000	1
	90	0.089	....	13,600	2,600	153,000	5
	60	0.119	....	11,700	3,900	98,000	5
	20	0.6	....	33,000	−200	55,000	5
	80	0.6	....	102,000	2,600	170,000	5
	80	0.052	16.5	17,000	400	326,000	9
	80	2.3	....	200,000	500	87,000	4
	40	2.3	....	128,000	820	56,000	4
Fe(OH)₃.............	10	0.28	21	42,000	300	150,000	9
	40	0.273	20	110,000	−3,000	402,000	9
	40.7	0.37	20	43,000	−90	116,000	7
	40	1.89	16	420,000	200	220,000	9
	60	1.73	17	485,000	1,300	280,000	9
	20	1.76	19.5	216,000	500	123,000	9
	20	0.275	23	76,000	200	276,000	9

during the run. However, a satisfactory correlation may be obtained for noncompressible sludges, which were filtered under conditions such that $\rho'\mu P^m$ was small, by plotting $(P\theta)/(V/A)$ vs. (V/A), from which the slope of the line is equal to $r''v\mu$. For compressible sludges it is possible to solve Eq. 7 as a series of simultaneous equations, choosing sufficient experimental points to evaluate the constants. An alternate method is to determine s from constant-pressure runs on the same sludge, and then to plot $(P\theta)/(V/A)$ vs. $P^s(V/A)$ for the constant-rate run. If $\rho'\mu P^m$ is sufficiently small, a straight line of slope $r''v\mu$ should result. In Fig. 120 the constant-rate filtration data[9] on ferric hydroxide are plotted, using s equal to 0.69 as determined from constant-pressure tests by the same investigator on the same sludge. From the slope of the line the value of $r''v\mu/a$ is calculated as 46,000,

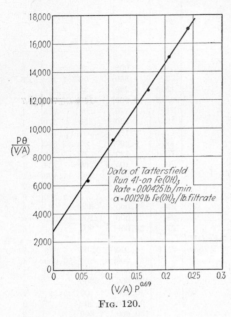

FIG. 120.

which may be compared with the value of the same group obtained by multiplying $(r''v\mu P^s/2a)$, given in Table I for the constant-pressure filtration test at 10 lb. per sq. in., by $\frac{2}{10}^{0.69}$, which gives $r''v\mu/a$ equal to 61,000.

General Applicability.—In the case of homogeneous compressible precipitates filtered under conditions such that decantation does not play a part in the filtering operation, the coefficients, s and r', determined thus from constant-pressure or constant-rate conditions check reasonably well. However, one should always determine experimentally these coefficients on the particular sludge for which the equation is to be employed under conditions as nearly similar as may be to those of actual operation; that is, if one proposes to operate at constant-pressure or constant-rate or constant-pressure gradient, the experimental data should be obtained on this particular type of cycle. On the other hand, given data obtained under one set of conditions, the equation may be safely used to secure a preliminary estimate of the influence of change in those conditions.

TABLE II

	Pressure range, lb./sq. in.	s	Investigator
Al(OH)₃.....................	20–80	0.65	4
	10–80	0.75	5
	10–40	0.88	1
	.....	0.56	6
Fe(OH)₃.....................	20–60	0.69	9
Cr(OH)₃.....................	5–100	0.81	2
ZnCrO₄.....................	10–70	0.72	4
Fe₂O₃.....................	.....	0.18–0.41	3
MgCO₃.....................	.....	0.10	6
CaCO₃.....................	.....	0.14	3
	.....	0.09	6
Kieselguhr..................	.....	0.05	3
	.....	0.02	6

Variability of Individual Sludges.—As has already been indicated, *compressible* sludges are extremely sensitive to the conditions under which they are produced and rapidly change in character with time, although this change usually becomes progressively less the longer this period. Data have been obtained on sludges produced and filtered under supposedly identical conditions, the filtering time of which varied fourfold. Because of this sensitiveness, laboratory data obtained from small-scale experimentation cannot be used with safety for purposes of engineering design except as a first approximation. It is possible in the laboratory to produce the precipitate in question under conditions that will yield a sludge of maximum specific resistance so that equipment based on such data will at least be safe. It is, however, impossible to estimate the magnitude of the factor of safety thus introduced. Consequently, where equipment is to be installed for a new process, on the basis of small-scale experimentation only, it should be designed on a reasonable basis, but with provision for expansion should this prove necessary.

Constancy of Operating Averages.—For one important purpose these equations are entirely dependable. Where a plant is in normal operation, the constants of these equations can be obtained from the *average* performance of the filtration equipment used on the sludge produced under normal conditions. Such constants obtained from average plant performance can be used with safety to estimate the result of proposed modification in operating conditions in the plant or for the design of filters for new installation provided the precipitate in the new plant is to be produced under conditions identical with those in the old one (see Illustration 1).

Washing.—While data on filtration can be used to secure an estimate on washing time, it is safer to obtain washing data directly, especially in the case of chamber or "plate and frame" type of filters, because in these the half-cake through which flow is reversed on washing is loosened up by this reversal and its resistance lessened. The extent of this effect can be determined only experimentally.

Constant Pressure vs. Constant Rate.—These equations show that for *homogeneous* sludges constant-pressure filtration is better than constant-rate filtration. On the other hand, the initial velocity in a constant-pressure operation is so high that it is very likely to cause the filtrate to run cloudy. Even in constant-pressure runs it is therefore better to start at low and substantially constant rate until a thoroughly formed layer of sludge is deposited on the filtering medium.

The maximum allowable pressure that can be tolerated in a filtering operation is determined by the strength of the filtering medium or by the tendency of the sludge to force its way through the filter. The higher the pressure, the less the life of the filter cloth and the greater the tendency toward cloudiness. In highly compressible sludges the gain by increased pressure is so slight that it is wise to restrict the pressure to a low figure. This maximum advisable pressure must, however, be determined experimentally with each individual sludge.

Illustration 1.—In the filtration of a certain sludge, the pump is operated at maximum capacity until the pressure rises to 50 lb./sq. in., and the filtration is then completed at constant pressure. The constant-rate operation requires 15 min. and one-third of the total filtrate is obtained during this period. On the assumption that the resistance of the filtering medium is negligible, determine (*a*) the total filtration time; (*b*) the filtration cycle if the filtrate per run is one-half that in (*a*), but the total filtration area is the same; (*c*) the per cent reduction in the time of filtration in (*a*) if a duplicate pump were installed in parallel with the present pump; and (*d*) the filtration cycle with the present pump and press to give the maximum amount filtered per day if the cake is not washed and if the time θ_c required for removing the cake and reassembling the press is 20 min.

Solution.—At the end of the constant-rate period, the pressure will be that prevailing in the constant-pressure period so that at this time the proportionality factor $P^{1-s}A^2/r''v\mu$ will be fixed. Calling this constant k and letting V_r and θ_r represent the volume of filtrate and time at the end of the constant-rate period, respectively, then Eq. 2*b* becomes $V_r/\theta_r = k/V_r$, or $V_r^2 = k\theta_r$ for the constant-rate period. Integration of $dV/d\theta = k/V$ for the constant-pressure period gives $V^2 - V_r^2 = 2k(\theta - \theta_r)$ where V and θ represent the total volume of filtrate and total filtration time, respectively, per cycle. The constant k can be eliminated from these relations, giving

$$\theta = \frac{\theta_r}{2}\left[\left(\frac{V}{V_r}\right)^2 + 1\right].$$

a. In this case V equals $3V_r$ and θ_r equals 0.25 hr.; hence

$$\theta = 0.25[9+1]/2 = 1.25 \text{ hr.}$$

b. In this case θ_r will be the same as in (*a*) and V' will be $(\frac{3}{2})V_r$, giving $\theta' = 0.406$ hr.

c. With two pumps V_r''/θ_r'' will equal $2V_r/\theta_r$ and the maximum allowable pressure will be reached when the cake is one-half as thick as before; hence the volume of filtrate V_r'' in the new constant-rate period will be $\frac{1}{2}V_r$ and θ_r''

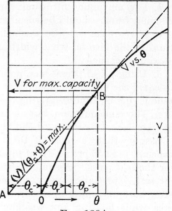

Fig. 120A.

will equal $\theta_r/4$, or 0.0625 hr. Since the total volume of filtrate is to be the same as in (*a*), V_r'' will now equal $V/6$ and θ'' will equal $0.0625(36+1)/2$ or 1.16 hr.

d. The filtration cycle for maximum daily capacity corresponds to maximum filtrate per cycle-hour, and may be found by setting the derivative of $V/(\theta + \theta_c)$ equal to zero, giving

$$\theta - \theta_r = \theta_c,$$

which means that for maximum capacity the constant-pressure filtration time should equal that required for removing the cake and reassembling the press, $\frac{1}{3}$ hr. in this case. Even if the resistance of the filtering medium is not negligible, the values of V and θ corresponding to maximum daily capacity are readily found by plotting the experimental data as a curve of V vs. θ, as in Fig. 120*A*, laying off θ_c horizontally to the left of the origin and drawing the straight line AB tangent to the filtration curve at the point B.

Illustration 2.—A precipitate of ferric and aluminum hydroxides is being filtered at substantially constant pressure in a chamber press having distance frames 3 ft. square and 1 in. thick. At the pressure used 4.5 cu. ft. of filtrate/sq. ft. of filtering area is obtained before the frames are full. The cake is not washed; 6.5 hr. is required to fill the press, and 40 min. to dump, clean and reassemble it.

a. It is desired to wash the cake in this press with an amount of wash water equal to one-third that of the filtrate. If this be done, how much will the present filtering capacity of the press be reduced?

A new press is to be purchased, which may be of the chamber or leaf type. The chamber press will be 3 ft. square as before. The leaf press will require 20 min. for dumping and reassembling and 15 min. for filling with wash water and removing excess. It is understood that the new press is to be operated at the present capacity and pressure (practically constant).

Parts *b* and *c* postulate a chamber press; parts *d* and *e* assume that a leaf press will be employed.

b. For maximum filtration capacity without washing, what thickness distance frames should be specified for the chamber press?

c. If the cake is to be washed with an amount of water equal to one-third of the filtrate, what width of distance frames should be provided for maximum capacity?

d. Using a leaf press, how many square feet of filtering area are needed to equal the filtration capacity of 1 sq. ft. of the present press, at the same time giving maximum filtering capacity without washing?

e. The same question, but assume the cake to be washed with an amount of water equal to one-third the filtrate.

Assume that the cost of the two types of press, including installation expense, is $2.50 per sq. ft. of filtering area for the chamber press, and $6.50 for the leaf press. Assume the total charge against investment, including interest, depreciation, maintenance, etc., is 45 per cent per year. The operating costs including overhead are 0.014 cent per hr. per sq. ft. of filtering area while filtering and washing and 0.11 cent per hr. per sq. ft. while dumping and reassembling.

f. If the presses are in operation 280 days per year, 10 hr. per day, what thickness of frames is to be specified for the chamber press, and what thickness of cake should be formed on the leaf filter?

g. The same questions, if the presses are operated 24 hr. per day for 360 days in the year?

Solution.—Assuming that the resistance of the filtering medium is small, the relationship between the volume of filtrate discharged, V, in the time θ, through the filtering area of the press, A, working at the pressure P, is expressed by $V^2 = 2kA^2P\theta$. Since in this problem the pressure remains constant, P may be disregarded and the equation simplified to

$$V^2/A^2 = K\theta.$$

Choosing as the basis of calculation the area of the present press, $\theta = 6.5$ hr and $V/A = 4.5$. Solving, K is found to be 3.12.

The calculation is simplified by calling the thickness of the frame one nth of 1 in.; *i.e.*, if the frame is ⅓ in. thick, n equals 3. The capacity measured in filtrate then becomes "$4.5/n$" cu. ft. for each sq. ft. of filter cloth, and the frame must be filled n times to obtain the required 4.5 cu. ft. of filtrate; that is, the press must be operated through n cycles to perform the present duty.

In considering the question of maximum capacity and minimum cost, it is advisable to tabulate the controlling factors as a function of some definite variable. In this case find how the time and cost for this definite amount of filtrate vary with the thickness of filter cake, and in so doing determine the following data:

TABLE III.—TIME SCHEDULE, CHAMBER PRESS
BASIS = 1 SQ. FT.

No. of cycles	Thickness of distance frame, $1/n$ inches	Filtering time per cycle	Washing time per cycle	Dumping time per cycle	Total time for n cycles (no washing)	Total time for n cycles (with washing)
				Time in hours		
1	1	6.5	17.33	0.67	7.17	24
2	½	1.62	4.33	0.67	4.59	13.2
3	⅓	0.72	1.92	0.67	4.17	9.93
4	¼	0.41	1.08	0.67	4.32	8.64
5	⅕	0.26	0.69	0.67	4.65	8.10
6	⅙	0.18	0.48	0.67	5.10	8.0
8	⅛	0.10	0.27	0.67	6.16	8.3

Differentiating the above equation, the rate of filtration at a given time is $dV/d\theta = 3.12A^2/2V$. Inserting the value of V at the *end* of a filtering cycle for any frame thickness $1/n$, one obtains the rate of filtration that existed at this time. Obviously the rate will also be the washing rate for a leaf press with a filter cake of thickness $1/n$; but for a chamber press the washing rate will be but one-fourth of this value, because washing is carried on through a cake twice as thick as that through which filtration has proceeded, and the effective filtering area is but one-half as great.*

The method of calculating the above data may be understood by taking as an example one thickness of frame; for example, n equals 4. Using the equation

$$V^2/A^2 = 3.12\theta,$$

with the ratio $V/A = 4.5/4 = 1.125$ (since the cake thickness is but one-fourth that employed when 4.5 cu. ft. was obtained), the time is 0.41 hr. The

* This neglects any difference in viscosity between solution and wash water.

rate of filtration at the end of the filtering period is obtained from the equation

$$\frac{d(V/A)}{d\theta} = \frac{3.12}{2(V/A)}.$$

as 1.39 cu. ft./(hr.) (sq. ft. of filtering area). The rate of washing in the chamber press is one-fourth this quantity, or 0.347. The volume of the wash water is 1.125/3 or 0.375 cu. ft./sq. ft., and the time of washing is this latter figure divided by the preceding one, or 1.08 hr. The time required per cycle for filtering, washing and dumping is therefore 2.16 hr., and the total time to do the work of a 1-in. frame, *i.e.*, to produce 4.5 cu. ft. of filtrate/sq. ft. of filtering area, is 8.64 hr.

Since cost data are given on a basis of 1 sq. ft. of filtering area, this basis is adhered to in figuring costs. For a chamber press operated 2800 hr. per annum, the investment charges are 250 (0.45)/2800 = 0.0402 cent per hr. per sq. ft. of filtering area and, similarly, for a leaf press 0.1045 cent. Therefore, in a chamber press the total cost per hr./sq. ft. of filtering area for filtering and washing is 0.0402 + 0.014 = 0.0542 cent and for dumping 0.0402 + 0.11 = 0.1502 cent. The corresponding figures for a leaf press are 0.1185 and 0.2145 cent.

Costs are obtained by multiplying the time required for each operation by the cost of that operation, and the following data result:

TABLE IV.—COST SCHEDULE, CHAMBER PRESS (BASIS = 1 SQ. FT.), n CYCLES
(280 Days, 10 Hours per Day)

No. of cycles	Thickness of distance frame, $1/n$ inches	Filtering cost per n cycles, cents	Washing cost per n cycles, cents	Dumping cost per n cycles, cents	Total cost no washing (n cycles), cents	Total cost with washing (n cycles), cents
1	1	0.352	0.94	0.1	0.452	1.392
2	$\frac{1}{2}$	0.176	0.469	0.2	0.376	0.845
3	$\frac{1}{3}$	0.117	0.312	0.3	0.417	0.731
4	$\frac{1}{4}$	0.0882	0.235	0.4	0.488	0.725
5	$\frac{1}{5}$	0.0705	0.187	0.5	0.571	0.759
6	$\frac{1}{6}$	0.0587	0.156	0.6	0.659	0.815
8	$\frac{1}{8}$	0.0433	0.117	0.8	0.843	0.960

It will be noted that, whereas, without washing, *maximum capacity* was obtained with a ⅓-in. frame, *minimum cost* is obtained with a ½-in. frame; with washing, maximum capacity is secured with a ⅙-in. frame, and minimum cost with a ¼-in. frame.

The methods of calculation for a leaf filter are entirely similar. The filtering time for such a filter will be the same for a ½-in. thickness of cake as for a 1-in. distance frame in a chamber filter, since with 1-in. frames the final filtrate flows through a thickness of ½ in. The results are given in the following tables, together with the costs for both chamber and leaf presses when operated 24 hr. per day, 360 days per year.

TABLE V.—TIME SCHEDULE, LEAF PRESS (BASIS = 1 SQ. FT.)

No. of cycles	Thickness of cake, inches	Filtering time per cycle	Washing time per cycle	Dumping time per cycle	Change time per cycle	Total time for n cycle (no washing)	Total time for n cycle (with washing)
				Time in hours			
1	½	6.5	4.33	0.33	0.25	6.86	11.44
2	¼	1.62	1.08	0.33	0.25	3.90	6.56
3	⅙	0.72	0.48	0.33	0.25	3.17	5.36
4	⅛	0.41	0.27	0.33	0.25	2.96	5.04
5	$\frac{1}{10}$	0.26	0.17	0.33	0.25	2.95	5.05
6	$\frac{1}{12}$	0.18	0.12	0.33	0.25	3.06	5.28
8	$\frac{1}{16}$	0.10	0.066	0.33	0.25	3.44	5.96

TABLE VI.—COST SCHEDULE, LEAF PRESS (BASIS = 1 SQ. FT.)
(280 Days, 10 Hours per Day)

No. of cycles	Thickness of cake, inches	Filtering cost per n cycle, cents	Washing cost per n cycle, cents	Dumping cost per n cycle, cents	Change cost per n cycle, cents	Total cost, no washing (n cycle), cents	Total cost, with washing (n cycle), cents
1	½	0.770	0.513	0.071	0.054	0.841	1.408
2	¼	0.385	0.257	0.143	0.107	0.528	0.892
3	⅙	0.257	0.171	0.215	0.161	0.472	0.804
4	⅛	0.193	0.128	0.286	0.215	0.479	0.822
5	$\frac{1}{10}$	0.154	0.103	0.357	0.268	0.511	0.882
6	$\frac{1}{12}$	0.128	0.085	0.427	0.322	0.555	0.962
8	$\frac{1}{16}$	0.095	0.063	0.569	0.429	0.664	1.156

It will be noted that *maximum capacity* is secured in this leaf filter without washing with a $\frac{1}{10}$-in. thickness of cake corresponding to a ⅕-in. distance frame in the chamber press. With washing the maximum comes at substantially the same point. Both with and without washing the *minimum cost* for 10 hr. per day comes at ⅙-in. thickness of cake corresponding to a ⅓-in. distance frame. The fact that in both presses it pays to build up a thicker cake than corresponds to maximum capacity is due to the saving in labor charges secured at the expense of lowered press capacity.

TABLE VII.—COSTS OF CHAMBER PRESS (BASIS = 1 SQ. FT.)
(360 Days, 24 Hours per Day)

No. of cycles	Thickness of distance frame, $1/n$, inches	Filtering cost per n cycles, cents	Washing cost per n cycles, cents	Dumping cost per n cycles, cents	Total cost, no washing (n cycles), cents	Total cost, with washing (n cycles), cents
1	1	0.176	0.468	0.082	0.258	0.726
2	½	0.0875	0.234	0.164	0.252	0.486
3	⅓	0.0583	0.156	0.246	0.304	0.460
4	¼	0.0443	0.117	0.328	0.372	0.489
5	⅕	0.0351	0.093	0.41	0.445	0.538
6	⅙	0.0292	0.078	0.492	0.521	0.599
8	⅛	0.0216	0.058	0.656	0.688	0.746

TABLE VIII.—COSTS OF LEAF PRESS (BASIS = 1 SQ. FT.)
(360 Days, 24 Hours per Day)

No. of cycles	Thickness of cake, inches	Filtering cost per n cycles, cents	Washing cost per n cycles, cents	Dumping cost per n cycles, cents	Change cost per n cycles, cents	Total cost, no washing (n cycles), cents	Total cost, with washing (n cycles), cents
1	½	0.311	0.207	0.048	0.036	0.359	0.602
2	¼	0.155	0.104	0.096	0.072	0.251	0.427
3	⅙	0.104	0.069	0.144	0.108	0.248	0.425
4	⅛	0.078	0.052	0.192	0.144	0.270	0.460
5	$\frac{1}{10}$	0.062	0.042	0.239	0.180	0.301	0.523
6	$\frac{1}{12}$	0.052	0.034	0.288	0.216	0.340	0.590
8	$\frac{1}{16}$	0.038	0.025	0.384	0.288	0.422	0.735

Notwithstanding the fact of nearly threefold apparatus cost on the leaf filter, the actual filtering cost is only slightly higher than that of the frame press on a 10-hr. basis, and lower on a 24-hr. basis.

The method of charging up such items as depreciation, maintenance, rental of floor space, etc., as a flat percentage against investment cost is open to criticism. The same statement applies to expressing the dumping cost of a leaf press as proportional to its size. The fact is that the character of each one of these items will vary from plant to plant and their distribution in calculating costs must be modified accordingly. No method could be given here which will cover the majority of cases but this particular method satisfactorily illustrates the principle.

The answers to the questions as stated are therefore as follows:

a. Since the total time for the present press without washing is 7.17 hr. and, with washing, 24 hr., the capacity per hr./sq. ft. will be reduced from 4.5/7.17 = 0.628 cu. ft./hr. to 4.5/24 = 0.1875 cu. ft./hr., a reduction of 70 per cent.

b. From Table III it will be noted that the total time without washing is a minimum for ⅓-in. distance frames.

c. The time with washing is seen from Table III to be a minimum when using ⅙-in. distance frames.

d. With a leaf filter the filtering time without washing is a minimum with ¹⁄₁₀-in. thickness of cake, filtration being completed in 2.95 hr. Since the present press requires 7.17 hr., it has only 41.1 per cent of the capacity of the new press. Hence the new press will require only 0.411 sq. ft. filtering area for each square foot of the present press.

e. Since the present press requires 24 hr. for washing, while a leaf press will do the work in 5.04 hr., the present press has only 21 per cent capacity of the leaf press, so that the size of leaf press required will be only 0.21 sq. ft. of filtering area/sq. ft. of area in the present press.

f. Inspection of Table IV shows that the minimum cost of filtration in a chamber press without washing is obtained with ½-in. frames and, with washing, by the use of ¼-in. frames.

The minimum cost with a leaf press *without washing* is found in ⅙-in. thickness of cake. This gives a total filtration time of 3.17 hr. as compared with 7.17 hr. in the present press, *i.e.*, the present press has 44.3 per cent the capacity of the proposed leaf filter. This means that the new filter must have 0.443 sq. ft. of filtering area for each square foot in the present press. *With washing*, the capacity of this new press is therefore such that 0.223 sq. ft. of filtering area will suffice in place of 1 sq. ft. in the present press.

The preceding paragraph must not be interpreted to mean that the capacity of a leaf filter so greatly exceeds that of a frame press. The comparison should be made, not with the present press, the frames of which are too thick, but with the chamber press at its best, *i.e.*, when using ½-in. frames without washing and ¼-in. frames with washing, requiring 4.59 hr. and 8.64 hr., respectively, as compared with the 3.17 hr. and 5.36 hr. required for the leaf press. In other words, the capacity of the chamber press is 69.1 per cent of that of the leaf press without washing and 62 per cent with washing. This means that the investment cost of a leaf press is correspondingly reduced.

g. Inspection of the tabulated costs for full-time work shows the thicknesses should remain unchanged except for washing in the chamber press, which should now be done with ⅛-in. frames. While all costs are lowered, the leaf press now has the advantage over the chamber press. It may be stated, in general, that large scale and continuity of operation tend to give the advantage to the leaf type of press.

It must not be forgotten that the numerical comparisons of the preceding paragraphs are dependent on the operating conditions and costs assumed and any variation in these will influence the results. However, the character and direction of the influence of these factors on the relative advantages of the two types will remain in all cases the same.

Nomenclature

A = total area of filtering surface, sq. in.

V = total weight of filtrate, pounds up to the variable time θ.

v = volume of cake, as it collects on the filter, cu. in./pound of filtrate.

P = total filtering pressure on cake.*

P_1 = pressure at interface between filtering medium and cake.*
       channels.

θ = total time of operation = minutes.

R = total resistance of cake divided by the viscosity.

r = specific resistance of cake, *i.e.*, the resistance of a unit cube.

r' = coefficient in the equation: $r = r'P^s$.

$r'' = r'(1-s)$.

L = thickness of cake at variable time θ = inches.

ρ/A = resistance of press channels and "plugged" filtering medium divided by the viscosity.

m = coefficient of "plugging."

s = coefficient of compressibility.

t = coefficient of velocity effect.

μ = viscosity, relative to water.

ρ' = coefficient of the equation: $\rho = \rho'(P - P_1)^m$.

References

1. ABRAMS, FARROW, HARTSOOK, S. M. Thesis, Massachusetts Institute of Technology, 1921.

2. ALMY and LEWIS, *Ind. Eng. Chem.*, **4**, 528 (1912).

3. CARMAN, *J. Soc. Chem. Ind.*, **52**, 280T, (1933); **53**, 139T (1934).

4. COMSTOCK, S.B. Thesis, Massachusetts Institute of Technology, 1913.

5. EVANS, S.B. Thesis, Massachusetts Institute of Technology, 1921.

6. MUNNING, S.B. Thesis, Massachusetts Institute of Technology, 1921.

7. RUTH, MONTILLON, MONTANA, *Ind. Eng. Chem.*, **25**, 153 (1933).

8. SPERRY, *Met. Chem. Eng.*, **17**, 166 (1917).

9. TATTERSFIELD, S.M. Thesis, Massachusetts Institute of Technology, 1922.

10. UNDERWOOD, *Trans. Inst. Chem. Eng.*, **4**, 19 (1926); *J. Soc. Chem. Ind.*, **47**, 325T (1928).

11. LEWIS, W. K., JR., Personal Communication, 1935.

* In the plots, pressures are expressed in pounds per square inch.

CHAPTER XII

BASIC PRINCIPLES OF VAPORIZATION PROCESSES

INTRODUCTION TO EVAPORATION, DISTILLATION, AND DRYING

That property of liquids by virtue of which they pass from the liquid to the vapor state, or the reverse, according to the temperature and pressure to which they are subjected, is the basis of very important industrial processes for separating one liquid from other liquids, or liquids from solids.

Industrial terminology distinguishes three cases in which separation is accomplished by utilizing differences in the volatility of substances, and, while the classification is not a rigorous one and is sometimes illogical, it will be adopted for the purpose of a general subdivision of this field into three chapters.

Evaporation is the removal by vaporization of a portion of the solvent from a solution of a solid or a practically nonvolatile liquid, when the vapor formed is valueless in comparison to the residue (except perhaps for its heat content). Since water is the only liquid that can be obtained in unlimited quantity, and hence can be economically discarded, evaporation processes are limited in practice to water solutions, for example, the concentration of aqueous solutions of inorganic compounds, glue, tannin, sugar, sulfuric acid, etc.

Distillation* is the removal by vaporization of one liquid from another when the vapor is of sufficient value to warrant recovery by recondensation. For example, the removal by vaporization of water from its impurities, of stearic acid from unsaponifiable matter, of alcohol from water, of gasoline from kerosene, of benzene from toluene, of benzene from mineral oil, of gasoline from extracted wool grease, etc., are distillation processes.

* Under the term *destructive distillation* are described those processes in which the material acted upon, such as wood, coal or bones, is first decomposed by heat and the volatile products of the reaction are then drawn off and recovered.

When one solid is separated from other solids by vaporization and subsequent condensation, the process is spoken of as **sublimation.** Phthalic acid, for example, is purified by sublimation

Drying is the removal, generally by vaporization, of a liquid from a solid. The term is also used to describe the removal of small amounts of water from liquid mixtures. For example, drying is represented by the vaporization of water from sand, ores, coal, leather, paper, fiber board, textiles, twine, starch, sugar, and wet crystals; again by the vaporization of carbon bisulfide from thio-carbanalide crystals, benzene from dipped rubber goods, organic solvents from impregnated and lacquered substances, emulsified water from oil, and the like. In the chapter on Drying, certain cases have been included where the separation is accomplished without resorting to the process of vaporization. While such cases should logically be classified under Mechanical Separation, the name Drying has been so firmly associated with these operations that they are taken up under this heading.

Certain inconsistencies exist in practical terminology which the reader must not take too seriously. For example, when water is separated from sea water in order to obtain the dissolved salt, the process is called evaporation; when it is the recondensed vapor that is wanted, *i.e.*, pure water, the process is called distillation. The apparatus employed in the two cases may, however, be practically identical. When the amount of water associated with alcohol is large, it is separated by distillation; when small, it is separated by drying with anhydrous copper sulfate. The vaporization of water from a glycerin solution is called evaporation although the apparatus used where glycerin loss must be avoided is identical with that employed for distillation.

These three processes have certain elementary principles in common. In order to lay a foundation for the development of the engineering problems involved in their consideration, these principles will be considered somewhat in detail.

MECHANISM OF VAPORIZATION

Vapor Pressure.—The molecules of a liquid are considered to be in a state of constant unordered motion, some moving with great velocity, while others move less rapidly. For any temperature, however, there is a certain mean velocity of the molecules, which for temperatures below the boiling point of the liquid is not sufficient to project them beyond the free surface of the liquid. But there are always some molecules that possess a velocity sufficiently greater than this mean so that, when they approach the free surface of the liquid, they overcome the mutual attraction exerted between them and other molecules in the liquid, and, continuing their motion, pass out into the surrounding space and exert a pressure upon the walls of the container as the resultant of the bombardment that their motion produces. Since they move in all directions, a certain number will strike the liquid surface from which they emanated, and again become a part of it. When the number of molecules reentering the surface is just equal to that leaving it, a condition of dynamic equilibrium exists, and the pressure exerted upon the walls of the container by these molecules is called the **vapor pressure*** of the substance at the existing temperature.

If the space surrounding the liquid is filled with molecules of some other substances, *e.g.*, air, at a pressure not materially exceeding 1 atmosphere, the voids between particles are sufficiently large and numerous to enable the above-described phenomenon to take place undisturbed. Since the pressure on the container is due to the sum of the molecular impacts, there will be present a final pressure made up of the pressure of the gas originally present plus the vapor pressure of the liquid. Should the liquid possess that attraction for the molecules of the original gas which results in solution, this relationship no longer holds; nor is it valid if the original gas is under a high pressure.†

If a liquid is made up of two kinds of substances *mechanically mixed* but of low mutual solubility, for example, benzene and water, each will give off its individual molecules, and each will establish an equilibrium between the escaping and returning molecules of its own kind, and hence a vapor pressure of its own irrespective of the presence of the other molecules. These pressures are additive and the sum of these partial pressures plus that of any gas originally present makes up the total pres-

---

* This is also called the *pressure of the saturated vapor* or *saturation pressure*.

† Deviations from the gas laws usually become large when the pressure is a considerable fraction of the saturation pressure of the liquefied gas (see p. 7).

sure within the container.*   In other words, the mixture behaves as though the surface were alternately entirely one liquid and then the other.

Vapor-pressure Lowering.—When the substances or components making up a liquid are mutually soluble, as, for example, alcohol and water, the escaping tendency of each substance is reduced owing to the presence of the other.   The partial pressure of each and, since they are additive, the total vapor pressure of the liquid are thereby reduced.   Even when one of the substances, for example, salt, has itself a negligible vapor pressure, nevertheless, when dissolved in water, it reduces the vapor pressure of the latter.   On the other hand, if the molecules of the dissolved substance are very large, the reduction in vapor pressure of the solvent is negligible.

It is important to visualize the reason for these facts.   Assume an equimolal solution of naphthalene dissolved in benzene.   At ordinary temperature the volatility of the naphthalene relative to that of benzene may be neglected.   Furthermore, there is good reason to believe that the size of the naphthalene molecule is not far from that of the benzene molecule.   In the surface of such a solution approximately one-half of the area is therefore occupied by benzene and one-half by naphthalene molecules.   The chance for benzene molecules to escape from the solution into the vapor space is therefore only half what it is in pure liquid benzene.   In order to have equilibrium with benzene vapor, it is therefore necessary for the vapor pressure above this solution to be only half that of pure benzene.   The reason for this is that any benzene molecule coming from the vapor toward the surface of the liquid at high velocity will force its way into the liquid whether it hits a benzene molecule or a naphthalene molecule in the surface of the liquid, because the difficulty of forcing either of these two out of the way is approximately equal.

On the other hand, assume a solution of glue and water of such concentration that one-half the surface of the liquid is occupied by glue molecules. When a water molecule from the vapor space impinges upon the surface of the liquid, it will force its way into the liquid if it happens to hit a water molecule in the liquid surface.   When it hits a glue molecule it is reflected back into the vapor since it cannot displace the large glue molecule.   The situation is much the same as though one-half the surface of the liquid were covered with a sheet of glass.   The result is that only half the liquid surface is available for entrance of water molecules from the vapor space.   Conse-

* If the mixture is not agitated, two layers will form and the lower liquid will vaporize through the upper much more slowly than if freely exposed. On the other hand, the evaporation is more rapid than might at first appear because the lower liquid dissolves to a finite extent in the upper and is carried by convection currents to the exposed surface, where it evaporates.

quently substantially the full vapor pressure of water is necessary in the vapor space in order to maintain equilibrium.

It will be noted that the molecular weight of the glue is so high that the mol fraction of glue is negligible. One can generalize the preceding facts by saying that the equilibrium partial pressure of a volatile material in the vapor is proportional to its mol fraction in the solution.

Heat of Vaporization.—If the molecules escaping from the surface of a body pass into air or other inert gas within a container, there is first formed this condition of equilibrium upon the inner surface of the relatively stationary gas film with which every surface is surrounded (see Chap. II, Fluid Films). From the outer surface of this film the molecules pass into and throughout the remaining space both by their own motion (diffusion) and by convection, until equilibrium is established in the entire container. Through the film itself they pass by diffusion. When the container is not closed, both diffusion and convection processes carry the vapor from the surface of the stationary film into the outside air, which is to a corresponding extent pushed back into space, and the normal atmospheric pressure is maintained. This total atmospheric pressure is now made up of the vapor pressure of the substance (which when equilibrium is reached is the same as though no air were present) and that amount of air which has not been driven back.

Therefore, in order for vaporization to continue at a constant temperature, the dynamic equilibrium which tends to establish itself must be destroyed. If the surface of the substance is exposed to the atmosphere, the molecules arising from it may be swept away by a current of air; this takes place in air drying and during evaporation of liquids into air. If the containing vessel is closed, these molecules will pass to a region of lower pressure, *i.e.*, where there are fewer of them. Such a region may be maintained by constantly removing the vapor molecules by dropping the temperature, thus decreasing the number and also the velocity of the molecules, and hence the resultant pressure, as in a condenser; or by pumping out mechanically as in the "vapor-compression" system of evaporation (page 392); or by absorbing the molecules in a medium that has for them a great attraction, *i.e.*, a medium which they will enter by impact, but from which they cannot return, such as drying over sulfuric acid and the like.

A constant temperature is not maintained of itself within a volatilizing liquid. Those molecules having the greater velocity possess also the greater amount of kinetic energy. Hence, as these leave the liquid, its mean kinetic energy decreases and the temperature falls. In order to maintain a definite temperature, therefore, heat must be added from an external source. This heat of vaporization varies with the substance, also somewhat with the ratio of pressure to temperature. The molal heat of vaporization (the heat of vaporization per unit mass multiplied by the molecular weight) for all liquids at their boiling point is of the same order of magnitude. The relation between heat of vaporization, molecular weight, temperature and pressure is given by the Hildebrand function (see Fig. 4, page 13).

Boiling Point.—Since molecular motion is a function of temperature,* the hotter a liquid, the higher will be the percentage of its molecules having sufficient velocity to escape from the surface, and hence the greater will be its vapor pressure. There must then be a temperature where the escaping molecules of a substance will maintain a pressure of their own equal to the atmospheric pressure. The air can then be forced back indefinitely and the substance will vaporize indefinitely so far as pressure is concerned. This temperature is called the **boiling point** of the substance.

FACTORS CONTROLLING VAPORIZATION

If the liquid is in a space in which the partial pressure of its vapor is less than the vapor pressure it possesses at this temperature, it will proceed to vaporize and its vapor will pass into space. But this change of state is accompanied by the large absorption of heat already noted. If this heat is not supplied from some external source, vaporization will nevertheless continue, and the necessary heat will be taken from the sensible heat of the liquid, with a consequent reduction of temperature. This fall in tem-

---

* According to Smithsonian Tables (p. 399, 1920 ed.), the mean velocity of gas molecules in feet per second equals $386\sqrt{T/M}$, where T is the degrees Fahrenheit absolute temperature and M is the molecular weight. Thus the mean diffusional velocity of air at 70°F. and normal barometer would be 1650 ft. per sec., or 1130 mi. per hr. However, owing to frequent collisions with other molecules, the average distance traveled between collisions is extremely small, with the net result that mass transfer by molecular diffusion is a slow process.

perature of the liquid is accompanied by a corresponding decrease in vapor pressure. Finally a temperature is reached where the vapor pressure of the liquid is equal to its partial pressure existing in the space and vaporization will cease.

Therefore, in order that vaporization may continue, two conditions must be met:

First, the heat necessary for vaporization must be continuously supplied.

Second, the equilibrium that forms between the vapor pressure of the liquid and its partial pressure in the surrounding space must be continuously destroyed.

If either one of these two conditions is neglected, vaporization will be retarded or even stopped.

CAPACITY

In all three processes (evaporation, distillation and drying) the rate of vaporization, and hence the capacity, are determined by the rate of heat supply. Where the heat is transferred by conduction and convection, as is often the case, the capacity is determined by the following integrated form of Newton's law:

$$Q/\theta = (U) \ (A)_{av.}(\Delta)_{av.}$$

where Q/θ is B.t.u. transferred per hour.

An inspection of this equation shows that the capacity (Q/θ) is determined by the product of three factors:

$A_{av.} =$ a proper average area of heating surface, sq. ft.

$(\Delta)_{av.} =$ a proper average overall temperature difference in deg. F. between the points from and to which heat is flowing.

$U =$ Overall coefficient of heat transfer, which may be experimentally determined, or estimated from a knowledge of each of the resistances to be encountered (see pages 106 to 142).

Where heat is transferred by radiation, the rate of heat supply is determined by

1. The areas of the surfaces, and their arrangement.

2. The difference of the fourth powers of the absolute temperatures.

3. The emissivities of the surfaces.

When heat is being supplied by both mechanisms, the rate of flow of heat is calculated by adding the rates calculated by the appropriate equation for each process.

For general discussion of the equations, data and illustrative examples for these mechanisms, the reader is referred to the chapter on Flow of Heat. However, the mechanism by which heat is carried into a vaporizing liquid, and by which the vapor forming on the surface of the liquid is removed, is so controlling in all these processes that it will be considered in detail in subsequent chapters.

CHAPTER XIII

EVAPORATION

BASIC FACTORS

To secure the evaporation of a volatile liquid, there are two and only two essentials that must be provided:

First, the necessary heat must be supplied to the liquid.

Second, the vapor evolved must be removed from above the surface of the liquid and not allowed to accumulate.

1. Heat Supply.—It is necessary to supply the heat to the liquid itself, because the vapor bubbles are developed there, and at the instant of their formation to absorb the heat incident to their evolution. The heat may be supplied in two ways:

1. By direct exposure of the liquid to the source of the heat.

2. Indirectly by transmission through a suitable solid retaining wall.

2. Vapor Removal.—The vapor evolved may be carried away in two conditions:

1. Mixed with an inert gas (*e.g.,* air, flue gas, etc.).

2. As undiluted vapor.

CLASSIFICATION OF EVAPORATION PROCESSES

Since there are two ways of supplying the heat and two conditions in which vapor may be removed, there are four combinations possible:

Case 1.—The heat is supplied through the free surface of the liquid, and the vapor is carried away by an inert gas.

Case 2.—The heat is supplied through the free surface of the liquid, and the vapor is evolved in undiluted form.

Case 3.—The heat is transferred through solid retaining walls to the liquid, and the vapor is swept away by an inert gas.

Case 4.—The heat is transferred through solid retaining walls to the liquid, and the vapor is evolved in undiluted form.

The various evaporation processes will be classified under these four subdivisions.

CASE I

The heat is supplied directly through the free surface of the liquid, and the vapor is swept away by an inert gas.

Evaporators in which the heat is supplied through the disengaging surface of the evaporating liquid possess the advantages that the apparatus may be built of material chosen with special regard to its resistance to corrosion irrespective of its heat conductivity, that the evaporator is practically unaffected by incrustation of solids depositing from the liquid, and that, when the initial source of heat is a hot inert gas, the heat transfer may be direct from the source to the liquid. The main limitation of this type is that hitherto no one has succeeded in adapting it to utilize the multiple-effect principle.

1. Solar Evaporation.—The cheapest, although in most localities least reliable, source of heat is the sun. Here the heat is transferred directly into the liquid by *radiation* from the sun, and also to the liquid surface from the air by convection. Salt solutions are sometimes concentrated in shallow rectangular pans by this method.

2. Ricks.—A simple evaporator of this type consists of piles or "ricks" of brushwood over which salt solution trickles from distributing troughs above, and the concentrated brine is collected in drains below, the evaporation being accomplished largely by the wind. Covers are unnecessary in this case, as during rain the flow of brine is discontinued. The gypsum in the brine soon covers the twigs with thick incrustations, and the ricks eliminate a large amount of this troublesome material.

3. Porion Evaporator.—A continuous apparatus using an artificial heat supply is the Porion evaporator. This consists of a horizontal chamber on the bottom of which flows the liquid to be evaporated, while above it the flue gases from the furnace underneath pass in an opposite direction. The liquid is given a large surface and intimate contact with the hot gases, being thrown by centrifugal force in the form of drops into the gaseous space by a series of disks on a rapidly rotating shaft placed crosswise in the evaporating chamber, the disks dipping partly into the liquid below. Because of the high temperature difference realized and the large surface exposed, the evaporative capacity is substantial; the disadvantage is contamination of the liquor with soot and dust from the flue gases.

4. Spray Evaporators.—Evaporation of a solution may be carried to completion and a dry dust obtained by spraying the solution into a chamber against hot gases (page 634). If, during their fall, the droplets can be exposed to direct radiation from the fuel bed, evaporation is accelerated and a large capacity realized. Thus, common salt may be so recovered, and the concentrated* waste liquor from pulp mills, operating the soda or the sulfate process, may be in this way, not only evaporated, but dried and incinerated. If the spray produces relatively small droplets, the resultant dust may be so fine as to present difficulty in its settling, thus causing loss of material up the stack. However, devices are available for recovering such dust (see pages 313 to 315).

5. Tower Evaporation.—Instead of subdividing the liquid into small drops, a large surface may be obtained by passing the liquid in a thin film over bricks or other filling in a tower up which hot flue gas is passing. When oil or dust-free producer gas is used as a fuel, no dust is introduced and rapid evaporation is effected.

The Glover tower of a sulfuric acid chamber plant, while fulfilling a number of functions, is an evaporator of this type. Dilute acid is fed to the top and is concentrated as it falls, the evaporation being at the expense of the sensible heat of the hot gases entering the bottom. In recent years installations of this type have been developed for the concentration of dilute sulfuric acid, the acid flowing down over the filling material of a tower, countercurrent to hot furnace gases from an oil burner located beside the bottom of the tower which serves as its flue (Gilchrist concentration system). Such an installation is peculiarly suited for this particular operation, because at the high temperature and acid concentration prevailing at the bottom of the tower relatively large quantities of sulfur trioxide are volatilized. The top of the large tower serves as a combination of rectifying column, partial condenser and final condenser, wherein this volatilized SO_3 is condensed and reabsorbed, thus avoiding its loss and the serious

* The dilute waste liquor is concentrated in a multiple-effect system of evaporators to a point such that, when fed into a rotary furnace, the heat evolved in combustion of the organic material is sufficient to evaporate the residual moisture.

nuisance created by its escape.   In view of the simplicity of the apparatus and the ease of operation, it is surprising that towers of this sort, fired directly with the flue gases from a furnace, are not more widely used.

6. Evaporation by Bubbling Gas through the Liquid.—Notwithstanding the low partial pressure of most liquids at moderate temperature, substantial evaporation can be effected by passing air or other gases through the solution at as high a temperature as the liquid will tolerate without serious decomposition.   The air should be injected in very fine bubbles and in large volume.   For example, a solution of lactic acid may be thus concentrated without deterioration, as a result of even, moderate heating.   The air is effective, not only for carrying away the vapor which springs into the small bubbles as they pass through the liquid, but also for agitation which maintains the liquid at a uniform (maximum) temperature.

CASE II

The heat is supplied through the free surface of the liquid, and the vapor is evolved in undiluted form.

There are no examples of this case in practice.   Conceivably, it could be realized by generating radiant heat electrically within a closed still, but such a system has no apparent advantages, while it has obvious disadvantages.   The case of evaporating water from a solution or suspension sprayed into a chamber containing superheated steam will be treated under Drying.

CASE III

The heat is transferred through solid retaining walls to the liquid, and the vapor is swept away by inert gas.

This combination is seldom found, except where the evaporator is direct-fired and the flue gases are allowed to flow over the free surface of the liquid.   In this case, heat may be transferred in two ways: conduction through the walls of the evaporator body and convection from the flue gases to the surface of the liquid in the evaporator.   The passage of the flue gas over the surface of the liquid will have no effect in increasing the capacity unless the rate of evaporation is so slow that the vapor is evolved at a pressure below atmospheric, as in the concentration of sulfuric acid in open pans or dishes.   In this case, the vapor pressure of the water is much less than 1 atmosphere because of the vapor-pressure lowering caused by the acid. A modification of this case is found in the salt industry in the form of apparatus known as "salt grainers." These grainers comprise large shallow rectangular chambers, built of wood, concrete or steel, fitted with large-diameter tubes with steam on the inside. Steam is admitted at such a rate that no ebullition takes place, the evaporation going on quietly with no disturbance of the liquor surface. Meanwhile salt crystals form on the surface and gradually sink to the bottom of the grainer.

For the evaporation of very corrosive liquids, pans may be constructed of special materials. Thus, for the concentration of sulfuric acid above 60°Bé., pans of platinum and gold were formerly widely used, direct-fired, and provided with draft hoods for removal of the fumes. At one time even glass, in the form of large evaporating dishes, was used for this purpose, but the breakage, due both to shock and to unequal heatings, was excessive. Later, dishes of fused silica of various shapes, arranged in cascade, so the acid under concentration flowed continuously through the apparatus, were introduced. To avoid breakage due to unequal expansion of setting and dish, these were placed on rings of asbestos packing in the top of the flue from a suitable furnace, and were thus directly heated by the flue gases. The flow of acid was countercurrent to that of the gases, to provide for the rising boiling point of the acid during evaporation. As before, draft must be provided for removal of fumes. These dishes are fragile and breakage is severe, especially in the expensive larger sizes. It has been attempted to replace them by dishes cast of high-silica iron but practice in this field is not yet standardized.

In the production of c.p. chemicals and other more expensive products, porcelain evaporating dishes up to 18 in. in diameter and 6 in. deep are used; they are resistant, but of poor conductivity, fragile and expensive.

CASE IV

The heat is transferred through retaining walls to the liquid, and the vapor is evolved in undiluted form.

By far the greater part of evaporative equipment falls in this class. The source of heat may be (1) fire or hot gases, (2) hot oil or other liquid, or (3) vapor usually steam. The most important of these is steam, and the rest of this chapter will be largely devoted to this case.

1. Direct-fired Evaporators.—These consist usually of a cast-iron pot or steel pan set over a fire. It is well to have combustion nearly complete before the flue gases strike the metal parts of the evaporator body, as the rate of combustion of the unburned gases is greatly decreased when the temperature of the gases is lowered. The main resistance to the flow of heat in direct-fired evaporators (or stills) is on the combustion side of the evaporator body, and hence stirring of the contents of the evaporator will not greatly increase the capacity. However, positive circulation in the evaporator may be necessary to overcome the tendency of certain parts to become overheated, for example, when a very viscous material is being heated. The capacity depends mainly, then, upon the area of "still" bottom exposed to heat and the difference in temperature between this and the source of heat.

A modern type of vapor generator, often called a "pipe still," consists of a number of horizontal tubes, joined by return-bend fittings, to form a long continuous passage. The fluid to be heated is pumped in at the bottom of an "economizer" section heated by the combustion gases flowing to the stack, and flows upward through this so-called convection section, and thence to tubes located in the combustion chamber of the furnace, where the outer surface is heated by both radiation and convection. The heated material then discharges into a vapor-liquid separator. Where desirable to reduce vapor generation in the tubes the pressure therein is controlled by a throttle valve just prior to the separator.

2. Oil-heated Evaporators.—Where a sufficiently high temperature cannot be obtained by using steam at commercial pressures, and where direct firing is undesirable, the heating may be accomplished by the use of hot oil. This method of heating may be applied to practically any form of apparatus designed for heating by means of steam, but usually it is applied to jacketed kettles.

The oil-heating system consists in a direct-fired "absorber," which is often similar to a water-tube boiler, together with a number of automatic safety devices designed to prevent overheating of the oil or "burning out" of tubes in the absorber.

3. Vapor-heated Evaporators.—It very frequently happens that steam can be used as a source of heat more conveniently than the direct combustion of fuel. The devices thus utilizing steam are many, but certain basic conditions must be met for the most economical practice. As previously indicated (page 371), capacity is directly proportional to the product of the following three factors: area of heating surface, overall difference in temperature between steam and boiling liquid, and overall coefficient of heat transfer from steam to boiling liquid.

In order that the heating surface may be as effective as possible, one must have provision for conducting the condensed steam (water) promptly out of the heating system and provision for preventing the accumulation therein of the fixed gases carried by the steam.

The value of the overall coefficient of heat transfer, as shown in the chapter on Flow of Heat, depends on a number of variables:

1. *The Coefficient of Heat Transfer on the Vapor Side.*— Primarily because of the higher thermal conductivity of the condensate, higher heat-transfer coefficients are obtained when condensing steam than when condensing organic vapors (page 135). With dropwise condensation of steam (page 138) much larger coefficients of heat transfer are obtained than with film-type condensation.

2. *The Thermal Conductivity and Thickness of the Walls of the Heat-transfer Surfaces.*—The thermal conductivity of copper is approximately nine times that of steel, and the thickness of copper tubes is usually about the same as that of seamless steel tubes; thus, if the thermal resistances of the heating surface were the controlling factor, a ninefold increase in capacity would be expected upon the substitution of copper for steel tubes. However, the thermal resistance of metal tubes in an evaporator is usually small compared to the total resistance, so only a small increase results from such a substitution. Obviously, the less the other resistances in comparison to that of the walls of the heating surface, the greater is the gain, but even under the most favorable conditions, *i.e.*, with practically pure steam condensing on one side and very rapid circulation of boiling liquor on the other, the gain rarely exceeds 30 per cent and is usually much less. However, where the walls of the heating surface are relatively thick and made of a material of low thermal conductivity, such as enameled iron, the overall coefficient from condensing steam to

boiling liquid may be considerably less than the value obtained with a thin all-metal wall.

3. *The Coefficient of Heat Transfer from the Heat-transfer Surface to the Solution.*—This depends on the effectiveness of the convection currents and the physical properties of the solution.

In *natural*-circulation evaporators the rate of flow of liquid past the heat-transfer surface is caused by differences in head due to differences in density brought about by the difference in temperature between the heating surface and the fluid, and is affected both by the resistance to fluid flow due to the dimensions and arrangement of the heating surface and by the physical properties of the solution and the vapor bubbles. Apparently part of the vapor is generated on the heat-transfer surface, but as the liquid, superheated by contact with the heating surface, circulates into the main body of the solution, additional vapor is generated.[1] For a given evaporator and solution, the viscosity of the solution and the temperature difference are important variables in determining the magnitude of the coefficient of heat transfer from the heating surface to the boiling solution (page 140). For a given solution in a given type of evaporator, a linear relation may be obtained by plotting on logarithmic paper the product of the overall coefficient of heat transfer and the viscosity of the boiling solution against the overall temperature difference between condensing steam and boiling solution (Fig. 121). However, this relation breaks down at high temperature differences, where U goes through a maximum value, as indicated by Fig. 52, page 141.

In *forced*-circulation evaporators the solution is caused to flow rapidly past the heating surface by means of a pump or stirrer, thus reducing film thickness and increasing the coefficient of heat transfer. With upward flow in vertical tubes, the vapor generation may be unimportant until near the outlet; in such case most of the surface is used in heating liquid and hence the coefficients approach those for *heating* liquids in tubes.[2] With a given solution in a forced-circulation evaporator, the mass velocity of fluid past the surface is the most important variable, but viscosity, thermal conductivity and specific heat are also involved. A rough correlation may be obtained by plotting the overall thermal resistance $1/U$ vs. a term that controls the thermal resistance on the boiling-liquid side, namely, $\mu^{0.4}/G^{0.8}$

where μ is the viscosity of the solution and G is the mass velocity (see page 140).

The thermal conductivities of aqueous solutions do not vary widely with the nature of the solute, and decrease somewhat with increase in the concentration of the solute. The viscosity of aqueous solutions varies with the nature of the solute, usually rises with increase in concentration of solute, particularly at high concentrations, and increases with decrease in tempera-

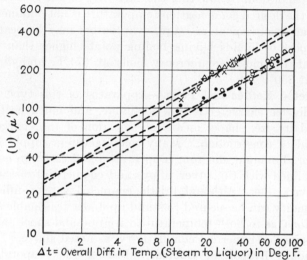

Fig. 121.—U = overall coefficient of heat transfer, as B.t.u./(hr.) (sq. ft.) (deg. F.); μ' = viscosity of boiling liquor in centipoises.

• Evaporation of Water, Badger and Shepard, *Chem. Met. Eng.*, **23**, 282 (1920).
○ Evaporation of Water, Claasen, *Zeit. Ver. Deut. Ing.*, **46**, 418 (1902).
△ Evaporation of Water, Torrey and Pratt, M.I.T. Thesis, 1913.
✕ Concentration of Ten Per Cent Salt Solution, *ibid.*

ture. An increase in viscosity not only increases the thickness of the film insulating the heating surface from the main body of the solution but also decreases the magnitude of convection currents, thus reducing the coefficient of heat transfer. In cases where the solubility of the solute decreases with increase in temperature, *i.e.*, for substances having "inverted solubility curves," such as calcium sulfate, a layer of solid of low thermal conductivity forms on the heat-transfer surface, reducing the overall coefficient of heat transfer. Scale may also be deposited owing to decomposition of the solute, corrosion of the surface and the presence of foreign matter.   In any event, scale deposits seriously reduce the rate of heat transfer (pages 138 and 415).

Uniformity of heating, completeness of control and general simplicity of operation are among the advantages incident to steam as a source of heat.   Obviously, if low-pressure exhaust steam is available, considerable economy is introduced by its use, even when it is necessary to obtain the desired difference in temperature between the steam and the boiling point of the liquid to be evaporated, by lowering this latter by means of a vacuum. Where the desired condensation temperature is not obtained with steam at a convenient pressure, evaporators may be heated by the vapors of liquids having boiling points higher than water. Thus at 1 atmosphere mercury boils at 674°F. and diphenyl oxide at 550°F.

Jacketed Kettles and Pans.—Apparatus of this type of the most diverse character is now available, and much latitude is enjoyed in size, shape, means of agitation of the charge, and material of construction.   Many manufacturers supply kettles made of aluminum, duriron, copper, steel and cast iron and also kettles lined with tin, silver, alloys and enamel to resist specific corrosive action.   Although brittle, enameled ware of sufficiently high quality can be secured to stand up under reasonable service conditions, as to both temperature variation and shock; a drawback is its lower thermal conductivity, as noted above.

Standard Evaporator Bodies.—Most of the evaporators in use are those heated by means of steam.   Various types are available and these will be discussed in detail in connection with multiple-effect evaporation under the heading Typical Evaporator Bodies (see pages 393 to 399).   However, it should be remembered that such types can be and are used for single-effect operation, both for continuous feed and discharge and for operation by the "batch" process.

Evaporation in Vacuum.—There is sometimes an impression that evaporation can be carried on under a vacuum at a less expenditure of energy than at ordinary atmospheric pressure. The actual saving is little or nothing, for, while less heat is required to bring the liquid to the boiling point, the heat of vaporization increases as the temperature falls (see Hildebrand chart, Fig. 4, p. 13), and furthermore a certain amount of energy is required to operate the vacuum pump.

The real advantages incident to the use of vacuum, are: (1) The boiling point of the liquid is reduced, and hence the temperature difference between the boiling point and condensing steam is increased, and evaporation is accelerated.* (2) Cheap low-pressure steam may be used. (3) Many substances, chiefly organic, deteriorate when their solutions are boiled at atmospheric pressure, as, for example, glue and tannin solutions, milk and concentrated solutions of sugar. (4) The size and character of many crystals may also be controlled by the temperature and rate of formation from an evaporating solution (page 400).

Maintenance of Vacuum.—As already indicated, operating an evaporator under vacuum increases its capacity because of the increased temperature difference between the source of heat and the boiling liquid. Since the pressure is below atmospheric, the vapor must be pumped out, though it is important to condense it before removal, thus reducing the work required to a very small value. Assuming free† vapor passages and the absence of noncondensable gases, the total pressure in such a system will be the vapor pressure of the liquid at the lowest temperature to which it is cooled in the condenser, while yet in contact with its vapor. Were the pressure lower, no condensation could take place; were it higher, the temperature of the condensed liquid would instantly rise owing to condensation of more vapor into it. In general, the pressure in such a system will be somewhat greater than the above owing to the presence in the vapor of inert noncondensable gases; if these are large in amount, the pressure will rise greatly. Provision must be made for taking these out of the condenser, either with the condensed liquid or separately. Obviously the heat of condensation evolved in the condenser must be removed; this requires adequate condensing surface and cooling medium.

Condensers.—The condenser may be of two types: (1) the cooling water is kept separate from the condensing vapor (*surface*

---

* However, when boiling liquids of low boiling point, it is easily possible to employ such a high temperature difference that the surface becomes insulated with vapor; in such cases a higher rate of heat transfer is obtained upon reducing the temperature difference (see p. 141).

† To make negligible any drop in pressure from point to point due to friction.

condenser) or (2) it mixes directly with the vapor as a spray or film (*jet condenser*), as in Fig. 122.

In *surface condensers*, to secure a high overall coefficient of heat transfer from condensing vapor to cooling medium, the requirements* are rapid circulation of the cooling medium to reduce the effective thickness of water film through which heat must flow by conduction, immediate removal of the condensed liquid and as nearly complete removal as possible of noncondensable gases to prevent the formation of an insulating film of relatively stationary gas.

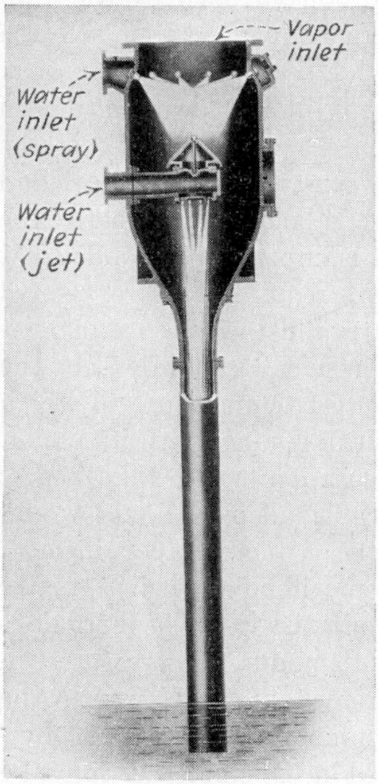

The disadvantages of the *jet condenser* are the necessity of lifting all the cooling water as well as the condensate and fixed gases from the prevailing vacuum to atmospheric pressure and the unavoidable escape of the permanent gases dissolved in the cooling water into the vapor space with corresponding rise in pressure.

The advantages of a *jet condenser* are that very rapid transfer of heat and hence large capacity per unit floor space are obtained because of the direct mixing of vapor and cooling water, that relatively simple construction is secured at a low cost, and the fact that, on account of dilution, corrosive vapors may be condensed without destruction of the containing walls or the use of specially resistant material. Because of their lower cost, jet condensers are ordinarily used, except when making "distilled" water.

Fig. 122.—Jet condenser. (*Courtesy of Schutte and Koerting Co.*)

In both types of condensers the liquid and gases may be removed by a wet-air pump, or separately by dry-air and liquor pumps. When a barometric leg is employed, no pumps are neces-

* See pp. 109 to 143.

sary,* but the vacuum is improved by the use of a dry-air pump connected to the top of the apparatus.

Heating Elements.—The small area of heating surface furnished by a jacket makes such an apparatus undesirable for rapid evaporation of large volumes. Recourse is had, therefore, to heating elements made from pipe, either in the shape of coils, which may be of most complex forms, or straight tubes set in tube sheets at either end.

Frothing and Entrainment.—Since the object of evaporation is the separation of vapor from residue, it is essential to secure such separation before the vapor passes to the condenser.

In rapidly boiling liquids, the escaping vapor has a strong tendency to carry liquid with it, sometimes as bubbles or froth and sometimes as suspended droplets, probably produced by the bursting of bubbles during the escape of the enclosed vapor. The former is called **frothing** and the latter **entrainment.**

Frothing.—With badly frothing liquids, where the bubbles are stable and persistent, it is sometimes difficult to prevent almost the whole body of liquid from lifting over with the vapor. Usually, however, the bubbles can be broken up by passing the froth over an additional heating surface; this causes further evaporation, with resulting distention of the bubbles to the point where they burst. This is readily accomplished where the heating surface is in the form of coils or closely packed tubes, but the heating elements must be well distributed through the path of the frothy vapor, as the conductivity of such a mass is poor. In practice, if the liquid in such an evaporator begins to froth, the liquid level may be lowered until a portion of the heating surface previously submerged is exposed to the vapor, thus lessening the amount of vapor disengaged below the surface of the main liquid mass and allowing the froth produced to play over the heating surface above the liquid, the level being so adjusted that the froth is broken up just at or above the top of the heating surface. Otherwise any heating surface in contact with vapor alone would be

---

* Although in a barometric condenser, *i.e.*, one so placed that the cooling water and condensate flow by gravity through a column of liquid equivalent to the prevailing vacuum, no pump is required, yet this quantity of cooling water must at some time have been pumped to the top of the condenser, with the expenditure of an equivalent amount of energy.

ineffective in evaporation. The proper location of the level between main liquid and froth is determined by experiment. The lowering of liquid level to reduce foaming has the disadvantage of the formation of scale on the heating surface; where this deposited matter does not dissolve readily, the disadvantage is serious. Foaming liquids are usually treated in film-type evaporators (see pages 395 to 403).

Entrainment.—It seems probable that the most important factor in determining entrainment is the "mass velocity" of the vapor rising from the free or disengaging surface of the liquid in the evaporator, *i.e.*, the pounds of vapor escaping through each square foot of disengaging surface per hour. The disengaging velocity allowable must, however, be determined for each specific case, as the viscosity, density and surface tension of the liquid affect the result. Since the first and last of these vary greatly with change in temperature, hence with change in pressure, and also with concentration, it is unsafe to determine the maximum allowable disengaging velocity at other than the actual conditions to be encountered in the evaporator. A determination made experimentally in a small apparatus will, however, enable one to estimate within reasonable limits the conditions that will be encountered in practice.

In evaporators with submerged tubes, to allow such particles to settle back into the evaporator, it is important to provide above the disengaging surface of the evaporator reasonable headroom in which there is no constriction of area of cross section, thus avoiding increase in the velocity of the rising vapor. In industrial apparatus, this headroom is rarely less than 30 in., and should be 6 to 15 ft. The disadvantages of increasing headroom come from the increased size of the apparatus and the greater heat loss to the surroundings. Owing to the small ratio of external surface to volume in large evaporators, it is possible in such to increase the height of the vapor space without increase in percentage heat loss beyond what would be found in a small evaporator.

It is found advisable to remove the droplets that remain in the vapor by utilizing centrifugal force. This is accomplished by passing the vapor through a vessel of greatly restricted section having a circular path, with provision for draining back into the evaporator the particles impinging upon the walls. Where appreciable decrease in pressure of the vapor is allowable, it is possible to produce a high velocity through a long path, against baffle plates, and thus secure very effective removal of drops. The passage of the vapor around and against baffles followed by temporary reduction in velocity is sometimes used to separate discrete particles therefrom, but the major action is the centrifugal effect at the points of change in direction.

Energy Required for Evaporation.—The measure of the theoretical difficulty of carrying out any reaction or separation is the minimum amount of work necessary to effect the change involved, if performed under theoretically perfect and reversible conditions, *i.e.*, the change in free energy. A process should be able to operate with a work consumption not greatly exceeding this value. It should be remembered that this energy must be supplied as work; mere heat is not its equivalent, though for convenience the energy is often expressed in heat units. On pages 422 to 423 equations are given for the minimum amount of work required, and it is shown that this is very small, amounting, in the case of a 10 per cent water solution of glycerin, to but 6.4 B.t.u. per lb. of water evaporated. It is evident that the more concentrated the solution, the greater is the theoretical energy required, but even for concentrated solutions this value remains small. For colloidal solutions, *i.e.*, those of high molecular weight, the reversible work is even less. Theoretically, therefore, the greater part of the heat supplied in evaporation should be recoverable, and such is the case.

It was emphasized that the free energy necessary was a work and not a mere heat requirement, but, since available heat engines actually convert 20 per cent or more of the heat supplied into work, the theoretical *heat* requirement for a 10 per cent glycerin solution is only 32 B.t.u. per lb. of water evaporated. From this point of view, a simple evaporator is a very inefficient mechanism. However, the heat required for evaporation is almost entirely converted into latent heat of vaporization, and is, in this form, carried out of the evaporator by the vapor and can be again utilized by condensing the vapor.

Suppose, for example, that in a given plant a certain amount of water is being evaporated at atmospheric pressure in the process of concentration of an aqueous solution. Most of the heat consumed appears as latent heat in the water vapor. It could not, however, readily and directly be employed to evaporate more water under these conditions, since on condensing it this heat is evolved at the boiling point (100°C.), so that no temperature difference exists to force the heat through the necessary heating surface into the fresh solution to be evaporated.   If, however, the same plant had a corresponding supply of alcohol to be distilled, the water vapor from the above evaporator could readily be used as a heat supply therefor, by condensation in the heating coils of the alcohol still, rather than by using boiler steam for this still.   If, in turn, this same plant had ether to be distilled, the heating coils of the ether still could be used as a condenser for the alcohol vapor, thus avoiding the use of boiler steam in the ether still.   In this way a succession of liquids of progressively lower boiling points can be evaporated with a single supply of heat. In other words, in the process of evaporation, the heat used is merely degraded in temperature and this degradation is slight.

Multiple-effect Principle.—However, the conditions above outlined, which allow a given quantity of heat to be used for evaporation a multiple of times by boiling a series of liquids of successively lower boiling points, do not frequently exist.   But it is true that the boiling point of a water solution depends upon the pressure above it, and by a judicious selection of pressures a solution can be made to boil at the temperatures given for alcohol and ether or any more suitable temperatures, and a similar economy of heat can be effected.   Each evaporator (kettle or pan) is called an **effect** and this process is called **multiple-effect evaporation.**

Suppose, for example, the steam entering the coils of effect *A* in Fig. 123 is saturated exhaust steam at 2.5 lb. gauge (17.2 lb. per sq. in. abs. pressure) and at 220°F., and the pressure in the vapor* space of *A* corresponds to a vacuum of 8.75 in. of mercury, or with normal barometer 10.4 lb. per sq. in. abs. pressure. The water in *A* will boil† at 195°F. and furnish steam to the heating coils of *B* at this temperature.   The vacuum in the

* For the sake of clearness, the steam evolved by a boiling solution will be referred to as "vapor" while the word "steam" will be used to designate the source of heat in any particular effect.   Obviously the vapor from one effect becomes the steam supply of the next.

† For the purpose of simplicity, in this illustration boiling-point raising has been neglected.

vapor space of B is 19.1 in. and hence water will boil at 165°F. The vapor coming from B and entering the heating coils of C at 165° will cause water to boil in C at 125°F. where the vacuum is 26 in. Vapor from C at 125°F. will then pass to the condenser.

Since the heating element of A is above atmospheric pressure, the condensed water in it can flow from it by gravity at a little below 220°F. But the condensed water in the heating space of B is under vacuum; hence the pump P' must be used to exhaust the heating space in B and deliver the water at atmospheric pressure. Similarly, the condensate in the heating space of C must be pumped out.

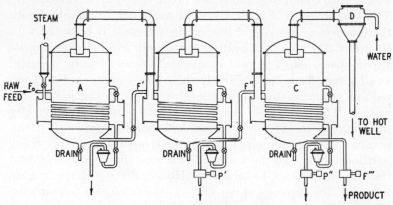

Fig. 123.—Multiple-effect system.

It is evident that the condensed water from the heater in B at about 195°F. is in position to give up part of its sensible heat to the liquid boiling in C at 125°F., and by leading it into the heating element of C part of it flashes into steam on account of the lower pressure, reducing its temperature to 165°F., the temperature of the steam in the coils of C. The hot condensate from the heater in A is generally returned to the boiler.

The solution to be evaporated is fed at 195°F. into the liquor spaces of effect A at F_o by means of a pump or by gravity. Since the pressures in B and C are progressively lower, it is evident that the solution can be drawn in sequence through the system by the pipes F' and F'' and finally lifted to atmospheric pressure by the pump F'''. This arrangement is called **parallel flow,** or forward flow. In order to permit the removal of fixed gases from the heating space of all the effects, each is connected by a small pipe to the vacuum condenser or to the body of the vapor space of the same effect which is obviously at lower pressure. Where the noncondensable gas is small in amount, the latter is better practice, as this method acts as a safeguard against the loss of steam due to its discharge with fixed gases.

Economy vs. Capacity.—Theoretically, therefore, in this case 1 lb. of initial steam should evaporate approximately 1 lb. of water in each of the effects *A*, *B* and *C*. In practice, for reasons discussed later, the evaporation per pound of initial steam, even for a fixed number of effects operated in series, varies widely with conditions, and is best predicted by a "heat balance." The *heat economy* of such a system must not be confused with the *evaporative capacity* of one of the effects. If operated with steam at 220°F. in the heating space and 26 in. vacuum in its vapor space, effect *A* will evaporate as much water (nearly) as all three effects costing nearly three times as much; but it will require approximately three times as much steam and cooling water. The capacity of one or more effects in series is directly proportional to (1) the *difference* between the condensing temperature of the steam supplied, and the temperature of the boiling solution in the last effect and (2) the overall coefficient of heat transfer from steam to solution. Hence, if these factors remain constant, the capacity of one effect is the same as a combination of three effects. On account of complications in construction and operation, multiple effects are not so frequently used for the evaporation of corrosive liquids, or where fuel is very cheap, or for small-scale processes, but they are of great value and impor tance in increasing the economy of large-scale evaporative proc esses, and are continually being simplified and improved. The savings resulting from the installation of additional effects are discussed on pages 408 to 410.

Efficiency vs. Economy.—In this connection, it may be noted that in the literature on evaporators the word "efficiency" is often erroneously used for the "capacity" of a system. The true efficiency of any evaporative system can be determined, as shown on pages 387 to 388, but, since the data for this are frequently inadequate and almost always inexact, it is wiser to express the performance of a given apparatus as its heat "economy," *i.e.*, the evaporation obtained per unit of steam consumption. This removes any uncertainty in the expression of the result.

Terminal Conditions.—The highest temperature employed in an effect is limited by the corresponding pressure, which must not exceed the working strength of the apparatus. At times it is, of course, limited by the pressure of the available steam supply,* also by the temperature to which the solution may be safely heated. The lowest pressure that can be realized depends upon the temperature of the cooling water. These limiting temperatures, together with the nature of the solution to be evaporated and the product required, are factors not usually within the control of the designer of evaporative equipment, but are already determined. Collectively, they are designated the "terminal conditions" of an evaporative system, and represent the fixed and accepted limitations under which the equipment must be designed to operate.

Theoretical Limit of Number of Effects; Boiling-point Raising. Every solution exerts a vapor pressure less† than that of the pure solvent at the same temperature, and corresponding to this vapor-pressure lowering is an equivalent boiling-point raising. That is, dissolved substances lower the vapor pressure of the solvent, such reduction increasing with the concentration of solute. Since a solution boils when its vapor pressure reaches that of its surroundings, it must be heated to a temperature above the boiling point of the pure solvent before ebullition can take place. The vapor rising from a solution is therefore superheated by an amount equal to this boiling-point raising (b.p.r.) and it must be cooled by this amount before it will condense and give up its heat of vaporization. While the amount of superheat is small when compared to the latent heat of the vapor, it should be noted that this latent heat of vaporization becomes available for use only when the vapor is cooled to a temperature lower than that of the solution from which it came by the amount of this b.p.r. This loss of temperature difference from condensing steam to boiling liquid in the next effect increases the heating surface required for the transfer of the heat. As is shown on page 414, a 33.3 per cent caustic soda solution has a b.p.r. of

---

* Where power is needed in the plant, boiler steam may be expanded down to nearly atmospheric pressure through turbines or steam engines, the exhaust steam being used for the evaporators. See p. 410.

† However, see p. 529.

34°F. Theoretically, the temperature difference from one effect to the next may be changed at will, but the drop due to the b.p.r. is a fixed quantity for any determined concentration of the solution. The possible number of effects, therefore, is limited to the total temperature drop available to force heat through the heating surface (and this is the difference in temperature between the steam supply and the cooling water) less the total b.p.r. in all effects.

Multiple Use of Steam through Mechanical Work.—In the above discussion, the point was made that work, rather than heat, is the essential thing in evaporation, and yet the methods of evaporation presented have involved heat transfer alone. It is, however, possible to use mechanical work effectively in evaporation, by mechanically compressing the vapor given off from an evaporating solution (more or less superheated by the b.p.r.), and again using the high-pressure steam thus secured, in the steam coils of the same effect from which the vapor came.

As was stated on page 388, the only reason that the vapor coming from effect A could not again be used in A to evaporate more solution is that it is at the same temperature as the solution boiling in A, and hence the heat would not flow from the heating space through the container walls into the solution. The heat units are present in the vapor as latent heat, but they are available at too low a temperature. If, now, this vapor is compressed to the proper pressure, its condensation temperature will be so raised as to be again available for transferring heat in the heating coils of effect A. The chief difficulty with such a process lies in the size of compressor needed for compressing large quantities of low-pressure vapor, having a large volume, from the saturation point up to a pressure high enough for use in the heating coils. Owing to cooling by heat loss and to entrainment, it is impractical to use an ordinary air compressor; the erosion of the mechanical parts is also a disadvantage. The only method heretofore adopted for overcoming this has been the use of a steam ejector, employing high-pressure boiler steam to compress part of the vapor to the degree required for re-use. The resulting mixture of steam from the evaporator and the boiler then flows to the steam coils of the evaporator itself. That part of the vapor which is not compressed flows directly to the condenser. With this system it is possible to evaporate about 3 lb. of water per lb.

of boiler steam, or the equivalent of a triple-effect evaporator; but with high compressive efficiency and small heat losses, it should be possible to evaporate much more water per pound of boiler steam than this. The development of this type of mechanical evaporator offers much promise, especially for use where power is cheap relative to fuel. In its present form, this evaporator should be considered for small installations, as it makes possible the realization of high heat economy in a single effect.

TYPICAL EVAPORATOR BODIES

In any evaporator effect there must be provided (1) means for supplying steam to the heating surface, (2) means for removing the condensate and noncondensable gases, (3) disengaging space for separation of vapor from boiling liquid, (4) means for admission and removal of the solution to be concentrated and (5) provision for removal of vapor evolved.

The heating surface of an effect is generally made up of tubes, straight on account of ease of construction and cleaning, either horizontal, vertical or inclined at an angle. The boiling liquid may be either outside or inside these tubes, the steam being in either case in contact with the other surface. Finally, the boiling liquid may lie over the heating surface as a deep layer, *i.e.*, the tubes submerged in the liquid, or the boiling liquid may be distributed over the heating surface as a thin film. Corresponding to these possibilities, evaporator effects may be classified under the following types:

Tubes horizontal.....

    Liquor *outside* tubes

        Submerged Tube Type. (1)

        Film Type. . . . (2)

    Liquor *inside* tubes

        Submerged Tube Type. (3)

        Film Type. . . . (4)

Tubes vertical (also inclined).............

    Liquor *outside* tubes

        Submerged Tube Type. (5)

        Film Type. . . . (6)

    Liquor *inside* tubes

        Submerged Tube Type. (7)

        Film Type. . . . (8)

Effects, corresponding to all but one of these types, are found in commercial operation. Formerly there were several types known by the names of their designers, but experience has standardized practice in construction and a few types are now accepted as having justified themselves, and can be obtained of any one of a number of manufacturers.

Type 1.   Tubes Horizontal, Liquor Outside, Submerged Heating Surface.—This is an important and widely used type.   In the evaporator shown in Fig. 124, the steam is supplied to one of the two steam chests, from which it is distributed to the steam tubes, and the condensed steam is trapped out from the bottom of the chest at the other end of the tubes.   The boiling liquid is in the main body of the evaporator around the heating tubes, and the space above the liquid serves for settling the entrained droplets from the vapor.   The dilute liquor is fed in through a supply pipe at one side of the evaporator either above or below the liquor level, and the more concentrated liquor flows out at the bottom as shown in Fig. 124.   The vapor leaving the top

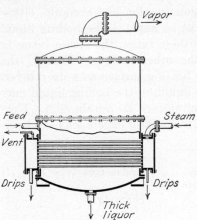

FIG. 124.—Evaporator, Type 1.   (*Courtesy of Swenson Evaporator Co.*)

of the disengaging space, before entering the vapor main leading to the next effect or to the condenser, may pass through a steam separator ("catch-all") containing one or more baffles for further separation of the entrained liquor from the vapors.   The steam tubes are fitted into the steam chest with gaskets of rubber or other suitable packing material, held tight by faceplates screwed down upon the gaskets from the steam chest side.   In order to insure circulation of the boiling liquid, a space entirely free from tubes is provided, either at the center or at the sides or both.   Evaporators of this type are constructed by practically all manufacturers.   The evaporator bodies may be either rectangular or cylindrical in cross section.   The differences lie mainly in the effectiveness of maintaining circulation and in simplicity, strength and perfection of mechanical construction. The relative location and size of heating surface and free circulation space have a large influence in determining the rate of circulation, and therefore the coefficient of heat transfer.

Type 2. Tubes Horizontal, Liquor Outside in Film Form.— The Lillie evaporator is the only representative of this class. In this type there is only one steam chest and each of the parallel tubes containing the steam is closed at the extreme end except for a small opening which allows the noncondensable gases to escape into the disengaging chamber that surrounds the tubes. The tubes slope slightly toward the steam chest to drain out the condensed water which is trapped out from the bottom of the chest. The feed liquor is distributed over the top row of steam tubes through a suitable distributing device, usually consisting of parallel perforated pipes or troughs. The concentrated liquor collecting in the bottom of the disengaging space is pumped out, and is either recirculated through the same effect, distributed into the next effect in series with the first or withdrawn as product. It is obvious that the total amount of liquid exposed to high temperature is small compared to the amount so exposed in Type 1, and hence the *time of exposure* of liquid to the high temperature is much less. Therefore, for materials which deteriorate on long heating, the use of a film-type apparatus is desirable. Other types of evaporators in which the time of exposure is short will be discussed later.

It has been shown that, if an evaporating liquid begins to froth, it is possible to stop this by lowering the liquid level, so that the liquid plays over the heating surface as a foam. Evaporators of Type 1, when used with frothing liquids, are operated in this way and should then be classified as Type 2.

Type 3. Tubes Horizontal, Liquor Inside, Submerged Heating Surface.—This type has never been realized owing to the impossibility of removing vapor from the tubes without at the same time carrying out the liquid. The nearest analogue is the water-tube boiler, but in this case the heating element is not steam.

Type 4. Tubes Horizontal, Liquor Inside in Film Form.—The Yaryan evaporator (Fig. 125) is equipped with horizontal tubes surrounded by steam. The feed liquor enters the tubes and flows through several horizontal passes, leaving at the opposite end to discharge into the disengaging chamber, in which the entrained liquor is separated from the vapor by suitable baffles. The liquid in the tubes flashes partly into vapor and rushes through the tubes as a froth consisting of alternate slugs of vapor and boiling liquid. The concentrated liquor is drawn off while the vapor passes to the steam space of the next effect in series, or to the condenser.

Type 5. Tubes Vertical, Liquor Outside, Submerged Heating Surface.—In the earlier days of evaporator practice, effects were constructed of large vertical cylindrical shells, the heating elements consisting of vertical steam tubes connected at top and

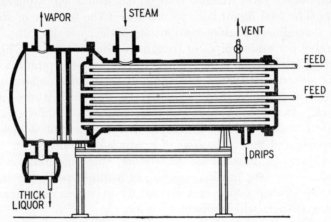

FIG. 125.—Evaporator, Type 4, Yaryan.

bottom into horizontal headers for supply of steam and removal of condensate. Such effects were at one time spoken of as the "standard"* type. It is, however, difficult to insert such heating elements so as to secure a maximum heating area in a given volume of the body of the effect; moreover, the steam headers interfere with the circulation of the boiling liquid, thus cutting down the heat-transfer coefficient. The use of this type has, in general, been abandoned.

Type 6. Tubes Vertical, Liquor Outside in Film Form.—The type described in the preceding paragraph, when used for frothing liquids, employing the method previously mentioned of lowering the level of the boiling liquid so that the major portion of the

* This term is now applied to Type 7 with central downtake.

heating surface is covered only with the foam and bubbles produced by ebullition, falls under this head. Since it suffers from all the disadvantages of the construction using submerged heating surface, it is no longer used.

Type 7. Tubes Vertical, Liquor Inside, Submerged Heating Surface.—This important evaporator type is usually built of a vertical cylindrical shell with, however, two available methods of insertion of the heating tubes. The ends of these may be expanded into plates or "diaphragms" extending clear across the evaporator body, and thus forming a suitable steam chest; in the center a large circular tube is provided for descent of the liquor, which rises through the heating tubes.

Frequently the steam chest consists of a short cylindrical shell, somewhat smaller than that of the evaporator itself, closed at the ends by tube sheets into which closely spaced heating tubes are expanded. This steam chest is supported concentrically within the main evaporator shell. From the shape of the steam chest, it is described as a "basket." In the case of single-effect finishing pans, such as "strike" pans for sugar, a central downtake is sometimes provided.

The notable advantage of Type 7 is the ease of cleaning the heating tubes from

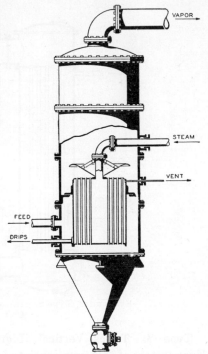

Fig. 126.—Evaporator, Type 7, basket type. (*Courtesy of Swenson Evaporator Co.*)

incrusted matter by running a rotary cutting tube cleaner through the tubes. To this end, the diaphragm type is provided with manholes, while the main body of a "basket" effect (Fig. 126) is flanged, so that the whole basket can be removed; extra baskets are usually kept on hand so that operation may be quickly resumed, and the incrusted basket is cleaned or repaired at leisure.

Salt solutions often contain gypsum, marked in its tendency to form a dense adherent scale of such low heat conductivity that the evaporative capacity of the apparatus is rapidly reduced. This type is well suited for use in concentrating such solutions, and is so widely used for this purpose that these effects are frequently termed "salt evaporators."

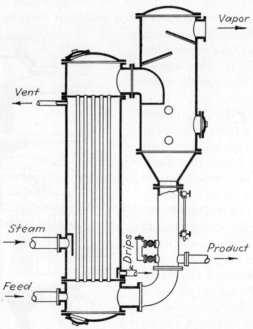

Fig. 127.—Evaporator, Type 8.   (*Courtesy of Buffalo Foundry and Machine Co.*)

Type 8. Tubes Vertical, Liquor Inside in Film Form.—

Evaporators of this type consist of a group of long vertical tubes, the ends of which are expanded into two plates which form diaphragms across a cylindrical shell near the ends, the space between these plates being the steam chest. The liquor is fed into the shell below the bottom plate, under sufficient head to rise a short distance into the tubes. There it boils, and the vapor rising as froth forces slugs of liquor ahead of it at high velocity up the tubes and out into the disengaging space in the evaporator shell above the upper tube plate. Where the disengaging space is small, as in Fig. 127, an externally located separator is used. Part of the liquid from the separator recirculates through the tubes and the remainder is sent to a second effect or is drawn off as product. For solutions sensitive to heat the time of contact is reduced by decreasing the diameter of the return pipe.

The distinctive advantage of this type lies in the high coefficient of heat transfer realized, due to the great velocity of the liquid over the heating surface. The character of the flow of liquid and vapor through the tubes guarantees a thorough and rapidly repeated wetting of the whole heating surface. This type is popular, particularly for handling foaming liquids.

Evaporators of Type 8 are also built with inclined tubes, thus reducing the head room required.

Forced-circulation Evaporators.—Pumps are sometimes installed to increase the velocity through the tubes, thus increasing the coefficient of heat transfer and increasing the evaporative capacity of the unit. The popularity of such units seems to be increasing.

Salting-out Evaporators.—Evaporator bodies that are to be used for solutions depositing crystals during the process of concentration must have provision for removal of the crystals. Since interference with continuity of operation is very undesirable, the evaporator is equipped with a type of double seal, known as a "salt catch." This consists of a chamber separated from the evaporator just above it by a gate valve and in the bottom of which is a second such valve. The bottom of the evaporator body is sloped downward, as in Fig. 126, page 397, to the upper valve, so that crystals deposited will fall upon it and flow through it when opened. Sometimes the salt receiver is fitted with a filter plate, so that, when full, the mother liquor may be drawn off and the crystals washed. They may then be dried, first by passing dry steam and then air through them. Or, as in the separation of salt from electrolytic caustic-soda solution, the salt, after being washed, is dissolved in hot water and pumped or forced out.

NOTES ON SINGLE-EFFECT EVAPORATORS

As already shown, to maintain a low temperature, the evaporation of liquids liable to injury by heat is conducted at the highest

available vacuum.   Since only the last effect of a multiple evaporator system can be under the highest vacuum and therefore at
the lowest temperature, this type of apparatus does not lend itself
to the concentration of liquids injured by heat except when the
same are very *dilute*, for example, solutions of sugar, glue, tannin,
etc.   Injury due to "burning" occasioned by localized lack of
circulation with resultant overheating is decreased by using a
lower steam pressure and a correspondingly larger heating surface.
Obviously, where the material in solution is sensitive to heat, it is
desirable to hold it at the temperature of the evaporator as short
a time as possible.   Since a film type of evaporator contains the
minimum of liquid at any given time, it is from this point of view
particularly desirable.   Unfortunately, however, in an apparatus
of this type intermittent wetting and drying of the heating
surface are very likely to take place and in the case of glue or
similar substances an adherent insulating film forms on the
heating element when dry which does not readily redissolve
when again wet.   The vertical tube type, however, is much
less subject to this drawback and should find here a promising
field for development.

Another advantage of film-type effects for handling liquids
injured by heat is the absence of any b.p.r. due to hydrostatic
head.   With submerged heating surface, the liquid at the bottom
of the pan is under a pressure greater than that at the disengaging
surface above, by an amount equal to the liquid head in the effect,
which may be several feet.   At high pressures, this additional
head may be negligible, but at very low pressures the increase
will cause a marked rise in temperature at the bottom of the pan.
It is true that the liquid at the bottom of such an effect often
does not boil, but is none the less raised in temperature and is
then brought by convection up to the surface where, being
superheated, it flashes partially into vapor, while the residual
liquid, cooled by this evaporation, then returns to the bottom of
the effect to repeat the cycle.   Thus in any case, hydrostatic head
produces an increase in the average temperature of the boiling
liquid (particularly important when operating under high
vacuum) which can be avoided by film evaporation.

In the refining of sugar it is essential to regulate the number of
crystallization centers formed and the rate of growth of the
resultant grains, by controlling (1) the concentration of the

solution, (2) its temperature, (3) the rate at which it is brought to any definite temperature and pressure, (4) the rate of cooling and (5) the extent of cooling to which it is finally subjected. The first three of these factors are determined entirely, and the last two to a certain degree, by careful manipulation of both heat supply and vacuum in the evaporator. For this purpose a single effect must be used, as the reaction of one effect upon the operation of another in series with it would render close control impossible.

Single effects are used, as already indicated, in small installations, where the amount of evaporation to be done is insufficient to justify the cost of installing and operating a multiple-effect system (see pages 390 to 391). Single effects are also used in many cases where it is desired to recover the solvent employed, but where otherwise an open pan could as easily be used.

It is desirable to bring together, even with danger of reiteration, the more essential details for which it is necessary to provide in order to secure satisfactory operation of evaporators. These requirements must be met in every effect, whether operated separately or in series with others; the modifications of these directions necessary in series operation will be pointed out in the discussion of multiple effects.

Steam Supply.—The steam feed of an effect should be through pipes large enough to insure no *appreciable* reduction in pressure caused by friction in the supply lines and valves (a point of great importance when using low-pressure steam), and should be drawn from an adequate source to insure the maintenance of full pressure in the steam chest at all times. Where the original supply is from a boiler or other source in which the pressure is too high for the safety of the evaporator, it is imperative that the supply line be equipped with a proper automatic reducing valve, to protect the effect and yet to insure, at all times, full working pressure on it. In this last case, a safety valve should also be provided.

Removal of Condensed Steam.—Provision for this is of utmost importance. The heating tubes must not be too long, as the downstream ends may fill with condensate, rendering that portion of the heating surface less useful. Where possible, the tubes should slope in the direction of flow of the steam in order to sweep out the condensate effectively. The condensed-steam chest must be equipped with an effective trap to remove condensate as soon as accumulated, without allowing escape of steam.   A gauge glass should be provided to detect inadequate removal of condensed steam from the steam chest.   The removal of the noncondensable gases always present in the steam is of great importance, as these gases will accumulate and entirely prevent the entrance of the steam.   This removal is effected by bleeding off a small part of the steam from the condensed steam chest, to the vapor space of the same effect or directly to the condenser.   The presence of noncondensable gases is detected by the discrepancy between the temperature in the steam chest and the pressure existing there.

Entrainment in an effect is indicated by the presence of solute in the condensed vapor.   *Frothing* is detected by inspection through sight glasses in the side of the effect, or by watching gauge glasses connected at various heights in the side of the vapor space and leading thence to any point of low pressure, such as the condenser, or a succeeding effect.   By the use of electrical contacts in a gauge glass or at definite heights in the disengaging space of the effect, an alarm may be given in the case of solutions of electrolytes.   Frothing is reduced by lowering the liquid level in the effect or by reducing the evaporative rate.

Liquor Feed and Removal.—By proper control of the feed, a single effect may be operated either intermittently or continuously.   The body of the effect is filled to the proper height with dilute liquor, and as concentration proceeds the level is maintained by admitting more dilute liquor at the proper rate, until ultimately the required concentration is realized; then the effect is emptied, and the cycle is repeated.   Or, instead of emptying the effect when the desired concentration is attained, the concentrated liquor may be drawn off at a definite, constant rate, determined by the evaporative capacity of the effect, the liquor level being maintained uniform by the continued admission of dilute liquor, thus securing continuity of operation.   Discontinuous operation requires constant attention to control the changing rate of evaporation consequent upon decreasing temperature drop (and hence decreasing heat flow) through the heating surface caused by the constantly rising boiling point of the solution, and to provide for emptying and refilling the effect.   Hence, continuous operation is generally used.   This involves the disadvantage that the entire evaporation is carried out at the high boiling point of the concentrated solution, the *average* b.p.r. of discontinous evaporation being much lower. In multiple-effect operation, on the other hand, this disadvantage largely disappears.

The liquor feed of an effect is controlled by a valve operated either by hand or automatically (as with a float valve) so as to keep the amount of boiling liquid in the effect at the proper level. Film-type effects usually require delivery of the feed at special points, as indicated in their description; but in the case of submerged heating surface, the liquor may be admitted anywhere, as boiling keeps the contents of the effect thoroughly mixed. The concentrated liquor is removed at a point some distance from the inlet, to prevent short-circuiting of the dilute feed liquor to the outlet pipe, and its flow is controlled by a throttle valve, operated to maintain the proper concentration of the effluent, usually determined by its density. The feed to effects under pressure and the discharge from those under vacuum must be by means of suitable pumps. The operator observes the amount of liquor in the effect through sight or gauge glasses.

Vapor Removal.—The vapor is removed by a condenser which, if operating under a vacuum, is fitted with an air pump. These two pieces of apparatus are of the types used in steam-engineering practice and their operation involves nothing unfamiliar. Jet condensers are used in a larger proportion of the cases in chemical practice than in steam engineering (see pages 383 to 384). The air pumps must be adequate for removal of all inert noncondensable gases present. Barometric jet condensers are used in many cases where corrosive gases enter with the steam. While this type avoids corrosion of pump parts, its height limits its use where space considerations are involved.

CHARACTERISTICS OF MULTIPLE-EFFECT SYSTEMS

It may at first thought seem that the maintenance of the proper conditions of temperature and pressure in each of the various bodies of a multiple-effect system is a difficult and complicated problem, but, since the adjustment of conditions between the pans is entirely automatic, such is not the case. When a number of effects are to be operated in series, the vapor from the first discharges into the steam coils of the second, the vapor from the second passes into the steam coils of the third, and so on; the vapor from the last effect passes directly to the condenser. In such a system the liquor feed and discharge of each body may be entirely separate, as though each were a single effect; however, this is seldom done.

Parallel Flow of Liquor and Steam.—It is advisable, however, to feed the dilute liquor to the first high-pressure effect, carrying on only a part of the concentration there, feeding the second effect from the first, the third from the second and so on, finally withdrawing the concentrated product from the last effect. There are two reasons for this. First, only two liquor pumps are required: the feed pump to the first effect (if it is under pressure), and the discharge pump from the last, since, as each effect is at a pressure lower than the preceding one, the liquor will flow directly from effect to effect. Second, since all effects before the last contain liquor which is but partly concentrated, the b.p.r. in these effects is correspondingly lower, thus giving a larger temperature drop through the heating surface of the effect, and hence a higher evaporative capacity.

When evaporation is carried on to high concentrations, this factor becomes important. Since the amount of water evaporated in each effect is often nearly the same, the concentration and hence the value of the b.p.r. is not large until the last effects are reached (see Counterflow, page 407).

Removal of Air.—The air or other noncondensable gases may be withdrawn from the system in either of two ways: first, the condensed steam chest of each effect may be connected directly to the condenser; second, the steam chest of each effect may be connected to the vapor space of the same effect. Since the presence of noncondensable gas in the steam chest of succeeding effects cuts down the rate of heat transmission (page 139), this second method is advisable only when the precentage of such gas is very small. If the volume of noncondensable gas is large, it is advisable to withdraw it directly to the condenser (see page 390).

Heat Recovery from Condensate.—The water leaving the condensed-steam chest in a single-effect evaporator, or in the first effect of a multiple system, is generally returned to the boiler and its heat content thus utilized. The condensate from the other effects of a multiple system is frequently contam inated through entrainment and requires special installation for the recovery of the heat contained therein. Because of the excellent coefficient of heat transfer from condensing steam to boiling liquid, it is more economical to lead the hot condensate from the chest of one effect into the heating coil of the next effect in series. Here, because of the lower pressure, some of this water flashes into steam at the same temperature as the condensing steam in this coil. The temperature of the condensate in the last effect is too low to make recovery easy and it is therefore discharged through the wet air pump or through the downtake pipe of a barometric condenser.

Starting Up.—To place a multiple-effect evaporator in operation quickly and without loss of liquor from boiling over calls for careful and accurate manipulation. Liquor levels must at first be kept very low, and, after the vacuum pump is started, water is admitted to the condenser. The first effect should be filled, followed by admission of steam to the steam chest. Feed liquor should be passed on to the following bodies only after it has been heated to the working temperature normally obtaining there. As soon as the liquor in the last effect has reached the desired concentration, it is allowed to discharge as rapidly as possible without fall in concentration, and the system now proceeds in smooth and continuous operation.

Such a system will soon adjust itself to a definite temperature and pressure in each effect. The vapor evolved in the first must condense in the coils of the second, where, in turn, it causes the evaporation of a corresponding amount of liquid. If this condensation in the coils of the second does not take place, the steam accumulates, and, backing up, raises the pressure in the first effect, stopping evaporation there. On the other hand, condensation in the coils of the second effect cannot occur without the dissipation of the corresponding heat, and there is no means of absorbing this heat except by evaporating from the boiling liquid in the second effect an approximately equal amount of steam. This interrelation holds for all effects throughout the system, and interference with, or acceleration of, evaporation at any point has its inevitable reaction upon the conditions at every other point. The heat flowing past each section of the apparatus equals that passing every other section, a condition maintained by self-adjustment of the temperature drops through the various heating surfaces and entirely automatic on the part of the system itself.

Probably the first sign of trouble which the operator observes will be a reduction in evaporative capacity, *i.e.*, it will be found necessary to reduce the rate of discharge of concentrated liquor from the last effect in order to maintain its strength. This undesirable result, however, develops only as a consequence of far-reaching changes in the operating conditions throughout the whole system. This will be made clearer by consideration of the results following specific modification of the operating conditions in the multiple-effect system.

Effect of Inadequate Condenser Capacity.—Assume, for example, that, in a system operating normally under given terminal conditions, the temperature of the condenser water rises. The resulting higher temperature of condensation produces immediately a rise in pressure in the last effect, followed by rise in temperature of the boiling liquid. This cuts down the temperature drop through the heating surface in that effect, thus reducing the heat transferred and the steam condensed in the coils. This causes rise of pressure in these coils, backing up the pressure in the effect before the last, and so on back through the whole system, resulting ultimately in reducing the temperature drop through the heating surface in each effect; hence the evaporation in each is reduced proportionally, with a corresponding decrease in the evaporative capacity of the entire system.

Effect of Decrease in UA-product.—Again, assume that the operator finds the evaporative capacity of his equipment reduced; but that in this instance the cause is either the cutting out of part of the heating surface or a reduction in the coefficient of heat transfer in a given effect. In either case, since the product of the coefficient of heat transfer and the area of heating surface is reduced, the heat current decreases in that particular effect. Since no effect can continue to receive a heat current greater than it can dissipate, the heat current decreases in *all* effects. As a result, the temperature drop increases in the effect in question, and decreases in all others. Hence the temperature of boiling rises in the preceding effects and falls in the succeeding ones. This automatic redistribution of the magnitudes of the temperature drop through the heating surfaces of the various effects, developing a *high* temperature difference in the body in which the coefficient of heat transfer or the area of the heating surface is decreased, and abnormally low values in the others, enables the operator to determine the location of the trouble.

The most likely causes in reduction of the effective heating surface are inadequate removal of condensate, which can readily be noted by inspection of condensate levels in the gauge glasses on the condensed-steam chests, or abnormally low liquor levels, which can be detected in the gauge glasses on the liquor space and corrected by properly adjusting the rates of liquor feed and withdrawal. Inadequate removal of noncondensable gas may be remedied by increasing the rate of bleed by adjusting the bleeder valve. If with normal terminal conditions (see page 391) the reduction in capacity of the system is not due to improper levels of condensate or liquor, or to inadequate bleeding of gases, the cause must be fouling of the heating surface.

Effect of Steam Leakage.—Three sources of steam leakage are encountered. The first is from the steam chest of an effect into the boiling liquid in that effect, usually through defective packing at the ends of tubes or through pinholes caused by corrosion. The second is caused by the bleeding of an excessive amount of steam out of the chest to remove permanent gases. The third is a direct flow of steam from the chest of one effect to that of the next due to imperfect traps in the condensed-steam line. The leakage of steam in any of these ways from the chest of an effect results in a relatively low evaporation in that effect although the evaporative capacity of the system may remain unchanged. Clearly a steam leak increases the steam consumption per unit of total evaporation since the multiple-effect principle is violated when steam fails to condense in each heating surface.

Modification in operating conditions at any point thus reacts upon and changes the conditions at every other point; but fortunately, as indicated above, analysis of the changes enables the operator to locate and remedy the trouble.

Counterflow of Liquor and Steam.—Occasionally one encounters solutions in the evaporation of which it is desirable to modify the above outline of multiple operation. Since the viscosity of a solution is greater when cold and concentrated, the coefficient of heat transfer is lowest* in the low-pressure effect of a multiple

* See p. 380.

system operated with parallel flow of liquor and steam. Where the product is very concentrated, the coefficient in the last effect may be only 10 per cent or even less of that in the first effect. Obviously, then, a higher coefficient will be obtained by evaporating the most concentrated solution at the highest temperature, *i.e.*, in the high-pressure rather than the low-pressure effect. In such cases, it may prove worth while to admit the dilute feed liquor into the low-pressure effect, pump it to the second effect and from there pump it to the high-pressure effect for the final concentration. This method of operation is called **backward flow** or **counterflow.** Sometimes a combination of backward and forward feed is used, which will eliminate a pump. The necessity for such changes from parallel flow is, however, not very frequent.

Choice of Terminal Conditions.—It will be recalled that the evaporative capacity of a multiple system is determined by the amount of heat that can be supplied to the boiling liquid and that this in turn is approximately proportional* to the temperature difference between the steam supply and the boiling liquid. The lowest temperature at which the liquid can boil depends on the vacuum in the condenser, which in turn is limited by the temperature of the cooling water. The highest allowable temperature is fixed by that pressure of steam supply which the mechanical strength of the apparatus will stand, or by the possible injurious effect that heat may have upon the material to be evaporated. However, the advantages that accrue to high-pressure steam through decrease in the area of the heating surface should be balanced against the resultant decrease in steam economy.

Determination of Number of Effects. *Economic Balance.*—The choice of the number of effects to be used in series in an evaporation system becomes an economic balance of cost of heat against fixed charges. If a single effect will handle a certain amount of evaporation, the addition in series of more effects duplicating the first does not greatly modify the evaporative capacity but does cut down the fuel cost. Although the size of the condenser can be reduced, the cost of the auxiliary equipment is not greatly changed; the air pump can be made smaller

---

* Since the coefficient of heat transfer increases with the temperature and the temperature difference (p. 141), an effect where a 25° difference is maintained will have more than two and one-half times the evaporative capacity where a 10°F. drop is used.

but not in proportion, because of the greater ratio of dead gas to steam. Liquor pumps remain unchanged. The cost of the effects themselves increases in direct proportion to their number. Therefore, the increase in total cost, and hence in fixed charges, is a little less than proportional to the number of effects. A point is soon reached beyond which the addition of further effects will increase fixed charges and maintenance to more than balance the decrease in cost of heat. This point varies with the ratio of costs of capital, repairs and the like to fuel cost; under American conditions more than five effects in series are seldom justified; triple and quadruple effects are more frequently met.

As an example of how the most economical number of effects may be calculated, consider the following problem:

Illustration 1.—It is desired to concentrate 400,000 lb. per day of liquor containing 10 per cent caustic soda to a 35 per cent solution. A suitable type of single-effect "salting-out" evaporator of sufficient capacity costs $6400 exclusive of pumps, condenser* and other accessories common to any number of effects. With fixed charges, amortization and interest amounting to 45 per cent per year, and steam at $0.40 per 1000 lb., what number of effects should be used to secure maximum economy? Assume 0.85n lb. of water evaporated per lb. of steam, where n is number of effects; there are 300 operating days per year, and labor is the same for any number of effects.

Solution. Basis.—One operating day.

$$\text{Steam cost} = 40,000 \times \left[\frac{9}{1} - \frac{65}{35}\right] \times \frac{1}{(0.85n)} \times \frac{(0.40)}{(1,000)} = \frac{\$134.40}{n}$$

(with diagonal labels: Lb. of Solids, Lb. of Evaporation, Lb. of Steam)

$$\text{Fixed charges} = \frac{(0.45)\ (6,400)\ (n)}{(300)} = \$9.60n.$$

	One Effect	Two Effects	Three Effects	Four Effects	Five Effects
Fixed charges.........	$ 9.60	$19.20	$28.80	$38.40	$48.00
Steam...............	134.40	67.20	44.80	33.60	26.88
Total...........	$144.00	$86.40	$73.60	$72.00	$74.88

* The condenser must be larger for one effect than for three, as in the latter case about two-thirds of the water evaporated is condensed in the heating surface of the last two effects. In order to simplify this illustration, the variation in the cost of condenser has been neglected as well as the variation in the amount of cooling water.

While these calculations show that the total cost is a minimum for four effects, the total cost for three is so little more that, in order to reduce the investment, three would be installed. Note that the saving when using three effects instead of one is over $70 per day. While the optimum number of effects varies with the ratio of the cost of steam to the charges on the apparatus, it varies only as the square root of this ratio.*

Where fluctuation in the rate of evaporation demanded is likely to arise, it is good engineering to install a multiple-effect system with a capacity sufficient for approximately the average load, but with the effects so connected that they can readily be thrown into parallel for the peak load. In this way, the normal load is carried with good steam economy, and yet the maximum demand for evaporative capacity is met without the installation of additional equipment, with the consequent fixed charges. It is true that the peak load is carried with poor steam economy but, if this load occurs only occasionally, the sacrifice is justifiable. This parallels the practice of the power engineer who designs his steam engine for the normal load, and carries the peak as an overload, though at a poor fuel economy. The auxiliary equipment, pumps, condensers and the like must be adequate for the maximum demand. If the increase beyond the capacity of the multiple system is not too great, the effects may be used partly in series and partly in parallel, with less of a decrease in steam economy. By providing for such connections and manipulation, considerable flexibility in the operating control of the capacity and heat economy of an evaporative system is possible.

Evaporators are generally operated with the exhaust steam from turbines or noncondensing engines. In plants having only small power equipment this arrangement is undoubtedly good, since cheap, yet efficient, reciprocating units are the best to be had. In large power plants, however, especially where turbines

---

* Since the equation of the total cost curve for this case is

$$\text{Total daily cost} = 9.6n + \frac{134.4}{n}.$$

the minimum point will occur where the tangent of the curve has a slope of zero. Hence, one may differentiate the total cost with respect to the number of effects and equate to zero, giving

$$n = \sqrt{\frac{\text{cost of steam}}{\text{charges on apparatus}}} = \sqrt{\frac{134.4}{9.6}} = 3.75.$$

are available for the low-pressure stages of the expansion, the steam can be used to as good advantage in the turbine as in a multiple-effect system, while the independence resulting from entire separation of the power and evaporator units insures better control of each. If the construction of the evaporator bodies or the character of the liquor is such that full-pressure boiler steam cannot be used in the effects, then it is imperative that the steam be expanded down to the safe working pressure for the first effect by passing through a suitable engine, so as to recover the corresponding power which would otherwise be wasted. The best plan, when possible, is to keep the power and evaporator houses entirely separate.

CALCULATIONS FOR EVAPORATOR DESIGN

General Assumptions.—Two important physical properties of a solution affecting evaporator design are, first, the boiling point of the solution as compared with that of the pure solvent, and, second, the heat of evaporation of the solvent from the solution. In the design of continuous evaporators for the concentration of relatively dilute solutions (up to perhaps 20 per cent), or for the concentration of stronger solutions under conditions such that the total pressure variations are small (not over twofold or threefold), the three following assumptions may be made: (1) the b.p.r. of a solution of definite concentration is independent of its temperature and pressure; (2) the heat consumed in the evaporation of a unit weight of solvent from the solution is the same as the heat of evaporation of the pure solvent when volatilized at the temperature of the boiling solution; and (3) the heat capacity of a solution is equal to that of the solvent in it (see Thomsen's Tables).[3] Thus the specific heat of a 10 per cent aqueous solution would be 0.9.

B.P.R. Due to Hydrostatic Head.—As shown on page 391, the presence of solute in a solution raises the boiling temperature of the solution above the boiling point of the pure solvent at a given pressure. Moreover, when the heating surface in an evaporator is below the surface of the liquid, the liquid in contact therewith has a higher boiling point than at the surface of the liquid. If the density of the solution is known, the b.p.r. due to hydraulic head can be readily calculated. While not strictly accurate, it is a satisfactory approximation for purposes of calculating heat transfer to assume the average temperature of the boiling liquid to be that at the point midway between top and bottom of the boiling mass.

Disadvantage of B.P.R.—As previously indicated, the total evaporative capacity of a multiple system is directly proportional to total available temperature difference, namely, the difference between the temperatures of the steam condensing in the coils of the first effect and the boiling temperature in the last effect, minus the total b.p.r. in all effects. Since, for a given capacity, the total heating surface required is an inverse function of the available temperature drop, the disadvantage of b.p.r. is obvious.

Estimation of Vapor Pressure.—In order to predict the b.p.r. due to solute, the vapor pressure of the solution as a function of concentration and temperature must be known. Raoult's law states that the vapor pressure of a solution divided by the vapor pressure of the pure solvent at the same temperature is equal to the mol fraction of the solvent in the solution. A corollary of this statement is that the vapor pressure of a solution divided by that of the solvent at the same temperature (normally spoken of as relative vapor pressure, r.v.p.) is the same at all temperatures. The major premise of Raoult's law, that the r.v.p. is equal to the mol fraction of the solvent, usually holds only in dilute solutions;* furthermore, for electrolytes it must be corrected for the degree of dissociation of the solute. Its use in connection with the normal problems of evaporator design is therefore inadmissible.

Since the vapor pressures of a solution are a function of two independent variables—concentration and temperature—the estimation of vapor pressures would be difficult and tedious in the absence of simplifying relationships. Such fortunately exist. The vapor pressure of any material rises rapidly with the temperature whether the material is a pure solid or liquid substance, a solution of definite constant concentration or a mixture of volatile components. The curvature is very high and a large number of points must be determined to make it possible to draw a satisfactory curve through them. On the other hand, these curves are all similar in shape and this similarity is the basis of the following relationships, stated by Dühring[4] in 1878. It is an experimentally determined fact that, if in plotting a

* For sucrose solutions Raoult's law applies even for saturated solutions.

vapor-pressure curve of any material, instead of plotting the pressures as ordinates against the temperature as abscissas, one plots as ordinates the temperature at which some suitable standard liquid, such as water, exerts the same pressure, the experimental points fall very nearly upon a straight line. The standard liquid chosen should, if possible, be chemically similar to the liquid the vapor-pressure curve of which is being studied. It is necessary that the vapor-pressure curve of the standard substance chosen be accurately known over a pressure range fully covering the limits desired, and it is desirable that interpolation tables which give the pressure for small temperature intervals be available. For most problems in evaporation, water is a satisfactory standard.

It will be clear from the preceding that, since the vapor pressure of a substance plotted in this way gives a straight line, two points in the vapor-pressure curve are theoretically sufficient to determine the line. While it is desirable to have more points, in order to guarantee accuracy, a large number is not essential. This means that, from a small number of determinations of the vapor pressure of any material of constant composition, the vapor-pressure curve of that material can be constructed with satisfactory accuracy.

To show the applicability of this method, a vapor-pressure curve for aniline is given in Fig. 128. The straight line represents tem-

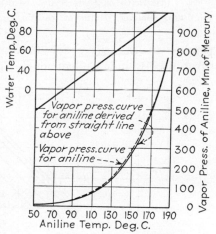

FIG. 128.—Dühring's rule applied to vapor pressure of aniline.

peratures of aniline (abscissas) plotted against temperatures at which water has the same vapor pressure. The solid curve is the vapor-pressure plot derived from the straight line. The dotted curve shows experimental values.[5] This indicates the accuracy of the method.

If it is possible to find in the literature the vapor pressure of a given solution at two different temperatures, it is theoretically

possible to construct its vapor-pressure curve for any temperature range. Further data serve as checks. For example, the
vapor-pressure curve of caustic-soda solutions has been determined at 0°C. by Dietterici[5]
and at 100°C. by Tamman,[5]
and the boiling points of these
solutions are also known (Fig.
129).

This gives, therefore, three
points on the vapor-pressure
curve of any caustic solution.
From these data Fig. 130 has
been constructed. According
to Dühring's rule, each of these
curves should be a straight
line, and it is found that the
curvature is very small. It is
noted that the curves for each
of the four solutions are nearly
parallel to the curve for water, showing that the b.p.r. is
substantially independent of temperature. In this case the

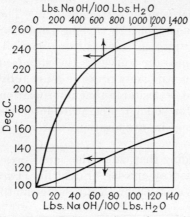

FIG. 129.—Boiling points of caustic
solutions.

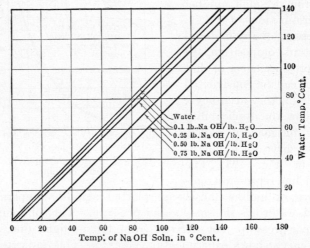

FIG. 130.—Dühring's rule applied to vapor pressures of caustic solutions.

b.p.r. is roughly proportional to the ratio of solute to solvent.
In general, for aqueous solutions of nonvolatile inorganic

materials, a straight line is obtained which is substantially parallel to the 45-deg. line for water, indicating a substantially constant b.p.r. due to solute independent of ionization or hydration of the solute and independent of the temperature or pressure.

Estimation of Heat of Vaporization.—The second important datum which it is necessary to have with regard to a solution is the heat of vaporization of the solvent from the solution. Assuming that the perfect gas laws are approximately applicable to the solvent vapor, it can be shown that the latent heat of evaporation of solvent from the solution is equal to the heat of vaporization of the solvent from pure solvent at the temperature of the solution, plus the heat of dilution, taken positive when heat is evolved on dilution. Primarily because of the absence of data on heats of dilution at temperatures encountered in general evaporation practice, this correction is practically always neglected. In dilute solutions the heat of dilution approaches zero; in more concentrated solutions it becomes more important; yet errors introduced by neglecting heat of dilution are generally far less than inaccuracies involved in estimating heat-transfer coefficients. For example, if an aqueous NaOH solution is being concentrated from 20 per cent to 40 per cent at 18°C., where the heat of vaporization of pure water is 1042 B.t.u. per lb., the corrected value for heat of vaporization of water from the solution is 1092 B.t.u. per lb.

Optimum Cleaning Cycle.—As pointed out on page 381, the overall coefficient of heat transfer decreases owing to the deposition of scale on the heating surface. Visualize an evaporator containing heating surface A and operating with temperature difference Δ from condensing steam to boiling liquid. At any time θ the overall coefficient of heat transfer is U and the instantaneous rate of heat transfer $dQ/d\theta$ equals $UA\Delta$. Assuming that the thickness of the scale is directly proportional to the heat Q transferred up to the time θ, the thermal resistance of unit area is the initial resistance $1/U_0$ plus that of the scale, βQ; hence $1/U = 1/U_0 + \beta Q$ and $-dU/U^2 = \beta \, dQ$. Eliminating dQ and integrating gives $1/U^2 = 1/U_0^2 + 2\beta A\Delta\theta$, *i.e.*, the reciprocal of the square of the overall coefficient should be linear in the time elapsed since cleaning:[6]

$$1/U^2 = a + b\theta. \tag{A}$$

Curve 1 of Fig. 131 shows a plot of U vs. θ and it is seen that U decreases as the run progresses. Curve 2 shows that the data

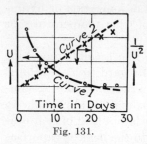

Fig. 131.

follow Eq. A for 20 days. After this time $1/U^2$ does not increase so fast as before, probably owing to failure of the scale to adhere so firmly to the heating surface as in the early part of the run. For that portion of the run in which Eq. A is followed the total heat transferred up to any time is found by integration to be

$$Q = \frac{2A\Delta[\sqrt{a+b\theta}-\sqrt{a}]}{b} \tag{B}$$

Even where the relation between Q and θ does not follow this rule, the actual relation may be determined experimentally. Given data as to the fixed charges on the evaporator, the time and cost for cleaning, the actual relation between Q and θ, the optimum cleaning cycle for any desired yearly capacity and the corresponding heating surface required are readily determined. In the case illustrated in Fig. 132, the sum of fixed charges and cost of cleaning reaches a flat minimum at a 10-day cycle, but in order to reduce initial investment a somewhat shorter cycle would be elected.

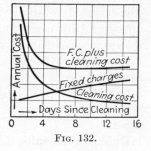

Fig. 132.

The solution of a few practical problems will illustrate these principles.

Illustration 2.—Assume a single vacuum pan of the submerged-tube type, operating continuously with a liquor depth of 4 ft. and provided with a condenser capable of giving a vacuum of 26 in. of mercury (bar. 29.91 in.). What is the heating surface required to concentrate 10,000 lb./hr. of 2 per cent NaOH solution, entering at 65°F., to a 25 per cent solution (sp. gr. = 1.3)? For the sake of illustration, assume an overall coefficient U of heat transfer of 100 B.t.u./(hr.) (sq. ft.) (deg. F) and exhaust steam at 6 in. vacuum.

Solution.—It is first necessary to calculate the terminal temperatures of the system. Since the liquor must leave the effect at a concentration of 25 per cent, the boiling liquor within the effect must be at this concentration. The temperature at the surface of the liquid will be that corresponding to the pressure maintained within the effect plus the b.p.r. of a solution of 0.333 lb. of NaOH per lb. of water. This latter is 11.5°C. or 20.7°F., as determined from Fig. 130, page 414. The absolute pressure above the boiling liquid is $(29.91-26)(14.7)/(29.91) = 1.92$ lb./sq. in., which corresponds to a temperature of 124.6°F. To this must be added the b.p.r. of 20.7°, giving the temperature of the liquid at the surface as 145.3°F. By the assumption that the heat necessary to vaporize water from a solution equals the heat of vaporization of the water alone, at the boiling temperature of the solution, the heat of vaporization at 145.3°F. is found from the steam tables to be 1011 B.t.u./lb. In each 10,000 lb. of liquor entering there are 9800 lb. of water and 200 lb. of NaOH. As the amount of NaOH is unchanged in passing through the system, it is taken as a basis of calculation; 600 lb. of water leave with each 200 lb. of NaOH (25 per cent solution) or 9200 lb. of water are evaporated per 10,000 lb. of entering liquor; the heat required to vaporize the water equals 9200×1011 B.t.u. The average temperature of the liquid into which heat flows from the steam coils will be substantially that corresponding to the average pressure on the liquid plus the b.p.r. of the dissolved NaOH. The pressure due to the average hydrostatic head $= (2)(1.3)(61.0)/144 = 1.11$ lb./sq. in.; the average total pressure $= 1.92 + 1.11 = 3.03$ lb./sq. in., which corresponds to a temperature of 141.4°F. To this must be added the b.p.r. of 20.7, giving the operating temperature of 162.1°F. By the assumption that the specific heat of a solution equals that of the water alone, to heat 10,000 lb. of entering 2 per cent liquor, $10,000(0.98)(162.1 - 65)$ B.t.u. are necessary. The area of the heating coils can now be determined:

$$q = 9800(162.1 - 65) + 9200(1011) = 100A(201 - 162.1)$$

whence A is 2640 sq. ft.

Failure to allow for the b.p.r. due to hydrostatic head would have given 1810 sq. ft.

EQUATIONS FOR MULTIPLE-EFFECT EVAPORATION (CONTINUOUS AND PARALLEL FLOW OF STEAM AND LIQUOR)

The following symbols will be used in the formulation of heat balances for multiple-effect evaporation:

c = parts solute per part solvent by weight.
W = weight of solvent in the liquor per unit of time.
t = temperature of solution.
T = temperature of steam in heating coils.
r = heat of evaporation of unit weight of solvent from either solution or pure solvent.
s = specific heat of solution.
A = area of heating surface in an effect.
U = overall coefficient of heat transfer through the heating surface, *i.e.*, from condensing steam to boiling liquor.
q = amount of heat transferred *through heating surface* per unit of time.

Subscripts

0 is for material entering the first effect.

1 applies to the first effect, or material leaving it.

2 applies to the second effect, or material leaving it, etc.

a before the symbol indicates that it applies to the condition within the heating coil.

b refers to the boiling solution.

Thus W_0 is the weight of solvent entering the first effect per unit time, and c_0 is its concentration. The temperature of the steam in the coils of the second effect is T_2, while the boiling solution is at t_2. The heat of condensation of this steam in the coils is $(_ar_2)$ while the heat of vaporization of the solution is $(_br_2)$.

If the solute is nonvolatile, the amount entering and leaving each effect of the series per unit time will be constant. Otherwise there would be an accumulation of the solute in some one effect. This is expressed mathematically by

$$c_0W_0 = c_1W_1 = c_2W_2, \text{ etc.}$$

The solvent evaporated in the first effect is $W_0 - W_1$, in the second $W_1 - W_2$, etc. The heat transmitted through the heating surface in the first effect must preheat the feed to the boiling temperature and evaporate the solvent.

$$q_1 = W_0[(1+c_0)(s_0)]*(t_1-t_0) + (W_0-W_1)\ (_br_1) = U_1A_1(T_1-t_1).$$

For the sake of illustration, assume that the condensed steam is removed from the system from each steam chest. The steam rising from the first effect is superheated, and cools on entering the second effect, giving up its superheat, and then condenses, giving up its heat of vaporization. Where the superheat, namely, the b.p.r., is small (20°F. or less), this superheat can be neglected, *provided* one remembers that $T_2 = t_1$ less the b.p.r. in the first effect. The heat transmitted through the heating surface of the second effect is

$$q_2 = (W_0-W_1)\ [(0.48)\ (t_1-T_2) + (_ar_2)] = U_2A_2(T_2-t_2).$$

The evaporation in the second effect is greater than corresponds to this heat supply through the heating surface, as the liquor entering from the first effect is superheated with respect

* Making the assumption that the specific heat of the aqueous solution equals the weight fraction of water in the solution, the term $(1+c)s$ equals unity.

to the pressure in the second effect, because it is at the boiling point corresponding to a higher pressure, namely, that in the first effect, and hence gives up a corresponding amount of heat, available for evaporation in this second effect. This is the so-called *self-evaporation* of a multiple-effect system, and is expressed by the second term in the following heat balance:

$$q_2 + W_1[(1+c_1)\ (s_1)](t_1-t_2) = (W_1-W_2)\ (_b r_2).$$

ILLUSTRATIVE PROBLEMS IN MULTIPLE-EFFECT EVAPORATION

Instead of using the above equations, one may develop the desired equations during the solution of the problem, using as tools the equality of input and output of matter and of heat, and Newton's law applied to the transfer of heat through the heating surface.

The following problem shows that, where high-pressure steam and *cold* feed liquor are used in multiple-effect practice, the evaporation per pound of steam is considerably less than the number of effects.

Illustration 3.—It is desired to design a film-type four effect evaporator with equal heating surface in each effect, to concentrate a solution from 20 per cent to 46 per cent solids by weight. The solute has a high molecular weight, and consequently the b.p.r. will be negligible. The rate of feed will be 10,000 lb./hr. and the feed temperature is 100°F. The available steam pressure is 52 lb./sq. in. gauge and the jet condenser water is at 100°F., giving a pressure in the last effect of 3.5 in. of mercury absolute, which corresponds to a boiling temperature in the last effect of 120°F. The condensed steam from each steam chest is withdrawn from the system. (*a*) Calculate the area of heating surface required per effect. (*b*) Calculate the pounds of water evaporated per hr. in each effect. (*c*) Tabulate the temperature difference across the heating surface in each effect. (*d*) Calculate the pounds of water evaporated per lb. of steam fed to the first effect. Explain why this figure is much less than 4 in this case.

Data and Notes.—Neglect heat loss to the surroundings. Take the latent heats of vaporization of water from the solutions to be the same as those of pure water at the same temperatures. Take the specific heats of all solutions to correspond to the water content of the solution, *i.e.*, neglect the heat capacity of the solute. Assume overall coefficients of heat transfer from steam to liquor to be 400, 350, 300 and 200 B.t.u./(hr.) (deg. F.) (sq. ft. of heating surface in the first, second, third and fourth effects, respectively).

Solution.—By an overall material balance on the system, it is seen that the total evaporation is 5650 lb./hr. Assuming for the moment that approximately equal weights of water are evaporated from each effect, 1413 lb./hr.

will be evaporated per effect. Therefore, the concentration of the solution leaving the first effect will be $0.2(10,000)/(10,000-1413) = 0.233$ lb. of solid/lb. of solution. Hence, the specific heat of this solution is 0.767. Similarly, the specific heats of the liquors leaving the second and third effects are found to be 0.721 and 0.653, respectively.

The solution to the problem now becomes one of successive approximations. As the first approximation assume that the *heat transferred* across the equal heating surfaces in each effect is the same, i.e., $q_1/A_1 = q_2/A_2 = q_3/A_3 = q_4/A_4$. Hence $U_1\Delta_1 = U_2\Delta_2 = U_3\Delta_3 = U_4\Delta_4$, or

$$400\Delta_1 = 350\Delta_2 = 300\Delta_3 = 200\Delta_4.$$

Solving for the temperature differences in terms of Δ_1, and noting that the sum of the four temperature drops is equal to the overall temperature difference, which is fixed by the steam and condenser pressures, the following equation is obtained:

$$300 - 120 = (1 + 1.14 + 1.33 + 2.00)\Delta_1.$$

Solving, Δ_1 is found to be $33°F$. Then

$$\Delta_1 = 33°F., \quad t_1 = 267°F.$$
$$\Delta_2 = 37°F., \quad t_2 = 230°F.$$
$$\Delta_3 = 44°F., \quad t_3 = 186°F.$$
$$\Delta_4 = 66°F., \quad t_4 = 120°F.$$

where t_1, t_2, t_3 and t_4 are the temperatures of the boiling solutions in each of the four effects.

It is now possible to make heat balances on each effect. Let y be lb. of steam fed/hr. to the first effect, and let E_1, E_2, E_3 and E_4 be lb. of water evaporated/hr. from the effects, respectively. A balance on the heat transferred in the first effect then gives

$$933E_1 = 910y - 10,000(0.80)(267-100)$$

from which $E_1 = 0.975y - 1431$. The heat balance on the second effect yields

$$959E_2 = 933E_1 + (10,000 - E_1)(0.767)(267-230)$$

from which $E_2 = 0.920y - 1055$. From similar heat balances on the remaining two effects, $E_3 = 0.834y - 625$ and $E_4 = 0.687y - 49$. However, the total evaporation, which is the sum of E_1, E_2, E_3 and E_4, was found to be 5650 lb./hr. Thus it is possible to solve for y, which is equal to 2580 lb./hr., of steam fed to the first effect.

Having a first approximation of y and values of q, the heat *transferred* across the heating surface may be calculated:

$$q_1 = 910y = 2,350,000 \text{ B.t.u./hr.}$$
$$q_2 = 933E_1 = 1,010,000$$
$$q_3 = 959E_2 = 1,264,000$$
$$q_4 = 986E_3 = 1,504,000$$

a. The corresponding values of the areas are $A_1 = 178$, $A_2 = 78$, $A_3 = 96$ and $A_4 = 114$ sq. ft., and the average value is 117. Using the above values of q and U, it is possible to make a second approximation, no longer assuming that the heat transferred in each effect is the same. However, it will be found that, although the individual values of Δ will change, the value of y will be practically unaffected. The individual areas will be more nearly equal, but their average will not differ materially from the value of 117 obtained in the first approximation. The second approximation actually yields an average area of 115* sq. ft. and a new value of y of 2500 lb./hr.

b.

	1st trial, lb./hr.	2d trial, lb./hr.
E_1	1084	1156
E_2	1318	1317
E_3	1525	1488
E_4	1723	1687

c.

	1st trial, °F.	2d trial, °F.
Δ_1	33	52
Δ_2	37	25
Δ_3	44	37
Δ_4	66	66

d. From the first approximation, the evaporation is $^{5650}/_{2580}$ or 2.2 lb. evaporated/lb. of steam consumed. By the second approximation this ratio is $^{5650}/_{2500}$ or 2.3.

By the first approximation, the heat transferred in the first effect is 2,350,000 B.t.u./hr., while that producing evaporation is 1,010,000 B.t.u./ hr., or the per cent producing evaporation is $(1,010,000/2,350,000)100$ or 43 per cent. The second approximation gives a value of 48 per cent. Thus it is seen that only 48 per cent of the steam consumed is used directly for evaporation, the remaining 52 per cent being stored up in the liquor and used in self-evaporation in the lower effects; this storing up of heat is a disadvantage, in that the heat stored is not re-used quantitatively as many times as there are effects. In a multiple system of any given number of effects, the greater the proportion of the heat supply stored in the liquor

---

* The problem has been solved on the basis of assumed values of the overall coefficients in each effect. These coefficients are a function of the viscosities of the solutions and the values of Δ in each effect. An exact solution would include allowance for these variations in the overall coefficient.

in the first effect, the less will be the total evaporation in all effects per pound of initial steam. In a given system operating under fixed terminal conditions, the percentage of heat obtained from the initial steam stored up in the feed liquor will be high where the ratio of weight of feed liquor to the evaporation in the first effect is high and where the temperature of the feed is far below the boiling temperature in the first effect. In the example just given, the steam economy calculated is poor (2.3 lb. of evaporation/lb. of steam). This is primarily due to the large amount of heat stored up in the liquor in the first effect, and to a lesser degree is due to the fact that the heat in the condensate from the various steam chests was not utilized. If the condensed steam from each chest, instead of being withdrawn from the system as assumed above, is passed on to the effect below, the lb. of evaporation/lb. of steam fed will increase somewhat.

EQUATIONS FOR THEORETICAL ENERGY REQUIRED IN EVAPORATION

To separate a solvent from its solution, if p_0 is pressure of the solvent at the temperature in question, p that of the solution, R the gas constant and T the absolute temperature, using as the basis of calculation an amount of solution containing 1 mol of nonvolatile solute and N mols of solvent, the free energy required (W) is

$$W = RT \int_{N_2}^{N_1} \ln \frac{p_0}{p} dN.$$

The units in which the work-energy involved is expressed depend on the units in which R is given. This expression is exact, barring deviations from the gas laws, which are usually small at the pressures at which evaporating processes are operated. For any given case the equation may be evaluated by graphical integration, but, to show how small is the real energy requirement in evaporation, it is possible to integrate this expression by the assumption of Raoult's law; in the worst case this will give a rough approximation, but in many cases the deviation will be only a few per cent. The result is

$$W = RT \ln \left[\frac{(N_2)^{N_2}(N_1+1)^{N_1+1}}{(N_1)^{N_1}(N_2+1)^{N_2+1}} \right]$$

where N_1 and N_2 represent the mols of solvent associated with 1 mol of solute at the beginning and end of the evaporation, respectively.

For the total removal of the solvent from a nonvolatile residue with which the solvent is completely miscible, i.e., where no crystallizing of the residue occurs or separation as a distinct phase, e.g., when $N_2 = 0$, this becomes

$$W = RT \ln N_1 \left(\frac{N_1+1}{N_1} \right)^{N_1+1}.$$

In the evaporation of a saturated solution of the solute, during which crystallization or separation occurs,

$$W = N_s RT \ln \frac{N_s+1}{N_s} = N_s RT \ln \frac{p_0}{p_s}$$

where N_s is mols solvent per mol of solute in the saturated solution and p_s is pressure of that solution. For the evaporation of a dilute solution to saturation, followed by crystallization, this last equation applies only to the second stage of the process, the work consumption of the first stage being determined by the general equation given above.

To illustrate, assume the complete removal of water from a 10 per cent glycerin solution at 90°F., *i.e.*, of 9 times 92 or 828 lb. of water from 1 lb. mol (92 lb.) of glycerin. $N_1 = 828/18 = 46$, $R = 1.99$

$$W = 1.99(550) \ln 46\left(\frac{47}{46}\right)^{47} = 5290 \text{ B.t.u.}$$

or $5290 \div 828 = 6.4$ B.t.u./lb. of water evaporated.*

It is evident that the more concentrated the solution, the greater the energy consumption per lb. of water evaporated, but even for strong solutions this quantity remains small. For colloidal solutions, *i.e.*, those of high molecular weight, the necessary work is negligible, as is obvious from the fact that the pressure of such solutions is practically the same as that of the pure solvent. For water, the theoretical work of evaporation is zero. As stated, even for true solutions the value is low.

References

1. JAKOB, N., and W. FRITZ, *Forsch. Gebiete Ingenieur.*, **2**, 435–447 (1931).

2. LOGAN, L. A., N. FRAGEN, and W. L. BADGER, *Ind. Eng. Chem.*, **26**, 1044–1047 (1934); ROBEY, N. T., Chemical Engineering Thesis, Massachusetts Institute of Technology, 1936.

3. THOMSEN, J., "Thermochemistry," pp. 161–164; Longmans, Green & Co., London, 1908.

4. "Neue Grundgesetz zur Nationelle Physik und Chemie," Erste Folge, Leipzig, 1878.

5. "Landolt-Börnstein Tables" (1912).

6. MCCABE, W. L., and C. S. ROBINSON, *Ind. Eng. Chem.*, **16**, 478 (1924)

* The equations given are for the batch free energy of separation, but apply to the flow process under conditions where the difference in the volume of the solution and the sum of the volumes of the solvent and the solid salt is small.

CHAPTER XIV

GENERAL PRINCIPLES OF DIFFUSIONAL PROCESSES

PART I. CLASSIFICATION OF PROCESSES

The problem of transferring materials by diffusion from one phase to another is repeatedly encountered in chemical-engineering operations. One type of problem that frequently involves such a mechanism is the separation of mixtures of fluids. For miscible liquids distillation, involving the interchange of material between liquid and vapor phases, is usually but not always the best. The same method is applicable to mixed gases. Thus, in the manufacture of oxygen and nitrogen from air, one can

Case	Character of mixture undergoing treatment	Character of treating agent
1	Gas	Gas
2	Gas	Liquid
3	Gas	Solid
4	Liquid	Gas
5	Liquid	Liquid
6	Liquid	Solid
7	Solid	Gas
8	Solid	Liquid
9	Solid	Solid

liquefy the whole mixture by compression coupled with refrigeration and separate the components by rectification.   If one of the components of a gas has a high condensing temperature relative to the others, it is possible to condense it completely by compression and cooling or by refrigeration, or by combination of the two. Other operations involving transfer of materials by diffusion from one phase to another are absorption, adsorption, humidification, drying, stripping, condensation, combustion and crystallization.

The individual cases falling under this classification are numerous and exceedingly diversified in detailed characteristics, but, because in all such operations the underlying principles and the general methods of applying them are the same, these cases will be first grouped together for a study of the factors common to all, to be followed with the later chapters on the specific processes.

The mixture to be treated may be solid, liquid or gas; thus there would be the nine possible cases shown in the table on page 424.

1. Treatment of Gas by Gas.—Since the phenomena under consideration involve treatment of a mixture by an agent immiscible with one of its components and since, in the absence of chemical combination or unusual affinity, all gases are miscible in all proportions, it follows that this particular case is never encountered.

2. Treatment of Gases by Liquid (Gas Washing or Scrubbing).—One of the best methods of separating the components of mixtures of gases or vapors is by means of selective absorption in liquid solvents. Thus, while the solubility of coal gas in water is very small, the solubility of ammonia in water is great. Consequently, if one treats coal gas with a relatively small amount of water, it is possible to remove from it by solution in the latter practically all the ammonia originally in the gas. Furthermore, the ammonia can then be readily separated from the water by distillation. Similarly, vapors of benzene, toluene and xylene in coal gas can be dissolved in various absorbent oils; gasoline can be removed from natural gas by these same solvents; sulfur dioxide can be recovered from smelter gases by water, carbon dioxide from flue gases by aqueous solutions of alkali carbonates, water vapor from air by sulfuric acid, and the like. In the last illustration the purpose is to free the air from water rather than to recover the water, whereas in most cases it is essential to recover the component dissolved. This difference in purpose, however, in no wise affects the character of the absorbing operation itself, although in general it will influence the method of treatment of the absorbent before re-use.

3. Treatment of Gases by Solids.—It has long been known that many solids show selective adsorption for specific gases and vapors. Thus, the adsorptive capacity of palladium for hydrogen is so high that this metal may be employed for the quantitative absorption of hydrogen from mixtures with other gases. Similarly, the adsorptive capacity of special charcoals for gases has long been known. During the war charcoal and other solid adsorbents were employed in gas masks for the removal of the poison gases employed in chemical warfare. Thus, a fraction of a liter of activated charcoal in a gas-mask canister was found capable of reducing the mustard-gas concentration of air, inhaled at a rate as high as 60 liters per min., to below 1 part in 100,000,-000. Largely as a result of improvements during the war in the manufacture of activated charcoal, silica gel and other highly active adsorbents, the use of these materials for adsorption of gases is being widely introduced in industrial plants. A number of plants for the recovery of gasoline from natural gas by charcoal are already in operation in this country.

4. Treatment of Liquid by Gas or Vapor (Steam Distillation and Stripping).—The benzene dissolved in absorbent oil in the recovery of light oil from coal gas, referred to under Par. 2, is removed from the relatively nonvolatile absorbent by heating to increase the volatility of the benzene and by blowing through steam to sweep out the benzene vapor. This operation is ordinarily described as oil stripping or denuding. In principle it is absolutely analogous to the steam distillation of a volatile component from a nonvolatile liquid. By bringing gases and liquids, such as air and water, into direct contact, the humidity of the air may be increased or decreased and the temperature of the water decreased or increased as discussed in Chap. XVIII.

5. Treatment of Liquid by Liquid.—It is sometimes advantageous to remove solutes from aqueous solutions by extraction with suitable organic solvents, such as ether, benzene, naphtha and the like, in which they are more soluble than in water. This makes it possible to separate them from other substances which may accompany them in the water solution but which are not soluble in the solvents employed. Thus, the standard method for the analytical determination of unsaponifiable oils and waxes in admixture with fatty material is to submit the mixture to vigorous saponification with alcoholic potash or, if necessary, sodium ethylate, and to dilute the product with water and extract with petroleum ether. The soaps remain in the aqueous solution while the unsaponifiable oils and waxes dissolve in the ether.* It is sometimes advantageous to modify

* Since the soaps are not entirely insoluble in the ether nor the unsaponifiable material not entirely insoluble in the aqueous solution, it is necessary

the relative solubilities by adding a material soluble in one liquid but not the other; thus the addition of salt to an aqueous solution prior to extraction with ether improves the separation.

Liquid SO_2 is employed to separate aromatic and highly unsaturated hydrocarbons from solution in liquid paraffins and naphthenes (Edeleanu process), taking advantage of the much greater solubility of the aromatics and unsaturateds in SO_2. Processes of this sort have not in the past been employed on an industrial scale to the extent that their promise seems to justify. It is likely that, as the manipulative technique required is developed, their utilization will become far more frequent.

6. Treatment of Liquids by Solids (Percolation or Adsorption Filtration).—Liquids contaminated with organic coloring matters of complex structure and high molecular weight can often be freed best from these impurities by treatment with suitable solid adsorbents such as bone char, activated charcoal, fuller's earth and the like. Such treatment is used for the decolorization of sugar syrups, animal, vegetable and mineral oils, etc. It is often advantageous to allow the liquor to percolate through the relatively coarse, granulated solid. The color is usually taken up by the solids by the mechanism of adsorption (see pages 436–440).

7. Treatment of Solids by Gases.—The necessity of removing water or other volatile liquids from solid materials is frequently met in industrial operation. This may be accomplished by passing a heated gas over the material and removing the liquid by evaporation. Thus, in the drying of wood or unburned brick, hot air is passed over the solid to remove the water. In case the liquid is valuable, it may be recovered by using a closed system and condensing the vapor from the exit gas, which then may be reheated and used again. In the case of inflammable liquids, gas containing a low concentration of oxygen may be used, thereby eliminating the danger of explosions. When gasoline or similar material has been adsorbed on charcoal, the gasoline may be removed by sweeping over the charcoal a current of superheated steam which picks up the gasoline and carries it to a

---

to extract the aqueous layer repeatedly with ether and to wash the ether solutions with water, these washings being added to the main aqueous solution. The unsaponifiable material is recovered by evaporation of the ether from the combined ethereal extracts.

condenser where both gasoline and steam are liquefied and separated by decantation.

8. Treatment of Solids by Liquids (Lixiviation, Leaching and Extraction).—Black ash consists essentially of a mixture of sodium carbonate and other water-soluble compounds, with insoluble constituents; caliche, of sodium nitrate mixed with insolubles; tanbark, of soluble tannic acid adsorbed on the fibers of the bark. All these materials can be recovered by solution in water, though the processes differ because in the first cases the materials dissolved are very soluble, while in the last they are quite firmly held by the insoluble residue. Also, wool grease is removed from wool and vegetable oils from press cake by solution in naphtha or other suitable organic solvents, etc. These processes are called **extraction,** but in principle do not differ from those already enumerated.

9. Treatment of Solids by Solids.—The transference of a material from one solid to another is so slow and the separation of mixed solids so difficult that this case does not arise in practice.

PART II. FACTORS CONTROLLING OPERATION

Equilibrium.—Whenever a substance distributes itself between two materials, a distribution equilibrium always tends to be set up. Thus, if SO_2 gas, whether or not mixed with inert gas, is brought into contact with water at 20°C., the SO_2 will continue to dissolve in the water until its concentration in the water is sixty times that in the gaseous phase. This condition represents equilibrium, and no further solution of the gas will occur unless this equilibrium is disturbed. If water containing dissolved SO_2 is brought in contact with gas containing less than one-sixtieth as much SO_2 per unit volume as the water, SO_2 will escape from the water and pass into the gas until the ratio of the concentrations in the two phases has reached the equilibrium value given above.

If one wishes to remove SO_2 from a gaseous mixture by water, it is obvious that this equilibrium sets an absolute lower limit on the amount of water necessary to employ for complete removal. Therefore equilibrium is a vital factor in controlling the operation of absorption systems. In the case cited above, the equilibrium is extremely simple in character, but frequently the relationships are complicated. Specific cases of importance will be discussed on pages 431 to 442.

Rate of Reaction.—The transference of a substance from one body to another obviously requires time. Other things equal, the rate of transfer will be proportional to the surface of contact between the phases and consequently, to secure rapid interaction, the interfacial surface should be made as large as possible. There are two main mechanisms of transfer, one by actual bulk motion of the gas (convection) and the other by molecular (true) diffusion as a result of concentration gradients. In most of these processes there exists a film of relatively stationary material which insulates the main body of fluid from the other phase and a main body where the fluid is turbulent and eddying. While the two mechanisms operate simultaneously throughout the fluid, actually in the true film where turbulence is practically negligible the transfer is mainly by molecular diffusion, while in the main body the transfer is largely by convection as a result of the rapid eddying. Thus a substance being transferred must pass through the two consecutively, being carried by turbulence through the main body of the fluid, and then by true diffusion through the film to the interface. In Chap. IV the conduction of heat through fluid films was taken up as one of the important cases in heat transfer; the problem in molecular diffusion is very similar. In diffusion, the material is transferred by means of the molecular motions, while the conduction of heat is a transfer of energy which is effected by the same motion. The rate at which heat is conducted is determined for each substance by a physical property which is termed the thermal *conductivity*, and in like manner the rate at which one gas diffuses through another is determined by a quantity which is termed the *diffusivity*. These two properties are analogous. Just as the density of the heat current (rate of transfer per unit area) is obtained by multiplying the conductivity by the temperature gradient, the mass-transfer rate per unit area is obtained by multiplying the diffusivity by the concentration gradient of the diffusing substance, and consequently will be greater the greater the distance from equilibrium. Factors, such as agitation, which decrease the thickness of surface films and increase turbulence will tend to increase diffusion rate and, similarly, factors which increase specific rate of diffusion, such as rise in temperature of a liquid, will also be helpful, though the latter will frequently throw equilibrium the wrong way to an extent more than compensating for increased diffusion rate. Reaction rate is no less important an influence in operation than equilibrium itself.

Countercurrent Action.—Since the transfer of a solute from one phase to another cannot possibly go beyond equilibrium and since, in general, low concentration of the solute in one phase corresponds at equilibrium to low concentration in the other, it follows that a single treatment of the original material cannot remove any large fraction of the substance to be transferred unless one employ a relatively large amount of treating agent or unless the treating agent has a great affinity for the substance absorbed. The disadvantages of employing excessive amounts of treating agent are obvious, and, where its affinity for the substance absorbed is great, the difficulty of removing it later is also serious. One can, therefore, lay down the rule that a single treatment is usually impractical and unsatisfactory. However, if one will treat the original material with treating agent which has been previously employed and which, therefore, is already partially saturated with the solute, it becomes possible, owing to the high concentration of solute in the original material to be treated, to raise the concentration of the solute in the treating agent to a point at least approaching equilibrium. At the same time it becomes practicable finally to reduce to a very low point the solute concentration in the original material by treating it ultimately, after a number of intermediate steps, with fresh treating agent in which the concentration of solute is negligible. This systematic, stepwise interaction of two materials is described as stepwise countercurrent treatment (see pages 465 to 512). Countercurrent action is capable of varied applications (see pages 118 and 209), but for diffusional processes its use in some form is almost always essential.

Temperature Control.—There is frequently a marked temperature effect accompanying the transfer of material from one phase to another. Thus, in the absorption of a vapor from a gas by a liquid, the latent heat of condensation of the vapor is set free, and this heat raises the temperature of both the liquid and the gas. Since, in general, rise in temperature decreases the solubility of the gas or vapor in the liquid, the equilibrium and therefore also the absorption rate are both adversely affected. Where the concentrations of the substance transferred are small, the heat capacity of the other materials present is usually so great that the temperature rise is not serious, but, where concentrations are high, this factor may be very important. It must never be forgotten and, where necessary, means must be provided to control the temperature.

Recovery of Treating Agent.—Occasionally the treating agent is either air or water and the material absorbed thereby is to be discarded, but ordinarily the treating agent must be freed from the material that it has taken up and used over again. It is therefore essential to choose the treating agent not only from the point of view of its effectiveness for the original absorption but also from the standpoint of ease of separation and recovery. Furthermore, in order to make the original treatment as complete as possible, it is necessary to remove the absorbed material from the treating agent completely before re-use. It is obvious that the larger the amount of treating agent employed, the greater the expense of purifying it. Consequently, from this point of view it is desirable to keep the amount of treating agent low and the concentration of absorbed material in it high, a result attainable only by effective countercurrent action. Reduction of the amount of treating agent, while it reduces the cost of its purification, tends to decrease the completeness of recovery from the material treated and, by reducing the rate of absorption, to increase the cost of treating. There is, therefore, an economically optimum ratio of treating agent to material treated, the value of which will depend on the cost factors governing each individual case.

PART III. EQUILIBRIA

Introduction.—If, in any *single* phase of matter, there exist at different points differences of concentration of any compound in it, that component tends to diffuse from a point of high to a point of low concentration. With diffusion through gases and liquids all are familiar, but diffusion also takes place through solids. Thus gold diffuses through solid lead and hydrogen through palladium. The diffusion of carbon through iron at temperatures hundreds of degrees below the melting point is exploited both in malleabilization and in casehardening. The last is diffusion through a multi-phase solid, but the first two are probably single phase. Fick's law states that the rate of diffusion is proportional to the concentration gradient at the point in question and is, of course, proportional to the area of cross section through which diffusion is taking place. Diffusion is therefore analogous to conduction of heat.

On the other hand, at the *interface* between phases, transfer of material from one phase to the other does not of necessity result from a concentration difference between the phases but depends on the *equilibrium* relation between them. Thus, while the concentration of water molecules in liquid water is far higher than in steam, the two phases can still be in equilibrium, or, if the steam is at a somewhat higher temperature, it will condense into the water, *i.e.*, water molecules will pass from a point of low concentration (the steam) to one far higher (the liquid water). Similarly, if air at 30°C. contains hydrochloric acid gas in a concentration of only 0.001 mg. per c.c. and this air is brought into contact with water, the HCl will continue to dissolve in the water phase until it has built up a concentration of over 20 per cent, *i.e.*, 210 mg. per c.c., a concentration 210,000-fold that in the air from which the acid came. Only in case the HCl concentration in the water is greater than this will HCl pass from the water into the gas. There is, therefore, in general, even at equilibrium, a sudden concentration break at the interface. It is obvious that these equilibria between phases are of controlling significance in processes of absorption, extraction and the like.

The technique of the determination of interphase equilibria is exceedingly important and data should never be accepted without reservation unless obtained by one skilled in the art. It is essential to approach equilibrium from both sides, to make sure that one is not dealing with false equilibria or other complicating phenomena. Furthermore, this frequently saves time, because the mean of the two approximate values thus obtained gives the desired result with a precision sufficient in many cases.

In discussing the various important types of equilibria, the following classification has been adopted.

1. Linear distribution:
    a. Gases and liquids.
    b. Liquids and liquids.
    c. Special cases.

2. Adsorption:
    a. Solids and gases.
    b. Solids and liquids.
    c. Gases and liquids.
3. Complete chemical combination.
4. Incomplete chemical combination.

1. Linear Distribution

Gases and Liquids.—There are certain important cases in which, at equilibrium, the concentration of the common component in one phase is proportional to that in the other. The most familiar case is that of the solubility of gases that follow Henry's law, *i.e.*, in which the concentration of the gas dissolved in the liquid is proportional to the partial pressure of that gas in the gaseous phase above the liquid, c equals Hp. Since the concentration of a gas in a mixture of gases is proportional to its partial pressure, the above is equivalent to saying that the concentration of gas dissolved in the liquid is proportional to the concentration of that gas in the gaseous phase in equilibrium with the liquid.

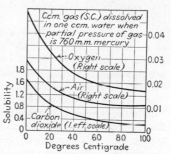

FIG. 133.—Effect of temperature on solubility of gases in water.

Figure 133 shows the solubility[3] of a number of important gases as a function of the temperature. It will be noted that rise in temperature decreases the solubility. It is important to remember that the solubility is proportional to the partial pressure of the gas and not to the total pressure above the liquid. Thus, the solubility of oxygen in water at 100°C. is 0.017 volume per unit volume of water, provided the partial pressure of the oxygen is 1 atmosphere. However, at this temperature, if the total pressure is 1 atmosphere, the vapor phase must consist entirely of water vapor* and the solubility of oxygen in the liquid under these conditions is zero. At this temperature, to dissolve the amount of oxygen quoted above, the total pressure must be 2 atmospheres, the partial pressure of the water and of the oxygen

* Since the depressing effect of the dissolved oxygen on the vapor pressure of the water is negligible.

each being 1 atmosphere. In other words, the solubility of gases in liquids at the boiling points of the latter is zero, a fact made use of in the deaeration of liquids. Modification of the form in which the concentration in the liquid is expressed will sometimes broaden the range over which Henry's law holds; acetylene dissolved in acetone is a case in point.

Since Raoult's law may be written in the form $p_A = P_A x$, it is obvious that it may be looked upon as a special case of linear distribution between the gaseous and liquid phase.

Illustration 1.—Flue gases, containing 1 per cent benzene vapor by volume, are to be washed with a mineral oil containing 0.5 per cent benzene by weight. Calculate the maximum percentage of the original benzene that could be absorbed (a) if the absorption were carried out at 20°C., and (b) at 30°C.

Notes.—The vapor pressures of pure benzene (Fig. 5, p. 14) are 75 mm. of mercury at 20°C. and 120 mm. of mercury at 30°C. The molecular weight of benzene is 78.0. Over the range of concentrations and temperatures involved, Raoult's law may be applied to the partial pressure of the benzene by taking the average molecular weight of this mineral oil as 230. Assume that the barometer is 760 mm. of mercury.

Solution.—Since it is desired to reduce the benzene concentration of the flue gas to the minimum value, the exhausted gas must be in contact with the leanest oil. In other words, one must employ the countercurrent principle (page 430). To obtain the maximum recovery, the absorber must be infinitely tall, so that the benzene concentration in the spent gases will be in equilibrium with the leanest oil at the top of the tower. Under these conditions, at 20°C., the partial pressure of benzene in the exit gases will equal

$$75 \frac{\dfrac{0.5}{78}}{\dfrac{0.5}{78} + \dfrac{99.5}{230}} = 1.10 \text{ mm. of mercury.}$$

Hence, at 20°C., the best that one can do will be to reduce the benzene from a pressure of 7.6 to 1.10 mm. To calculate the percentage of the original benzene, absorbed by the oil, take a basis of 1 mol of inert or benzene-free gas.

$$\text{Then } 100 \frac{\dfrac{7.6}{760-7.6} - \dfrac{1.10}{760-1.10}}{\dfrac{7.6}{760-7.6}} = 85.6 \text{ per cent recovery.}$$

Similarly, at 30°C., the maximum percentage recoverable is found to be 77.2, emphasizing the importance of low temperature as regards maximum per cent recovery (see, however, p. 455).

Figure 134 shows the effect, on the per cent recovery, of changing the temperature of the treating agent.

Liquids and Liquids.—Similarly, the distribution of a solute between two immiscible liquids is frequently linear; *i.e.*, at equilibrium the concentration of the solute in liquid *A* is proportional to its concentration in liquid *B*.

These two simple distribution laws are usually but not always valid at low concentrations. Thus, Henry's law almost always applies for sparingly soluble gases, because in such case it is

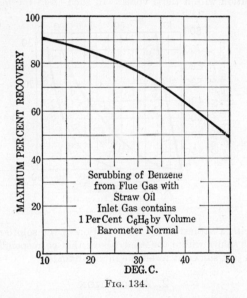

Fig. 134.

obvious that the concentration of gas in the liquid phase cannot possibly be high. It likewise frequently applies to very soluble gases so long as the concentration in the liquid phase is low or, what is equivalent to the same thing, the partial pressure in the gaseous phase is very low. Similarly, the distribution of a solute between two liquids of limited miscibility is usually linear so long as the concentration in the two phases is small. Whenever the concentration in a liquid phase becomes high, deviations from proportionality almost always begin to develop.

Special Cases.—Many solids are porous and, when impregnated with solutions, hold these solutions within their voids. In order to remove the solute from such a solid, it may be necessary to allow the solute to diffuse

from the voids within the solid out into a less concentrated external surrounding solution, thus to be washed away.   The amount of solute held by
such solids is obviously proportional to the concentration of the solution
in the internal voids.   Since such an internal solution will obviously be in
equilibrium with an external solution, outside the solid, of equal concentration, it follows that the concentration of solute within the solid, expressed
as a relation between the amounts of solute and solid, is proportional to that
of the external solution with which it is in equilibrium.   Such cases are
illustrated by leather, wood pulp, fabrics, etc., saturated with solutions of
nonadsorbed materials.

One can have within the internal voids solutes present as solids in excess
of that in solution within those voids.   In such cases the mass will be in

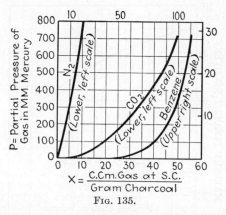

Fig. 135.

equilibrium with a saturated external solution of the solute at all concentrations of the solute within the solid, above that corresponding to a saturated solution just sufficient to fill the internal voids.

2. Adsorption

Solids and Gases.—Certain solids and gases combine to form
compounds which may be loose or very stable, but which differ
from compounds such as calcium carbonate, formed by interaction of calcium oxide and CO_2, in that, first, the combination
does not take place in constant stoichiometric proportions and,
second, the decomposition pressure is not independent of the
amount of gas combined with the solid provided excess solid is
present, but varies progressively with the gas quantity held by
the solid.   The data of a characteristic adsorption reaction,
namely, that of CO_2 gas[5] on activated charcoal, are shown in
Fig. 135.

It will be noted that, at very low partial pressures of the CO_2,
relatively large quantities of the gas are held on the solid.   As the

partial pressure of the gas is increased, the amount held on the solid at equilibrium also increases, but at a much less rapid rate than would correspond to linear distribution. Finally a point is reached at which a relatively large increase in partial pressure of the gas is required to force a given increase of gas on the solid. Figure 135 shows also the data for the adsorption of benzene vapor on charcoal.[2]

A similar curve for a more loosely held gas, nitrogen,[5] is also shown in Fig. 135. While the general shape of the curve is the same, the difference lies in the fact that much less gas is held by the solid at low partial pressure of the gas.

Mechanism.—The exact mechanism of adsorption is still a matter of dispute. It seems certain that in some cases adsorption is due to chemical combination of the gas with the free valences of atoms on the surface of the solid. In other cases the evidence indicates that adsorption is due to liquefaction of the gas and its retention by capillary action in the exceedingly fine pores of the adsorbing solid. In some cases the two phenomena are probably superimposed. Often one encounters curves of the type shown in Fig. 194 (page 620) for water adsorbed on cotton, in which at low pressures one gets a characteristic adsorption relationship, the water held flattening out to an approximately asymptotic value, followed later by a further rise in adsorption at high partial pressures of the adsorbed gas. It has been surmised that the first part of the diagram may represent chemical adsorption and the latter, capillary effects; or it may be that the first part represents liquid held in exceedingly fine capillaries and the latter, the influence of capillaries an order of magnitude larger in size.

Freundlich Equation.—Whatever the mechanism, the equilibrium between a gas or vapor and an adsorbing solid is generally exponential in character over certain ranges in concentration. This relation is expressed by the Freundlich equation,

$$p = bX^n$$

where p is the partial pressure of the gas in equilibrium with the solid and X is the amount of the gas adsorbed per unit quantity of adsorbent; b and n are constants. In true adsorption, n is always greater than unity.* The more firmly the gas

* If $n = 1$, one is dealing with a phenomenon of solution which follows Henry's law and which is not classified as adsorption. The solubility of

is adsorbed, the greater is the numerical value of n. The quantity b is proportional to the active surface of the adsorbing solid. While it has been claimed that this equation has theoretical basis, it is probably safer to regard it as empirical in character. The data demonstrate that it is not exact, but as an interpolation formula over very wide ranges it is extremely valuable. Numerical illustrations of this equation will be found on pages 508 and 512. From the form of the equation it is obvious that if one plots on logarithmic paper the partial pressures of the gas as ordinates against the equilibrium concentrations on the adsorbing solid as abscissas, the equation demands that the data fall on a straight line, the slope of which is equal to the exponent n. This offers a ready means of testing the applicability of the Freundlich equation to any given set of data.

While adsorptive phenomena are to no small degree specific in character, it is nonetheless possible to lay down the general rule that the higher the molecular weight and the lower the volatility of any gas, the greater its tendency to adsorb on any solid. So marked is the influence of volatility, *i.e.*, the vapor pressure of the liquefied gas in the pure state, that it is often better to express the concentration of the adsorbed gas, not as its partial pressure in the gaseous phase, but as the ratio of its partial pressure to its saturation (vapor) pressure.* Expressed in this way, it is found that the influence of temperature on the equilibrium is relatively slight.† The adsorption equilibria of water on textile fibers at various temperatures are plotted in Fig. 194 (page 620). As vapor saturation is approached, the Freundlich equation always breaks down.

CO_2 in solid rubber is a case in point. See VENABLE and FUWA, *J. Ind. Eng. Chem.*, **14**, 139 (1922). If n is less than unity, the phenomenon is sometimes called *negative adsorption*, but is of minor technical importance.

* In the case of water, this ratio is the relative humidity, (see page 577). The term *relative humidity* is not infrequently applied to the concentration of vapors other than water when expressed in the same way: $h = p/P$.

† In certain cases, as in the adsorption of SO_2 by silica gel, equilibrium data at various temperatures may be correlated by the Freundlich equation modified as follows:

$$X = b(h\gamma)^{1/n}$$

where γ is the surface tension. Expressing X as cubic centimeters of liquid SO_2 per grams of gel, McGAVACK and PATRICK, *J. Amer. Chem. Soc.*, **42**, 946 (1920), found n to be 2.24 between $-80°C$. and $+100°C$.

Selective Adsorption.—So important is the effect of volatility that it is frequently possible for a gas of low volatility to displace one of high volatility. Thus, if activated charcoal is brought in contact with natural gas, it adsorbs a certain amount of all the hydrocarbons of the gas. On the other hand, per unit partial pressure, the high-boiling constituents of the gas are adsorbed selectively, *i.e.*, far more completely than the low-boiling constituents. Furthermore, if this same charcoal is treated with additional gas, the high-boiling components of this second quantity of gas will adsorb on the charcoal and, in order to do so, will to a large degree displace the low-boiling constituents already adsorbed. In this way a charcoal that has picked up from a gas relatively large quantities of methane, ethane and propane will, when treated with further gas, adsorb pentane, hexane and higher hydrocarbons by displacing the lower-boiling ones already picked up. This is the reason for the fact that by the intelligent use of activated charcoal in recovering gasoline from natural gas it is possible to produce a product relatively free from gases of low molecular weight.

Importance of Surface.—The concentration of adsorbed gas or vapor per unit area of adsorbing solid is exceedingly low, *i.e.*, the adsorbed film is very, very thin. Therefore, in order to adsorb large quantities of gas, it is essential to have an enormous amount of adsorbing surface. This might be secured by having the adsorbing agent finely subdivided. Because of the difficulties of handling powders, however, it is preferable that the adsorbing agent consist of a spongy, porous material, agglomerated into granules so that each individual lump is relatively large, but, because of its porous structure, the total surface is enormously greater than could be realized with a dense solid of the same grain size. Thus the apparent density of the individual granules (best called "grain density") of well-activated charcoal is about 0.83,* while that of the carbon itself is 1.89. Thus the granule itself contains 56 per cent capillary voids.

Solids and Liquids.—Solids can adsorb solutes from solution in liquids by a mechanism entirely analogous to the adsorption of gases. Here also the Freundlich equation applies. Cases in point are the adsorption of direct dyestuffs by textile fibers,

---

* This must not be confused with apparent density, *i.e.*, the weight, per unit volume of the granules in bulk, which in this case is 0.46 gm. per c.c.

the adsorption of tannic acids by both hide substance and vegetable fibers and the adsorption of organic colors by fuller's earth, bone char, activated charcoal and the like. Computation methods do not differ in principle from those employed for the adsorption of gases by solids.

Illustration 2.—Water contains organic color which is to be extracted with alum and lime. Five parts of alum and lime per million parts of water will reduce the color to 25 per cent of the original color, and 10 parts will reduce the color to 3.5 per cent.

Estimate how much alum and lime as parts per million are required to reduce the color to 0.5 per cent of the original color.

Solution.—Let y be the residual color in the solution, expressed as a fraction of the original value, and X be the ratio of adsorbed color to adsorbent. Since $y = bX^n$, log $y = $ log $b + n$ log X. Applying this equation to the data, one finds

$$\log \frac{y_1}{y_2} = n \log \frac{X_1}{X_2} \quad \text{or} \quad \log \frac{0.25}{0.035} = n \log \frac{75/5}{96.5/10}$$

whence $n = 4.45$. Also, log $(y_1/y_3) = 4.45$ log (X_1/X_3) or log $(0.25/0.005) = 4.45$ log $(15/X_3)$, whence X_3 equals $6.23 = 99.5/z$ and the parts of adsorbent z are found to be 16.0.

Gases and Liquids.—While gases and vapors adsorb on the surface of liquids, it is but rarely that liquids can be employed in a permanent state of subdivision sufficiently great to furnish the surface necessary to adsorb appreciable quantities. On the other hand, liquids dissolving gases sometimes give equilibrium diagrams extremely similar to adsorption curves. These are usually liquids which combine chemically with the dissolved material. A case in point is that of sulfuric acid and water, the equilibrium diagram for which is given in Fig. 136.[9] In such cases computations may be made by the same methods employed for solid adsorbents.

3. Chemical Combination

When a gas is treated with an absorbent with which it combines chemically to form a stable compound, so long as there is excess of this absorbing agent, at equilibrium the partial pressure in the gaseous phase is negligible. Thus, if ammonia is being absorbed in excess sulfuric acid, as in the manufacture of ammonium sulfate from illuminating gas, or CO_2 in excess caustic, as in gas analysis, or the like, the gas left undissolved after thorough contact between the gaseous and liquid phases is negligible. Similarly, if one is absorbing a gas by a solid with which it firmly combines chemically, such as CO_2 by calcium oxide in the purification of air for liquefaction, the absorption is complete so long as contact is adequate and the absorbent is present in excess.

4. INCOMPLETE CHEMICAL COMBINATION

In many cases the combination is a loose and unstable one, *i.e.*, the compound is subject to partial dissociation. Such cases are obviously governed by the law of mass action. Other cases undoubtedly involving loose chemical combination are of a character such that it is difficult to demonstrate this quantitatively. A case in point is the absorption of water vapor by sulfuric acid, the equilibrium data for which are found in Fig. 136.

An interesting case of chemical combination is found in the distribution of certain substances between liquids in which the substance in question exists in different degrees of polymerization. Thus, acetic acid dissolves in benzene in the form of double molecules and in ether as single molecules. If one grants the presence in the benzene solution of a small

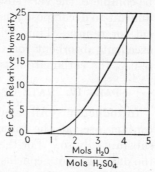

FIG. 136.—Equilibrium distribution of water between air and H_2SO_4.

proportion of single molecules, the concentration of which is in equilibrium with both the double molecules in that solvent and the single molecules in the ether, the law of mass action requires that at equilibrium the distribution of the acetic between the two solvents be determined by the following equation:

$$y^2 = jx,$$

where y is the concentration of acetic acid in ether, x is the concentration of acetic acid in benzene and j is the distribution constant.

When a gas combines chemically with a solid to form a second solid phase present as such, the compound must dissociate, giving a constant partial pressure of the gas so long as any of the compound and both its dissociation products are present. Thus, if calcium oxide absorbs CO_2 to form calcium carbonate, so long as all three of these substances are present, equilibrium can exist only at a certain partial pressure of CO_2, the value of which depends on the temperature and on nothing else. Because of this fact it can be laid down as a general rule that chemically combining solid absorbents are unsatisfactory; for, if the compound formed is one readily dissociating, its partial pressure is relatively high and, since combination cannot take place if the partial pressure of the gaseous component is below the equilibrium pressure, it is impossible to get complete absorption; on the other hand, if the compound is a stable one and the equilibrium pressure is correspondingly low so that absorption can be complete, the very stability of the compound formed makes it difficult to decompose it and therefore hard to recover the absorbent for re-use. Thus, while it is true that calcium oxide is an excellent absorbent for CO_2, to recover tne calcium oxide for re-use, the carbonate must be heated to approximately 900°C.

PART IV. RATE OF ABSORPTION AND EXTRACTION

Introduction.—All available data indicate that phases in contact are, at the interface itself, always at equilibrium, or substantially so. For the interaction between liquids and gases, the data are quite conclusive; in interaction of solids and liquids, equilibrium at the interface has been demonstrated to exist when crystals dissolve in suitable solvents; in the case of solid absorbents, whether reacting with gases or liquids, the phenomena are complicated and the available data sufficiently accurate to serve as a basis for a conclusion are decidedly limited, but none of the data are incompatible with the above generalization, and throughout this treatment equilibrium at the interface will be assumed.

This assumption of equilibrium at the interface is equivalent of the assumption of such rapid interaction between the phases at the exact point of contact that this interaction is not a controlling factor in delaying the ultimate result. Hence, it follows that the thing which controls the rate of interaction of phases is transfer through the phases themselves and that, therefore, the capacity of every apparatus for absorption or extraction is limited by and dependent upon mass-transfer phenomena. Consequently, in process of absorption and extraction, the quantitative mass-transfer relationships are just as important as the equilibrium itself.* As pointed out on page 429 the transfer through a single phase involves both the transfer through the main body by turbulence or eddy diffusion and transfer through the surface film by molecular diffusion. Since the two mechanisms are quite different, the rate of transfer for each will first be considered separately.

Molecular Diffusion in Gases.—The fundamental differential equations for diffusion of gases were first derived by Maxwell. They were later reexamined along somewhat different lines by Stefan, who also applied the diffusion laws to liquid mixtures.

Visualize a single molecule of one component A, diffusing unidirectionally through a binary gaseous mixture of A and B. The experimental evidence is conclusive that the frictional resistance to motion by diffusion is proportional both to the relative velocity of the diffusing component past the interfering one and to the diffusion distance dz. It is to be anticipated that the resistance will be proportional to the number of molecules of B which block the path, a quantity which is in turn proportional to the partial molal density of B, ω_B. Granting that these two terms determine the friction encountered by a single molecule of A, the total frictional resistance to diffusion of component A will equal this resistance met by the individual molecule times the number of the molecules. This latter quantity is proportional to the partial molal density of A, ω_A, and the total frictional resistance to diffusion of A is given by the expression $\beta_{AB}\omega_A\omega_B(u_A - u_B)\,dz$, where u_A and u_B are the velocities of components A and B, respectively, measured in the z-direction, and β_{AB} is the coefficient of resistance to diffusion of component A through B.

Excluding the influence of external forces and temperature variations, this frictional resistance must be overcome by an equivalent drop in the partial pressure of A, $-dp_A$, over the section in question. In other words, $-dp_A = \beta_{AB}\omega_A\omega_B(u_A - u_B)\,dz$, or

$$-dp_A/dz = \beta_{AB}\omega_A\omega_B(u_A - u_B). \tag{1}$$

Clearly a similar equation may be written for the other component:

$$dp_B/dz = \beta_{BA}\omega_A\omega_B(u_A - u_B). \tag{2}$$

If there is no major bulk motion of the gas in the direction of diffusion, the total pressure P of the gas must be the same at all points in this direction.

* When a material diffuses from one substance to a second substance existing as a separate phase, the principles are the same regardless of whether the materials diffused from a gas into a liquid or from a liquid into a gas. This applies to the transfer of a vapor from gas to solid, and from solid to gas. To cover such diffusion in either direction, the term *interaction* is here employed.

Since the total pressure equals the sum of the partial pressure, $P = p_A + p_B$, differentiation gives $dp_A + dp_B = 0$, *i.e.*, dp_A and dp_B are equal and have opposite signs. This last relation combined with Eqs. 1 and 2 results in $\beta_{AB} = \beta_{BA}$, *i.e.*, the coefficient of resistance to diffusion of A through B must be numerically equal to the corresponding coefficient of diffusion of B through A. The subscripts may, therefore, be dropped and β considered as the common resistance coefficient for the mixture of the two components.

It is more convenient to work with molal rather than volumetric units. The partial molal density ω_A multiplied by u_A equals the molal rate of interchange of A per unit interfacial surface, *i.e.*, $\omega_A u_A$ equals dN_A/dA and similarly $\omega_B u_B$ equals dN_B/dA. Also ω_A equals p_A/RT, where T is the absolute temperature and R is a suitable value of the gas constant, ω_B equals p_B/RT. Equations 1 and 2 may now be written

$$\frac{-dp_A}{dz} = \frac{+dp_B}{dz} = \frac{1}{D_m}\left(\frac{p_B\,dN_A}{dA} - \frac{p_A\,dN_B}{dA}\right) \tag{3}$$

where the term RT/β is replaced by the "diffusivity" D_m, expressed in molal units.

These equations for "point conditions" may be integrated into several forms depending on the diffusion conditions.

1. *Gaseous Diffusion of One Component Only.*—This case was discussed by Stefan in connection with a special technique employed by him for determining the coefficient of diffusion of a vapor through a gas. Its engineering importance is very great, particularly in the evaporation of a liquid into a gas or the condensation, absorption or adsorption of a vapor from a binary gaseous mixture. In such cases the vapor must diffuse through the gas film separating the liquid-gas interface from the main body of the gas.

Where there is no net diffusion of B, dN_B is zero, and Eq. 3 becomes

$$\frac{dN_A}{dA} = -\frac{D_m\,dp_A}{p_B\,dz}, \tag{3a}$$

which shows that the molal rate of transfer of A between gas and liquid is directly proportional to the product of the diffusivity and the partial pressure gradient through the film, and inversely proportional to the partial pressure of the nondiffusing gas.

Where the fractional variation in p_B through the film is small, p_B may be considered constant at an average value, $(p_B)_{\text{av.}}$, and Eq. 3a may be integrated across the true gas film from 0 to B_f and from p_{Ai} to p_A', giving

$$-\frac{dN_A}{dA} = \frac{D_m}{(p_B)_{\text{av.}}B_f}(p_A' - p_{Ai}). \tag{4}$$

Where the fractional variation of p_B is too large to be neglected, $-dp_A$ in Eq. 3a is replaced by dp_B, giving upon integration

$$\frac{-dN_A}{dA} = \frac{D_m}{B_f}\ln\frac{p_{Bi}}{p_B'} \tag{5}$$

Equation 5 may be rearranged to involve the potential difference $p'_A - p_{Ai}$ by multiplying through by an identity $(p'_A - p_{Ai})/(p_{Bi} - p'_B)$, giving

$$-\frac{dN_A}{dA} = \frac{D_m(p'_A - p_{Ai})}{B_f(p_B)_{\text{l.m.}}} = \frac{(p' - p_i)}{r_f} \tag{5a}$$

where $(p_B)_{\text{l.m.}}$ is the logarithmic mean of p_{Bi} and p'_B, $p' - p_i$ represents $p'_A - p_{Ai}$, and r_f is the resistance of the film to diffusion.

2. *Gaseous Diffusion under Steady Conditions in Binary Mixtures, Both Components Diffusing But in Opposite Directions.*—These are essentially the conditions obtained at any particular point of contact of liquid and vapor in a rectifying unit operating continuously. Thus, in the case of the rectification of a mixture of water and ammonia, at a given element of contact between vapor and liquid in the column, ammonia is diffusing from the liquid interface out through the gas film into the vapor and a corresponding amount of steam diffuses in the opposite direction from the body of the vapor through the film into the interface. The concentration of water in

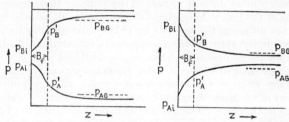

Fig. 137.—Left, outward diffusion of component A; right, inward diffusion of component A.

the vapor at the point in question is maintained constant, despite this diffusional loss, by the steady flow of vapor up the column from below. Similarly, the ammonia concentration in the body of the liquid is maintained by the flow of reflux down the column from above. Thus liquid and vapor concentrations at the point are maintained constant and diffusion takes place under steady conditions. For the usual case, where dN_B equals $-dN_A$, Eq. 3 becomes

$$-\frac{dp_A}{dz} = \frac{1}{D_m}\left(\frac{p_A\,dN_A}{dA} + \frac{p_B\,dN_A}{dA}\right) = \frac{P\,dN_A}{D_m\,dA}. \tag{6}$$

Noting that the mol fraction y in a vapor equals p_A/P and that dy equals dp_A/P, Eq. 3 reduces to $dN_A/dA = -D_m(dy/dz)$. Integrating through the film from 0 to B_f and from y_i to y' gives

$$\frac{dN_A}{dA} = \frac{D_m(y_i - y')}{B_f} = k_y(y_i - y') \tag{7}$$

where dN_A/dA represents the molal rate of evaporation of the more volatile component per unit surface and y_i is the mol fraction of the same component at the interface between liquid and vapor.

Values of D_m and B_f are necessary for the use of these equations.   Values of D_m can be satisfactorily predicted by using Maxwell's theoretical equation with an empirical constant.   For a given binary mixture D_m is directly proportional to the square root of the absolute temperature and independent of the total pressure.   For different mixtures D_m is proportional to the square root of the sum of the reciprocals of the molecular weights of the two gases, and is also a function of the effective volume of the molecules.   Table I on page 460 gives the diffusivity for a number of common binary mixtures.

The value of the film thickness, B_f, depends on the flow conditions in a way similar to the film thickness for heat transfer.   In the case of given flow conditions and for concentrations of the diffusing substance low enough so that the properties of the mixture are not appreciably changed, the film thickness should be the same for all substances. It is probable that under comparable conditions the film thickness for heat transfer is the same as for mass transfer.

3. *Multicomponent Diffusion.*—Diffusion equations are available for systems containing more than two gases, but because of their complexity they are much more difficult to use.   They indicate that, where the concentrations of the gases undergoing diffusion are small, *i.e.*, the main component is not diffusing, the equation for binary mixtures may be used as an approximation for each diffusing component, considering all other gases as the stationary component.   Thus, in the scrubbing of a dilute mixture of ammonia gas and air with cold water, the two-component equation, when applied to the diffusion of ammonia or water vapor, will give results within a few per cent of the more complicated equation for a ternary system.

Diffusion in Liquids.—Stefan has given similar derivations for the diffusion in liquids which may be given as

$$-\frac{dN_A}{dA} = \frac{D_L}{B_L}(\Delta c_A) = k_L(c_i - c_L) \tag{8}$$

where D_L is the diffusivity through the liquid phase, having the equivalent film thickness B_L; Δc_A is the potential difference, *i.e.*, the concentration of A at the interface between phases, minus the concentration of A in the main body of the liquid; and k_L is the diffusion coefficient in Eq. 8.

The correlation of diffusivities in the liquid phase is less satisfactory than for the gas phase; this is undoubtedly due to the complicating effects of ionization, association and dissociation, and to the difficulty of eliminating natural convection.   However, for a given temperature, it is possible to correlate D_L for systems in which there is little ionization or association.   Thus the diffusion of many organic compounds through other organic liquids and the diffusion of gases through liquids give values of D_L which agree well with certain "semitheoretical" equations.   For such binary systems the diffusivities are inversely proportional to the square root of the sum of the reciprocals of the molecular weights.   Owing to the high viscosity-temperature coefficient of liquids compared with gases, the effect of temperature on the diffusivity in the liquid phase is much greater than in the gas phase.   Experimental data are meager but indicate that the diffusivity in the liquid phase is approximately proportional to the inverse three-halves power of the viscosity. Table II on page 461 gives values of liquid-phase diffusivities.

Transference in Main Body.—The problem of transference through the main body of the gas phase by convection or eddy diffusion has not been solved so satisfactorily as the transfer by molecular diffusion. This is largely due to the lack of an adequate knowledge of the mechanism of convection.

Experimental data for the evaluation of the rate of transfer by eddy diffusion are meager, but consideration of the mechanism would indicate that for given flow conditions the current density of transfer should be independent of the physical properties of the component being exchanged so long as the latter does not appreciably alter the flow conditions or turbulence. Thus a turbulent body of fluid would have the same resistance for all substances so long as its own properties were not altered significantly.

Transfer Coefficients.—In engineering calculations the net transfer coefficient is desired rather than the individual coefficients for the film and main body.

These rate coefficients are defined by the equation

$$-\frac{dN_A}{dA} = k_G(p - p_i) = k_Y(Y - Y_i) \tag{9}$$

where k_G is the coefficient used when the driving force is expressed in terms of the partial pressures of the diffusing constituent and k_Y is the coefficient where the driving force $(Y - Y_i)$ is expressed in mols of A per mol of B in the gas phase.* By analogy with the corresponding case in heat transfer (page 109), the mass transfer from the main body of the gas to the interface can be visualized as meeting two resistances in series, that of the turbulent main body of gas and that of the gas film. The gross gas-phase resistance r is then the sum of the two individual resistances $r_c + r_f$. Algebraically expressed,

$$-\frac{dN_A}{dA} = \frac{p_G - p'}{r_c} = \frac{p' - p_i}{r_f} = \frac{p_G - p_i}{r_c + r_f} = \frac{(p_G - p_i)}{r} = k_G(p_G - p_i).$$

* In dealing with problems in humidification and dehumidification, it is convenient to express the driving force in terms of absolute humidity H, expressed as a mass ratio of A to B, rather than in terms of the mol ratio Y, and to replace dN_A/dA by dW/dA, where dW is the rate of evaporation expressed in mass units. Equation 9 then takes the form

$$-\frac{dW}{dA} = k_H(H_i - H). \tag{9a}$$

When using consistent units, k_H equals $M_B k_Y$.

As shown by Eq. 5a, r_f equals $B_f(p_B)_{l.m.}/D_m$, giving

$$\frac{1}{k_G} = r_c + \frac{B_f(p_B)_{l.m.}}{D_m}. \tag{10}$$

At present the only satisfactory evaluation of r_c is by the use of Eq. 10 together with experimental determinations of k_G. The direct experimental evaluation of B_f is difficult but fortunately is not necessary for the utilization of the above equation, since values of k_G can be measured for two substances with different diffusivities when these substances are allowed to diffuse separately or simultaneously through a third component, under conditions such that the diffusing substances do not alter the flow conditions of the third component. These two values of k_G, together with known values of D_m and the fact that the flow conditions were such that r_c and B_f were the same for both substances, allow the calculation of both r_c and B_f. These values may then be used to predict values of k_G for the transfer of other substances under similar conditions. The utility of Eq. 10 will be demonstrated by numerical examples (Chap. XV on Absorption and Extraction). Actually the transfer of heat may be utilized in place of one of the substances and this illustrates the complete analogy between mass and heat transfer. The applicability of this analogy will be considered in Chap. XVII on Humidity.

Both r_f and r_c decrease with increasing velocity of the fluid past the interface. Prandtl's study of the relation between heat transfer and friction would indicate that r_f decreased with increasing velocity faster than r_c, and that at very high velocities the main resistance to transfer would be eddy diffusion. The experimental data on mass transfer are not sufficiently precise to evaluate the effect of velocity on the relative value of the two resistances, but they indicate that any such effect is relatively minor in comparison with the large change in magnitude of r_c plus r_f. For given flow conditions the ratio of r_c to r_f depends on the diffusivity of the system in question: thus in systems with relatively large diffusivities the resistance to transfer will be mainly in the main body while small diffusivities increase the relative importance of the resistance of the film. For a given film thickness, in the first case an increase of turbulence in the main body would materially aid the transfer, but in the latter case it would be of much less value.

Transfer coefficients have been correlated by methods similar to those for heat transfer, using dimensionless groups. Thus $k_G D_d (p_B)_{l.m.}/D_m$ is found to be a function of Reynolds number and a group μ/MD_m, which is analogous to the Prandtl group in heat transfer. Another method of correlating mass-transfer data has been to visualize a fictive film of thickness B such that its resistance to molecular diffusion would equal the observed transfer resistance: $B(p_B)_{l.m.}/D_m = 1/k_G$;* the values of B so calculated were then correlated by dimensionless functions. The correlations of experimental values of the transfer coefficients will be given in the chapters on Humidity, Absorption and Extraction, and Distillation.

1. Gases and Liquids

The foregoing considerations indicate that transfer through the gas phase proceeds at a rate that is proportional to the difference between solute concentrations in the main body of the gas and at the interface.† Transfer through the liquid phase, on the other hand, is controlled by the difference between the concentration of the solute in the liquid at the interface and its concentration in the main body of the liquid. Since the surface films are generally thin, the actual amount of solute contained in them at any one time is usually negligible compared with the amount diffusing through them. It follows, therefore, that all the solute which passes through one film must also pass through the other, and the two films may be considered as two diffusional resistances in series.[5] Under certain circumstances the resistance of one of the films may be so much greater than that of the other that the second film may be neglected and the problem treated as if only one film existed.

---

* Upon comparing this relation with Eq. 10, it is seen that, except where r_c is negligible relative to r_f, the fictive thickness B is greater than B_f. Nevertheless this concept of the effective film, whose resistance equals the actual resistance $1/k_G$, is allowable and is frequently used.

† Resistance to diffusion due to a gas film is, of course, nonexistent in the special case where an absolutely pure gas is being absorbed. This problem is very rarely encountered in practice, however, since the presence of very small amounts of inert gas, which will concentrate at the liquid surface, is sufficient to create an effective gas film.

The amount of solute transferred per unit time by diffusion through the two films is dN (see table of nomenclature on page 458 for résumé of all symbols). The rate of transfer is obviously proportional to the surface of the interface dA and it is convenient to refer to the current density dN/dA. This quantity is equal to the transfer coefficient (k_G for a gas phase or k_L for a liquid phase) multiplied by the concentration difference available as a driving force, *i.e.*,

$$-\frac{dN}{dA} = k_G(p_G - p_i) = k_L(c_i - c_L) \tag{11}$$

where p is the partial pressure of the diffusing substance in the gas and c is its concentration in the liquid. The subscripts G, i and L refer, respectively, to conditions in the main body of the gas, at the gas-liquid interface and in the main body of the liquid.

It is clear that the numerical value of the transfer coefficients k_G and k_L will depend upon the units in which the gas and liquor concentrations are expressed. The choice of these units is purely arbitrary. In this chapter, unless otherwise specified, solute concentration in the gas is expressed as its partial pressure in atmospheres and concentration in the liquid as grams per cubic centimeter because this makes the separate values of k_G and k_L of the same order of magnitude for many cases.

The data at present available indicate that at the true interface between liquid and gas the two phases are substantially at equilibrium (p_i in equilibrium with c_i), even though there may be rapid diffusion and therefore high concentration gradients through the films on the two sides of that interface. This fact puts one in a position to visualize clearly what takes place in an absorption process. Conditions at the interface are determined by two factors: first, the equilibrium between gas and liquor concentrations; and second, the fact that all the solute diffusing through the gas film must also diffuse through the liquid film. Thus, p_i is a function of c_i,

$$p_i = f(c_i), \tag{12}$$

this function being the solubility equilibrium relationship. If the values of k_G and of k_L are known, the values of p_i and c_i, the interfacial concentrations, are at once determined by Eq. 11.

If, for example, k_G should be just equal to k_L, to satisfy Eq. 11, $(p_G - p_i)$ would have to equal $(c_i - c_L)$.

Overall Coefficients.—It is generally convenient to utilize an overall coefficient for the gas and liquid phases rather than the individual coefficients. However, the concentration difference to be used with the overall coefficients is the total difference between the main bodies of the gas and liquid, expressed in comparable units. Thus, if gaseous concentration is expressed as partial pressure p_G, the liquid concentration must be given as $p_L^\star$ corresponding to equilibrium with the actual liquid concentration c_L. Similarly, if the liquid concentration c_L is used, the gaseous concentrations must be expressed as $c_G^\star$ (the liquid which would be in equilibrium with p_G). In these units Eq. 11 becomes

$$-\frac{dN}{dA} = K_G(p_G - p_L^\star) = K_L(c_G^\star - c_L). \tag{13}$$

On such a basis of comparable units the ratio of the resistance of either phase to the total resistance is given by the ratio of the decrease in driving force through that phase to total concentration difference across both films, *i.e.*, the fractional resistance of the gas phase $1/k_G \div 1/K_G$ is $(p_G - p_i)/(p_G - p_L^\star)$ and for the liquid phase $1/k_L \div 1/K_L$ will equal $(p_i - p_L^\star)/(p_G - p_L^\star)$. Comparable expressions may be obtained in terms of differences in liquid concentration.

Effect of Solubility.—The overall coefficients are most conveniently obtained in terms of the individual coefficients by setting $\Delta p = n \Delta c$, where n is the proportionality constant of solubility, which will usually be a function of both temperature and concentration, but for the special case where Henry's law applies n will be a function of temperature only. Expressing Eqs. 11 and 13 in pressure units:

$$-\frac{dN}{dA} = K_G(p_G - p_L^\star) = \frac{K_L}{n''}(p_G - p_L^\star) = k_G(p_G - p_i) = \frac{k_L}{n'}(p_i - p_L^\star)$$

where n' is equal to $(p_i - p_L^\star)/(c_i - c_L)$ and n'' equals $(p_G - p_L^\star)/(c_G^\star - c_L)$, from which

$$\frac{1}{K_G} = \frac{1}{k_G} + \frac{n'}{k_L} = \frac{n''}{K_L} \tag{14}$$

and, for Henry's law where $p = c/H$, n' and n'' are both equal to $1/H$, giving

$$\frac{1}{K_G} = \frac{1}{k_G} + \frac{1}{Hk_L} = \frac{1}{HK_L}. \tag{15}$$

Since in the units specified on page 450 the values of k_G and k_L are often approximately the same, it is apparent that the relative

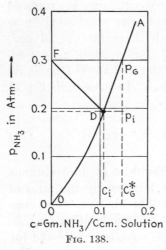

c=Gm. NH_3/Ccm. Solution

Fig. 138.

value of the gas-phase resistance $1/k_g$ to the liquid-phase resistance n'/k_L will be largely controlled by the value of n'. The value of n' is determined by the solubility relationships of the system involved. Thus for gases of high solubility the value of n' will be very small and the resistance to diffusion will be essentially $1/k_g$, and the condition is called one of "gas phase controlling"; for very slightly soluble gases the value of n' will be large and n'/k_L will be large relative to $1/k_G$, and the main resistance will be the liquid phase, giving a condition of "liquid phase controlling." Gases of intermediate solubility will give conditions intermediate between the above extremes, and the resistances of both the liquid and the gas phases will be significant.

These conditions are easily visualized by graphical representation in a plot of partial pressure $vs.$ concentration. Equation 11 when rewritten as $k_L/k_G = (p_G - p_i)/(c_i - c_L)$ represents a line of slope $-\dfrac{k_L}{k_G}$ in a partial pressure-concentration diagram. Likewise the equilibrium curve between gas and liquid may also be plotted and, since p_i and c_i must be on the equilibrium curve, a graphical representation of Eq. (11) is possible. Figure 138 represents such a plot for the system ammonia-water (a case of intermediate solubility) at a temperature of 30°C. where OA represents the equilibrium curve. Consider the absorption of ammonia from a gas in which its partial pressure is 0.300 atmosphere, by an aqueous solution containing 0.005 mg. of ammonia per c.c. These conditions can be represented by the point F, whose ordinate is p_G and whose abscissa is c_L. If the flow conditions were such that k_L were equal to k_G, the equation would indicate that a line through point F of slope $-\dfrac{k_L}{k_g}$ would intersect the equilibrium curve at the point p_i, c_i. Thus for the case given above p_i would equal 0.195 atmosphere and C_i 0.105 gm. per c.c. The value of $p_L{}^\star$ is seen to be approximately zero and the ratio of the gas-phase resistance to the total resistance, $(p_G - p_i)/(p_G - p_L{}^\star)$, is 0.105/0.3 or 0.35, and in this case the gas phase offers about 35 per cent of the total resistance and the liquid phase 65 per cent. The value of n' is the *slope* of the chord passing through p_i, c_i and $p_L{}^\star$, c_L, or through points O and D. It is apparent that the significant factor is the ratio of the slope between points F and D, which is $-\dfrac{k_L}{k_g}$ to the slope between O and D, which is n'.* If n' is equal to $-\dfrac{k_L}{k_g}$, the resistances of the two phases will be equal; if n' is greater than $-\dfrac{k_L}{k_g}$, the liquid-phase resistance will exceed the gas-phase resistance; and if n' is smaller than $-\dfrac{k_L}{k_g}$, the reverse will be true. These conditions are illustrated in Figs. 139 and 140 where similar constructions are given for the system oxygen-water (high value of n') and the system HCl-water (low value of n') for $-\dfrac{k_L}{k_G}$ equal to 1 and for the same liquid and gas concentration as used in Fig. 138. The

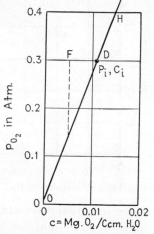

FIG. 139.—Absorption of O_2 in water.

* In terms of liquid concentrations the ratio of the gas-phase resistance to the total resistance $(c_G{}^\star - c_i)/(c_G{}^\star - c_L)$ is 0.04/0.145 or 0.276. In general, the ratio of gas-phase resistance to liquid-phase resistance will be different when measured in pressure units than when measured in liquid concentration units, but, for the case where the equilibrium curve is a straight line between c_L and c_G, the ratio will be the same in both units.

figures indicate that in the first case the resistance to diffusion is almost completely (99+ per cent) in the liquid phase, while in the latter the reverse is true (98+ per cent gas phase).

It is possible for the solubility relationships to be such that under one condition in a particular system the gas-phase resistance may be controlling while under other conditions the same system may offer the main resistance to transfer in the liquid phase, and there must obviously be conditions under which the resistances of both phases must be significant. These changes of relative resistance can be brought about by concentration changes in either or both of the gas and liquid phases, or by changes in temperature. These conditions are shown in Fig. 140, for the system HCl-water. First consider the conditions represented by point F, which give the interfacial conditions represented by point D, and it is apparent that the liquid phase offers less than 2 per cent of the total resistance. However, if at the same liquid concentration and temperature the gas-phase concentration is raised to the condition represented by F', then the interfacial conditions are those at D' and the liquid phase offers approximately 30 per cent of the total resistance.

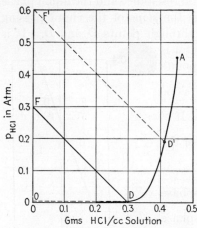

FIG. 140.—Absorption of HCl in water.

Other Variables.—The discussion has so far considered only the effect of solubility of the gas in determining absorption rate per unit area. The other important variables are the transfer coefficients k_G and k_L, which can be varied considerably by the character of the absorption process. Any factors that tend to cut down the thickness of the surface films or to increase the main body turbulence should increase the coefficients and correspondingly speed up the absorption rate. Thus, agitation of liquid increases transfer through the liquid, while higher gas velocities past the surface cause more rapid transfer through the gas (see pages 499 to 505).

The effect of such factors will be decidedly dependent upon whether the process is controlled by gas-phase or liquid-phase resistance. Thus, a change that decreased the resistance of the gas phase but did not affect the liquid phase would increase the absorption of hydrogen chloride but would not affect the rate of oxygen absorption.

Changes in temperature influence several factors, and it is necessary to distinguish clearly between the effect of temperature on the equilibrium and its effect on the transfer coefficients. Increase in temperature makes the gas less soluble, thus tending to lower the rate of absorption. The transfer coefficients themselves may, however, be either raised or lowered by temperature, depending upon the changes in turbulence, film thickness and diffusivity. Liquid-phase coefficients k_L rise rapidly with increasing temperature, both because of decreased film thickness and increased turbulence due to lowered viscosity and because of greater diffusivities. On the other hand, data regarding effect of temperature on the gas-film coefficient k_G are inconclusive, but the effect of temperature is not large (see page 502). Although the molal diffusivity of gases increases as the square root of the absolute temperature, it seems probable that this effect is less than that due to decreased turbulence and to increased film thickness.

A type of apparatus in which gas bubbles up through a liquid would represent vitally different conditions from one where liquid drops are sprayed through a gas. In the first instance, a rising gas bubble would continuously expose fresh liquid surface and the liquid-phase coefficient would be high, whereas the gas phase would be relatively undisturbed. Such a device should therefore be most satisfactory for absorbing the less soluble gases where liquid-phase resistance is controlling. In the other case, a falling drop might be expected to have only a very thin gas film but a fairly stagnant liquid phase. Apparatus of a spray type will therefore, other things equal, be well suited for absorbing very soluble gases.

From these suggestions it is evident that the ratio of the transfer coefficients (k_L/k_G) varies with the type of apparatus and with the conditions of operation. It is therefore quite possible that the absorption of a gas of intermediate solubility might be controlled primarily by liquid-phase resistance in one piece of equipment and by gas-phase resistance in another.   This point is illustrated by the case of sulfur dioxide, which is almost entirely governed by the liquid phase when passed over a free surface of liquid, but which is largely affected by the gas phase when absorbed by bubbling through water.

It is possible to predict comparative performances of different solutes in the same equipment on the basis of this general concept. Under similar operating conditions the effective film thicknesses will in most cases be independent of the solute that is being absorbed.

2. FLUIDS AND SOLIDS

In the majority of cases solid absorbents pick up gases by adsorption, the equilibria being of the type shown in Fig. 135. The data available on adsorption rates are incomplete, but the indications are that the mechanism is one of gas-phase transfer, the film being, however, not merely on the outside of the grain but also to no small degree within the solid.   Consequently there is a very definite limit to the possibility of reducing the gas-film resistance by high gas velocity past the adsorbent.

The reason lies in the structure of solid adsorbents.   Thus the individual grain of activated charcoal is not a dense solid, but is permeated by a labyrinth of exceedingly fine capillaries upon the walls of which the adsorbed gas is held (see page 439). It has been estimated that in the case of highly activated charcoal the active surface of these capillaries is of the magnitude of 20 acres to the pound.   Gas is adsorbed not merely in those capillaries near the outer surface of the grain but in the inner ones as well.   To penetrate the grain, however, the entering gas must diffuse along the capillaries, and this, rather than diffusion through the gas film around the outside of the grain as a whole, offers the major resistance to rapid adsorption.   This resistance increases as adsorption proceeds, for at the start the entering gas is adsorbed and held at the very mouths of the capillaries, whereas later increments of gas adsorbed must diffuse farther into the capillaries, past the outer layers of carbon surface already saturated, to points located progressively deeper in the grain and not yet saturated with gas.   In the case of gases and vapors, however, this diffusion is rapid—so much so, that for small grain sizes equilibrium rather than adsorption rate is often the controlling factor in the process.

In the adsorption of solutes from liquids by solid adsorbents, the situation is very different. While the capillary structure of the adsorbent granule remains the same, these capillaries in the interior of the grain are normally ineffective, because the material adsorbed from liquids almost always possesses very high molecular weight. For example, the organic color removed from sugar syrups by bone char and from oils by fuller's earth is in both cases complex in structure and colloidal or semicolloidal in character. In consequence, the diffusion rate through the capillaries is exceedingly slow and, indeed, the indications are that the capillaries act in a certain sense as filters, their mouths on the outer surface of the grain becoming choked with adsorbed color.

There are two important consequences. In the first place, when the mouths of the capillaries closely approach equilibrium with the color in the external solution, further adsorption becomes exceedingly slow, despite the fact that the total adsorptive capacity of the grain has been only partially utilized. In other words, there develops a false equilibrium, which, however, sets a practical limit to the adsorptive capacity of the solid. It is this false equilibrium in which the engineer is interested and which must be experimentally determined as the basis for computations and design. In the second place, the total effective adsorptive capacity of the solid is proportional, not to the total surface of the capillaries (*i.e.*, to the total weight of the solid), but rather to the surface of the grains themselves, because the effective capillary surface is limited to that in a thin layer below the outer surface of the grain. Thus, whereas it has been found experimentally that grinding 20-mesh carbon to particles less than 0.001 mm. in diameter increases the total adsorptive capacity for gases only 8 per cent, the capacity of similar solids for decolorization is approximately proportional to the total grain surface exposed, *i.e.*, for a given weight of adsorbent, inversely proportional to the average grain size (see page 468). Consequently, while it is advantageous to use solid adsorbents for gases in the form of coarse grains, because this avoids the evils of dusting and high-pressure drop without introducing serious concomitant disadvantages, when employing similar adsorbents for liquids, the use of them in the form of relatively fine powders greatly increases both adsorbing capacity and rate per unit weight of adsorbent employed.

While from the preceding discussion it is obvious that the mechanism of diffusion of a solute from a liquid into a solid adsorbent is complicated and, even for the same concentration difference, will be more rapid at the start of the adsorbing process than toward its end, nonetheless the data indicate that the adsorption rate is substantially proportional to the total surface of the adsorbing grain and to the difference in concentration between that in the solution around those grains and that in a solution in equilibrium with the material already adsorbed.

Because the total adsorptive capacity of the material is proportional to its surface rather than to its weight, the determination of the adsorption equilibrium is very unsatisfactory. It is difficult to get two samples of material of the same grain size and the same size distribution.   Indeed, if one takes a granular material and separates it into two parts, there is a very marked tendency toward segregation of grains of varying size, and of these two samples the one with the smaller average grain size will have both the higher adsorptive capacity and the higher adsorption rate.   Added to this is the still greater difficulty of duplicating the quality of an adsorbent in the preparation of separate samples.   Thus, in the activation of charcoal by selective oxidation, it is difficult, if not impossible, to carry the activation to exactly the same point in successive runs.   Obviously, in the regeneration of old adsorbent for re-use, as is practiced in the reactivation of charcoal, bone char and fuller's earth by furnacing, the chances for variation in quality of product are even greater.   Because of these facts it is difficult to get satisfactory experimental checks in determination of either equilibrium or rate.   In practice, it is best to secure these data from analysis of operating data under plant conditions, but it is imperative to making sure that the data obtained are representative, by using results of a large number of tests.   Furthermore, in employing such data as the basis for design, liberal factors of safety must be used.

Nomenclature

A = area.

b = constant.

B_f, B_L, B = film thickness for true gaseous diffusion, liquid diffusion and effective film thickness, respectively.

c, c^* = liquid concentration.

D_m, D_L = diffusivity in gas and liquid, respectively.

D_d = diameter.

d = prefix indicating differential.

H = Henry's law constant, in $p = c/H$.

h = relative humidity.

K_G, K_L = overall transfer coefficients.

k_G, k_Y, k_y = transfer coefficient for the gas phase, with driving force expressed in partial pressure, mol ratio and mol fraction, respectively.

k_L = transfer coefficient for the liquid phase.

M = molecular weight.

N = molal rate of transfer.

n = exponent, slope of chord.

P = total pressure.

p_G, p', p^* = partial pressure in the main body of the gas, at the outside of the true gas film and in equilibrium with the liquid, respectively.

R = gas-law constant, in molal units.

r, r_f, r_c = overall, film, and core resistances, respectively.

u = net diffusional velocity in z-direction.

X = ratio of adsorbed material to amount of adsorbent.

x = mol fraction in liquid.

y, y', y^* = mol fraction in the main body of the gas, at the outside of the true gas film, and in equilibrium with the liquid, respectively.

Y = molal ratio of solute to carrier.

z = distance.

β = resistance factor in Stefan equation.

γ = gamma, surface tension.

Δ = potential difference, driving force.

μ = mu, absolute viscosity.

π = pi, total pressure.

ω = omega, partial molal density = p/RT.

Subscripts

A, B refer to components.

c refers to core, *i.e.*, fluid lying outside true film.

f refers to film.

G refers to main body of gas.

i refers to liquid-gas interface.

L refers to main body of liquid.

l.m. refers to logarithmic mean.

TABLE I.—DIFFUSIVITIES IN GASES AT 25°C.

$D_m =$ gm. mols/(cm.) (sec.)

System	$D_m{}^* \times 10^4$	System	$D_m \times 10^4$
Air—H_2O	0.090	Air—$CH_3COOC_2H_5$	0.034
Air—NH_3	0.089	Air—CH_3COOH	0.046
Air—CO_2	0.062	Air—CH_3OH	0.062
Air—H_2	0.281	Air—C_2H_5OH	0.048
Air—O_2	0.077	Air—C_6H_6	0.035
Air—SO_2	0.055	Air—n—C_8H_{18}	0.026
Air—CO	0.090	H_2—$CH_3COOC_2H_5$	0.137
H_2—SO_2	0.227	H_2—CH_3COOH	0.182
H_2—N_2O	0.248	H_2—CH_3OH	0.225
H_2—CH_4	0.268	H_2—C_2H_5OH	0.183
H_2—C_2H_4	0.239	H_2—C_6H_6	0.146
H_2—N_2	0.278	CO_2—$CH_3COOC_2H_5$	0.027
CO_2—N_2	0.062	CO_2—CH_3COOH	0.037
CO_2—CH_4	0.072	CO_2—CH_3OH	0.050
CO_2—C_2H_4	0.055	CO_2—C_2H_5OH	0.038
		CO_2—C_6H_6	0.029

* Calculated from Eq. 6, *Ind. Eng. Chem.*, **26**, 681, (1934).

For example, the diffusivity of the system air—NH_3 is 0.0000105 gm. mols/(cm.) (sec.

Note $D_m = (D_v\pi)/(RT)$, where D_v is expressed in volumetric units.

TABLE II.—DIFFUSIVITIES IN LIQUIDS
$$D = cm.^2/sec.$$

Solvent	Solute	Temperature, °C.	$D_L \times 10^5$	Reference
Water.............	H_2	20	5.94	1
	O_2	20	2.08	1
	CO_2	20	1.74	1
	NH_3	20	2.04	1
	CH_3OH	20	1.48	1
	C_2H_5OH	20	1.16	1
	CH_3COOH	20	1.02	1
	HCl	12	2.3	1
	H_2SO_4	20	1.73	1
	NaCl	18	1.20	1
CH_3OH.............	CH_3COCH_3	20	2.68	8
	CCl_4	15	1.69	8
	C_6H_5Cl	15	2.07	8
C_2H_5OH.............	$CHCl_3$	20	1.23	6
C_6H_6.............	$CHCl_3$	15	2.11	8
	C_6H_5Cl	15	1.90	8

For example, the diffusivity D of O_2 in liquid water is 0.0000208 cm.^{2}/sec.

References

1. ARNOLD, J. H., Sc.D. Thesis, Massachusetts Institute of Technology, 1931.
2. BERL and ANDREWS, *Z. angew. Chem.*, **34**, 381 (1921).
3. BOHR and BOCK, *Wied. Ann.*, **44**, 318 (1891).
4. GILLILAND, E. R., *Ind. Eng. Chem.*, **26**, 681 (1934).
5. LOWRY and HULETT, *J. Am. Chem. Soc.*, **42**, 1393 (1920).
6. OHOLM, *Z. Physik. Chem.*, **70**, 378 (1910).
7. WHITMAN, W. G., *Chem. Met. Eng.*, **24**, 147 (1923).
8. THOUERT, *Compt. rend.*, **135**, 579 (1902).
9. WILSON, R. E., *Ind. Eng. Chem.*, **13**, 326 (1921).

CHAPTER XV

ABSORPTION AND EXTRACTION

PART I. METHODS OF OPERATION: EQUIPMENT

1. Treatment of Gases by Liquids (Gas Washing and Scrubbing).—Efficient absorption of gases from gases by liquids demands both counterflow and large interfacial contact between the phases (see page 430).   The problem is entirely analogous to that arising in rectification, and the apparatus employed in that art is also frequently used in absorption (see pages 547 to 551).   Attention should be called to the fact that filled towers give less efficient contact than bubble-plate columns but possess the advantages of much less back pressure and smaller liquid content.   The latter advantage may be particularly important where frequent starting and stopping are necessary.   All filled towers, however, are likely to channel badly, especially at low liquor rates; and under this condition contact is lost because only a small fraction of the surface is properly wetted.   In consequence, filled towers are unsatisfactory where under operating conditions the rate of liquid flow is subject to wide variations (see page 550).

Many types of tower filling are available.   Thus, columns packed with coke are employed in the absorption of CO_2 from flue gas in bicarbonate solutions; slat-packed towers are sometimes preferred for absorption of light oil in mineral seal oil; packings of quartz, earthenware and tile are valuable for acid liquids, and perforated sheet metal is also used in various cases. In absorbing light naphtha in suitable hydrocarbons, as in the washing of refinery gases, horizontal screens may be placed in a vertical column to expose fresh surfaces of the oil flowing down the tower.

Spray chambers of the type shown in Fig. 190 (page 597) may be used for absorption, but, where liquid is recirculated through the sprays, it is necessary, to obtain an approach to counterflow of gas and liquid, to employ a number of chambers in series.

The Ceco spray device secures contact between gas and liquid by feeding the liquid upon a revolving disk. Figure 141 shows a section of the B.-H. washer, a recent modification of the Fels scrubber, designed to give a contact between liquid and gas which is independent of the net flow of liquid through the tower. This type is especially suited to cases where extensive contact is required and the amount of liquid is small, as in absorbing very soluble gases. Within limits, the amount of contact can be controlled by regulating the speed of the shaft which rotates the inclined vanes attached thereto.

2. Treatment of Gases by Solids.—Whenever a fluid, gas or liquid, is to be treated by a solid, one is handicapped by the

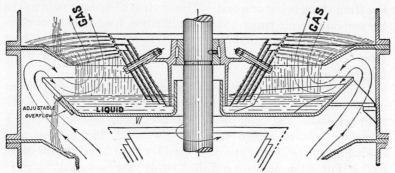

Fig. 141.—Longitudinal section of Bartlett-Hayward washer.

difficulty of moving solids smoothly and continuously. This difficulty is so serious that it is the almost universal practice to place the solid in position and pass the fluid over it, leaving the solid undisturbed until its interaction with the fluid is complete. Thus, in the absorption of gasoline from natural gas, the absorbent charcoal in granulated form is packed in cylindrical containers several feet deep, through which the gas to be treated is allowed to flow. Three of these cylinders are operated together, the gas first entering a cylinder partly saturated with gasoline from previous treatments and flowing thence to a cylinder recently stripped of its gasoline content. The third cylinder is out of the gas circuit, in process of being stripped of its gasoline content by passing superheated steam through it. The mixture of gasoline vapor and steam leaving this cylinder is condensed and the gasoline recovered by decantation. When the charcoal in the first cylinder in the gas circuit becomes saturated with gasoline, it is cut out, the gas now entering what was previously the second cylinder in the line and flowing thence to the gasoline-free charcoal in the third cylinder, now stripped of its gasoline. The cylinder cut out of the line is then subjected to the stripping operation.   It is thus seen that the plant operation is divided into three cycles, at the end of which conditions return to those originally obtaining.   By this means the charcoal is used repeatedly with no physical movement or handling so long as it remains in process; this has the important advantage of lessening deterioration and loss of char by dusting.   Such an operation is described as semicontinuous and represents two stages of countercurrent action.   As many stages may be introduced as desired, the use of less than three being unusual.   This system of operation involves the same principle employed in rectification (page 547), countercurrent drying (page 631) and countercurrent transfer of heat (page 118), but the principle is applied as in the operation of the ring furnace (page 209).

Attempts have been made to secure a continuous movement of the solid treating agent in a direction opposite to that of the fluid treated.   For example, it has been proposed to employ a traveling belt or screen to carry the solid, in an apparatus analogous to the band-type drier used for soap (see Fig. 199, page 627).   For solids that do not dust easily, the so-called "Jacob's ladder" type of apparatus has been suggested, in which the solids slide down over a series of inclined shelves alternately projecting from the sides of a vertical container.   Another proposal is that the gases be brought into contact with the pulverized solid, in a stepwise countercurrent apparatus involving dust collectors and bag filters.

3. Treatment of Liquids by Gases or Vapors (Stripping or Denuding).—These operations are carried out in the same types of apparatus as described above for the treatment of gases by liquids.   A familiar illustration is the stripping of benzene from absorbent oil, accomplished by blowing steam up through a tower at the top of which oil to be treated is fed.   The denuded oil leaving the bottom is cooled before returning to the absorption tower, and for this purpose heat exchange is generally employed so far as practicable.   The mixture of benzene vapor and steam leaving the top is condensed and the benzene is separated by decantation.   In order thoroughly to strip the oil and at the same time conserve steam, the temperature must be maintained high. If this be done by the condensation of live steam alone, the temperature limit is that corresponding to the pressure of steam in the stripping tower, *e.g.*, at atmospheric pressure to about 212°F. There is no need to adhere to this temperature limit, and less steam is required as the temperature is raised. The column should be heated, usually by steam condensing under pressure in closed coils. The temperature in the lower part of the column can be raised above that at the top of the column, even though a certain amount of vaporization of the absorbent oil results, since this vaporization can be rectified out in the upper part of the column by the refluxing action of the feed or, if desired, by the use of a refluxing section above the feed plate. It is important to realize that the closed coils used for heating should be distributed throughout the column below the feed plate, in proportion to the heat consumption due to vaporization and rise in temperature occurring in each section. A further large saving in the live steam injected directly into the column may be made by applying vacuum (see pages 539 to 543). If one wishes, the whole separation may be made by ordinary rectification, but the temperature required at the bottom of the still may cause decomposition.

4. Treatment of Liquids by Liquids.—These operations are usually carried out in tanks, provided with the proper auxiliaries to prevent loss of solvent, if volatile, with agitating devices of various types for securing intimate contact. After the treating agent has extracted its quota of material, the agitation is discontinued and the two layers are separated by decantation (see pages 315 to 316).

5. Treatment of Liquids by Solids.—Where necessary to remove a component from solution in a liquid by means of a solid adsorbent, the classical method is to allow the liquid to flow through a deep bed of the adsorbent in granular form. The mass is called a **percolation filter,** although the mechanism of removal is in no sense filtration, the voids between the grains of the adsorbent being far too large to prevent the passage of the largest particles of the solute. The mechanism of removal is pure adsorption (see pages 436 to 440).

Countercurrent flow is desirable, but study of the equilibria relationships (see Fig. 161, page 509) makes it clear that the more intense the adsorption (*i.e.*, the greater the value of n in the Freundlich equation, page 437), the less the advantage of counter-current flow over batch operation. Consequently, such filters are frequently employed in single units, the solutions flowing through them until the concentration of the effluent liquor is no longer satisfactory. Where liquids of varying initial concentration are available for treatment, a filter is frequently employed first for weak liquors and later for stronger ones, without attempt to make the flow positively countercurrent. The flow is usually by gravity. Whether the liquid should flow upward or downward depends upon the change of density produced by the adsorption; if treatment makes the liquid lighter, it should flow upward and, if heavier, downward, in order to avoid the mixing by convection currents of purified liquid with impure material in earlier stages of filtration. Because the rate of adsorption is very small (see page 457), time must be allowed, *i.e.*, flow of liquid through the filter must be slow. It is frequently possible to increase the adsorption rate by increasing the temperature of the operation, the increased rate of diffusion more than compensating for the decreased affinity of the adsorbent for the solute.

By far the most serious difficulty encountered in the operation of percolation filters is channeling. It is impracticable to produce a granular adsorbent of absolutely uniform grain size and shape, and, when charging the filter, the tendency for segregation of granules of varying size is marked, the more so the greater the variation in size. Thus, if the material entering the filter is discharged at any given point, a cone is built up at that point and the larger granules roll to the bottom, while the core of the cone consists of the finer particles. If the adsorbent is fed to the middle of the filter, this segregation of large particles at the side is very serious. This coarse material offers far less resistance to flow of liquid; hence the major portion of the liquid goes through this section and the flow through the finer material is negligible. Various mechanical devices have been tried for securing uniform distribution of the granules while charging the filter but, though it is possible to localize segregation, it is difficult to eliminate it altogether. So long as segregation is sufficient to offer through the filter some path of relatively low resistance to liquid flow, channeling occurs and the utilization of the adsorbent is greatly impaired, because the liquid fails to flow through the finer material, which is most efficient from the points of view of both capacity and rate.* Where the adsorption produces in the liquid an appreciable change in density, the evils of channeling may be reduced to a minimum by using such low liquor velocities that the differences in liquor density developed by the adsorption itself maintain uniformity of liquor concentration at each horizontal section through the filter. Thus, assume that adsorption decreases the density of the liquid. In such case the liquid should obviously flow upward through the filter. At the start the liquid at any particular horizontal level in the bed tends to flow predominantly through the coarse material, but this soon saturates that material and consequently there is no further decrease in density of this liquid. This develops an additional pressure head, which does not exist through the fine material, in which, owing both to the smaller liquor flow through it and to its greater adsorptive capacity, adsorption and consequently decrease in density have gone much further. Hence, there is developed a greater pressure gradient through the fine material than through the coarse, and, provided the velocity is sufficiently low so that the greater friction through the fines does not overbalance this excess-pressure gradient, the liquid will now flow predominantly through the fines. Unfortunately, however, in the majority of cases the change in density due to adsorption itself is too small to make this method of overcoming the evils of channeling effective.

Percolation filters are frequently employed for removing from liquids or solutions a relatively small amount of impurity, as, for example, in the decolorization of oils by fuller's earth or of sugar syrups by bone char. When the adsorbent has become saturated, it is obvious that the liquid held in its voids, both those between the grains and the capillary spaces within the grains themselves, must be recovered. From the voids between the grains a certain amount can be removed by draining the filter. The rest is usually removed by washing; in the case of oils this may be done with petroleum ether, and in the case of sugar syrups with water. The wash liquid is usually lower in density than the liquid under treatment, and consequently downward flow should be employed to prevent convection. It is frequently best not to drain the filter before starting the washing operation, since other-

* See p. 457.

wise a great deal of unnecessary mixing results, due to the rush of the washing liquid applied to the top of the filter down through the empty voids between the grains.   The rate of washing should be low, particularly at the start, so that the heavy liquid, even that entrapped in the capillary voids within the grains, may flow down and out from the filter ahead of the wash liquid, which follows it through the filter like a piston.   Insofar as this piston action is effective, it results in removal of the original liquid without dilution with the wash liquid, but the final removal is always by diffusion and is correspondingly slow.

The wash liquid is almost always removed from the adsorbent by evaporation.   In the case of water, the adsorbent is usually removed from the filter and dried; in the case of organic solvents, such as petroleum naphtha, the solvent is usually vaporized by blowing in steam, the vapors going to a suitable condenser for recovery.   It is frequently possible to revivify or reactivate the adsorbent.   Thus, in the adsorption of organic color by bone char and fuller's earth, these materials are ignited to a moderate temperature in the presence of a certain amount of air.   This chars the color that was adsorbed, burning out a certain amount of it and converting the residue into a carbon which is itself decidedly adsorbent.   It is thus possible to re-use the material a large number of times.   In the case of the bone char, the limit to the life of the adsorbent is often dusting, but the fuller's earth becomes less effective with revivification and is seldom employed more than ten to fifteen times.   After furnacing, the adsorbent must, of course, be cooled and reintroduced into the filter.

The potential advantages of increasing adsorbent capacity and adsorption rate by the use of finer granules are very attractive, but fine material clogs the percolation filter.   The possibility of securing the necessary contact between solid and liquid by agitating the adsorbent in the liquid in the form of very fine granules and separating the adsorbent after saturation by filtration is obvious, but, before the development of the modern leaf and rotary filters, the filtering operation was too expensive to make this method practicable.   In recent years, however, the method has come into widespread use.   The rotary filter has proved best suited to the purpose.   The grain size of the adsorbent must not be so small that the filtration rate is seriously reduced or that dusting develops in any subsequent operations, such as revivification. The smaller the amount of adsorbent relative to the volume of liquid treated, the simpler and more efficient is the process. Hence, this method is particularly advantageous when employing treating agents of high adsorbent capacity such, for example, as activated charcoal. Unfortunately, in this system the advantages of counterflow can be secured only at the expense of multiplicity of operations. In practice one seldom employs more than one or at the most two agitations with a given body of liquid. However, where adsorption is marked, *i.e.*, the value of n in the Freundlich equation is high, the advantages of countercurrent action are far less than where adsorption is low (see pages 508 to 512).

Systematic sedimentation (see page 472) offers certain obvious advantages for this treatment of a liquid by a solid and will sometimes commend itself. Sedimentation is impossible under conditions of violent agitation, however, and for adsorption filtration agitation is very essential because of the extremely high molecular weight and correspondingly low diffusion rate of the material removed from the solution (see page 457). Consequently, therefore, agitation followed by mechanical filtration of the solid from the liquid in which it is suspended is usually the better method.

6. Treatment of Solids by Gases or Vapors.—The operation is the reverse of the treatment of vapors by solids but the principles governing it are identical. Furthermore, because of the difficulty of handling the solids, it is usually conducted in the same container used for the original adsorption. The removal will be the more complete the larger the amount of gas swept over the solid and the higher the temperature. In the case of adsorbed organic liquids, the best treating agent is steam, because, by condensing both it and the adsorbed vapor, the two can be separated by decantation. It is obviously desirable to keep the amount of steam necessary for treatment down to a minimum, and this can be done by raising the temperatures. Most solid adsorbents, however, are very poor conductors of heat, and the problem of distributing the heat throughout the adsorbent is a very real one. Sometimes coils are imbedded in the adsorbent, for water cooling during the adsorption phase of the operation and steam heating during the stripping. The danger of leakage is serious, and the coils should be so constructed that, where necessary, leaky units can be shut off without stopping operation.   Where the concentration of vapor adsorbed is high, cooling units of this sort are often essential during the adsorption operation, since it would otherwise be impossible to dissipate the heat, but where the adsorbent is dilute, *i.e.*, under those conditions for which solid adsorbents are peculiarly advantageous, the heat capacity of the diluent gas is enough to prevent serious temperature rise during adsorption.   In stripping it is usually best to supply the necessary heat in the form of highly superheated steam.   This has the advantage that the very flow of the steam itself distributes the heat perfectly throughout the adsorbent mass, despite its poor heat conductivity.   Furthermore, during the evaporation of the adsorbed vapor from the solid, the heat absorption lowers the temperature of the steam, while, as soon as stripping is complete, the temperature of the steam leaving the unit rises substantially to that at entrance. This gives a convenient and dependable control of the stripping operation.   After stripping, the adsorbent mass can be cooled by blowing through it cold air or inert gas.

Toward the end of the stripping operation it is obvious that a unit amount of steam can remove but little adsorbed vapor, because of the low partial pressure of the latter.   Such steam still possesses a large vapor-carrying capacity, which can be utilized by allowing the steam to flow through a number of containers in series.   Owing to the complications involved, however, this is seldom done.

7. Treatment of Solids by Liquids (Lixiviation or Leaching).— The technique of the art of lixiviation was developed in connection with the leaching of tannin from various barks and in similar important processes, and led to the adoption of what has been described above as a stepwise countercurrent system.   In the extraction of solids by liquids it is called the **Shank's system.** In the common case where water is used as the treating agent, the fresh bark is treated with a solution already rich in tannin, while the exhausted bark is given a final wash with fresh water.   In Shank's system the solid to be extracted is charged into large tanks, where it remains undisturbed until the extraction is completed, then to be replaced by fresh charge.   Where necessary, the charge is first broken up into granules.   The grain size should be as nearly uniform as possible, since for large lumps extraction is slow, whereas fine material packs and interferes with flow of liquid through the mass. For the reasons given on page 466, in charging the tanks precautions should be taken to prevent segregation of particles of varying size, though usually the change of density of the liquid as extraction proceeds is sufficient to overcome this evil if rate of flow is slow (see page 467). Since the liquid almost always increases in density, the flow is downward. The tanks are usually arranged in parallel rows, similar in principle to the arrangement of the cells in a ring furnace (see page 209). They should obviously be identical in size and level. The water or other lixiviant enters the most nearly exhausted tank of the series, flows down through it, and thence up to the top of the next tank in order.

Where gravity head is used, there must be a difference in liquid level between tanks sufficient to overcome the friction through the material and, in addition, the head corresponding to the difference between the density of the effluent liquor from the tank and the average of that in the tank itself. Where the number of tanks in series is large, this difference in head becomes a serious factor, because the charge in the fresh tank must be covered with liquid and consequently the full depth of the tank cannot be utilized for charge. The lixiviant is usually employed hot, to increase both solubility and rate of extraction. Where extraction is slow, heat losses, not only by radiation and conduction but also by evaporation, are sometimes serious.

A difficulty sometimes encountered is the packing of the charge due to its reduction by the extraction process to a finely subdivided residue. This is particularly likely to develop when the percentage of solute in the charge is high. Thus, in the manufacture of black ash in the LeBlanc process, it is essential to modify the composition of the charge to the black-ash furnace to secure a product that will, to a reasonable degree, retain a porous structure and mechanical strength as leaching proceeds. Fortunately, however, solids containing a high percentage of soluble matter can usually be leached by simple agitation, followed by separation of the residue by sedimentation.

The Shank's system was originally developed primarily because of the mechanical difficulties of moving solids under proper conditions of control. This difficulty was avoided by leaving the solid stationary and letting all the movement, during the extraction process itself, be that of liquid past the solid. The advent of the modern developments in the mechanical conveying of solids obviously made possible a new technique in lixiviation. It became practicable to move both solid and liquid simultaneously, countercurrent to each other, in intimate contact, independently of the state of subdivision of the solid. The Dorr classifier (Fig. 103, page 310) consists essentially of a scraper conveyor which drags a granular solid up an inclined plane against a countercurrent of lixiviant. The solid is fed at the lower end of the incline and is discharged at its top. While the motion of the scrapers is slow, nonetheless their agitating action is such that this type of equipment is not well suited for the treatment of finely subdivided slow-settling solids. Furthermore, the agitation distinctly interferes with the countercurrent action, owing to the mixing of liquids at different points in the trough. This may be offset by using these units in series. The apparatus has large capacity and low operating cost. The grain size can be sufficiently small so that extraction is rapid. An important illustration is the leaching of copper salts from pyrites cinder.

For finer materials it is best to reduce the agitation to a minimum and to let the solid move through the liquid by gravity sedimentation. This is accomplished in the Dorr continuous thickener (Fig. 105, page 321). The suspension is fed into the middle of the top, the clear decanted liquor overflows at the periphery, and a concentrated sludge is continuously removed from the bottom. There is no countercurrent flow in a given unit, but the units may be successfully used in series. A typical application is found in the extraction of caustic soda from calcium carbonate sludge in the causticization of soda ash.

In principle the washing of a sludge in a filter comes under this heading. This has already been discussed in Chap. XI.

PART II.   DESIGN: GASES BY LIQUIDS

1. Packed Towers

In the absorption of gases by liquids the conditions of operation are usually countercurrent and continuous or at least reasonably so over definite time intervals. Consequently the discussion of quantitative methods of design will be restricted to such conditions.*

* Computation methods adaptable to other cases will, however, be found on pages 506 and 513.

Figure 142 represents a countercurrent absorption unit. The incoming gas is indicated entering at the bottom and leaving at the top and the liquid absorbent is flowing in the opposite direction. The entering gas carries the material to be absorbed, which dissolves as solute in the liquid absorbent. The exit gas carries only the residual solute not dissolved in the absorbent liquid flowing from the bottom. It is advisable to express the concentrations of material being absorbed, *i.e.*, of solute as parts of solute per part of solute-free gas for the gas phase and parts of solute per part of solute-free absorbent for the liquid phase. Unless otherwise stated, both gas and liquid concentrations will be expressed as mols per mol.

Call the mols of incoming, solute-free gas per unit time G and the mols of liquid absorbent L. The concentration of solute in the liquid, expressed as mols per mol of absorbent liquid is X. This has the value X_1 at the bottom of the tower in the effluent liquid and X_2 at the top of the tower in the incoming liquid. Y is the concentration of solute in the gas, expressed as mols of solute per mol of solute-free gas. Its value is Y_1 in the incoming gas and Y_2 in the outgoing. Consider any section in the middle of the tower, taken at right angles to its axis. At this section the concentrations are X and Y, the numerical values of these quantities differing of course with the point at which the section is taken. Consider a second section at a differential distance dl below the first, at which point the corresponding concentrations are $X+dX$ and $Y+dY$. Since equality of input and output demands that any

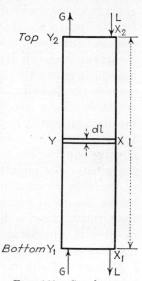

Fig. 142.—Steady counterflow of liquid and gas through a tower.

solute removed from the gas in this section be taken up by the liquid, it follows that $GdY = LdX$. Furthermore, since continuity of operation is assumed, L and G are constants for any fixed conditions of operation. It is, therefore, possible to integrate this equation directly, obtaining $GY = LX +$ constant. This equality may also be written

$$G(Y - Y_2) = L(X - X_2) \tag{1}$$

Inspection of this equation shows that in any such continuous countercurrent system, Y must of necessity be linear in X. Because this relation was derived solely from an equality of input and output, it must hold whatever the character of the equilibria between the phases, the type of apparatus, the intimacy of contact, the relative velocities of flow or any other similar relationships, however important from other points of view. It does, however, postulate steady rates of flow of both gas and liquid.

Ratio of Liquid to Gas.—Consider a countercurrent gas washing system in which not only the component desired is soluble in the absorbent but also some other component of the gas is at least somewhat so. Both these components will dissolve, but the second less than the first. If one employs an absorption column sufficiently long and efficient, one can saturate the absorbent with the desirable component at the point where the absorbent leaves the column, but it is impossible completely to dissolve the desired component with a smaller amount of absorbent than this; in general, one will have to use more absorbent, the excess quantity depending upon the size and efficiency of the tower. Even this minimum amount of absorbent will, however, dissolve some of the undesirable constituents and, furthermore, the greater the quantity of excess absorbent, the more of the undesirable constituents will go into solution. Since, however, excess absorbent cannot possibly dissolve more of the desired constituent, because the theoretical quantity, *properly used*, will dissolve it all, excess absorbent merely increases the ratio of undesirable to desirable material.

Minimum Ratio of Liquid to Gas.—As a specific case consider the drying of air by sulfuric acid. The equilibrium relationship between air and sulfuric acid is given by the curve $OABC$ in Fig. 143.[21] If one assumes air entering such a system with a moisture content $Y_1 = 0.028$ (Fig. 143) being treated with H_2SO_4 with an initial moisture content $X_2 = 2$, the moisture in the air being ultimately reduced to $Y_2 = 0.008$ and the water content of the acid rising to $X_1 = 9$, it follows from the preceding paragraph that the concentrations of moisture in both the air and the acid throughout the apparatus must be represented by the line *EF*. Such a line must always lie to the *left* of the equilibrium curve, and furthermore it can never cross that curve, although, theoretically at least, it can touch it. However, if it touches the equilibrium curve, tangentially or otherwise, at that point gas and liquid are at equilibrium or only differentially separated from it, so that rate of transfer of solute from gas to liquid in the neighborhood of that point is negligible, requiring, therefore, infinitely large surface of contact, which is equivalent to a negligible capacity for any apparatus of finite size.

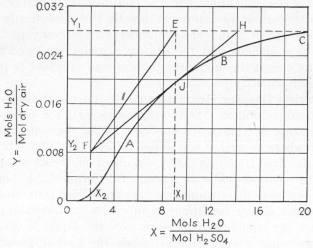

Fig. 143.—Absorption diagram, using mol-ratio units.

Inspection of Eq. 1 shows that the slope of the line *EF* is the ratio of liquid absorbent to gas treated, in this case 0.00286 mol of H_2SO_4 per mol of bone-dry air. Since, in general, it is desirable to use as little absorbent as practicable, it is important to keep this slope low. Assume, for example, that it is required to dry air down to a moisture content $Y_2 = 0.008$ with acid entering the system with a concentration $X_2 = 2$. This corresponds to point *F* on Fig. 143. The flattest line that can be drawn through *F* and reach the high water content $Y_1 = 0.028$ without crossing the equilibrium curve is obviously the line *FH*, tangent to the equilibrium curve at *J*. The slope of this line $(0.028 - 0.008)/(14.2 - 2) = 0.00164$ mol of H_2SO_4 per mol of bone-dry air therefore represents the smallest ratio of acid to air which it is theoretically possible to employ in drying air of high moisture content Y_1 to the low moisture content Y_2 by the use of acid with initial water content of X_2.   Furthermore, since in such a system one would of necessity approach equilibrium in the middle of the absorber, it follows that the air-treating capacity of the absorber would be negligibly small or else the size of the absorber would be infinitely great.

If, however, the initial air to be treated contains less moisture than corresponds to point J, it then becomes possible to draw flatter lines, *i.e.*, to use less acid per mol of air and still stay on the left of the equilibrium curve.   This diagram therefore makes it possible for one to determine directly the theoretically minimum amount of liquid absorbent necessary for any particular case.   It is obvious that the amount actually employed will of necessity exceed this minimum by a margin sufficient to furnish reasonable capacity.

Materials Obeying Henry's Law.—If the vapor dissolved in the absorbent follows Henry's law, $(p = Hx)$, the equilibrium relationships are greatly simplified.   While the following discussion will be general, it will be illustrated by the case of benzene vapor dissolved from flue gas by absorbent oil, the oil being later denuded by distillation with steam.   It is assumed that both the absorption and the stripping are conducted by countercurrent flow, under steady conditions of operation.   At constant temperature the equilibrium pressure over the liquid is given by the expression $p = HX/(1+X)$, while the partial pressure of benzene in the gas is $p_g = \pi Y/(1+Y)$, where π is the *total* pressure. At equilibrium p_g equals p whence

$$Y = \frac{HX}{\pi - (H - \pi)X} \tag{2}$$

For the special cases to which Raoult's law applies, H becomes equal to P, the vapor pressure of the pure benzene at the temperature of the operation.   This equation represents a rectangular hyperbola with axes parallel to the major axis.

Case 1: $H > \pi$.—When stripping a volatile component from a nonvolatile absorbent by steam, it is advantageous to have the temperature as high and the pressure as low as possible (see page 465).   Generally, therefore, the operating conditions are such that $H > \pi$.   In this case inspection of the equilibrium

(Eq. 2) shows that Y becomes infinite when the denominator on the right-hand side is zero, *i.e.*, when $X_a = \pi/(H-\pi)$, where X_a is the asymptotic value above which the concentration of the dissolved constituent in the absorbent liquid cannot exist. If the absorbent enters the stripping column richer than this, the excess of dissolved vapor boils out spontaneously, reducing the concentration to the asymptotic value. The equilibrium curve is represented by Fig. 144.

If, in this figure, X_2 represents the concentration of the incoming rich absorber stock, inspection will make it clear that, if one wishes to secure complete stripping, *i.e.*, to have the operating line go through the origin, the steepest line that can be drawn is one tan-

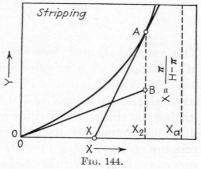

Fig. 144.

gent to the equilibrium curve at the origin, cutting the vertical line through X_2 at the point B, this point corresponding to the highest possible degree of saturation of the steam leaving the stripping column under these conditions.

Inspection of the equilibrium (Eq. 2) shows that its slope at $X=0$ is $dY/dX = H/\pi$ or $dX/dY = \pi/H = G/L$, where G/L is the mols of steam required per mol of oil. Furthermore, it is obvious in this case that the equation of the operating line is $Y = (H/\pi)X$ and that the steam consumption is proportional to the total pressure on the system and inversely proportional to the Henry's law constant at the operating temperature. In other words, the lower the total pressure the less the steam consumption necessary for complete stripping, and the lower the volatility of the absorbed component the greater the steam necessary to do the work. Inspection, both of the diagram and of these equations, shows that the steam consumption for complete stripping is independent of the initial concentration of the rich absorber stock. From this it follows that, if one is stripping from the oil a mixture of a number of dissolved components, since the more volatile strip out first, the steam necessary for complete stripping is that computed for the least volatile component, just as though the others were not present.

If one wishes to saturate the steam leaving the stripper, *i.e.*, to bring it into equilibrium with the incoming rich stock, the steepest operating line attainable is a tangent to the equilibrium curve at point A, cutting the horizontal axis at point X, corresponding to the best possible stripping compatible with the assumption made. The equation of this line can be calculated from its slope, and at the bottom of the apparatus, where $Y = 0$,

$$X = X_2 - Y_2 \frac{[\pi - (H - \pi)X_2]^2}{H\pi}.$$

This value of X represents the lowest attainable concentration of the stripped oil compatible with steam saturation at the top.

If $X_2 = X_a$, inspection of the diagram makes it clear that it is impossible to strip at all and at the same time have the vapors leaving the still at equilibrium with the absorber stock entering it. This is true because, under these conditions, the partial pressure of the entering absorber stock is equal to the total pressure on the still, so that the presence of any steam whatever would lessen the partial pressure of the solute and therefore destroy the equilibrium.

If, as is usually the case, a large fraction but not all of the benzene in the feed is to be removed, then X_1 is small but finite. The minimum steam consumption would then correspond to equilibrium at some value of X intermediate between X_2 and X_1, the operating line being tangent to the equilibrium curve at $X_t = \sqrt{\pi X_1/(H - \pi)}$. Obviously this value of X is independent of X_2 and depends only on X_1, π and H. Since the values of Y_t, X_t and X_2 are known, Y_2 is computed by proportion: $Y_2 = Y_t(X_2 - X_1)/(X_t - X_1)$.

Case 2: $H < \pi$.—Absorption should take place at the highest practicable total pressure and the lowest possible temperature, *i.e.*, at high values of π and low values of H. In other words, the conditions of this case ($H < \pi$) are those normally existing in absorption processes but not in stripping.

Inspection of the equilibrium equation makes it clear that it corresponds to the curve of Fig. 145, being asymptotic to the horizontal line, $Y = H/(\pi - H)$.

It is obvious that, if one desires to denude the gas completely, the operating line must go through the origin and cannot possibly have a slope less than that corresponding to tangency there.

Since at $X=0$, $dY/dX=H/\pi$, the corresponding operating line is $Y=HX/\pi$ and the amount of absorbent required per mol of inert gas treated is $L/G=H/\pi$. It will be noted that the absorbent required for a given amount of gas is proportional to the volatility of the solute absorbed and inversely proportional to the total pressure on the system. Here, too, the absorbent needed is independent of the initial concentration in the other phase at the other end of the unit. Since $Y=HX/\pi$, it is obvious that $X_2=\pi Y_2/H=$ the maximum saturation of oil compatible with complete denuding of the gas treated.

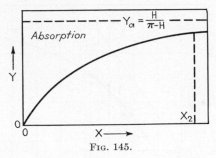

FIG. 145.

To bring the oil into equilibrium with the gas entering the absorber,

$$Y_1=Y_2-\frac{H\pi X_2}{[\pi+(\pi-H)X_2]^2}.$$

This gives the lowest value to which the concentration of solute vapor in the exit gas can be reduced if the oil is brought up to equilibrium with the entering gas.

Case 3: $H=\pi$.—For this case at equilibrium $Y=X$ and it is therefore possible to have equilibrium at all points in the system, provided the capacity of the equipment is sufficient to carry out the absorption under a negligible driving force.

It is worth noting that, in both stripping and absorption, one normally operates on the unfavorable side of the equilibrium curve, *i.e.*, it is theoretically impossible to secure equilibrium at both ends of the operating line. However, this disadvantage is more apparent than real, because the height of the equilibrium curve corresponding to stripping conditions, secured by raising the temperature and lowering the pressure, far more than compensates for its unfavorable shape and the same is true of the advantages gained by lowering the equilibrium curve for absorption, through decreased temperature and increased pressure.

Absorption Rate.—On pages 442 to 456 it was shown that the instantaneous rate of transfer of material from the one phase to the other is proportional to the surface of contact between the phases and to the concentration gradient through each of the two surface films on the two sides of the interface, the two phases being at equilibrium at the interface itself. It therefore follows

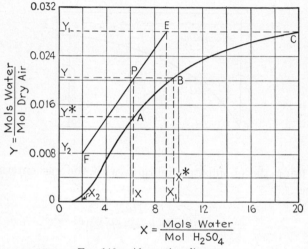

Fig. 146.—Absorption diagram.

that in Fig. 143 the equilibrium curve $OABC$ represents the interfacial conditions, *i.e.*, at each point in the apparatus the concentrations there existing at the interface must fall somewhere on this curve. Calling k_Y and k_L the individual or film coefficients of the gas and liquid films, respectively, S the area of cross section of the apparatus, a the interfacial surface of contact between the gas and the liquid per unit volume of the apparatus* and X_i and Y_i the liquid and gaseous concentrations at equilibrium and therefore also at the interface, the rate of transfer of material can be expressed as follows:

$$dN = L\ dX = k_L aS(X_i - X)\ dl = G\ dY = k_Y aS(Y - Y_i)\ dl. \quad (3)$$

* Obviously A, the total interfacial surface, equals aSl.

Liquid-phase Controlling.—In Fig. 146 the equilibrium curve and the line FE of Fig. 143 are reproduced. The point P on the line FE represents the conditions in liquid and gas, respectively, at a certain point in the absorber, where the liquid and gas concentrations are X and Y, respectively. Assume for the instant that in this particular case the type of equipment and the operating conditions are such that the resistance to transfer is mainly in the liquid phase and that the gas-phase resistance is negligible, *i.e.*, that the liquid phase is the controlling factor (see page 452). This is equivalent to saying that the concentration gradient through the gas phase is negligible, or that the gas concentration at the interface is essentially identical with the concentration Y in the bulk of the gas. It therefore follows that the interfacial conditions are represented by point B in Fig. 146, at which the concentration in the gas film at the interface is equal to that in the main body of the gas, while the concentration in the liquid film at the interface has the value $X^\star$. Therefore, the driving force causing transfer in Eq. 3 is numerically equal to $X^\star - X$, corresponding to the length of the line PB.

Rewriting Eq. 3 in the form

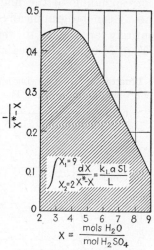

FIG. 147.—Graphical integration, liquid-phase resistance controlling.

$$\frac{dX}{X^\star - X} = \frac{k_L a S d l}{L},\tag{4}$$

it is seen that granting a knowledge of the constants k_L, a and S, one can calculate the length of absorber necessary by evaluating the integral $\dfrac{dX}{(X^\star - X)}$. This may be done by plotting the reciprocal of $(X^\star - X)$ vs. X. This has been done in Fig. 147 and the crosshatched area represents the value of the integral in question, and is numerically equal to $k_L a S l / L$. In this way it is possible to determine the height l of absorber necessary for any desired operation, once the constants of the equipment are known for the case in question.

Gas-phase Controlling.—Assume, on the other hand, that the equipment and operating conditions are modified until the gas phase is controlling, *i.e.*, the resistance of the gas phase is considerable and that of the liquid phase negligible (see pages 451 to 452). Since the concentration in the liquid phase at the interface will be substantially equal to that in the main body of the liquid X, it follows that the interfacial conditions will correspond to the point A (Fig. 146). Furthermore, the driving force causing transfer through the gas phase is $Y - Y^\star$, corresponding to the line PA in Fig. 146. It is obvious that Eq. 3 can be graphically integrated for this case by a method entirely analogous to that given above, *i.e.*, by plotting $1/(Y - Y^\star)$ vs. Y, the area under the curve being equal to $k_Y a S l/G$.

Illustration 1.—In drying air for a certain process, a sulfuric acid absorption tower is employed. The entering acid contains 92 per cent H_2SO_4 by weight, and its concentration drops to 47.6 per cent H_2SO_4 in passing through the tower. The air enters at 25°C. with a relative humidity of 70 per cent, and analysis of the effluent air shows 3.09 gm. of moisture/cu. m. of bone-dry air at 25°C. and normal barometer. The tower is equipped with lead cooling coils to maintain it at substantially constant temperature throughout and operates at 25°C.

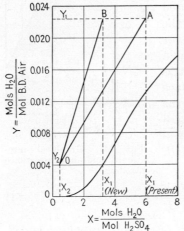

It is necessary to build a second tower for the same capacity as the present one, to meet the same operating conditions, except that the new tower is to be designed for a rate of flow of acid twice that now employed. What will be the necessary size of the new tower, expressed as a percentage of the size of present tower?

Fig. 148.—Absorption diagram for Illustration 1.

Notes.—For equilibrium data, see Fig. 143 (page 475). Vapor pressure of water at 25°C. is 23.76 mm. of mercury. Assume the gas-film resistance of controlling importance.

Solution. Present Conditions:

$$X_2 = \frac{\text{mols } H_2O}{\text{mols } H_2SO_4} \text{ in entering acid} = \frac{(100-92)}{(92)}\frac{(98)}{(18)} = 0.473.$$

$$X_1 = \frac{\text{mols } H_2O}{\text{mols } H_2SO_4} \text{ in exit acid} = \frac{(100-47.6)}{(47.6)}\frac{(98)}{(18)} = 5.99.$$

The partial pressure of water vapor in the entering air is $(23.76)\ (0.70) = 16.63$ mm. of mercury.

$$Y_1 = \frac{16.63}{(760 - 16.6)} = 0.0224 \frac{\text{mols } H_2O}{\text{mol dry air}}.$$

$$Y_2 = \frac{(3.09)(273 + 25)(22.4)}{(1000)\ (273)\ (18)} = 0.0042 \frac{\text{mols } H_2O}{\text{mols dry air}}$$

Figure 148 shows the operating line OA, based on these coordinates, plotted on the equilibrium diagram.

The following table gives the value of $Y^\star$ corresponding to the values of Y as read from Fig. 148, based on the operating line for the present tower.

Y	$Y^\star$	$Y - Y^\star$	$1/(Y - Y^\star)$
0.0042	0	0.0042	238
0.006	0.00007	0.00593	169
0.008	0.0005	0.0075	133
0.0120	0.0029	0.0091	110
0.016	0.0067	0.0093	107.5
0.020	0.0110	0.0090	111
0.0224	0.0131	0.0093	107.5

In Fig. 149 the values of $1/(Y - Y^\star)$ are plotted vs. Y for values of Y from 0.0042 to 0.0224.

The area under the curve BC is 56.5 squares. Each square is (20) $(0.002) = 0.04$ units; hence the area is 2.26 units, *i.e.*

$$\int_{Y_2 = 0.0042}^{Y_1 = 0.0224} \frac{dY}{Y - Y^\star} = 2.26 = \frac{k_Y \sigma Sl}{G}.$$

New Conditions.—The slope of the operating line equals mols H_2SO_4/mol of bone-dry air. The operating line for the new conditions will have a slope twice as great as in the present tower.

Slope for present conditions $= \dfrac{0.0224 - 0.0042}{5.99 - 0.473} = 0.0033.$

Slope for new conditions $= \dfrac{0.0224 - 0.0042}{X_1 - 0.473} = 0.0066$

whence $X_1 = 3.23.$

Y	$Y^\star$	$Y - Y^\star$	$1/(Y - Y^\star)$
0.0042	0	0.0042	238
0.006	0	0.006	167
0.008	0.00008	0.00792	126
0.012	0.0005	0.0115	87
0.016	0.00145	0.01455	69
0.020	0.00295	0.01705	58.5
0.0224	0.00405	0.01835	54.5

Figure 148 also shows the operating line for the new tower. The table at the bottom of page 483 gives the values of $Y^\star$ corresponding to various values of Y as read from Fig. 148, based on the operating line for the new tower. These values of $1/(Y-Y^\star)$ for the new tower have been plotted vs. Y in Fig. 149, for values of Y from 0.0042 to 0.0224.

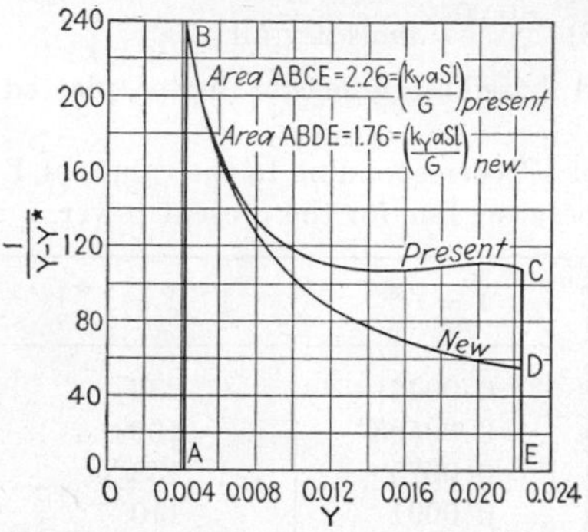

The area under the curve BD is 44.0 squares. Therefore the area is $44 \times 0.04 \doteqdot 1.76$ units $= k_Y a S l/G$.

Inasmuch as the exact effect of gas velocity on $k_Y a$ for this case has not been determined, the gas velocity G in the new tower will be made the same as in the present tower, requiring the same value of the cross section S as at present.

Hence

$$\frac{l_{\text{new}}}{l_{\text{old}}} = \frac{(1.76G/k_Y aS)\ \text{new}}{(2.26G/k_Y aS)\ \text{present}} = 0.78.$$

Fig. 149.—Graphical integration for Illustration 1.

Therefore the height of the new tower should be 78 per cent of the height of the present tower.

General Case.—In those important cases in which both gas- and liquid-phase resistances must be taken into account, the graphical method of computation is of especial value. It is clear from Eq. 3, page 480 (see also page 452), that $k_L/k_Y = (Y-Y_i)/(X_i-X)$. Granting now that the ratio of the liquid- and gas-phase coefficients is known, by drawing through point P a line PD (Fig. 150), the slope of which equals k_L/k_Y, it will be clear that the intersection D of this line with the equilibrium curve $OABC$ is the only point on the equilibrium curve which can possibly fulfil this last relationship. It therefore follows that for such a case the concentration gradient through the gas phase $Y-Y_i$ is equal to the line DM or PN, and that the gradient through the liquid phase X_i-X is equal to the line DN or PM. In such a case the area curve is obtained by using these lines instead of one of the

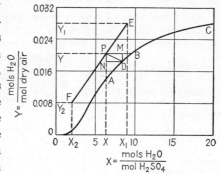

Fig. 150.—General case.

lines PA or PB, as before. From inspection it is seen that PN is always less than PA, and PM less than PB, *i.e.*, the area under the reciprocal curves is always greater. In other words, the rate of transfer through two resistances in series is less than if only one resistance were substantial.

The preceding discussion has been based on the assumption that the driving forces or differences in potential Δp and Δc are proportional to the concentration differences ΔY and ΔX, respectively. It can readily be shown that, where concentrations are low, this is substantially true, but, where concentrations are high, it is not true. In the latter case the diagrams of Figs. 146 to 150 should be constructed, not in terms of Y and X, but in terms of partial pressures and concentrations p and c, or of whatever units of concentration must be chosen such that differences in concentrations expressed in these units are proportional to transfer rates. On this diagram of p vs. c the equilibrium curve should be drawn. The actual curve, corresponding to the line FE, can be drawn by computation most conveniently by constructing first an auxiliary X-Y diagram and transferring the corresponding points from this diagram to the p-c plane. The FE line will not be straight in the p-c plane.

Henry's Law.—Figure 151 is a diagram similar to the two preceding ones for the case in which the equilibrium concentration in the liquid phase is directly proportional to that in the gaseous phase. Study of this diagram will show that, whatever the ratio k_L/k_Y, provided only that this ratio remains constant throughout the apparatus, at any particular cross section of the apparatus, the actual driving force PN through the gas phase, divided by the vertical line PA, *i.e.*, the driving force on the assumption that the resistance is entirely in the gas phase, is numerically identical with this ratio at any other point. Since this ratio is constant throughout the apparatus, it therefore follows that the assumption of gas-phase resistance only or, what is the equivalent to the same thing, the use of the line PA as the driving force will give a computed driving force proportional to the true one. In other words, it is allowable to assume a single resistance for such a case, for, while the coefficient thus computed will differ from the true one, it will be constant and can be employed without hesitation. Similar analysis will show that it is equally allowable to assume the liquid phase as controlling, for analogous reasons.   In consequence, in those cases where Henry's law applies, it is usual and entirely allowable to assume either gas-phase or liquid-phase resistance only, neglecting the other one.   It must, however, be kept in mind that the coefficients thus computed are not true gas-phase or liquid-phase coefficients, but are *overall* in character.   Furthermore, their numerical values will vary with any changes in operating conditions which modify either the absolute or the relative resistances of the two phases.

Further study of Fig. 151 (shown below) will make it clear that in this case the average driving force is the *logarithmic mean* of

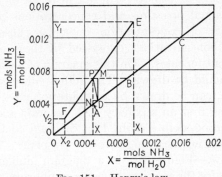

Fig. 151.—Henry's law.

the driving forces at the beginning and end of the system.[*] The possibility of using the logarithmic mean makes it easier to compute the performance of such a system algebraically than by the use of the graphical method outlined above, the equations to be employed being as follows:

$$G(Y_1 - Y_2) = N = K_Y a Sl(\Delta Y)_{av.} \tag{5}$$

where $(\Delta Y)_{av.}$ is the logarithmic mean of the overall driving forces at the top and bottom of the tower.

[*] The logarithmic-mean driving force is the proper driving force not only for cases in which Henry's law applies but for all cases where the operating line and equilibrium line are straight over the region in question, *i.e.*, the equilibrium curve may be of the form $Y^\star = qX^\star + p$, where q and p are constants.   It is to be noted that for the case of gas-phase controlling the logarithmic mean requires the equilibrium curve to be straight from X_2 to X_1, but for liquid-phase controlling the straight portion of the equilibrium curve must be between Y_2 and Y_1.

$$L(X_1 - X_2) = dN = K_L a l S(\Delta X)_{av.} \qquad (6)$$

where $(\Delta X)_{av.}$ is the logarithmic mean of the overall driving forces at the top and bottom of the tower.

In Eqs. 5 and 6, for low concentrations the values of ΔX and ΔY may be expressed in the stoichiometric units defined on page 473; for higher concentrations, ΔY must, in general, be expressed in terms of pressure difference Δp, and ΔX as concentration difference Δc (see page 459). For very high concentrations the graphical methods must be used in terms of Δp and Δc.

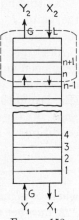

FIG. 152.—Diagram of plate tower.

2. PLATE TOWERS

Plate towers (see page 548), as well as packed towers, are used in absorption, stripping and extraction. The most convenient design method for plate towers is based on the concept of a theoretical plate. Consider the diagrammatic sketch of a plate column shown in Fig. 152, where the horizontal lines represent plates. The concept of a theoretical plate assumes that the contact between the liquid and gas on a plate is sufficiently good, that the vapor and liquid *leaving* a plate are in equilibrium with each other. The material balance for such a tower can be written in general terms for the nth plate as

FIG. 153.—Diagram for plate-type absorber.

$$Y_{n-1} = \frac{L}{G} X_n + \left(Y_2 - \frac{L}{G} X_2 \right). \qquad (7)$$

This balance represents the operating line of slope L/G on a $Y-X$ plot and passes through the points Y_2, X_2 and Y_1, X_1. These conditions are shown in Fig. 153 where OM represents the equilibrium curve and AI represents the operating line of slope L/G through the coordinates of the terminal conditions. Starting at bottom of the absorber, the compositions of the gas entering and of the liquid leaving the bottom plate are represented by point A. Now, using the concept of a theoretical plate, the vapor rising from this plate must be in equilibrium with the liquid leaving the plate, *i.e.*, in equilibrium with X_1. This condition is represented by the point B on the equilibrium curve corresponding to a vapor composition of Y', which is in turn related to the composition of the liquid on the plate above by the operating-line equation at point C, giving X' as this liquid composition. In this way it is possible to reach the point I, and such a *stepwise* procedure gives the number of theoretical plates required, four in this case.

Algebraic solutions, instead of the above graphical procedure, have been developed[11] for the cases where the equilibrium curve is a straight line through the origin.   Using the material balance (Eq. 1) and the equilibrium expression $Y^\star = K^\star X^\star$, where $K^\star$ is the *slope* of the equilibrium curve, the relation of the terminal conditions is given by

$$\frac{Y_1 - Y_2}{Y_1 - K^\star X_2} = \frac{(L/K^\star G)^{n+1} - (L/K^\star G)}{(L/K^\star G)^{n+1} - 1} \qquad (8)*$$

where n is number of theoretical plates in the tower.

A number of quantitative conclusions were derived for packed towers under the limiting condition for which the operating line touched the equilibrium curve (see pages 474 to 480).   All these conclusions are directly applicable to plate towers, because, when the operating line touches the equilibrium curve, an infinite number of plates is necessary and the steps become differential in this region, causing the differences between a stepwise countercurrent (plate tower) and a true countercurrent (packed tower) operation to vanish.

Plate Efficiency.—In general, the number of plates in an actual column is greater than the number of theoretical plates although in some cases it may be less.   This is due to the fact that the vapor rising through the liquid on the plate does not come to equilibrium with the liquid.   This inefficiency is somewhat offset by the concentration gradient across the plate, a condition which was neglected in the definition of a theoretical plate, but this gradient aids the operation by making it more nearly true countercurrent.   Also droplets of liquid are thrown into the vapor space above the liquid by the rising vapor; this increases the contact surface between the liquid and vapor and makes the

* For $\dfrac{L}{K^\star G} = 1$; $\dfrac{Y_1 - Y_2}{Y_1 - K^\star X_2} = \dfrac{n}{n+1}$.

approach to equilibrium more complete, but increases the possibility that liquid droplets will be carried from one plate to the plate above, a process that tends to destroy the counter-current action of the tower. Depending on the relative magnitude of these effects, the efficiency of an actual plate may be smaller or greater than that of a theoretical plate.

There are several definitions of plate efficiency, of which the *overall plate efficiency* is the simplest. This efficiency is defined as the ratio of the number of theoretical plates to the number of actual plates required for the operation; thus it is the factor by which the number of theoretical plates must be divided to give the actual number of plates required. Experimental data indicate overall plate efficiencies of 7 to 90 per cent, but are too meager to enable a correlation suitable for the prediction of overall efficiencies. These efficiencies varied with the design of the plate, with the chemical and physical properties of the system being treated and with the operation conditions. Except where data are available on an operation very similar to the proposed design, the estimation of overall plate efficiencies becomes largely a matter of guesswork, and pilot plant data on the proposed operation are extremely desirable before constructing a large unit.

H.E.T.P.—In the design calculations for given operating conditions, the equilibrium curve and operating line are identical for both plate and packed towers. However, except for the case of a straight equilibrium curve for which algebraic methods can be used, a graphical integration is necessary for a packed tower, which is more time-consuming than the simple stepwise operation involved for plate towers. For this reason one of the common methods of designing packed towers has been to determine the number of theoretical plates that would be required if the operation were carried out in a plate tower, and then to convert to the height of a packed tower by multiplying the number of theoretical plates by the height of packing equivalent to one theoretical plate, called H.E.T.P.[13] In other words, the H.E.T.P. is the height of packing that will give the same separation as one theoretical plate, *i.e.*, a section of packing of a height such that the vapor leaving the top of the section will have the same composition as the vapor in equilibrium with the liquid leaving the bottom of the section. The H.E.T.P. values are experimentally determined by calculating the number of theo retical plates necessary to be equivalent to some actual packed tower; the H.E.T.P. is then simply the height of the packed tower divided by the number of theoretical plates. Such a unit varies with mixture being treated, the operating conditions, the diameter of the tower, the size and type of packing and the concentration of the gas and liquid. Values of H.E.T.P.'s have been reported from a few inches for small laboratory columns up to several feet for large towers with coarse packing. Theoretically, the use of the H.E.T.P. is unsound because it substitutes a stepwise countercurrent for a true countercurrent operation; however, where the operation is such that the number of theoretical plates is large and the change in concentration per plate small, the error so introduced is well within the accuracy with which such towers can be designed.

H.T.U.—Another design method[4] for packed towers is the use of the height of a transfer unit, H.T.U. The number of transfer units is defined as equal to $\int_{Y_2}^{Y_1} dY/(Y-Y^\star) = k_Y a Sl/G$, and a similar expression in terms of X may be obtained from page 481. The H.T.U. is then the height of the tower divided by the number of transfer units. Its advantage over the H.E.T.P. is that it is defined on the basis of the true differential countercurrent process rather than the incorrect stepwise countercurrent. Ordinarily over the height of one transfer unit the difference $Y-Y^\star$ does not change greatly and the arithmetic average may be used without introducing appreciable error.

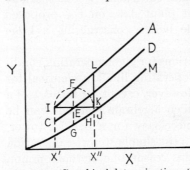

Fig. 154.—Graphical determination of number of transfer units[4a].

This may be approximated by the use of a relatively simple stepwise calculation for the determination of the number of transfer units[4a]. In the usual design diagrams (Fig. 154), the line CD is drawn so that its ordinates are equal to the arithmetic mean of the ordinates of the equilibrium curve and the operating line. On the above assumptions, one transfer unit would correspond to a step giving a change in Y equal to the arithmetic average of $Y-Y^\star$ at the two ends of the step. Thus, if one starts at the point I and proceeds not to J (as would be the case for a theoretical plate) but to K, so that $IE = EK$, and then steps up to L, it is easily shown that LK, the change in Y, is equal to GF, which, if the curvature of the equilibrium curve is not too great, approximates closely the arithmetic average of $Y^{\star} - Y$ at X' and X''; thus the step corresponds to one transfer unit. Such a stepwise procedure is continued to the other terminal of the tower; the number of steps so obtained is the number of transfer units. If the design calculation is based on X instead of Y, the midway line must be drawn at the average abscissa of the operating line and the equilibrium curve rather than the average ordinate. The H.T.U.'s thus found are used similarly to the H.E.T.P.'s, and for the case where the operating line and the equilibrium curve are parallel the two units become identical.

3. Heat Effects

The foregoing discussion has assumed isothermal operation, an assumption that is usually satisfactory where dilute gases and liquid are being handled. However, in cases such as the absorption of hydrochloric acid gas in water, the heat evolution is sufficient to raise appreciably the temperature in the tower. The changes in temperature may be sufficient to alter the equilibrium conditions, and, since the temperature effects are usually such as to hinder the desired operation, the capacity of the operation may be seriously limited. Hence, in the absorption of hydrochloric acid in water, it is customary to provide cooling simultaneously with the absorption, in order to maintain equilibrium conditions favorable to the production of a strong acid solution. These temperature effects may be allowed for by the use of the material balance line and a heat balance.

The material balance relates Y to X, and, on the assumption that the temperatures of the vapor and liquid are the same at any given section, using thermal data, such as heats of solution, specific heats, etc., it is possible to estimate by a heat balance the temperature difference between the section in the tower where the liquid composition is X and either of the terminals. Thus it is possible to obtain the temperature gradient in the tower as a function of the liquid composition. In constructing the design diagram, the equilibrium curve is not constructed isothermally, but the temperatures corresponding to various values of liquid composition chosen for plotting the equilibrium curve are used to determine the equilibrium values of $Y^\star$. This equilibrium curve is then used in the same manner as the usual isothermal curve.

4. Allowable Gas and Liquor Velocities

Flooding in packed towers is caused by the friction of the rising gas holding up a certain amount of the liquid in the tower.

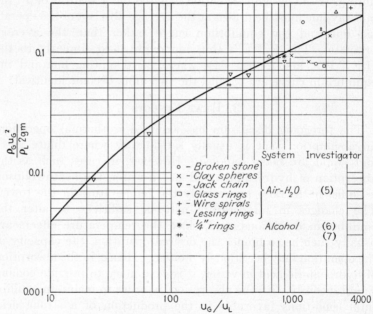

Fig. 155.—Maximum allowable actual velocities of gases and liquids through the free areas in packed towers.

The gas friction is given by the familiar expression $fL\rho_G u_G^2/2gm$ where f is a friction factor, l is the length of the tower, ρ_G is the density of the gas, u_G is the actual gas velocity, g is the acceleration of gravity and m is the mean hydraulic radius (free volume divided by the total contact area).* However, the friction effective in holding up liquid is clearly not the total friction, but the friction per unit length. The friction factor f is undoubtedly some function of the liquid and gas velocities, and it seems

---

* u equals u_0/F and m equals F/a where u_0 is the superficial velocity, *i.e.*, volumetric rate of flow per unit ground area, a is the specific contact are (square feet per cubic feet of tower), and F is the friction voids, *i.e.*, cubic feet of free volume per unit volume of packed section.

possible that these two velocities should occur as a ratio. At the flooding velocity this friction may be looked upon as the head necessary to hold up the liquid in the tower. This latter head should be proportional to density ρ_L of the liquid being held up. Equating the friction head to the liquid head and rearranging,

$$\frac{\rho_G}{\rho_L} \frac{u_G{}^2}{2gm} = \phi\left(\frac{u_G}{u_L}\right),$$

The data of several investigators are correlated in Fig. 155, including data on both absorption (air-water) and distillation for a variety of different packings.

Illustration 2.—Ammonia is to be removed from a 10 per cent NH_3–90 per cent air mixture by countercurrent scrubbing with water at 1 atmosphere pressure. The tower will be provided with adequate cooling, so that the entire operation may be carried out at 68°F., and the scrubber is to be designed to recover 99.5 per cent of the ammonia in the entering gas.

Equilibrium data for ammonia and water are given in Fig. 156.[17] An entering gas rate of 735 lb./(hr.) (sq. ft.) will be used. (a) Calculate the minimum water rate necessary for such an absorption. (b) If a water rate 20 per cent greater than the minimum is employed, calculate the necessary height of an absorption tower filled with 3-in. spiral tile, using the logarithmic driving force. (c) Repeat (b) using the graphical integration of the driving force.

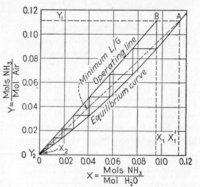

FIG. 156.—Absorption diagram for Illustration 2.

(d) Calculate the number of theoretical plates required for the same operation. (e) Calculate the average H.E.T.P. (f) Calculate the number of transfer units required for the absorption. (g) Calculate the average H.T.U.

Solution.—(a) $Y_1 = 0.10/0.90 = 0.1111$ mol NH_3/mol air.

$$Y_2 = Y_1(.005) = (0.1111)(.005) = 0.000555 \text{ mol } NH_3/\text{mol air.}$$

Since the water enters with no dissolved NH_3, $X_2 = 0$. The slope of the operating line is L/G and the minimum L will correspond to the straight line with the lowest slope that can be drawn through Y_2, X_2, without cutting the equilibrium curve. In the accompanying figure this is seen to be the line OA, which just touches the equilibrium curve but does not cross it, and the maximum liquor concentration consistent with the design condition that can be obtained is $X_1' = 0.1143$. Per square foot of cross section, the air rate is

$$\frac{G}{S} = \frac{735(0.9)}{(0.9 \times 29 + 0.1 \times 17)} = \frac{23.8 \text{ lb. mols air}}{(\text{hr.})(\text{sq. ft.})}$$

and the minimum water rate is obtained by an overall material balance.

$$(23.8)(0.1111 - 0.000555) = L'(0.1143 - 0)/S$$

giving $L'/S = 23.0$ lb. mols $H_2O/(hr.)(sq. ft.)$.

b. A 20 per cent increase in the minimum water rate will give $L/S = 23 \times 1.2 = 27.6$ lb. mols $H_2O/(hr.)(sq. ft.)$.

The operating line may be constructed either by drawing a line of slope L/G through the point Y_2, X_2 or by calculating X_1 and drawing a line through Y_2, X_2, and X_1, Y_1; using the latter method,

$$23.8(0.1111 - 0.000555) = 27.6(X_1 - 0),$$

from which $X_1 = 0.0953$ lb. mol $NH_3/$lb. mol H_2O. The operating line OB is then drawn through these terminal concentrations.

From Fig. 156 the driving force $(Y - Y^\star)$ at $X_2 = 0$ is $(0.000555 - 0) = 0.000555$ and at $X_1 = 0.0953$ is $(0.1111 - 0.0881) = 0.023$. The average driving force is then

$$(Y - Y^\star)_{av.} = \frac{(0.023) - (0.000555)}{\ln (0.023/0.000555)} = 0.00604.$$

The transfer coefficient for this system may be taken as $K_Ga = 0.122$ $(V_{av.})^{0.8}$ where $V_{av.}$ is the average of mass rate of flow entering and leaving.

$$V_{av.} = \frac{735 + [735 - (0.1111)(0.995)(17)(23.8)]}{2} = \frac{713 \text{ lb.}}{(hr.)(sq. ft.)}.$$

$k_Ya = K_Ga = (0.122)(713)^{0.8} = 23.6$ lb. mols$/(hr.)(cu. ft.)$ (mols $NH_3/$mol air) and the height of the tower $l = G(Y_1 - Y_2)/K_GaS(Y - Y^\star)_{av.} = (23.8)(0.1111 - 0.000555)/(23.6)(0.000604) = 18.5$ ft.

c. For the graphical integration the equilibrium curve and operating line are used to obtain the required values of $Y - Y^\star$ at several values of Y.

Y	$Y^\star$	$Y - Y^\star$	$(1/Y - Y^\star)$
0.000555	0	0.000555	1800
0.004	0.0021	0.0019	526
0.0071	0.0044	0.0027	370
0.0119	0.0073	0.0046	218
0.0233	0.0150	0.0083	121
0.0350	0.0230	0.0120	83
0.0581	0.0408	0.0173	58
0.0815	0.0609	0.0206	48
0.1111	0.0881	0.0230	43

A plot is then made (Fig. 157) of $1/(Y - Y^\star)$ vs. Y and the area under the curve is found to be 12.7 units, and

$$l = \frac{G}{K_GaS} \int_{Y_2 = 0.000555}^{Y_1 = 0.1111} \frac{dY}{(Y - Y^\star)} = \frac{(23.8)(12.7)}{23.6}$$
$$= 12.8 \text{ ft.}$$

d. To obtain the number of theoretical plates, starting at $X_1 = 0.0953$, $Y_1 = 0.1111$, steps are drawn between the operating and equilibrium lines down to $X_2 = 0$, as shown in Fig. 156. The number of theoretical plates is thus found to be 10.5.

e. The average H.E.T.P. = $12.8/10.5 = 1.22$ ft.

f. The number of transfer units is obtained by constructing the curve *OC* (Fig. 158) so that its ordinates are midway between the equilibrium curve and the operating line, and steps are laid off such that the horizontal length of each step is twice the distance from the operating line to the midway curve *OC*. A little more than 12 such steps are required to pass from Y_2 to Y_1, indicating that 12 transfer units are required.

g. The average H.T.U. = $12.8/12 = 1.07$ ft.

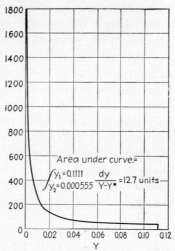

Fig. 157. Graphical integration, for part (*c*) of Illustration 2.

DESIGN METHODS FOR MULTICOMPONENT SYSTEMS

It is often desired to absorb or strip two or more solute vapors

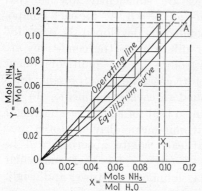

Fig. 158.—Graphical determination of number of transfer units, part (*f*) of Illustration 2.

simultaneously. This is particularly true in the absorption of benzene, toluene, xylene and other high-boiling hydrocarbons from coke-oven gas and in the absorption of volatile hydrocarbons in natural or petroleum gases. Both of these absorptions are followed by a stripping operation to recover the absorbed materials. Where it is desired to recover a number of components, one should design an apparatus for recovering the least soluble of these. The others will then be recovered even more completely than the first, provided they are not present in preponderating amounts. In the latter case the absorption system must be designed for the one most difficult to dissolve in view of both its solubility and its quantity.

Equation 1 for the operating line applies to any one solute component regardless of the number of other components present, and indicates that for any component the operating line is a straight line of slope L/G, passing through the points Y_2, X_2 and Y_1, X_1 for the particular component in question, *i.e.*, the operating lines for the different components will be a series of parallel lines. In the systems involving hydrocarbons the equilibrium relationships can usually be expressed by $y = K^\star x$, where y and x are the mol fractions of one component in the vapor and liquid, respectively, and $K^\star$ is an equilibrium constant, which is a function of temperature, of pressure and usually to a small degree of the liquid and vapor composition. In mol ratio units this becomes

$$\frac{Y^\star}{1 + \Sigma Y^\star} = K^\star \frac{X^\star}{1 + \Sigma X^\star}$$

where $\Sigma Y^\star$ is the sum of all the mol ratios per mol of carrier gas in the vapor except the carrier gas itself, which corresponds to the 1 mol, and $\Sigma X^\star$ is the analogous function for the liquid phase. Often the compositions are sufficiently low so that $\Sigma Y^\star$ and $\Sigma X^\star$ may be neglected and $Y^\star = K^\star X^\star$ for each component. This is identical with conditions developed on page 485 for a single solute gas, and for dilute gases the conditions are essentially the same for each solute in the multicomponent mixture, as though the other solute gases were not present; for a plate tower Eq. 8 may be applied to each component. In the case of a packed tower it was shown that for such a case (straight equilibrium curve) the logarithmic-mean driving force was applicable, and the amount of each solute absorbed will be proportional to the product $K_Y(\Delta Y)_{\text{l.m.}}$ for that particular component since the wetted area, volume of the tower and height of the tower are the same for all components.

Illustration 3.—In a continuous light-oil recovery plant, light oil is absorbed from coke-oven gas by solution in mineral oils in a counterflow absorption tower. The mineral oil enters the top of the tower with a negligible concentration of light oil, and the rich oil leaves the bottom with 2 lb. of benzene/100 lb. of mineral oil. The gas treated contains 1.2 per cent by volume of benzene, toluene, xylenes and similar hydrocarbons. The absorber recovers 86 per cent of the benzene in the entering gas and operates at 20°C. and at substantially normal barometric pressure.

What percentage recovery of the toluene, xylenes and other hydrocarbons may be expected in this tower (a) if it is a plate tower? (b) if it is a packed tower?

Data.—The light oil in the entering gas contains 67 mol per cent of benzene, 12 per cent of toluene and 7.1 per cent of xylenes. The remaining hydrocarbons, while constituting a very complex mixture, have an average boiling point of approximately 136°C. and an average molecular weight of 110. The light-oil solutions at 20°C. follow Raoult's law when the average molecular weight of the oil is taken as 220. The gas-film resistance may be assumed to be of controlling importance.

Vapor pressure at 20°C.	Benzene	Toluene	Xylenes	Remaining hydro-carbons
Millimeters of mercury..........	75	22	5.2	5.4
Average molecular weight........	78	92	106	110

Solution. a. Since the gas is dilute, Eq. 8 may be used (see page 488). Basis: 100 mols gas entering tower:

	Mols entering	Y_1
Carrier gas...........	98.8	1.0
Benzene............	$1.2 \times 0.67 = 0.804$	$0.804/98.8 = 0.00813$
Toluene............	$1.2 \times 0.12 = 0.144$	$0.144/98.8 = 0.00146$
Xylene.............	$1.2 \times 0.071 = 0.0852$	$0.0852/98.8 = 0.00086$
Remaining hydrocarbons.......	$1.2 \times 0.139 = 0.167$	$0.167/98.8 = 0.0017$

For benzene:

$$Y_2 = 0.804(0.14)/98.8 = 0.00114.$$

At the top of tower $X_2 = 0$.

The oil leaving the tower contains 2 lb. of benzene/100 lb. of oil, and

$$X_1 = \left(\frac{2}{78}\right)\frac{(220)}{(100)} = 0.0564.$$

Since Raoult's law holds and the gas is dilute $Y^\star = P/\pi X^\star$, or $K^\star$ is the vapor pressure divided by the total pressure, for benzene $K^\star = 75/760 = 0.0987$.

The mols of oil required are

$$L = \frac{(0.804)(0.86)}{0.0564} = 12.26 \text{ mols}$$

and $L/G = 12.26/98.8 = 0.124$.

$$\frac{L}{K^\star G} = \frac{0.124}{0.0987} = 1.259$$

and from Eq. 8 the number of theoretical plates in the tower can be estimated

$$\frac{Y_1 - Y_2}{Y_1 - K^\star X_2} = \frac{(L/KG)^{n+1} - (L/KG)}{(L/K^\star G)^{n+1} - 1}$$

$$\frac{0.00813 - 0.00114}{0.00813 - 0.0987(0)} = 0.86 = \frac{(1.259)^{n+1} - 1.259}{(1.259)^{n+1} - 1}$$

from which $(n+1) = 4.55$.

By using this same value of $(n+1)$ together with appropriate values of $K^\star$ in Eq. 8, the per cent recovery for the other components may be estimated.

Thus for toluene:

$$K^\star = \frac{22}{760} = 0.02895$$

$$\frac{L}{K^\star G} = \frac{0.124}{0.02895} = 4.29$$

$$\% \text{ recovery} = 100\left(\frac{Y_1 - Y_2}{Y_1 - K^\star X_2}\right) = 100\left[\frac{(4.29)^{4.55} - 4.29}{(4.29)^{4.55} - 1}\right] = 99.6\%.$$

Similar calculations for xylene and the remaining hydrocarbons indicate approximately 100 per cent absorption.

b. For a dilute gas the absorption (page 486) in a packed tower is

$$G(Y_1 - Y_2) = K_G a S l (\Delta Y)_{\text{l.m.}}$$

or the relative absorption of benzene to toluene is

$$\frac{G(Y_1 - Y_2)_{\text{benzene}}}{G(Y_1 - Y_2)_{\text{toluene}}} = \frac{[K_G a S l (\Delta Y)_{\text{l.m.}}]_{\text{benzene}}}{[K_G a S l (\Delta Y)_{\text{l.m.}}]_{\text{toluene}}}.$$

The values of Y are the same as those calculated in part (a) and G, S, a and l are the same for all components.

For benzene: $Y_1^\star = K^\star X_1 = (75/760)(0.0564) = 0.00556.$

$\Delta Y_1 = 0.00813 - 0.00556 = 0.00257$

$\Delta Y_2 = 0.00114 - 0 = 0.00114$

$$(\Delta Y)_{\text{l.m.}} = \frac{0.00257 - 0.00114}{\ln (0.00257/0.00114)} = 0.00176.$$

Data are not available on the ratio of the $K_G a$'s for benzene and toluene, but as an approximation they will be assumed proportional to the square root of their molal diffusivities. Taking the carrier gas to be methane, these are estimated to be

	D_m	$D_m^{1/2}$	$(D_1/D_2)^{1/2}$
Benzene......................	4.15×10^{-5}	2.04×10^{-3}	1.05
Toluene......................	3.8×10^{-5}	1.95×10^{-3}	
Xylene+H.C.................	3.5×10^{-5}	1.87×10^{-3}	1.04

giving, for toluene,

$$\frac{0.00813 - 0.00114}{0.00146 - Y_2} = 1.05 \frac{(0.00176)}{\left[\dfrac{(0.00146 - Y_1^\star) - (Y_2 - 0)}{\ln\dfrac{(0.00146 - Y_1^\star)}{(Y_2)}}\right]} . \qquad (A)$$

$$Y_1^\star = (^{22}\!\!/_{760}) X_1 = 0.029 X_1 \qquad (B)$$

and

$$(Y_1 - Y_2) = (L/G)(X_1 - X_2)$$
$$(0.00146 - Y_2) = 0.124 X_1. \qquad (C)$$

Trial-and-error solution of (A), (B) and (C) gives $Y_2 = 0.00006$.

$$\text{Recovery of toluene} = \frac{0.144 - 98.8(0.00006)}{0.144} \times 100 = 96\%.$$

A similar computation for xylene and other hydrocarbons indicates an absorption of these two approximately equal to 97.2 per cent.

Summary	Recovery, per cent	
	Plate tower	Packed tower
Benzene....................	86	86
Toluene....................	99.6	96
Xylene....................	100	97.2
Other hydrocarbons..........	100	97.2

CAPACITY COEFFICIENTS FOR PROCESSES OF ABSORPTION AND DESORPTION

This section of the chapter is devoted to a discussion of the quantitative capacity coefficients for different types of apparatus as affected by factors such as gas velocity, liquid velocity, temperature, nature of gas and liquid used and the dimensions of the apparatus. As shown on page 451, the relationship between the overall coefficients K and the individual coefficients k is given by the following equations:

$$\frac{1}{K_G} = \frac{1}{k_G} + \frac{n'}{k_L} = \frac{n''}{K_L}$$

or for Henry's law

$$\frac{1}{K_G} = \frac{1}{k_G} + \frac{1}{Hk_L} = \frac{1}{HK_L}.$$

Unless otherwise specified, data will be given in the following units given under nomenclature, page 512.

Absorption in Packed Towers. *Gas-phase Controlling.*—For the case of gas-phase controlling, the resistance of the liquid phase becomes negligible and the overall resistance $1/K_G$ is equal to $1/k_G$. The experimental data indicate that the transfer coefficient k_G varies with the mass velocity in a manner similar to coefficient of heat transfer. Since the wetted area per unit volume of tower, a, is not usually known, the data are expressed as the product $k_G a$. For wide variations in tower sizes, types of packing and operating conditions the gas-film coefficients may be satisfactorily correlated as

$$k_G a = \phi V^{0.8}$$

Table I gives experimental values of ϕ for absorption in packed towers under conditions such that the major resistance was in the gas phase.

For the absorption of SO_2 in water in towers packed with wood grids, the following empirical equation[9] has been given:

$$k_G = \frac{6.7 \times 10^{-4}}{d_s^{0.4} d_G^{0.2}} \left[\frac{V(d_s + d_T)}{d_s} \right]^{0.8}$$

where k_G is the pound mols of SO_2 per hour per square foot per atmosphere, V is the superficial mass velocity of the gas as pounds of gas per hour per square foot of total cross section, d_s represents the clearance between grids in feet, d_G represents the height of the individual grid section in feet and d_T is the thickness of the grid slats in feet.

Generally the liquor rate affects the gas-phase coefficient. This is undoubtedly due largely to an increase in the wetted area a with increasing liquor rates, and to a minor degree to an increase in k_G due to increased relative velocity between the liquid and gas. Thus, in the absorption of ammonia by water

TABLE I.—COMPARISON OF PACKINGS FOR MASS TRANSFER WITH GAS-FILM CONTROLLING, CARRIER-GAS AIR AT ROOM TEMPERATURE AND ATMOSPHERIC PRESSURE[14]*

Packing	Solute	Solvent	Estimated surface, sq. ft./cu. ft.	Liquor rate, lb./(hr.)(sq. ft.)	ϕ constant in relation, $k_Ga = \phi V^{0.8}$	Tower dimensions, diameter × packed height, in.	Investigators
0.25-in. ×0.4-in. glass rings	Benzene	Wash oil	...	163–408	0.046	2.8 × 36	18
0.5 to 0.75-in. coke	Benzene	Wash oil	...	500	0.057	2.35× 0.27	19
0.73-in. glass balls	Benzene	Wash oil	...	75–573	0.034	2.35× 27	19
0.35- to 0.63-in. coke	Ethylene Dichloride	Wash oil	...	120–4790	0.071	2.85× 27	12
	Ammonia	Water	...	323	0.083	....	16
0.25-in. crushed stone	Ammonia	Water	123	500	0.116	6 × 48	5
0.50-in. crushed stone	Ammonia	Water	79	500	0.105	6 × 48	5
0.75-in. crushed stone	Ammonia	Water	53	500	0.071	6 × 54	5
0.50-in. balls	Ammonia	Water	94	500	0.103	6 × 48	5
0.75-in. balls	Ammonia	Water	64	500	0.058	6 × 48	5
1.0-in. balls	Ammonia	Water	55	500	0.057	6 ×105	5
1¼ to 1¾-in. broken quartz	Ammonia	Water	30	500	0.147	16 × 48	10
3-in. spiral tile	Ammonia	Water	30	500	0.122	16 × 48	10
4-in. partition ring	Ammonia	Water	22	500	0.135	16 × 48	10
Wood grid, 3 in.×1½ in. spaced ½ in. apart	Ammonia	Water	32	500	0.122	16 × 48	10

* k_Ga is expressed in lb. mols/(hr.)(cu. ft.)(atm.) and V is expressed in lb./(hr.)(sq. ft. ground area). These values of k_Ga are substantially equal to k_Ya expressed in lb. mols/(hr.)(cu. ft.)(unit ΔY in mol ratio units). H.T.U. in ft. is approximately equal to $V^{0.2}/M_B\phi$.

in a packed tower 4 ft. high and 16 in. in diameter filled with 3-in. spiral tile, the transfer coefficient $k_G a$ at a given gas rate doubled for an increase in the water rate from 60 to 600 lb. per hr. per sq. ft. of tower cross section.

The data on the effect of temperature on $k_G a$ are meager, but on the whole substantiate the conclusion given on page 455 that the effect is very slight, the increase of the diffusivity with temperature being offset by an increase in thickness of the gas film due to increased viscosity.

Liquid-phase Controlling.—When the liquid phase is controlling, the liquor rate has a large effect on the rate of absorption, while the effect of gas velocity is much less than for the case of gas-phase controlling. The small amount of experimental data available may be expressed as $k_L a = \psi L^n$. Table II gives the values of ψ and n for the results of four experimental investigations.

The effect of temperature on the rate of transfer where liquid phase is controlling is very large, owing to the rapid increase of the diffusivity and convection with small increases in temperature. The effect is so large that it often more than compensates for the less favorable absorption equilibrium that results from an increase in temperature, and in such cases there is usually an optimum temperature of absorption.

TABLE II.—COMPARISON OF PACKINGS FOR MASS TRANSFER WITH LIQUID-FILM CONTROLLING, CARRIER-GAS AIR

Packing	Solute	G	$k_L a$	Tower dimensions, diameter × packed height, in.	Investigators
1-in. carbon rings	CO_2	150–157	$0.016L^{0.92}$	10 ×56	15
0.73-in. glass balls	CO_2	5–27	$0.0185L^{0.86}$	3.5×33	19
1.0-in. coke	Cl_2	47–116	$0.028L^{0.78}$	6 ×48	1
Small glass rings, 0.4-× 0.25-in. o.d	CO_2	10	$0.108L^{0.60}$	3.5 ×33	3

General Case.—The absorption of sulfur dioxide by water is a case in which the resistance of both phases is significant. Henry's law may be assumed to apply to this system and the treatment of page 452 used to interpret the data. The overall resistance may be expressed as $1/K_G a = (1/Hk_L a) + (1/k_G a) = 1/Hk_L a + (1/\phi V^{0.8})$, where $\phi V^{0.8}$ has been introduced for $k_G a$. This equation indicates that, if $1/K_G a$ is plotted vs. $1/V^{0.8}$ under conditions such that $k_L a$ is substantially constant, a straight line should result with an intercept of $1/Hk_L a$ at $1/V^{0.8} = 0$. This method of plotting is not a crucial test of the data, since the occurrence of an intercept does not necessarily indicate that the liquid-phase resistance is significant. The same data plotted against the reciprocal of the mass velocity to a power slightly different than 0.8 gives about the same correlation but with differing values of the intercept. It is also very probable that $k_L a$ changes with the gas velocity and is not constant as assumed. However, the method is convenient for presenting a qualitative picture of the various resistances. Figure 159 shows data on the absorption of sulfur dioxide plotted in this manner.

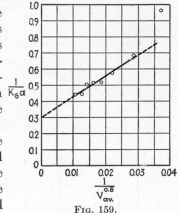

FIG. 159.

Spray Towers.—The spray type of absorption tower is best suited to cases in which the gas-phase resistance is controlling, since there is little motion within the liquid drops as they fall through the gas, which results in low transfer rates through the liquid. They are often used for humidification, where the liquid-phase resistance is negligible. Figure 160 gives the values of $K_G a$ for the absorption of ammonia in water, obtained in spray towers as a function of the liquor rate. In this absorption the value of $K_G a$ increased as the 0.7 to 0.8 power of the gas velocity. Coefficients for humidification and dehumidification in spray towers are given on page 607.

Wetted-wall Towers.—Wetted-wall towers have been widely used to obtain experimental data on the transfer through a gas phase, because of the definite interfacial area and controllable flow conditions in the gas stream. By evaporating pure liquid in such an apparatus, it is possible to eliminate the liquid phase and have a system with the entire resistance in the gas phase.

The data on the evaporation of various liquids into air have been correlated for the turbulent-flow region as

$$\frac{D_t}{B} = 0.023\left(\frac{D_t V}{\mu}\right)^{0.83}\left(\frac{\mu}{M D_m}\right)^{0.44}$$

where D_t represents the diameter of the wetted-wall tower; D_m the molal diffusivity; V, μ and M the mass velocity, viscosity and average molecular weight of the gas stream; and B the fictive film that would offer a resistance to true molecular diffusion

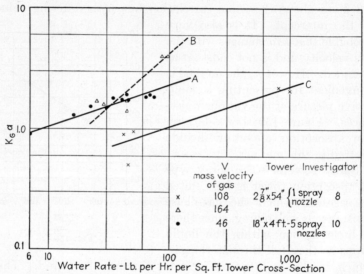

FIG. 160.—Absorption of ammonia in water in spray towers.

equal to the observed resistance to transfer (see page 449.) This method of correlation, while convenient, is undoubtedly unsound since in the film the rate of transfer is proportional to the first power of the diffusivity, while in the turbulent core the transfer should be independent of D_m and the actual effect of diffusivity will have to be between these two extremes. A correlation based on the sum of the resistances of the core and film is probably better than an exponential function of D_m. Thus these same data may be satisfactorily correlated by

$$\frac{1}{K_G} = \left[1080 + \left(\frac{0.008}{D_m}\right)\right]\left(\frac{\mu}{D_t V}\right)^{0.83} \quad \text{where} \quad \frac{1080}{1080 + (0.008/D_m)} \quad \text{repre-}$$

sents the fraction of the total resistance due to the turbulent core and $\dfrac{0.008/D_m}{1080+(0.008/D_m)}$ represents the fraction due to the film.* Data on the absorption of ammonia in water in wetted-wall towers give lower values of K_G than predicted by the above equation, indicating that for this case the liquid-phase resistance is not negligible.

Estimation of Transfer Coefficients

The prediction of an overall transfer coefficient involves the estimation of the transfer coefficients for both the gas and liquid phases. For transfer in a wetted-wall type of apparatus, when the liquid-phase resistance is negligible, the coefficients may be estimated from the equations given for the evaporation of pure liquids in wetted-wall towers. The effect of different components on the gas-phase resistance in packed towers is not known, but this resistance is undoubtedly a function of the diffusivity. This function is probably of the form $s+(b/D_m)$; however, since data are not available for the evaluation of the constants s and b, it is generally more convenient to assume the function to be of the form $1/D^n$, where n will have to be between zero (turbulent transfer) and 1 (molecular diffusion). A value of n equal to 0.5 is probably satisfactory. Thus, to convert the gas-phase resistance for one gaseous system to another under comparable transfer conditions, it is necessary to correct the resistance as the inverse ratio of the square roots of the diffusivities. For variations in gas velocity, the experimental data indicate that the transfer coefficients vary as about the 0.8 power of the mass velocity. The experimental data relative to the liquid-phase resistance are even less conclusive than those for the gas phase, but the liquid-phase transfer coefficients vary as the 0.6 to 1.0 power of the liquor rate, and are dependent on the physical properties of the system, particularly upon the viscosity. By the use of these approximations it is possible to obtain a rough estimate of the transfer coefficient for one system when the coefficient for another system is known.

For cases where the gas phase is controlling, it is possible to estimate the transfer coefficient from heat transfer in a similar-type apparatus by substituting μ/MD_m for the Prandtl group and $k_G D_t (p_B)_{\text{l.m.}}/D_m$ for hD_t/k.

---

* D_m in these equations is gram mols per second per centimeter.

PART III.   DESIGN: GASES BY SOLIDS AND SOLIDS BY LIQUIDS

The adsorption rate of gases and vapors by solid adsorbents is usually rapid.   Thus, the air inhaled through the canister of a gas mask is, under extreme conditions, in contact with the adsorbent a total time of only 0.1 or 0.2 sec., and yet in this time the adsorbent will reduce the concentration of mustard gas, for example, to a point below 1 part in 50,000,000 of air.   In consequence of this rapidity of adsorption, rate is seldom a controlling factor in determining the capacity of equipment, at least where the adsorbent is in a reasonably fine state of subdivision and possesses high activity.   Theoretically, therefore, the amount of solid adsorbent necessary for treating gaseous mixtures is exceedingly small.   Thus, for continuous treatment of gas, one could employ two containers, stripping the adsorbed gas from the solid adsorbent in one container while passing the gas through the other.   With only a small amount of char in each container, the adsorbing and stripping periods would be very short, requiring too frequent shifting of the gas from one container to another. Hence, the amount of adsorbent employed is ordinarily determined by the practical engineering considerations governing the length of this cycle.   This also determines the size of the apparatus.

Under normal conditions it is found inadvisable to move solid absorbents, and consequently true continued countercurrent operation is not encountered.   Where, however, one employs containers of solid adsorbents in systematic rotation (see page 463), the action is substantially continuous and countercurrent, provided the number of absorbers in series at any one time is considerable (5 or above).   The effective length of the system, however, is less than the total number of absorbers in operation at any one time.   The net length may be assumed to be the total number in actual operation in series, less one-half a unit. Otherwise, the computation methods for such a case are identical with those developed above for continuous countercurrent interaction of gases and liquids.

Frequently, however, one employs a small number of absorbent containers, or occasionally gases pass through a single absorber under semi-batch conditions, the gas flowing continuously but the absorber being used until its absorbing capacity is exhausted and then being regenerated or else replaced by a new one.

Illustration 4.—Assume that one has 3000 cu. ft./min. of a gas, at 25°C. and normal barometric pressure, containing 1 volume per cent of benzene. It is desired to recover this benzene by adsorption on activated charcoal. Laboratory data show that, at this temperature and concentration, equilibrium will correspond to 0.08 lb. of benzene/lb. of carbon. This is somewhat less than the adsorptive capacity of fresh charcoal to allow for the slight decrease in activity that results from continued use. Assume that stripping can be satisfactorily accomplished in 2 hr.

Estimate the minimum number of tanks it is advisable to use and the total tons of char required.

Solution.—Inspection of a characteristic adsorption diagram, such as Fig. 160A, shows that in a true countercurrent system equilibrium is approached only at the end of the system, whereas in the middle conditions are far removed therefrom. Evidently, therefore, in a stepwise countercurrent system the entering gas will saturate successive layers of the absorbent to equilibrium with itself, the cleanup of the gas taking place in the remainder of the system. If, now, the first unit which the gas enters is not too large a percentage of the whole system, it is entirely practicable to have this unit completely saturated when it is cut out for stripping. Furthermore, because of the extreme rapidity of adsorption in the middle of the system consequent upon the large distance from equilibrium there obtaining, the final unit need be but a small percentage of the total. Normally, 33⅓ per cent is enough; that is, if one operates with three units in series, it is possible to saturate the first unit, at least where the adsorption is at all strong, *i.e.*, where the value of the exponent n is great (page 437). Obviously, it is advisable to cut out a tank each 2 hr., *i.e.*, to operate with four tanks in all.

The amount of benzene removed per hour is calculated as follows:

$$3,000 \ (60) \ \left(\frac{273}{298}\right)\left(\frac{0.01}{359}\right) \ (78) = 359 \text{ lb.}$$

The char required per tank = $(2)359/0.08(2000) = 4.5$ tons. With four tanks one would need a total of 18 tons.

Figure 160A is a modified case of Fig. 146, showing the equilibrium curves OAB for benzene on charcoal and OC for benzene in straw oil* at 25°C. Since in any absorption operation the operating line must always lie to the left of the equilibrium, inspection of this diagram makes it clear that, if one wishes to treat a gas of reasonable benzene concentration, such as represented by Y_1, and reduce its concentration to a low figure Y_2,

---

* The equilibrium curve for the oil is based on Raoult's law and on average molecular weight of 230 for the oil.

not only will it be possible to do this with the use of a much smaller quantity of charcoal than of oil, but, in the range of operation where the concentrations are low, it is possible to build up a far higher driving force with the charcoal than with the oil. In other words, from the point of view of both rate of absorption and carrying power of absorbent, charcoal has the advantage.

Illustration 5.—Referring to Fig. 160*A*, assume that the value of Y is 0.10 lb. of benzene/lb. of flue gas in the entering gas and 0.02 in the exit gas, corresponding to 80 per cent recovery. Further, assume the operating

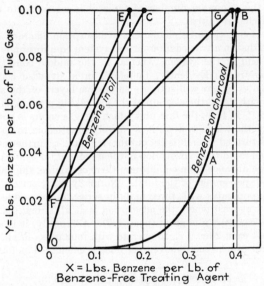

Fig. 160*A*.—Removal of benzene vapor from flue gas (Illustration 4).

lines as shown, *FE* for the oil and *FG* for the charcoal, the fresh treating agent being free of benzene in both cases. Per pound of benzene-free flue gas, this requires only 0.20 lb. of charcoal as compared with 0.47 lb. of oil. Inspection of Fig. 160*A* makes it obvious that the driving force $Y - Y^\star$ is on the average far higher for the char than for the oil. Moreover, this advantage is greater the lower the concentration of benzene in the initial gas and the more completely it is necessary to strip the gas. It is found that for high concentrations of benzene the many advantages of liquid absorption make the use of straw oil advisable, but for very lean gases the charcoal is superior.

Illustration 6.—A batch of sugar syrup is to be decolorized by finely divided activated vegetable char, free from color. It is proposed to agitate the char with the syrup at a temperature of approximately 180°. As soon as the syrup is decolorized to 5 per cent of the initial color, the suspension will be sent to a filter for the separation of the decolorized syrup and the spent char. Laboratory data show that at equilibrium between the color to be removed and the char employed in this case the value of n in the Freundlich equation is 3.

Per unit of syrup treated, calculate the ratio of the minimum weight of char required for batch decolorization to the minimum weight of char necessary for ideal countercurrent treatment.

Solution.—Figure 161 is a plot of the concentration of color in the syrup *vs.* the color on the char X. The curve OAE represents the equilibrium data. For the ideal single batch treatment, it is obvious that at the end of the operation the char will be in equilibrium with the syrup, *i.e.*, the abscissa X_2 represents the final color on the char.

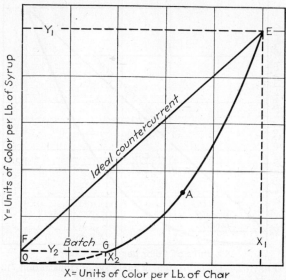

Fig. 161.—Decolorization of sugar syrup (Illustration 6).

The line FE in Fig. 161 represents the operating line for the ideal, continuous, counterflow percolation filter. Since the equilibrium curve OAE is concave upward, the best one can do is to obtain equilibrium at the point E where the syrup enters, corresponding to the value X_1 on the char. Since in both cases the color is reduced from Y_1 to Y_2 and the initial char is free from color, a color balance shows that the ratio r of the minimum weights of char in the two cases is equal to X_1/X_2. The values of X_1 and X_2 can be read quantitatively from Fig. 161, or one can use the Freundlich equation:

$X_1 = (bY_1)^{\frac{1}{n}}$, and $X_2 = (bY_2)^{\frac{1}{n}}$, whence $r = (Y_1/Y_2)^{\frac{1}{n}} = 20^{\frac{1}{3}} = 2.71$. Hence, for this case a single batch treatment would require 2.7 times as much char as continuous countercurrent percolation, both processes operating under ideal conditions. It is interesting to note that the ratio of the minimum char requirements of single batch to continuous countercurrent percolation depends only upon the ratio of initial to final color and upon the value of n in the equation for the adsorption equilibrium, and is independent of the value of the constant b of the Freundlich equation. Furthermore, the smaller the value of n, the greater is the advantage, as regards minimum requirements of char, of continuous counterflow over a batch treatment.

Illustration 7.—Sugar syrup is to be decolorized by vegetable char as outlined in the preceding illustration, except that two successive batch agitations with color-free char are to be employed instead of one, ultimately reducing the color to 5 per cent of the original value.

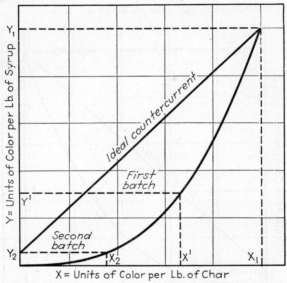

Fig. 162.—Decolorization of sugar syrup (Illustration 7).

Calculate the total minimum char required, expressed as a ratio to the minimum char required in a continuous countercurrent decolorization, and report what percentage of the total char should be used in the first of the two batch treatments. Also, compare the total minimum char necessary for two batches with that required for one batch, as computed in the preceding problem.

Solution.—Figure 162 shows a plot of the equilibrium data, with Y expressed as units of color per pound of syrup, and X as units of color per pound of char. The color in the syrup is reduced from Y_1 to Y' in the first batch, and from Y' to Y_2 in the second. As specified, $Y_2 \div Y_1 = 0.05$. In the ideal case, at the end of a batch treatment, the color in the liquor would be in equilibrium with the color on the char. Thus, at the end of the first batch, each pound of char would contain X' units of color, and after the second batch, X_2. From a color balance, based on 1 lb. of syrup, remembering that the char added in each case is free from color, the total char required W_b would be $\dfrac{Y_1 - Y'}{X'} + \dfrac{Y' - Y_2}{X_2}$.

For the ideal countercurrent treatment, since the equilibrium curve OAE^* is concave upward, one could have equilibrium at the point E, where the operating line FE intersects the curve. Hence the minimum char for countercurrent W_c would equal $(Y_1 - Y_2)/X_1$. Hence the ratio R of the total char for double batches, to the minimum char for continuous countercurrent, is given by the following equation:

$$R = \frac{W_b}{W_c} = \frac{\dfrac{Y_1 - Y'}{X'} + \dfrac{Y' - Y_2}{X_2}}{\dfrac{Y_1 - Y_2}{X_1}}. \tag{A}$$

One can determine the minimum value of numerator by several methods.

First Method.—If Fig. 162 is drawn to scale, one can arbitrarily select a value of Y', and, by reading the corresponding value of X', the total char for the case is determined by the above equation. After assuming various values of Y', R could be plotted vs. X' and the minimum value of R determined by inspection. From the value of X' corresponding to the minimum value of R, a material balance would immediately show what fraction of the total char should be used in the first batch.

Second Method.—If Fig. 162 is not drawn to scale, an algebraic solution can be made as follows: Let z represent that fraction of the initial color Y_1 removed in the first batch. The following equations can be written by inspection:

$$Y_1 - Y' = zY_1; \quad Y' = (1-z)Y_1; \quad Y_2 = 0.05Y_1; \quad X_1 = (bY_1)^{\frac{1}{n}}; \quad X' = (bY')^{\frac{1}{n}};$$

$$X_2 = (bY_2)^{\frac{1}{n}}.$$

By combining these expressions with Eq. A, one obtains

$$R = \frac{1}{0.95}\left[\frac{z}{(1-z)^{\frac{1}{n}}} + (0.95 - z)20^{\frac{1}{n}} \right].$$

The minimum value of R may now be found by differentiating R with respect to z and equating to zero, or by assuming various values of z, *i.e.*, by trial and error. One finds that the minimum value of R is 1.81, corresponding to $z = 0.7$. Since 70 per cent of the original color is removed in the first batch, $Y' = 0.3Y_1$, and the proper value of X' is determined. From a color balance, one finds that 60.4 per cent of the total char should be used in the first batch.

In order to reduce the color to 5 per cent of the original value, the minimum total char for two successive batch treatments is 1.81 *versus* 2.71 for the single batch, both expressed in terms of the minimum char required for the continuous countercurrent decolorization.

* See Fig. 161, p. 509.

Char consumption may be still further reduced by using fresh char only for the second batch and treating the original syrup with spent char from a prior second operation. This may be called stepwise countercurrent operation.

Nomenclature *

A = total interfacial surface, sq. ft.

a = interfacial surface per unit volume, sq. ft. per cu. ft.

B = effective film thickness, ft.

b = constant.

D_m = molal diffusivity, mols/(hr.)(ft.).

D_t = diameter of tower, ft.

G = mols solute-free gas per hr.

g = acceleration due to gravity.

H = Henry's law constant.

K_Y, K_G = overall transfer coefficients, units same as k_Y, k_G.

K_L = overall transfer coefficient in
         lb. mols/(hr.)(sq. ft.)(driving force in X).

$K^\star = Y^\star/X^\star$.

k_Y, k_G = gas-phase transfer coefficients, see footnote page 501 for units.

k_L = liquid-phase transfer coefficient, units same as K_L.

L = mols solute-free absorbent per hr.

l = height of packed tower, ft.

M = molecular weight.

m = mean hydraulic radius.

N = mols solute transferred per hr.

n = exponent and number of plates.

p = partial pressure.

q = constant.

S = area of cross section, sq. ft.

s = constant.

u_G, u_L = actual velocities of gas and liquid, respectively, in packed
         towers.

V = mass velocity, lb. gas/(hr.)(sq. ft. of ground area).

X = concentration of solute in liquid, mols/mol of solvent.

$X^\star$ = equilibrium value of X corresponding to Y.

Y = concentration of solute in gas, mols/mol of solute-free gas.

$Y^\star$ = equilibrium value of Y corresponding to X.

x, y = mol fraction of solute in liquid and gas, respectively.

θ = time.

μ = viscosity.

π = total pressure.

* Throughout this book the Nomenclature closely follows the "Tentative Standard System of Nomenclature for Chemical Engineering Unit Operations" adopted by the American Institute of Chemical Engineers on Oct. 11, 1935.

ρ_G, ρ_L =density of gas and liquid, respectively.

ϕ, ψ =constants.

Subscripts

1, 2 =conditions at gas inlet and outlet, respectively.

a =asymptotic value.

av. =average value.

G =gas.

L =liquid.

l.m. =logarithmic mean.

t =tangential value.

References

1. ADAMS, F. W., and R. G. EDWARDS, paper to appear in *Ind. Eng. Chem.*

2. BAKER, T., T. H. CHILTON, and H. C. VERNON, *Trans Amer. Inst. Chem. Eng.*, **31**, 296–315 (1935).

3. CANTELO, R. C., C. W. SIMMONS, E. M. GILES and F. A. BRILL, *Ind. Eng. Chem.*, **19**, 989 (1927).

4. CHILTON, T. H., and A. P. COLBURN, *Ind. Eng. Chem.*, **27**, 255, 904 (1935).

4a. BAKER, T., *Ind. Eng. Chem.*, **27**, 977 (1935).

5. CHILTON, T. H., H. R. DUFFEY and H. C. VERNON, *Ind. Eng. Chem.*, **29**, 298 (1937).

6. FENSKE, M. R., C. O. TONGBERG and D. QUIGGLE, *Ind. Eng. Chem.*, **26**, 1169 (1934).

7. HASLAM, R. T., W. P. RYAN, and H. C. WEBER, *Trans. Amer. Inst. Chem. Eng.*, **18**, 1291 (1926).

8. HIXSON, A. W., and C. E. SCOTT, *Ind. Eng. Chem.*, **27**, 307 (1935).

9. JOHNSTONE, H. F. (see T. K. SHERWOOD, "Absorption and Extraction," p. 181, McGraw-Hill Book Company, Inc., New York, 1937).

10. KOWALKE, O. L., O. A. HOUGEN and K. M. WATSON, *Bull. Univ. Wis., Eng. Expt. Sta. Series* 68 (1925).

11. KREMSER, A., *Nat. Petroleum News*, **22**, No. 21, 42 (1930).

12. OSBORNE, H. B., and C. W. SIMMONS, *Ind. Eng. Chem.*, **26**, 856 (1934).

13. PETERS, W. A., JR., *Ind. Eng. Chem.*, **14**, 476 (1922).

14. SHERWOOD, T. K., "Absorption and Extraction," p. 178, McGraw-Hill Book Company, Inc., New York, 1937.

15. SHERWOOD, T. K., F. C. DRAEMEL and N. E. RUCKMAN, *Ind. Eng. Chem.*, **29**, 282 (1937).

16. SHERWOOD, T. K., and A. J. KILLGORE, *Ind. Eng. Chem.*, **18**, 744 (1926).

17. SHERWOOD, T. K., *Ind. Eng. Chem.*, **17**, 745 (1925).

18. SIMMONS, C. W., and J. D. LONG, *Ind. Eng. Chem.*, **22**, 718 (1930).

19. SIMMONS, C. W., and H. B. OSBORNE, *Ind. Eng. Chem.*, **26**, 529 (1934).

20. WHITMAN, W. G., and J. L. KEATS, *Ind. Eng. Chem.*, **14**, 186 (1922).

21. WILSON, R. E., *Ind. Eng. Chem.*, **13**, 526 (1921).

CHAPTER XVI

DISTILLATION

INTRODUCTION

In Chap. XII the phenomena of vapor pressure were discussed in detail, and it was pointed out that, if two substances at any temperature possessed a marked difference in their vapor pressures, this difference could be made the basis of a method of separation of the two; and if one or both of the substances were recovered by condensation, the process was called **distillation.** *
As there explained, an equilibrium is established at any temperature between a liquid or a mixture of liquids held in a containing vessel, and the vapor existing above it. Since it is this vapor which ultimately passes out of the containing vessel and when condensed forms the product of the process, the question arises, what is the relation of the composition of this vapor to the composition of the liquid from which it came and with which it is in equilibrium? The answer to this question is different for different kinds of mixtures; and to comprehend the problems of distillation, these kinds of mixtures must be considered from this point of view.

Obviously, if a volatile component is to be separated from a nonvolatile one, the operation is comparatively simple, and has in principle been described under Evaporation on page 385. It is necessary only to volatilize it in one vessel and to condense it in another to accomplish this purpose.

In a mechanical mixture of two mutually insoluble liquids sufficiently well agitated to prevent stratification (for example, turpentine and water, heavy fatty acids and water), a dynamic equilibrium is established between the liquid and the vapor

---

* Destructive distillation may be described as a thermal decomposition of nonvolatile material with the formation of products that lend themselves to separation by the methods here described.

when the number of each kind of molecules leaving the liquid is just balanced by the number of molecules of each kind again entering the liquid. Since they are not mutually soluble, each liquid will exert a vapor pressure of its own just as though it alone were present. The pressure existing over the liquid mixture will, therefore, be the sum of these individual pressures, and it follows that a pressure *equal to the atmosphere will be reached and boiling will therefore result at a temperature below that at which either of the component liquids would boil alone.* * These facts form the basis of a highly important type of distillation in which a high-boiling liquid is distilled at a comparatively low temperature by the injection of some low-boiling immiscible liquid or its vapor into the still (see Steam Distillation, page 537).

Referring again to Chap. XII, it is noted that, where two liquids are mutually soluble, the vapor pressure of each is decreased by the presence of the other, and therefore the sum of their vapor pressures is less than the sum of the vapor pressures of the two liquids before mixing.† In this case the composition of the vapor is not independent of the relative amount of the components of the mixture, but is profoundly influenced thereby. Sometimes this composition can be calculated from the known vapor pressures of the individual pure liquids. When the molecules of two liquids are of relatively the same size, and when there are no complicated effects when mutually dissolved, such as molecular association, chemical reaction and the like, the composition of the vapor is given by what is known as *Raoult's law.* This law states that that part of the total vapor pressure of a solution of two liquids which is caused by one of the components will equal the product of the vapor pressure of that component in its pure state, and its mol fraction in the liquid. This law, together with *Henry's law,* will be further discussed and applied in the design of distillation apparatus. But it may be said that, in general, the composition of the vapor arising from a solution of one liquid in another is an empirical function of the composition of the solution and must be experimentally determined.

* If the liquids are to any extent mutually soluble, the individual vapor pressures are decreased, and the mixture must be heated to a higher temperature to reach its boiling point (see pp. 367 to 369).

† However, see p. 529.

Liquid Mixtures, with Components Volatile and Miscible in All Proportions

Simple Distillation.—A mixture of liquids that are mutually soluble evolves a vapor, the composition of which is usually different from that of the liquid. If such a liquid mixture is partially volatilized, the residual liquid will be poorer in the more volatile component, and the vapor evolved correspondingly richer. But the vapor will not be free from the less volatile component, and the separation will be incomplete. Such a single vaporization used to separate partially two or more volatile liquids will be called *simple distillation*.

Such distillation processes have heretofore been much used in the refining of crude coal tar, petroleum and materials of this kind. The stills consist of very large boiler-plate cylindrical vessels with rounded ends and are direct-fired. In the refining of petroleum it was common practice to build these stills in multiple, setting each succeeding still somewhat lower so that the residuum from still 1 might overflow by gravity to still 2, and so on through the series. A more intense fire is maintained under each succeeding still so that there is a temperature gradient from the first to the last, thus producing a series of products of progressively increasing boiling point. The condenser is generally a tubular heat exchanger. When the condensate is insoluble in water and can be easily separated from it by stratification, an efficient and economical condenser is made by passing the vapor and water countercurrent over packing material in a short tower.

The separation of the components in such a still must of necessity be incomplete, and the product is rerun to obtain the fractions sought. More recently such stills are being equipped with rectifying columns which function as described on page 547, and thus a better separation with larger capacity and less expense of fuel is effected.

The transfer of heat is low in such a still, and in the more modern installations pipe or tube stills are used in which the charge is heated by forcing it at high velocity through a bank of tubes set in a direct-fired high-temperature furnace and discharging the same into a vessel where the vapor is separated from the liquid.

Simple distillation processes are divided into two classes depending on whether the process is continuous or batch. In the first case the material to be distilled is fed continuously to the still or vaporizer, from which a certain fraction is evaporated and taken overhead, and the unvaporized portion, or residue, is continuously removed from the still. Such a continuous process is called **equilibrium** distillation. A simple distillation can also be carried out as a batch operation, in which case the mixture is charged into the still, and the distillation of this charge is then carried out without feeding additional material. This latter operation is termed **batch** or **differential** distillation. Simple equilibrium distillation has all the advantages resulting from continuity of operation, such as constant rates of flow for all fluid streams, constant temperature and constant heating and cooling requirements, but has the disadvantage that with one still it is possible to obtain only one overhead and one bottom product, and, as will be shown later, the relative composition of these two products is fixed by equilibrium relationships. In batch or differential distillation, the process is differential in that a given charge of material is vaporized and the vapors are continuously removed from the still. Since the vapors, in general, are of different composition than the liquid from which they come, it necessarily follows that in such cases the vapor leaving the still and the liquid remaining in the still must continuously change in composition, which for constant-pressure operations results in a changing still temperature. However, since the overhead vapor does continuously change in composition, batch distillation allows the production of a large number of fractions or products, by simply condensing successive portions of the overhead vapor separately. Since the first portions of distillate of a differential distillation will be rich in the volatile component, it is apparent that for a given per cent of the original mixture vaporized the combined distillate of a differential distillation will contain a higher percentage of the more volatile component than the distillate from an equilibrium distillation.

Vapor Enrichment; Redistillation.—Since the separation of two volatile liquids by simple distillation is so incomplete, means for its improvement must be developed. In the last analysis there are but two methods of accomplishing this; one is by condensing the vapor obtained from a simple distillation and revaporizing it, namely, redistillation. The first distillate is richer in volatile component than the original liquid. If this is condensed and redistilled, the second distillate will be yet richer. By repeated redistillation the separation can be carried, theoretically at least, to any desired point. It is obvious, however, that such repeated redistillation involves a large number of steps and a large heat consumption.

Partial Condensation.—The second method for improving the separation is to cool somewhat the mixed vapors from a simple distillation producing a *partial condensation* of the vapor. From the structure of the liquid-vapor equilibrium curves on page 526, it will be seen that the condensate will be poorer in volatile component than the remaining vapor, and that the vapor has therefore been enriched in volatile component. In other words, the partial condensation of a vapor has the same sort of effect on its composition as has redistillation. Thus, simple distillation coupled with properly controlled partial condensation is capable of effecting the separation of two volatile liquids as completely (though not so easily or efficiently) as can be done by more complicated distillation processes.

Partial condensers have been built in many forms, one of the older and more simple types consisting of a series of metal bulbs immersed in cooling water, from each of which the condensate collecting therein may be drawn. An ordinary tubular surface condenser may be employed and, to insure effective counter-current action, it should be long relative to its diameter. As explained on page 551, when efficient separation in the condenser itself is desired, it is best not to use it as a preheater, as is often done. Condensers of this type have been built as a combination of plate tower and feed-liquor preheater, but the best results are realized by building tower and condenser separately, each designed to perform its own function. The cooling medium must be under accurate control with a very low temperature difference between it and the condensed vapor; so far as possible, localized total condensation should be avoided. For effective partial condensation a large area of condensing surface is required.

VAPOR-LIQUID EQUILIBRIA

Quantitative design calculations for simple distillation require knowledge of vapor-liquid equilibria for the mixtures being distilled. Although quantitative relationships of vapor pressures of liquid mixtures are extremely complex, certain quantitative relationships may be established which are valid in some important cases and which apply within narrow limits to a great many cases. Possibly more important, the laws that may thus be laid down serve as valuable criteria for estimating the normal behavior of a distillation process, and help to clarify and explain the divergencies that are frequently noted. In the following discussion isothermal conditions are considered first, after which is given an analysis of constant-pressure operations of a character sufficiently general to serve as the basis of the solution of most industrial problems in distillation.

Vapor Pressures of Completely Miscible Liquid Mixtures at Constant Temperature

Raoult's Law.—When one liquid is dissolved in another, the partial pressure of each is decreased. Assume two liquids, the molecules of which are the same size, which mix without the complicating effects of molecular association, chemical combination and the like. In an equimolecular mixture of two such liquids, each unit of surface area of the liquid mixture will have in its face half as many molecules of each component as exist in the liquid surface of that component in the pure state. Hence, the escaping tendency or partial pressure of each component in the mixture will be half that of the same component in the pure state. Similarly, in a mixture containing 25 mol per cent of the first component and 75 mol per cent of the second, the first will exert a partial pressure 25 per cent of that of this component in the pure state. Therefore, in more general terms for any such mixture, the partial pressure of any component will equal the vapor pressure of that component in the pure state times its

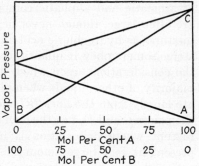

Fig. 163.—Raoult's law diagram for a binary mixture at constant temperature.

mol fraction in the liquid mixture. This generalization is known as *Raoult's law*. It is expressed in the relationship, $p_A = P_A x_A$, where p_A is the partial pressure of the component A in the solution, x_A is its mol fraction in the solution and P_A is the vapor pressure of the component A in its pure state. If P_B is the vapor pressure of pure B, and p_B that in the mixture, $p_B = P_B x_B$. This relationship is shown graphically in Fig. 163, where the abscissas are the mol per cent or mol fraction of the two components, A and B, in the liquid portion. The ordinates are pressures, C being the vapor pressure of pure A, and D that of pure B. The lines AD and BC represent the partial pressures of the components over any mixture, while the line CD is the total pressure of the mixture.

Deviations from Raoult's Law.—In view of the above assumptions as to equal molecular size, absence of association, etc., it is not surprising to find Raoult's law honored more in the breach than in the observance. Nonetheless some organic liquids, such as benzene-toluene, deviate from it but little. The deviations of mixtures of hydrocarbons of the same series can usually be neglected for a great deal of engineering work, and even for mixtures of a number of series this is often true. For mixtures of aromatic and aliphatic compounds, however, the deviations are often large, though never of the order of magnitude of such mixtures as hydrochloric acid and water, and the like. Organic stereoisomers obey it quantitatively as would be expected from the considerations upon which it is based. However, the great majority of other liquids when plotted as shown in Fig. 163 deviate largely from the lines BC and AD except when very near to the points C and D, *i.e.*, the deviation for any component is slight (except where dissociation is involved) if that component is present in very large amount. This is ordinarily expressed by saying that in dilute solutions Raoult's law applies to the *solvent*. Since the deviation from Raoult's law may be either positive or negative, great or small, where results are presented graphically this generalization serves as a convenient standard of comparison.

Henry's Law.—A modification of Raoult's law applies to the vapor pressure of the *solute* in dilute solutions, just as Raoult's law applies to that of the *solvent*. Henry's law states that the partial pressure of the solute is proportional to its concentration in the solution. In analogy with Raoult's law it may be expressed by the equation $p_A = k x_A$, where p_A is a partial pressure of the solute, x_A is its mol fraction and k is an experimentally determined constant. Comparison with Raoult's law $p_A = P_A x_A$ shows that they differ only in the constant that determines the slope of the line. This constant is P in the one case, while it must be experimentally determined in the other. A typical partial pressure curve for one component of a liquid mixture is shown in Fig. 164, where BD is the range over which Henry's law applies, while Raoult's law holds over the section EC, where C is the vapor pressure of pure A.

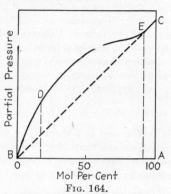

Fig. 164.

Volatility.—The term "volatility" is loosely used in the literature, generally as equivalent to vapor pressure when applied to a pure substance; as applied to mixtures its significance is very indefinite. Because of the convenience of the term, the volatility of any substance in a homogeneous liquid will be defined as its partial pressure in the vapor in equilibrium with that liquid, divided by its mol fraction in the liquid. If the substance is in the pure state, its mol fraction is unity and its volatility is identical with its vapor pressure. If the substance exists in a liquid mixture that follows Raoult's law, its volatility as thus defined is still obviously equal to its vapor pressure in the pure state, *i.e.*, its volatility is *normal*. If the partial pressure of the substance is lower than that corresponding to Raoult's law, as, for example, that of hydrochloric acid in dilute aqueous solutions, the volatility according to this definition is less than that of the pure substance, *i.e.*, is abnormally low. Similarly, if the partial pressure is greater than that indicated by Raoult's law, *e.g.*, that of aniline dissolved in water, the volatility is abnormally high. The volatility of a substance in mixtures is therefore not necessarily constant even at constant temperature but depends on the character and amount of the components.

Relative volatility is the volatility of one component divided by that of another. Since the volatility of the first component of a mixture, v_A, is its partial pressure p_A divided by its mol fraction x_A, and that of the second, $v_B = p_B/x_B$, the volatility of the first relative to the second is $v_A/v_B = p_A x_B/p_B x_A$. Since the relative amount in the vapor of the components of any mixture (expressed in mols) is $y_A/y_B = p_A/p_B$,

$$\frac{v_A}{v_B} = \frac{y_A}{y_B}\frac{x_B}{x_A} = \alpha.$$

In any constant-boiling homogeneous liquid mixture the composition of the liquid is identical with that of the vapor in equilibrium with it, *i.e.*, $x = y$; hence the relative volatility α is unity.

Volatility, like vapor pressure, increases rapidly with rise in temperature. The *ratio* of the pressures of pure substances does not change rapidly with change in temperature and the same is true of relative volatilities, but, whereas vapor pressures always increase with temperature, *relative volatility* may, in a given case, either rise or fall, depending on the nature of the components. At constant temperature the relative volatility is independent of the liquid composition for systems that obey Raoult's law; however, for most systems α is a function of the liquid composition, and frequently will be greater than unity for one range of concentrations and less than unity for another range. Relative volatility is the most important factor in determining ease of separation of components by distillation.

Duhem Equation.—A general isothermal relationship based upon the second law of thermodynamics and upon the gas laws, and hence approximately applicable to all binary mixtures, is the Duhem equation,

$$dlnp_1/dlnp_2 = -(1-x)/x.$$

It can be used as a check upon the accuracy of empirical determinations of vapor compositions, but is otherwise of little practical help. Assume a solution where Raoult's law applies to the solvent. Differentiating the equation of Raoult's law, $p_2 = P_2(1-x)$, and substituting in the Duhem equation, one obtains upon integration $p_1 = kx$. In other words, if one component of a mixture obeys Raoult's law over a definite range, within that range the other component must follow Henry's law.

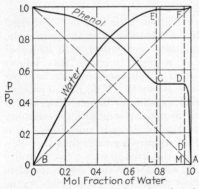

FIG. 165.—Equilibrium data for phenol and water at 58.4°C.

PARTIALLY MISCIBLE LIQUIDS AT CONSTANT TEMPERATURE

In those ranges of concentration within which partially miscible liquids are soluble in each other, they fall under the preceding classification. As soon as the limits of solubility are exceeded, the two liquids exist as separate layers or phases side by side, each being a saturated solution of the other in itself. The vapor pressure of each phase is exerted independently of the presence of the other, and, since the two phases are in equilibrium, the partial pressure of either component in one liquid phase must equal that of the same component in the other. These facts are represented graphically in Fig. 165 for the system phenol-water at 58.4°C. The partial pressure of each component divided by the vapor pressure (P_0) of the pure component at

58.4°C. is plotted *vs.* the mol fraction in the liquid. The limit of solubility of water in phenol corresponds to a mol fraction of water of 0.776, while the solubility of phenol in water is 0.045 mol fraction phenol. For mol fractions of water between 0.776 and 0.955 the components exist as two layers of liquids. Throughout this range in which two liquid phases are present, and where the compositions of these phases are therefore constant, the partial pressures remain constant and are represented by the horizontal lines *EF* and *CD*. Both components deviate appreciably from Raoult's law (the 45-deg. lines) even when the other component is present in only small amounts; however, Henry's law is seen to apply approximately for values of p/P_0 up to about 0.3.

The two points of importance regarding this diagram are, first, constancy of the partial pressures so long as two liquid phases are present, and second, the character and extent of the deviations from Raoult's law. The diagram shows that the partial pressure of phenol when dissolved in water is abnormally high, *i.e.*, is much greater than is called for by Raoult's law, the line *AD'*. Limited miscibility of two liquids implies that the molecules of one find it difficult to force their way into the other. Thus it requires a relatively high pressure of phenol to force a relatively small amount of it into water. This is equivalent to saying that, when phenol is dissolved in water, the volatility of phenol is abnormally high. The less the mutual solubility, the more abnormal is the vapor pressure, and hence the greater the volatility of the dissolved component. The practical results of these relationships are shown in the following examples.

Despite the fact that aniline boils 80°C. higher than water, the volatility of aniline in an aqueous solution is greater than that of water, *i.e.*, the vapor given off by such a solution is richer in aniline than the solution itself. If, therefore, one distills an aniline-water solution in a column still, the water is discharged from the bottom substantially free of aniline which is found in the distillate. The vapor from the top of the column is condensed and allowed to run into a separator, from which the aniline layer (saturated with water) is withdrawn as product while the water layer (saturated with aniline) returns to the column as reflux.

Another important application is found in the dehydration of organic solvents. Thus, while water boils 20°C. higher than benzene, benzene saturated with water can be successfully dehydrated by the distillation of less than 5 per cent of the mixture, as the volatility of the water in the solution is abnormally high.

Assume a binary mixture in which one component when present in small amount exerts an abnormally high pressure, *i.e.*, $p_1 > P_1x$. Since the value of p_1 when x equals unity must be P_1, the curve becomes abnormally flat at high values of x and $dp_1/dx \leqq P_1$. Combined with the Duhem equation (page 522), these inequalities give $-dp_2/p_2 < dx/(1-x)$. In words this means that the fractional *lowering* of the pressure of the second component must within these limits of concentration be less than that corresponding to Raoult's law. In other words, in the range in question, if the pressure of one component is higher than predicted by Raoult's law, that of the other will be higher, and consequently the total pressure of the mixture will be higher; there is then a tendency to form a mixture with minimum boiling point. Similarly, if the partial pressure of one component is abnormally low, that of the other tends to be low.

Complete immiscibility is the case in which the mutual solubilities are negligibly small and the points L and M coincide with the points B and A. The lines EF and CD would then correspond to the pressures of the pure components A and B. It is perhaps true that absolute immiscibility never occurs.

BINARY LIQUID MIXTURES AT CONSTANT PRESSURE

Boiling Point—Composition Curves.—It follows from the preceding discussion that, if isothermal conditions are to be preserved, arbitrarily predetermined pressure differences must be maintained. This is so impracticable that distillations are never carried out at constant temperature, but rather at constant pressure and variable temperature. The vapor composition and boiling point which correspond to any definite liquid mixture are sometimes plotted as shown in Fig. 166, the abscissas being liquid compositions and the ordinates boiling points. In this figure the curve ABC represents the boiling points at atmospheric pressure of all mixtures of benzene and toluene from pure benzene (100 per cent of benzene) at the right to pure toluene (zero per cent benzene) at the left. A second curve, ADC, can be constructed from empirical data which will show, by following a horizontal line, the composition of the vapor in equilibrium with any mixture of the two components at its boiling point. Suppose, for example, a mixture of 20 per cent benzene and 80 per cent toluene is heated. It will boil when the temperature reaches the point E (102°C.) on the curve, and the vapor that comes off will have the composition represented by the point F on the second curve. This vapor if condensed would give a liquid of the composition 38 per cent benzene and 62 per cent toluene. Obviously the liquid remaining in the still will now contain less than 20 per cent benzene and will boil at a higher temperature, *i.e.*, farther up the curve ABC, and will yield a vapor of a composition determined by the curve ADC. It is seen that, while by such an operation the distillate

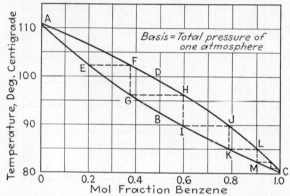

Fig. 166.—Boiling point as a function of composition of liquid for benzene-toluene.

will at any time be richer in the lower boiling component than the liquid remaining in the still, *complete* separation is impossible.

Liquid-Vapor-Composition Curves.—For the solution of problems at constant pressure, the diagram just considered, though frequently used, is inconvenient because it is indirect and because a change in pressure makes a relatively large error on the vertical temperature scale. The value of greatest interest is the relation between *liquid composition* and *vapor composition*, plotted as shown on the ethanol-water diagram (see Fig. 167, page 526). This method is advantageous, first, because the data are actually obtained in this form as the result of experimentation, and, second, because the values thus expressed change but slightly with moderate variation in pressure or temperature. A single curve obtained at an average pressure can generally be used over a pressure range of 20 or 30 per cent with an error of not more than 2 per cent.

Again, assume a mixture of two liquids A and B, in which p_A is the partial pressure of A in a mixture in which the mol fraction of A is x_A, and p_B that of B. The mol fraction of compo-

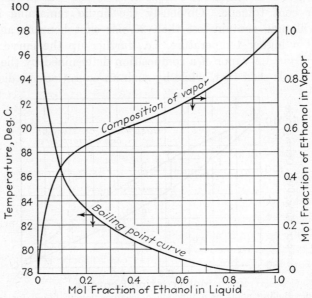

Fig. 167.—Equilibria for ethanol-water at 1 atmosphere absolute: y vs. x, and t vs. x.

nent A in the *vapor* evolved from this mixture is y_A. Hence, as shown on page 521,

$$\frac{y_A}{1-y_A} = \alpha_{AB} \frac{x_A}{1-x_A}$$

where α is determined experimentally. This states that the mol ratio in the vapor is α times that in the liquid. The relative volatility α changes very little with moderate changes in temperature, from which it follows that changes in temperature have little effect upon vapor composition. The amount of low-boiling constituent in the vapor is

$$y_A = \frac{\alpha x_A}{1+(\alpha-1)x_A}.$$

It can be shown algebraically that the equation is identical in form, when x represents fraction by weight in the liquid and y fraction by weight in the vapor, the numerical values of alpha remaining unchanged. If both of the liquids follow Raoult's law then $\alpha = P_A/P_B$ where P_A and P_B are vapor pressures of pure A and B, respectively.

The great majority of mixtures of liquids miscible in all proportions do not follow Raoult's law even approximately, and hence the vapor compositions must be determined experimentally.* This may be conveniently done by boiling the liquid mixture and analyzing the vapors given off from it. Experimental results show that the vapor evolved from such a boiling liquid is in equilibrium with it as it escapes from the surface, owing doubtless to perfect agitation incident to boiling. In this distillation, entrainment must be rigorously avoided on the one hand, and partial condensation on the other. It is well to jacket the portion of the flask above the liquor line with hot gas, inasmuch as superheating does not change the composition of a vapor while partial condensation does.

With these precautions the experimental determination of vapor composition is relatively easy, and a convenient apparatus for carrying out these determinations has been developed.[6],[14]

In this discussion the composition of both liquid and vapor will be expressed as the mol fraction of the *lower* boiling constituent (see page 521). The percentage of this component in the liquid is called x, while the percentage of this same component in the vapor is called y. When in equilibrium, y is a definite function of x and can best be expressed graphically by what will be termed the y vs. x curve. For most liquid mixtures this y vs. x curve has been determined at atmospheric pressure only; but fortunately the shape of this curve changes but little with moderate changes in either temperature or pressure.

The y vs. x curve of any known binary liquid mixture of components miscible in all proportions has a shape similar to one of the five types shown in Fig. 168. In this figure the vertical line at the left corresponds to the pure high-boiling component B, while that at the right represents the low-boiling substance A, numerical values referring in all cases to the mol fraction of A in the mixture. The vapor-composition curve of the first

* However, see p. 520.

type is the straight 45-deg. line, curve 1, indicating that the vapor evolved from all possible mixtures has the same composition as the liquid from which it came. In this case no separation whatever by distillation is possible. Illustrations of this type are found in mixtures of stereoisomers. The second type, which may be described as the normal one, is represented by curve 2. In this case the vapor evolved from the liquid contains more of the low-boiling component than the liquid from which it came. An illustration is methanol-water. In curve 3

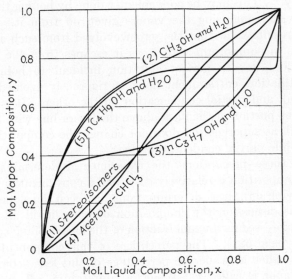

Fig. 168.—Five types of vapor-liquid equilibrium curves.

are represented liquids which, when they contain small amounts of A, evolve a vapor richer in A than themselves, but when the amount of A in the liquid reaches a certain value the composition of the vapor becomes identical with that of the liquid, while beyond this point the liquid evolves vapor richer in the high-boiling component B than themselves; that is, the volatility of the components is reversed. Curve 4 represents a mixture in which a dilute solution of the low-boiling substance A evolves a larger percentage of B than it contains. In all solutions coming under this type a concentration of A is finally reached at which liquid and vapor compositions are equal, and beyond which the behavior of the mixtures is normal. Curve 5 represents the vapor-liquid relationship for a system of partially miscible liquids. Those liquids having curves of Type 3, which cross the diagonal with a slope flatter than the slope of the diagonal, possess *minimum boiling points* at the intersection, while the intersection of curves of Type 4 (curves with steeper slopes than the diagonal at the point of intersection) are mixtures that possess *maximum boiling points* at the point where $y = x$.

The constant-boiling mixtures of the type represented by the intersection of curves 3 and 4 with the diagonal are termed

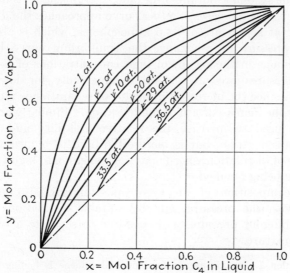

Fig. 169.—[3]Effect of total pressure on the vapor-liquid equilibrium curves for mixtures of n-C_4H_{10} and n-C_6H_{14}.

azeotropic mixtures, while the type represented by curve 5 is termed **pseudo-azeotropic**.

Effect of Pressure.—It was pointed out (page 527) that a moderate change in pressure had only a slight effect on the y-x curve; however, large changes in pressure significantly change the vapor-liquid equilibria. As a general rule, as the pressure is increased, the relative volatility decreases and the y-x curve approaches the diagonal, and the difficulty of separating the mixture increases. At pressures higher than the critical pressure of the mixture only one phase can exist and separation by distillation becomes impossible. In a binary mixture, one component will generally have a lower critical pressure than the other, and, as the pressure is increased above this lower critical pressure, the y-x curve will exist in the region of concentrations where a sufficient concentration of the component with the higher critical pressure is present to make the critical pressure of the mixture greater than the total pressure. However, in the region of high concentrations of the component with the lower critical pressure, only one phase is possible and the y-x curve becomes discontinuous. These conditions are illustrated in Fig. 169 for the system n-butane–n-hexane.[3] This figure shows that, as the pressure increases, the y-x curve approaches the diagonal, and that at a pressure of 33.5 atmospheres, which is above the critical pressure of n-hexane, the equilibrium curve becomes discontinuous in the region of high concentrations of n-hexane. High pressures are often used commercially for low-boiling materials since the increased difficulty of separation is more than offset by the increased ease of condensation. Similarly a vacuum may be used to increase the relative volatility and thereby facilitate separation, but is more often used to reduce the temperature of distillation where materials sensitive to high temperatures are being handled.

The composition of an azeotropic mixture also generally varies with the pressure, and by suitable distillations carried out at different pressures it is possible to separate a constant-boiling mixture.

Illustration 1.—A mixture of benzene and toluene is boiling at 45°C. under a total pressure of 200 mm. Evaluate, using Raoult's law, the composition of the vapor and liquid in equilibrium under these conditions. At 45°C. the vapor pressures of pure benzene and pure toluene are 224 and 75 mm., respectively.

$$P_B x_B + P_T(x_T) = \pi$$
$$224 x_B + 75(1 - x_B) = 200$$

from which $x_B = 0.839$. The mol fraction of benzene in the vapor is obtained by dividing the partial pressure of benzene by the total pressure, *i.e.*, $y_B = (224)(0.839)/200 = 0.940$. Thus a mixture of benzene and toluene containing 0.839 mol fraction benzene would boil at 45°C. under a total pressure of 200 mm., and would evolve an equilibrium vapor containing 0.940 mol fraction benzene, giving a relative volatility equal to (0.940) $(0.161)/(0.839)(0.060) = (224)/(75) = 3.0$. A similar calculation for the same liquid boiling at 760 mm. gives a temperature of 84°C. and an equilibrium vapor of 0.93 mol fraction benzene corresponding to a relative volatility of 2.56. It is to be noted that for a given liquid composition, increasing the total pressure almost fourfold, made only a small change in the equilibrium vapor composition and the relative volatility, but made a large change in temperature.

Complex Mixtures

In the case of more complex mixtures these relationships are extremely involved. Mixtures of hydrocarbons, the types and boiling points of which do not differ widely, usually follow Raoult's law within the experimental error. For other mixtures the vapor compositions must be determined experimentally (see page 527).

Petroleum.—In the distillation of petroleum the number of components in the mixture is very great and it is not usually desired to separate the individual substances but rather mixtures of these within certain limits. However, it is often desirable to fractionate the lower hydrocarbons present in refinery and other petroleum gases to obtain relatively pure fractions of ethylene, propane or butane. In these distillations it is advantageous to use relatively high pressures in order to raise the condensing temperatures. Under such conditions, it is found that deviations of the vapors from the perfect gas laws often constitute the major error in the application of Raoult's law. Generalized corrections for such deviations have been developed[2],[8],[9] which allow satisfactory prediction of the y-x relations of such mixtures.

Ethanol.—The behavior of fusel oil (amyl alcohol) in the distillation of the fermented mash in the manufacture of ethanol is interesting. The fusel oil boils at about 130°C., but is only sparingly soluble in water. Therefore, as shown on page 523, its volatility when dissolved in water is abnormally high. If in an ethanol column fusel oil gets down on the lower plates where there is practically nothing but water, its volatility is such that it is carried up the column. On the other hand, any fusel oil that gets into the top of the column is in the zone of nearly pure ethanol and here, because of its complete miscibility, its volatility is normal. It is obvious, therefore, that the fusel oil must concentrate in the middle of the column. In a batch operation it will remain in the middle until a large part of the ethanol is over and then it will distill with the low-test tailings. In a continuous column its concentration reaches such a point that it can be removed continuously from one of the plates in the middle of the column. The liquid removed contains both ethanol and water but the fusel oil has been concentrated to such an extent that its recovery from this liquid is easy.

METHODS OF CALCULATION

Equilibrium Distillation.—In the case of a continuous (steady state) simple distillation, a material balance relates the composition of the feed to the composition of vapor and residue produced. Consider the operation during the period of time such that F mols of feed with a mol fraction of A equal to x_f enter the still. In this same period of time V mols of vapor are removed with a vapor composition of y and $(F-V)$ mols of residue with the composition x_w are removed from the still. By material balance in component A,

$$Fx_f = Vy + (F-V)x_w. \tag{1}$$

Similar equations may be written for $(n-1)$ of the component present in the feed mixture. If the equilibrium relation between y and x_w is known, it is possible for a given value of x_f to solve Eq. 1 for V/F, the per cent vaporized, as a function of y or x_w; or for a given per cent vaporized it is possible to calculate y and x_w.

Differential Distillation, Rayleigh Equation.—The computation of the separation realizable in this type of simple distillation was first made by Lord Rayleigh.[12] Since the composition of the liquid in a still will change continuously during distillation, the analysis must be a differential one.

At any given time during the distillation the still contains L mols of liquid whose composition with respect to one component is x. Distill off the small amount $-dL$, the composition of which will be y, where y is determined as a function of x by the equilibrium curve. The total mols of this component in the still, Lx, will change an amount equal to $-d(Lx)$, which must equal the mols of this component vaporized, $-y \, dL$, i.e., $-y \, dL = -d(Lx)$, giving

$$\frac{dL}{L} = \frac{dx}{(y-x)},$$

which is the Rayleigh equation in the differential form. Integrating between the limits x_1 and x_2, with corresponding values L_1 and L_2,

$$\ln_e \frac{L_1}{L_2} = \int_{x_2}^{x_1} \frac{dx}{y-x}.$$

In the few cases where a mathematical relationship between x and y is known, this integral may be evaluated thereby, but in general resort must be had to the graphical determination of the area under the curve of $1/(y-x)$ vs. x.

For the special case of a binary mixture in which Raoult's law applies and in which, over the temperature range under consideration, the ratio of the pressure of the two components, P_1/P_2, is approximately constant, $y = \alpha x/[1+(\alpha-1)x]$ and this equation integrates to

$$\ln_e \frac{L_1}{L_2} = \frac{1}{\alpha-1} \ln \left\{ \frac{x_1}{x_2} \frac{(1-x_2)}{(1-x_1)} \right\} + \ln \frac{(1-x_2)}{(1-x_1)}$$

where $\alpha = P_1/P_2 =$ relative volatility (see page 521).

For the special case of dilute solutions which follow Henry's law, one may write $y = kx$, whence the integral becomes

$$\ln_e \frac{L_1}{L_2} = \frac{1}{k-1} \ln_e \frac{x_1}{x_2}.$$

Obviously, L and x may be expressed in mols and mol fraction, respectively, or in weight and fraction by weight.

Another form of the Raleigh equation applying to any two components of a multicomponent mixture is

$$\frac{-dA}{-dB} = \alpha_{AB} \frac{A}{B}$$

where A is the mols of the more volatile of the two components left in the liquid in the still at any time and B is the mols of the less volatile component remaining in the liquid at this time. For cases where α_{AB} does not vary significantly, the equation can be integrated giving

$$\ln \frac{A_1}{A_2} = \alpha_{AB} \ln \frac{B_1}{B_2}.$$

Partial Condensation.—Theoretically there are two diametrically different ways of producing a partial condensation; these form two limiting cases between which all actual condensations lie. The first, which is called **equilibrium condensation,** is characterized by keeping the condensate in contact and in equilibrium with the residual vapor. The second, **differential condensation,** consists in continually removing the condensate from the system as soon as formed. Continuous equilibrium condensations may be perfectly and easily realized by maintaining a certain amount of liquid condensate in the condenser, bubbling the incoming vapors through the liquid with sufficient contact to secure equilibrium, producing the partial condensation by cooling the liquid itself, and removing the excess of liquid formed by a continuous overflow at the surface where the vapor escapes. There is no mechanical device to accomplish a perfect differential condensation, though it can be closely approximated.

Equilibrium Partial Condensation.—Given a number of mols of vapor of composition y_1, to be enriched by *simple* condensation to a composition of y_2, it is obvious that the condensate must have a composition x_2, connected with y_2 by the x vs. y curve. Let the residual weight of vapor be V_2. Equating the original and final amounts of volatile component,

$$y_1 V_1 = y_2 V_2 + x_2 (V_1 - V_2),$$

or

$$(y_2 - y_1) = \frac{(y_1 - x_2)(V_1 - V_2)}{V_2}.$$

Differential Partial Condensation.—If the condensation is a differential one, the change in mols of volatile composition in the vapor $-d(Vy)$ is equal to the amount of volatile component condensed $-x\,dV$, *i.e.*, $-d(Vy) = -x\,dV$ and $-dV/V = dy/(y-x)$, ฺhence

$$\ln_e \frac{V_1}{V_2} = \int_{y_1}^{y_2} \frac{dy}{y-x}.$$

A differential condensation is more efficient than one, or any number of successive finite simple condensations between the same limits, and represents the theoretical maximum efficiency of separation. It may be considered as an infinite series of infinitesimal simple condensations. For purposes of comparison the performance of a partial condenser should be given in per cent of this theoretical maximum, which may be determined by measuring the area under the curve of $1/(y-x)$ vs. y.

Illustration 2.—An equimolal mixture of benzene, toluene and xylene is to be distilled at atmospheric pressure to recover 95 per cent of the benzene. It is desired to estimate the molal per cent which should be distilled and the composition of the distillate and residue if the distillation is carried out as (*a*) simple equilibrium distillation, (*b*) differential distillation collecting all the distillate together and (*c*) differential distillation if the distillate in (*b*) is collected in two equimolal portions.

The variation of temperature during the distillation will cause only a small change in α and for purposes of estimation an arithmetic mean will be used. The initial temperature of distillation will be approximately 100°C. and the final temperature will be somewhat less than the boiling point of xylene, probably about 130°C. The relative volatilities of benzene to toluene at these two temperatures are 2.40 and 2.17, respectively, or an average $\alpha_{BT} = 2.29$. The corresponding values for the relative volatilities of toluene to xylene are 2.35 and 2.15 or average $\alpha_{TX} = 2.25$.

Solution.—*a.* Continuous equilibrium distillation. The relative volatility equation may be rewritten as

$$\frac{Y_B}{Y_T} = \frac{\alpha_{BT} X_B}{X_T}$$

where Y_B and Y_T are the mols of benzene and toluene in the vapor, respectively, and X_B and X_T are the corresponding figures for the liquid. On the basis of 100 mols of material charged, Y_B would equal 31.67 and X_B would equal 1.67, and Y_T plus X_T would equal the toluene charged, or 33.33 mols. Using these values gives

$$\frac{31.67}{Y_T} = 2.29\left(\frac{1.67}{33.33 - Y_T}\right),$$

from which $Y_T = 29.73$ and $X_T = 3.60$. Similarly

$$\frac{Y_T}{Y_X} = \alpha_{TX}\frac{X_T}{X_X}$$

$$\frac{29.73}{Y_X} = 2.25\left(\frac{3.60}{33.33 - Y_X}\right),$$

giving $Y_X = 26.14$ and $X_X = 7.19$. These values are summarized in the following table:

Component	Distillate		Residue	
	Mols	Mol %	Mols	Mol %
Benzene.................	31.67	36.2	1.67	13.4
Toluene.................	29.73	33.9	3.60	28.9
Xylene.................	26.14	29.9	7.19	57.7
Total.................	87.54	....	12.46	

b. Using the integrated form of the Rayleigh equation

$$\log\left(\frac{B_1}{B_2}\right) = \alpha_{BT} \log\left(\frac{T_1}{T_2}\right),$$

$$\log 20 = 2.29 \log\left(\frac{33.33}{T_2}\right),$$

$$20^{\frac{1}{2.29}} = \frac{33.33}{T_2} = 3.69,$$

$$T_2 = 9.03.$$

$$\log\left(\frac{33.33}{9.03}\right) = \alpha_{TX} \log\left(\frac{33.33}{X_2}\right),$$

$$(3.69)^{\frac{1}{2.25}} = \frac{33.33}{X_2},$$

$$X_2 = 18.65.$$

Component	Distillate		Residue	
	Mols	Mol %	Mols	Mol %
Benzene.................	31.67	44.9	1.67	5.68
Toluene.................	24.30	34.4	9.03	30.80
Xylene.................	14.68	20.7	18.65	63.52
Total.................	70.65	....	29.35	

c. If the distillate of (*b*) had been collected in two equimolal portions of 35.3 mols each:

$$\left(\frac{33.33}{B_2{}^1}\right)^{\frac{1}{2.29}} = \frac{33.33}{T_2{}^1}$$

and

$$\left(\frac{33.33}{T_2{}^1}\right)^{\frac{1}{2.25}} = \frac{33.33}{X_2{}^1}$$

Solving these two equations together with the condition that $B_2{}^1 + T_2{}^1 + X_2{}^1 = 100 - 35.3 = 64.7$ gives $B_2{}^1 = 13.93$, $T_2{}^1 = 22.73$ and $X_2{}^1 = 22.03$. The mols of each component in the first portion of the distillate are obtained by subtracting each of these values from 33.33, and the amount of each component in the second distillate is obtained by taking the difference between the values obtained in part (*b*) and those of the first distillate.

Component	1st distillate		2d distillate		Residue	
	Mols	Mol %	Mols	Mol %	Mols	Mol %
Benzene........	19.40	55.0	12.27	34.7	1.67	5.68
Toluene.........	10.60	30.0	13.70	38.8	9.03	30.80
Xylene.........	5.30	15.0	9.38	26.5	18.65	63.52
Total.........	35.3	....	35.35	....	29.35	

To recover 95 per cent of the benzene requires the distillation of 88 per cent of the charge when the process is carried out as an equilibrium distillation and of only 71 per cent when the process is made differential. Since less distillate is made by the differential process, the distillate will therefore contain a higher percentage of benzene. It should be noted that the enrichment obtained by such simple distillations [parts (*a*) and (*b*)] is relatively small. Part (*c*) suggests a method for improving this separation; thus, if

35 per cent is distilled off as a differential process, it will contain 55 mol per cent benzene; an additional 35 per cent (based on original charge) may then be distilled and collected separately. This latter distillate has a composition approximately that of the original charge and may be added to the still for the next distillation. By this means it is possible to obtain the 95 per cent recovery of benzene in a distillate containing 55 per cent benzene. This latter operation would, of course, require more heat and larger equipment to take care of the redistillation.

Steam Distillation.—Volatile organic liquids containing non-volatile impurities in relatively small amounts frequently have boiling points so high that incipient decomposition may take place if they are distilled directly at atmospheric pressure. Even where this would not occur upon the distillation of the pure liquid, the impurities may be sufficiently soluble in it so that, when they are concentrated, the viscosity of the liquid and its boiling point may become so great that local superheating due to imperfect mixing will cause decomposition. Aniline, glycerin, fatty acids recover from cottonseed foots and many other materials illustrate this point. Advantage is here taken of the fact that in a mixture of liquids *not mutually soluble* the partial pressure of one component reduces the partial pressures of the other components necessary for vaporization.

When the gas laws apply, the weight ratio of two components in a vapor is equal to the molal ratio multiplied by the ratio of the molecular weights, *i.e.*, $W_A/W_B = (y_A/y_B)(M_A/M_B) = (p_A/p_B)$ (M_A/M_B) where y and p are the mol fractions and partial pressures, respectively, of the actual vapor. If water is one component of such a vapor, $W_A/W_W = (P_A/P_W)(M_A/M_W)$ and, for a binary mixture at the constant total pressure π,

$$\frac{W_A}{W_B} = \left(\frac{p_A}{\pi - p_A}\right)\frac{M_A}{M_B}. \qquad (2)$$

If the material distilled is entirely insoluble in water, the partial pressure p_A is the vapor pressure of the pure substance, and p_w is the difference between the pressure reigning in the system and p_A. Even where mutual solubility is appreciable, the vapor pressures of the pure components may be employed, since the *fractional* reductions in the vapor pressures are approximately equal and the ratio is but slightly affected. When, however, the mutual solubility of the two substances is great, these considerations do not apply.   In these cases one must determine experimentally the vapor-liquid equilibria.

Unless the steam used is highly superheated or unless heat from an external source is supplied in addition to that of the steam, water will always be present in the still.   This follows from the fact that, when the heat of vaporization of the substance distilled is taken from the steam, an equivalent amount of water must be condensed.   When a water layer is present as well as the water-insoluble layer, then $(\pi-p_A)$ must equal vapor pressure of pure water and the temperature then becomes fixed at a value such that the sum of p_A and the vapor pressure of water is equal to the total pressure.   It is obvious that this temperature is less than the boiling point of either component alone at the same total pressure.

Liquids are purified by "steam distillation," not only because this lowers the temperature at which the liquid distills, but also because the injected steam keeps the liquid mass thoroughly agitated.   Thus aniline, for example, boils at 180°C. under atmospheric pressure.   Under a high vacuum it can be boiled at 100°C., but such a vacuum may be hard to maintain.   If steam is injected into the still at atmospheric pressure, the aniline is heated to approximately 98°C., where the combined partial pressures of aniline and water equal 1 atmosphere, and vaporization proceeds, the mixed vapors distilling together.   It is possible to use any inert gas instead of a condensable vapor for the distillation, although in this case the heat must come either from the cooling of the hot gas or from some external source. Since the gas is saturated with the vapor of the material distilled when it leaves the condenser, it must be recirculated through a preheater to avoid this loss of vapor from the system.

Steam distillation is generally carried out in a cylindrical still, sometimes externally heated by either steam jacket or direct fire, and with injection of the steam through coils placed in the bottom of the still with numerous perforations to secure uniform distribution.*   The still must be connected with a condenser for the liquefaction of the mixed vapors, the components of which are separated by gravity.   The use of steam is a matter

* The relation between the number and size of these distributors and the pressure drop and rate of flow through them may be determined by considering the perforations as orifices (see p. 61).

of convenience and cheapness, as other vapors not appreciably soluble in the material to be distilled may thus be employed.

The method for calculating most of the points involved in the design of stills and auxiliaries for steam distillation, such, for example, as the heat quantities that must be supplied in vaporization and removed in condensation, the volumes of vapors and liquids to be handled, the heating and condensing surfaces necessary, etc., are but the application of principles already described.

The ratio of the substance distilled to the steam coming over with it is always below that calculated from the steam distillation Eq. 2, owing to imperfect contact of the steam with the substance. If the steam comes through in large bubbles that rise rapidly and if the layer of liquid being distilled is shallow, the time of contact in the still may be too small to secure equilibrium between the steam and vapor, and it leaves the still carrying less than the maximum amount of vapor. This equation gives a statement of the theoretically possible performance of a still, and thus furnishes an exact measure of the efficiency of the operation.

Steam Distillation in Vacuum.—While most steam distillations are carried out at atmospheric pressure and at less than 100°C., one must occasionally deal with a material of such low volatility that a higher temperature and less than atmospheric pressure must be used. An important illustration is the purification of oleic and other fatty acids by steam distillation where the highest allowable temperature and the lowest obtainable vacuum are desirable.

The steam consumption of such a distillation is in any case strikingly small, but decreases as the total pressure is reduced and becomes zero when the pressure on the system is reduced to the vapor pressure of the material being distilled, for under this condition the material will boil without the presence of steam. Just because liquids of higher volatility, such as aniline, can be steam distilled at atmospheric pressure is no reason why they should be so distilled. For the greatest economy in steam distillation, the still should be heated from an external source of energy to the highest allowable temperature, and should be operated under as high a vacuum as the cooling water will permit. The only equipment needed in addition to that usually employed is a wet-air pump for the removal of the condensed liquid and any permanent gases originally dissolved or due to leakage of air. As is obvious from ordinary steam-condenser practice in power plants, such a pump is cheap both to install and to operate.

In the separation of glycerin from impurities by steam distillation, the volatility of the glycerin is so low that the distillation must be carried out at the best attainable vacuum and at a high temperature, approximating 180°C. At this temperature and pressure the solubility of water in glycerin is very small, and the vapor pressure of the glycerin is therefore practically that of the pure substance. However, unless separated by fractional condensation, the glycerin and steam condense together as a single liquid mixture and must be separated by a subsequent distillation. Because of the widely different boiling points, little glycerin is then volatilized, and this process is generally called *evaporation*.

Use of Superheated Steam.—If the substance to be distilled is maintained at the highest allowable temperature by an external source of heat, and at a pressure sufficiently low to prevent the formation of a water layer, the steam consumption of the process is greatly decreased. The partial pressure of the steam is found by subtracting from the total pressure in the system that of the material being distilled. The total pressure is determined by the cooling water and condensing apparatus employed.

In this type of distillation it is especially important to prevent any condensation of the mixed vapors arising in the still until they have passed the highest point in the goose neck at the top of the still and are on their way down toward the condenser. Lagging the top of the still is insufficient, as this merely reduces but does not eliminate the evil. The still should, wherever possible, be externally heated up to and above the top. A steam jacket can be used, but this is expensive to construct and is likely to develop leaks, and the realizable temperature is limited by the strength of the still. Where direct firing is used, it is best to allow the flue gases to flow up and over the top of the still at such a temperature as to avoid appreciable superheating of the vapors and yet to prevent all heat loss from the vapor zone.

Illustration 3.—In a direct-fired still operating by the semi-batch method, stearic acid is being purified by steam distillation in a vacuum. Superheated steam is injected into the mass by means of perforated pipes in such a manner that the steam leaves the liquid phase at a temperature of 240°C., 70 per cent saturated with acid, *i.e.*, in a ratio equivalent to 70 per cent of the equilibrium value. Assume the following operating conditions to obtain: barometer, 748 mm. of mercury; vacuum in still, 662 mm.; and temperature of material when charged, 70°F.

DATA

Average specific heat of solid stearic acid... 0.4
Average specific heat of stearic acid vapor.. 0.47
Latent heat of fusion of stearic acid....... 47.6 gm. cal./gm.
Melting point of stearic acid............. 64°C.
Average specific heat of liquid stearic acid.. 0.55
Latent heat of vaporization of acid at
240°C............................. 66.0 gm. cal./gm.

Vapor pressure of stearic acid in mm. of mercury:

At 240°C....................................... 19 mm.
At 220°C....................................... 8 mm.
At 200°C....................................... 3 mm.

Total heat of dry *saturated* steam at 240°C. above liquid water at 70°F. = 1167 B.t.u./lb. Specific heat of low-pressure superheated steam = 0.46. Molecular weight of acid = 284.4.

1. Calculate the pounds of acid passing to the condenser per pound of steam, on the assumption (*a*) that the top of the still is so jacketed by combustion products that no heat is lost by the vapors leaving the acid in the bottom of the still until they reach the condenser; (*b*) that the still is not thus jacketed and that the vapors cool 40°C. before leaving the top of the still; (*c*) that the still is lagged but not jacketed, so that the vapors cool 20° before leaving the still.

2. In cases (*b*) and (*c*) what per cent of the acid initially evaporated in the still is refluxed back into it for reevaporation, and what per cent of the total heat consumed in the initial distillation of the acid is lost by radiation and convection from the top of the still?

3. What is the total consumption of heat required for the distillation in the three cases, expressed as B.t.u./lb. of product?

Basis: 1 lb. of steam leaving still at 240°C.
Partial pressure of acid = (0.70)(19) = 13.3 mm.
Total absolute pressure = 748 − 662 = 86 mm.
Partial pressure of steam = 86 − 13.3 = 72.7 mm.
Heat consumption in C.h.u./lb. of acid:

To heat solid acid: $0.4(64-21)$ = 17.2
To melt solid acid: = 47.6
To heat liquid acid: $0.55(240-64)$ = 96.9
To vaporize acid: = 66.0
                                   ——
Total   227.7

Pounds of acid/lb. of steam $= \dfrac{13.3 \times 284.4}{72.7 \times 18.02} = 2.89.$

Hence the heat used by the acid evaporated by 1 lb. of steam is $2.89 \times 227.7 = 657$ C.h.u. or $1.8 \times 657 = 1185$ B.t.u. To this, one must add the 1167 B.t.u. in the steam, or a total of 2352 B.t.u., which is $2352 \div 2.89 = 813$ B.t.u./lb. of product.

At 200°C. the weight of acid per lb. of steam (figured similarly to the above) is $(3)(284) \div (86-3)(18.02) = 0.57$ lb., *i.e.*, 2.32 lb. are condensed and refluxed, or 80.3 per cent of the total evaporated. The heat lost is $1.8(240-200)(0.46) = 33$ B.t.u. due to cooling of the steam; $1.8(240-200)(0.47)(0.57) = 19$ B.t.u. due to cooling of acid vapor; $1.8(66)(2.32) = 276$ B.t.u. due to condensation; $1.8(240-200)(0.55)(2.32) = 92$ B.t.u. due to cooling of the condensed acid; this makes a total of 420 B.t.u. The heat consumption per lb. of steam is 1167 B.t.u. in the steam; $0.57(227.7)(1.8) = 233$ B.t.u. to preheat and vaporize the acid distilled; $2.32[66+0.55(240-200)](1.8) = 367$ B.t.u. to reheat and vaporize the acid refluxed; this gives a total of 1767 B.t.u. The heat loss is therefore 23.8 per cent of the heat consumed.

Similarly, at 220°C., the acid distilled per lb. of steam is 1.62 lb., while the reflux is 1.27 lb. or 44.0 per cent. The heat consumption is 2006 B.t.u. per lb. of steam, and the heat lost is 220 B.t.u. or 11 per cent.

Obviously, the heat consumption per lb. of product is found by dividing the total used per lb. of steam by the yield. Hence, the answers are as follows:

1*a*. 2.89 lb. of acid evaporated/lb. of steam.

1*b*. 0.57 lb. of acid evaporated/lb. of steam.

1*c*. 1.62 lb. of acid evaporated/lb. of steam.

2*b*. 80.3 per cent of the acid is refluxed for 23.8 per cent heat loss.

2*c*. 44.0 per cent of the acid is refluxed for 11 per cent heat loss.

3*a*. 813 B.t.u./pound of product.

3*b*. 3100 B.t.u./pound of product.

3*c*. 1240 B.t.u./pound of product.

The recovery of benzene and toluene from illuminating gas, recovery of gasoline from natural gas and processes of this type are frequently accomplished by dissolving the vapors in a suitable solvent, such as a heavy paraffin oil or cresol. There is thus produced a solution so dilute with respect to the benzene that removal of the benzene by simple distillation is impractical on account of the high boiling point. The situation is met by distilling the mixture with steam at a temperature so low that the volatility of the oil is negligible. Condensation of the steam and benzene makes possible the separation of the two by gravity.

As the benzene or other vapor is removed from the oil, its concentration decreases, and, according to *Henry's law*, its partial pressure decreases proportionately. This means that the necessary quantity of steam progressively increases during the distillation. Since, however, steam saturated with benzene at a low concentration of benzene in oil is still capable of picking up benzene from a solution of higher benzene content, it is obvious that countercurrent flow of steam and benzene is demanded. Such countercurrent flow is obtained in rectifying columns of the general type described on pages 547 to 551.

The steam consumed in such a process may be greatly reduced by the use of a vacuum, for reasons entirely analogous to those already described; and although a vacuum is not usually employed in this work, its desirability is clear.

A study of the rectifying columns mentioned above shows that the pressure on the lower plates is always higher than that on the upper ones. This increase of pressure at the bottom of such a column interferes with the removal of the volatile component by the steam. By allowing a free passage for the vapors up through the column, at the same time providing for effective counterflow of the liquid down through the column, this difficulty is reduced to a minimum. For this reason, the tower fillings described on page 550 can here be used to advantage.

Volatile Solid Component; Sublimation.—Certain solid substances possess at temperatures below their melting points vapor pressures so high that distillation without melting is practical. This process is called **sublimation** and is used for the separation of solids when only one component is volatile. Except in the respects noted below it does not differ from the distillation of a material containing a single volatile liquid.

If the material sublimed contains only a slight amount of nonvolatile impurities, the volatilization can be carried out without difficulty in a direct-fired or steam-jacketed still or retort. The material is in immediate contact with the hot wall of the retort and, as it volatilizes, fresh charge comes into contact with the heating surface. If, on the other hand, there is a large percentage of infusible, nonvolatile impurity in the material, the escape of the volatile portion that is in immediate contact with the retort wall leaves behind an insulating layer of impurities which makes it difficult to heat the whole mass without danger of localized overheating. In such a case direct contact of every portion of the charge with the retort wall must be effected by some sort of agitation.

The most serious problem in sublimation is in the condensation of the vapors. If a surface condenser is used, the cooling surface is quickly coated with a layer of the sublimate which insulates the vapors from the condensing surface and greatly reduces the capacity. In some cases the condenser can be equipped with mechanical scrapers, but such an apparatus must generally be made of steel or cast iron and there is danger of contamination of the product. It is usually best to condense the vapors by diluting them with large quantities of cold gas, most frequently air. Where necessary, inert gases can be used for dilution.

If the vapors are cooled very quickly by admission of gas at a temperature far below the sublimation point, the material condenses as an extremely fine powder. When it is desired to produce large crystals, the temperature and quantity of diluent gas must be so controlled that the vapors are not greatly supersaturated. If these vapors are now passed through a large chamber in which strings or other centers for crystallization are suspended, the supersaturated vapor will condense slowly and large crystals will result.

The disadvantage of condensation by dilution is that the gas leaving the condenser chamber is saturated with the vapors of the material sublimed. While the partial pressure of the material at this low temperature may be small, the quantity lost can be large since the molecular weight may be high and the gas quantities very great. These difficulties are met by cooling and recirculating the gas. If, however, a surface cooler is used, it will choke up with crystals deposited from the saturated gas. This can be overcome by using a spray cooler and by filtering out the crystals that separate from the water withdrawn from the chamber, or by evaporation if the material is soluble. In the latter case the spray water may be recirculated through a surface cooler. Where the material sublimed is sensitive to water, other suitable liquids, such as organic solvents, can be used for the spray cooling and recirculated through a surface-type water cooler.

In the sublimation of materials sensitive to heat, it is sometimes advisable to admit gas or steam in the retort itself to volatilize the material at a temperature below its normal sublimation point, in a way entirely analogous to that used in steam distillation; however, this introduces additional difficulties in condensation.

UNDERLYING PRINCIPLES OF SEPARATION

Referring again to Fig. 166, which gives the relationship between the composition of the liquid and the composition of the vapor in equilibrium, a possible method of separating components becomes evident. If, now, the vapor which was given off when the liquid boiled at temperature E and which in composition is represented by F is condensed and heated by itself, it will boil at temperature G and give off vapor having the composition H. If this in turn is condensed and again heated, it will boil at I, producing a vapor of the composition J, and so on until almost pure benzene is obtained near C. Or, what amounts to the same thing, if the vapor formed at E with the composition F is cooled from the temperature at F (102°C.) to the temperature at G (96°C.), vapor of the composition H, much richer in benzene, will persist, and the remainder of the vapor will condense to form a liquid poorer in benzene, with the composition corresponding to G. Thus by controlled condensation the same result will be obtained as by complete condensation followed by revaporization.

When the vapor of composition H falls in temperature to the point I, some of it will condense to a liquid poorer in benzene than that represented by I, by the amount of benzene which has remained in vapor form of the composition represented by J. This liquid poorer in benzene than I will, if returned to the still, immediately boil, again taking heat from the still. When the vapor of composition F falls in temperature to the point G and partly condenses, it must give off heat equal to the heat of condensation of the liquid formed. If now the liquid condensing at I, which is richer in benzene than that condensing at G, can come in contact with the vapors condensing at G, the heat of condensation here set free will immediately boil the liquid condensing at I, and no heat will be taken from the still. In other words, the hot vapor rich in toluene will boil the cooler liquid rich in benzene, forming from the first a liquid yet richer in toluene, and from the latter a vapor yet richer in benzene without the consumption of more heat from the still.

An apparatus in which these conditions are realized is shown in Fig. 170, where E, G and I are stills, each supplied with a heating coil and a discharge for the vapor, and in which are placed mixtures of benzene and toluene having the composition represented by the points E, G and I corresponding to the boiling points E, G and I on the curve ABC in Fig. 166, page 525.   The coil in E is heated by steam which boils the liquid of the composition E, evolving vapor of the composition F, at the temperature of E, which passes into the heating coil of the still G.   Here the vapor condenses and liquid of the composition F runs out of the coil into a receiver.   But the condensing vapor in the coil boils the liquid in G, and vapor of the composition H passes into the coil of the still I, and so on.   In this way successive stills will deliver vapor ever richer in benzene until, if enough are employed, almost pure benzene will be obtained.

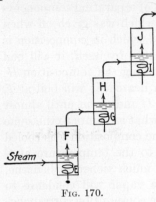

Fig. 170.

But the effluent from the coils in the still G is of the same composition as the contents of still G and can be added to it. Since this is the case, one can as well allow the vapor from still E to pass directly into still G and condense therein a liquid richer in toluene and evolve a vapor richer in benzene.

An apparatus in which this direct interchange of heat and consequent condensation and evaporation can take place is called a **rectifying column,** and the process carried on within it is called **rectification.**

Such a system is shown in Fig. 171, where S is a still body or kettle.   Resting on the outlet of the still is a column divided into compartments by plates perforated with small holes.   Each plate has an overflow pipe discharging into a pool of liquid on the plate below.   The layer of liquid on each plate is prevented

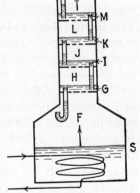

Fig. 171.—Perforated-plate rectifying column.

from passing down through the holes by vapor which is passing up through these holes, from the compartment next below.   Any excess liquid accumulating on the plate flows down through the overflow pipe.   The letters on the apparatus correspond to

those on Fig. 166, page 525. Vapor from the still at temperature
E and composition F passes up and partly condenses at temperature G in compartment G, with a composition slightly poorer in
benzene than that corresponding to G. Here is evolved vapor of
the composition H which bubbles up through the liquid on the
next higher plate which is richer in benzene, with the composition
I. Here again condensation takes place at the temperature of I
and the heat evolved sends off vapor of composition J, even
richer in benzene. This can be repeated any number of times,
and the vapor finally issuing from the apparatus at the top and
into the condenser is practically pure benzene. As in the
previous illustration, each one of the compartments in the
column may be considered a small still in which the source of
heat is the hot vapor coming from below and the cooling element
(condenser) is the cooler liquid from the plate above.

The relationship here pictured is in fact valid only in case the
molal ratio of liquid overflowing from plate to plate to the vapor
rising through the plates is practically unity, *i.e.*, the ratio of
distillate to liquid vaporized is exceedingly small. In practice
less overflow must be employed to reduce the heat consumption,
and the rate of enrichment is much less rapid than that indicated in the explanation. This special case is discussed here
because it brings out clearly the nature of the underlying
phenomena. It corresponds to the asymptote of Fig. 181,
page 568.

Rectification.—A study of the liquid-vapor equilibrium curves
shows that the condensate formed upon partial condensation of a
vapor is necessarily richer in the volatile component than the
liquid from which the vapor was originally evolved. Therefore,
this condensate cannot be in equilibrium with the vapor rising
from the still, and if it is brought in contact with it some sort
of interaction must take place. From the liquid-vapor diagram
it is seen that this interaction must involve the condensation
from the vapor rising from the still of part of the less volatile
component, with evolution of a new vapor richer in the more
volatile component. The heat of condensation thus set free
tends to raise the temperature of the liquid, but, since it is
already at its boiling point, there results a new vapor richer in
the more volatile component. This interaction of a vapor
rising from the still with the condensate from a part of the vapor

previously evolved is called **rectification** which affords an efficient means for separating volatile liquids.

Since rectification in its result is equivalent to a series of redistillations without the consumption of additional heat, it is analogous in this respect to multiple-effect evaporation; however, it is only the result that is similar and not the mechanism of attaining it.

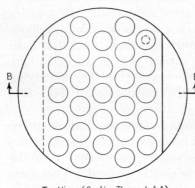

Side View (Section Through B-B)

Top View (Section Through A-A)

Fig. 172.—Bubble plate rectifying column.

As already indicated, the enrichment of a vapor in the more volatile constituent by cooling it sufficiently to separate out as liquid a part of the less volatile component will be here designated **partial condensation;** the interaction of such a partial condensate with the vapor rising through a column, resulting in further enrichment of the vapor in low-boiling constituent, will be called **rectification.**

Plate Columns.—In order to be efficient, the contact between the vapor rising from the still and the liquid reflux resulting from a previous partial condensation must be countercurrent and as intimate as possible. Experience has developed the bubbling plate column as one of the best devices for securing this result. This rectifying column, as it is called, consists of a series of plates over which flows the liquid reflux and through which the rising vapors are made to bubble. The reflux flows from plate to plate through suitable overflow pipes and the vapor rises through each of the plates in series countercurrent to the flow of the liquid.

A section of such a column is shown in Fig. 172, in which overflow weirs and partitions are used instead of overflow pipes.

The height of the overflow weir regulates the depth of the liquid remaining on the plate and the lower end of the partition is sealed in the liquid on the plate below in order to prevent the vapor from passing up the overflow space. The bubble caps are of various design, one common type being shown in Fig. 173. The vapor passes up the central vapor riser and reverses direction and passes downward inside the annular space between the cap and riser and then out through the slots into the liquid. The amount of opening of the slots, *i.e.*, the portion of slot discharging vapor, depends on the quantity of the vapor flowing, being zero for no vapor flow but increasing with vapor flow until the entire slot area is being used; if such a cap is overloaded sufficiently, vapor will escape around the lower periphery. Long rectangular

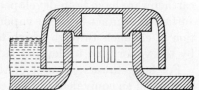

Fig. 173.—Slotted bubble cap and vapor riser.

bubble caps have been used in place of the round caps illustrated in Fig. 172.

A simple type of plate sometimes employed consists of perforated sheet metal or even of a wire screen, Fig. 171, page 546. This type has the disadvantage that, when the vapor velocity is low, the liquid leaks through the vapor holes from the plates into the still. Consequently, such a column cannot be operated at low capacity. With a high vapor velocity the friction through the holes is very large and, if such a plate is not absolutely level, all the liquid will run through the low side and the vapor pass up the high side. However, these plates when properly placed give a high plate efficiency because of the exceptionally small bubbles produced and their excellent distribution, and they also have high capacity for a given amount of entrainment.

A relatively large pressure is required to force the vapor through the column against the resistance of the orifices and the liquid head, which is a disadvantage in many gas-washing operations; but this disadvantage disappears in distillations where increased temperatures do not harm the materials being distilled, because the necessary pressure can be easily developed within the still by merely allowing the temperature of the boiling liquid to rise (but see page 551).

Tower Fillings.—The interaction between vapor and refluxing condensate can be efficiently secured by the use of a plain tower filled with suitable packing material over the surface of which the reflux flows to the still and through the voids of which the vapor rises. When dealing with excessively corrosive liquids, as, for example, in the separation of nitric and sulfuric acids,* such a tower can be built of resistant material and filled with broken quartz. A number of tower fillings made from refractory earthenware have been developed, all designed to present a large surface of contact between vapor and liquid, to avoid the formation of channels through which the liquor may pass undisturbed by the vapor, and to develop as little back pressure as possible.

For large towers the cost of the packed column often exceeds the cost of an equivalent bubble cap tower and generally the latter is used; however, where corrosive materials are being handled, or where the pressure drop must be kept low, packed towers can be advantageously employed. In small pilot plant operation, the small-diameter columns can be made cheaper as packed towers than as bubble plate towers, and in small laboratory columns very efficient fractionation can be obtained by the use of special types of packing which would be too expensive for even moderate-size towers.

A very popular packing for columns is a cylinder of earthenware having a diameter equal to its height. These rings are thrown into the tower at random, their uniform size and dimensions insuring an even, homogeneous packing. The area presented for reaction is large, while the frictional resistance to the moving vapor is small. An even and uniform distribution of the partial condensate over the top of the tower filling is controlling in the efficient operation of such a tower, especially if it is relatively short. There exists a strong tendency for the ascending vapor to seek out channels of least resistance, and these "chimneys," once formed, seem to perpetuate themselves, allowing the liquid to flow down undisturbed. It has been shown[1] that, if the

* Nitric acid may be efficiently concentrated by mixing it with strong sulfuric acid and allowing this mixture to flow down a filled tower against an ascending current of steam. The heat of condensation of the steam combined with the heat of dilution of the sulfuric acid distills the nitric acid. The fractionating effect of the tower enables the operator to withdraw concentrated acid from the top of the tower and completely denitrated sulfuric acid from the bottom.

diameter of a tower is approximately ten times the diameter of the packing, the liquor will tend to distribute itself more or less evenly, but, if the liquor is introduced at the top in one large stream, it may be a considerable distance down the tower before satisfactory distribution is obtained, and a distributor for introducing the liquor is desirable.

Rectification under Vacuum.—If the operating temperature in a rectifying tower must not exceed a low maximum, as in the dealcoholizing of beer, a vacuum must be maintained in the system. Under this condition a tower or column with an open filling to give the least frictional resistance to the flow of vapor is better than a column equipped with plates (see page 550).

Condensers.—It has already been pointed out that a partial condenser can be used to effect a partial enrichment of the vapor, and this separation can be used to aid the rectifying column. However, to attain simplicity in operation it is customary to omit the partial condenser altogether and employ a final condenser which completely liquefies all vapor leaving the column, a part of this condensate being deflected as reflux to the column and the rest taken off as product. It is, however, difficult to construct and operate a single condenser of this type which will both cool the product and at the same time preheat the feed. It is usually better practice to employ a single condenser for the production of reflux and product, cooling the latter in a liquor cooler.

Where the vapor is insoluble in water, the final condenser may be of the jet-condenser type. If the heat to be absorbed is large and the condensate separates readily from water, as in the refining of heavy petroleum oil, a short tower packed with Raschig or similar earthenware rings, over which cooling water flows, is both inexpensive and efficient in its condensing action.

Intermittent Operation of Distillation Apparatus.—A rectifying apparatus can be operated in two fundamentally different ways. In *intermittent operation* the still below the column is filled with a charge of the liquids to be separated (*e.g.*, benzene and toluene) and distillation is begun. In Fig. 174, S is the still, D the rectifying column, F the partial condenser, C the final condenser and W an auxiliary cooler for the product. G is a glass dome covering the overflow chamber A, where the rate of distillation can be observed and where a hydrometer may float, indicating at all times the density of the liquid product.   As a volatile constituent (benzene) is removed, the residuum in the still becomes progressively richer in the less volatile substance (toluene).   This means that the vapor rising from the still grows continually poorer in benzene, and hence to free it from toluene, since the rectifying

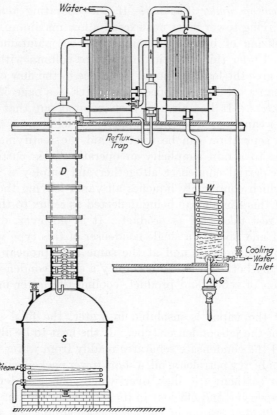

Fig. 174.—Still, bubble plate rectifying column, partial condenser, final condenser, and distillate cooler.

column is of a fixed length, the ratio of condensate refluxed at the top of the column to the distillate must be progressively increased.   This necessity for continually modifying the operating conditions in an intermittent distillation is a serious disadvantage, but satisfactory separation of the constituents can be realized, except at the very end of the operation, when the distillate always contains some of the higher boiling constituent and must be collected separately for admixture with the next charge. This inability to effect complete separation at the end of the operation is occasioned by the fact that there is insufficient low-boiling component in the system to maintain the necessary concentration gradient through the column, *i.e.*, there remains only the high-boiling component on the bottom plates. The effective length of the column is thus reduced below that essential for complete separation.

Continuous Operation of Distillation Apparatus.—Just before the end of the operation in an intermittent unit as above considered, toluene exists in the still free from benzene, while there is being discharged from the condenser practically pure benzene. The percentage of benzene in the vapor and liquid in the column increases progressively from the bottom to the top plate. Assume that the original feed to be separated contains 80 per cent of benzene. On some plate in the column a liquid of practically this composition will be found. If, now, the feed containing 80 per cent of benzene is introduced continuously onto this plate, the conditions in the system will tend to perpetuate themselves, *i.e.*, concentrations at all points will remain unchanged, benzene will be discharged from the final condenser, while toluene will work its way down into the still from which it may be continuously withdrawn. This method of distillation is called **continuous rectification.** It may be shown mathematically that the heat efficiency of a continuous operation is greater than that of an intermittent operation, while, as above noted, the operating conditions are less complicated. Intermittent rectification is justified only when working on such a small scale, or where it is desired to produce more than two fractions of high purity with a single column. Rectification, especially if continuous, offers various opportunities for the economy of heat through the use of heat economizers or exchangers. The best "routing" of the feed through the heat-recovery system varies with conditions.

METHODS OF CALCULATION

The mathematical theory of the rectifying column as applied to the distillation of binary mixtures was first developed by Ernst Sorel,[15] who calculated the enrichment from plate to plate by equating the amount of energy and of matter entering and leaving each plate and by assuming that equilibrium was realized between the vapors and the liquid leaving the plate. Sorel applied his method successively from one plate to the next in a column. In consequence the computations become involved and it is difficult to visualize what is taking place. The following is a modification of Sorel's method, which simplifies computation and makes it possible to present results in graphical form.

The derivation will assume a column in continuous operation, with the feed, *i.e.*, the binary mixture to be separated, entering on a plate somewhere between the top and the bottom of the column. The results may, however, be applied to a discontinuous column at any particular instant during the operation, provided the amount of condensate in the column is small in proportion to the amount in the still.

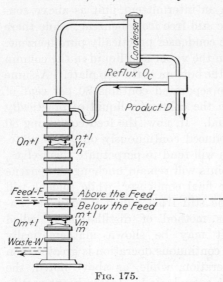

Fig. 175.

Nomenclature.—The nomenclature is indicated by Fig. 175, where, for the sake of simplicity, there is shown a single condenser, so that the overflow back into the column is of the same composition as the product. However, this has nothing to do with the derivation and does not affect the validity of the equations. Heat is supplied by conduction at the bottom of the column, as by means of steam condensing in closed coils or by externally firing the still.

Call any particular (variable) plate above the feed plate the nth and that below it the mth plate. Call the amount of vapor, measured in mols per unit time passing any particular section, V, and the amount of overflow passing the section, O. On the same basis, F, D and W represent the respective amounts of feed, overhead product and residue. These quantities are to include in each case the mols of both components. Designate the point of origin of the particular vapor or overflow referred to by the use of a subscript; thus V_n is the mols of vapor rising from the nth plate, while O_{n+1} is the mols of overflow coming down to that plate from the plate above. Use the subscripts f and c to refer to the feed line and to the condenser, respectively. Call the mol fraction of the more volatile component in the liquid x and the mol fraction in the vapor y. Indicate the liquid to which reference is made by subscripts; thus x_w is the mol fraction of volatile component in the residue leaving the bottom of the still, while y_m is the mol fraction of the same component in the vapor rising from the mth plate. The quantities required in discussion are assembled in the following table:

x = mol fraction of more volatile component in liquid.

y = mol fraction of more volatile component in vapor.

D = mols of distillate withdrawn as product per unit of time = P.

x_c = mol fraction of more volatile component in the distillate.

O_{n+1} = mols of overflow from plate $n+1$ to plate n, per unit time.

x_{n+1} = mol fraction of more volatile component in overflow, O_{n+1}.

V_n = mols of vapor passing from plate n to plate $n+1$ per unit time.

y_n = mol fraction of more volatile component in vapor, V_n.

F = mols of the mixture fed to the column per unit time.

x_f = mol fraction of more volatile component in feed, F.

W = mols of residue per unit time.

x_w = mol fraction of more volatile component in residue, W.

O'_{n+1} = theoretical minimum overflow from plate $n+1$, per unit time.

n = the number of the plate under consideration, counting from the feed plate up.

m = the number of the plate under consideration, below the feed plate, counting up from the still.

Q_n = *total* latent heat in the vapor V_n.

r_1 = molal heat of vaporization of more volatile component.

r_2 = molal heat of vaporization of less volatile component.

It is easy to visualize each step and appreciate its significance by discussion of a special illustrative case; consequently the following will refer to the separation of ethanol and water, ethanol being the more volatile component.

Consider the whole apparatus above a section drawn between the nth and the $(n+1)$th plate, just below the latter. The only thing entering this section is the vapor from the nth plate, V_n. Leaving this section is the product D, and the overflow from the $(n+1)$th plate, O_{n+1}. Therefore, by a total material balance,

$$V_n = O_{n+1} + D. \qquad (3)$$

The total ethanol entering this section must equal that leaving it, *i.e.*,

$$y_n V_n = x_{n+1} O_{n+1} + x_c D. \tag{4}$$

By eliminating V_n from these two equations, one obtains

$$y_n = \frac{O_{n+1} x_{n+1}}{O_{n+1} + D} + \frac{D x_c}{O_{n+1} + D}. \tag{5}$$

Similarly, for conditions below the feed plate one obtains

$$y_m = \frac{O_{m+1} x_{m+1}}{O_{m+1} - W} - \frac{W x_w}{O_{m+1} - W}. \tag{6}$$

Since these equations represent nothing but equality of input and output, for conditions of steady operation their validity cannot be questioned. Furthermore, inspection of Eq. (5) shows that under these conditions it contains only three variables, x_{n+1}, y_n and O_{n+1}. Similarly, the only variables in Eq. (6) are x_{m+1}, y_m and O_{m+1}. Obviously, therefore, one needs to find only one other independent relationship between these variables to determine the value of both the others if that of any one is known at any point in the column, and this relation is a heat balance. While the principle underlying such a heat balance is simple, its details become, in the general case, sufficiently involved to interfere with a clean-cut visualization of the significance of the results. Hence, to avoid this difficulty, at the start certain simplifying assumptions will be made, which in many important cases are close approximations to the facts.

The heat supply to that part of the column above the nth plate is obviously restricted to the heat content of the vapor V_n entering it. Part of this heat may be lost through the walls, part is consumed in heating the liquid overflow going down the column, and the rest goes to furnish the heat in the vapor rising to the plates above. Since heat loss from the walls of the column should be eliminated, so far as practicable, by lagging or otherwise, it will now be assumed that this has been done to a point such that heat thus lost is a negligible fraction of the total.*

---

* Where a column is large in cross section and operated to its full vapor capacity, the ratio of surface to volume becomes so small that heat losses from the sides are sometimes a negligible fraction of the total, so far as these calculations are concerned, even though the column is uninsulated and the losses are large in absolute value.

The heat of mixing of liquids that do not react chemically or exhibit the phenomena of dissociation, molecular association and the like is usually small, particularly in comparison with the latent heats of vaporization. The heat of mixing of the vapors is even smaller. The second assumption will be that these factors are not appreciable. The heat required to heat the liquid flowing down the column is in part compensated for by a decrease in temperature of the vapor as it passes up the column. Generally the sensible heat of the liquid flowing down the column exceeds that of the vapor passing upward and the difference in these two quantities is made up at the expense of the latent heat of the vapor; the net result is a decrease in enthalpy of the vapor.

Liquids can be divided into two groups, the associating and nonassociating types. Within each group the molal heat of vaporization divided by the absolute temperature decreases at constant pressure with decreasing values of the temperature (see Fig. 4, page 13). This results in a decrease in the molal latent heat of the vapor as it passes up the column. Since both the enthalpy of the vapor and its molal latent heat decrease in passing up the column, it is possible that the total mols of vapor may remain constant, increase or decrease, depending on the relative decrease of these two quantities. The decrease in enthalpy of the vapor is mainly due to the sensible heat of the liquid, and in the portion of the actual column above the feed, where the mols of vapor exceed the mols of liquid, this decrease is often less than the decrease in the molal latent heat and there results an increase in the total mols of vapor as it passes up the column. In the portion of the column below the feed, where the mols of liquid exceed the mols of vapor, the reverse may be true and the total mols of vapor may decrease as they pass up this section. Experimental data indicate that, if all the components are associating (water, ammonia, alcohol, etc.) or if they are all nonassociating (hydrocarbons and most organic liquids), up to moderate pressures (about 10 atmospheres) the total mols of vapor (and liquid) are substantially constant except as affected by the introduction of the feed or by the return of cold reflux to the column.* In

* In distillating petroleum fractions, the feed often contains appreciable percentages of heavy fractions, which are essentially nonvolatile under the column operating conditions, and these fractions simply flow down the column and out with the bottoms, taking up large quantities of sensible

other words, above the feed plate both the molal overflow from plate to plate and the vapor passing up the column are substantially constant throughout this section, and the same applies below the feed, but the mols of vapor and overflow cannot be the same in both sections. Since it is impossible to condense the vapor from the top plate without cooling it, the reflux from the condenser will be cooler than the boiling liquid on the top plate; hence the amount of overflow in the column is greater than the reflux from the condenser. The effect of this is often negligible but may be large.

Under such conditions, therefore, the molal overflow from plate to plate above the feed plate, *i.e.*, the term O_{n+1} in Eq. 5 is constant and, similarly, O_{m+1} in Eq. 6 is constant; however, O_{m+1} is greater than O_{n+1}. Hence, it follows that x_{n+1} is linear in y_n and x_{m+1} is linear in y_m.[13] Furthermore, for fixed operating conditions, *i.e.*, definite quantities and concentrations of feed, distillate and residue and a given overflow, the slopes of these lines are known and the location of a single point upon either of them determines the whole line. Since these lines, based as they are only upon energy and material balances in the column, represent the conditions necessarily existing at each section in the column between the vapor rising and the overflow passing down through that section, they are called the *operating* lines. To distinguish between conditions above and below the feed plate, the former may, in any specific case, be called the *enriching* and the latter the *exhausting* or *stripping* line.

It must be emphasized that, so far as a bubble plate column is concerned, the preceding discussion has been limited to the relations between the composition of the vapor rising from a plate and that of the overflow onto it from the plate above. The relation between the composition of the vapor and that of the liquid on the plate below from which it came must now be considered.

All available data indicate that the vapor evolved upon boiling any mixture of volatile liquids is, at the moment of its evolution,

---

heat, which results in a decrease in the total mols of vapor as it proceeds up the column in this section. At high pressures the sensible heat content of both the liquid and vapor becomes large relative to the latent heat of vaporization and large variations in the total mols of vapors may result at different sections of the column.

in substantially complete equilibrium with the liquid from which it is given off. The vapor rising from a given plate of a column is, however, by no means all evolved from the liquid on that plate; it consists largely of vapor from lower plates, which, because of inadequate contact with the liquid on the plate in question, has not had opportunity completely to react and come into equilibrium with it. Furthermore, the liquid on a plate

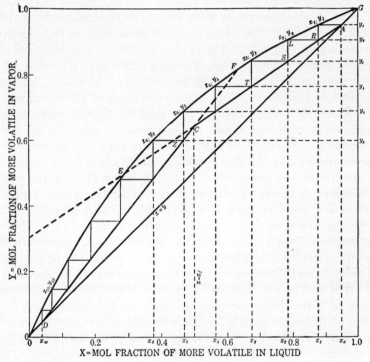

Fig. 176.—Diagram illustrating graphical stepwise method of McCabe and Thiele.

is not uniform in composition but grows progressively poorer in volatile constituent as it flows from the point of discharge of the overflow from the plate above, across the plate, to the entrance to the overflow pipe leading to the plate below. For purposes of computation, bubble plate columns are usually designed on the basis of the "theoretical plate," *i.e.*, a plate such that the vapor rising from the plate has the same composition as the vapor in equilibrium with the overflow leaving the plate. Such an ideal column serves as the standard of performance of rectifying equipment. In it the relation between the composition of the vapor at a given section and that of the liquid leaving the plate from which that vapor came must, therefore, be given by the equilibrium x-y curve.

It follows, therefore, that the conditions existing in a column operating continuously, with a constant value of the molal overflow above the feed plate and another, larger, constant overflow below it, in which the vapor rising from each plate is in substantial equilibrium with the liquid leaving that plate, may be represented by a diagram similar to Fig. 176. Equilibrium is represented by the curve $OEFG$. The operating lines are AE and DF, corresponding to Eqs. 5 and 6, respectively. Consider, for the moment, a plate from which the composition of the overflow is x_2. Since the vapor rising from this theoretical plate is in equilibrium with this liquid, its composition must be y_2, corresponding to a point L on the equilibrium curve. Furthermore, the composition of the vapor rising from the plate below must be y_3, determined by the point S vertically below L, since the relation between the compositions of the vapor rising into a plate and of the overflow from it is given by the enriching line AC. Similarly, the composition of the overflow from the plate above the one in question must be x_1, *i.e.*, the abscissa of that point R on the enriching line which has the same vapor composition y_2 as point L, and therefore lies on the same horizontal level with it. In other words, the changes in concentration, as one goes from plate to plate down the column, are found quantitatively by going stepwise alternately from the enriching line to the equilibrium curve and back again, first horizontally and then vertically, as indicated in Fig. 176. Thus, if x_1 is the composition of the liquid on one plate, x_2 is that on the plate below, x_3 on the next, and so on.

To start this stepwise operation, one must know the composition of the liquid leaving some one plate or else that of the vapor from it. In the case of the arrangement of Fig. 175, inspection makes it clear that the composition of the vapor from the top plate must be identical with that of the product x_c, since no separation or enrichment of this vapor takes place in the condenser. Calling the composition of the overflow from the top plate x_1, and the corresponding vapor y_1, it follows that $y_1 = x_c$.

Hence y_1 is found by locating x_c at A on the diagonal line $ODAG$ $(y=x)$ and drawing a horizontal line from x_c to intersect the equilibrium curve at y_1; the corresponding abscissa is x_1.

Furthermore, if in Eq. (5) one inserts top plate conditions for this case, namely, $y_n = x_c$, one obtains $x_{n+1} = y_n = x_c$; in other words, the enrichment line must go through point A, as above determined. Rearranging* Eqs. (5) and (6)

$$y_n = \frac{O_{n+1}}{V_n} x_{n+1} + \frac{Dx_c}{V_n} \qquad (5a)$$

and

$$y_m = \frac{O_{m+1}}{V_m} x_{m+1} - \frac{Wx_w}{V_m}, \qquad (6a)$$

it is obvious that the ratio of reflux to vapor, O_{n+1}/V_n, is the slope of the enrichment line. Hence, when this ratio is known, the line AE is fully determined and readily drawn. Therefore, for the conditions in question the following rule may be formulated. On the x-y diagram plot the equilibrium curve $OEFG$ and the diagonal $ODAG$. Determine point A corresponding to the abscissa $x = x_c$. Draw the line AE with the slope O_{n+1}/V_n. Conditions from plate to plate in the column are determined by going from point A horizontally to the equilibrium curve, then vertically down to the operating enrichment line AE, and so on.

By eliminating y from Eq. (6) and from the equation $y = x$, one finds that the exhausting line must of necessity go through the point D, on the diagonal $ODAG$, corresponding to the abscissa $x = x_w$. Furthermore, its slope is O_{m+1}/V_m, though this slope is normally numerically larger than above the feed plate. In any case, this line DF is determined by the operating conditions and is readily drawn. In the stepwise determination of plate-to-plate conditions below the point of feed, this operating line must be employed instead of the line AE.

In going down the column along the enrichment line, one must face the question as to where it is necessary or desirable to

---

* Equation (5a) may also be obtained *directly* from Eq. (4), which represents equality of input to output of the more volatile component in the section above the feed plate. Equation (6a) is a similar balance on the section below the feed plate.

change to the exhausting line, *i.e.*, on what plate in the column the feed should be introduced.

Feed-plate Location.—A step on the enriching line AE corresponds to a plate above the feed plate and a step on the exhausting line DF corresponds to a plate below the feed. Obviously the step that passes from one operating line to the other must correspond to the feed plate. In Fig. 176 x_5 would be the liquid on the feed plate and y_5 the vapor leaving this plate. The composition of the feed plate is limited to that portion of the diagram where it is possible to step from one operating line to the other. A little consideration will show that this region is the area bounded by the equilibrium curve and the lines EC and CF, and the composition of the liquid leaving the feed plate must be between the liquid compositions corresponding to F and E. Thus, starting at x_c, it is possible to step down the enriching line to the point E before changing to the exhausting line, but to do so would require an infinite number of plates. Commercially it is desirable to use the least number of plates possible to obtain a given separation, and from Fig. 176 it is apparent that, as steps are taken from x_c down the enriching line, the largest steps (corresponding to fewest plates) are obtained if the change from the enriching line to the exhausting line is made such that the feed step passes from a liquid composition higher than that corresponding to the intersection of the operating lines to a liquid composition lower than the intersection composition. In other words, while the feed can be introduced into the column at any point below the point F and above E in Fig. 176, it will shorten the column, and therefore reduce construction expense with no counterbalancing disadvantages whatsoever to introduce it, *i.e.*, to shift from the enriching line to the exhausting line, at the highest possible point below C.

In the ideal column the final step must of necessity fall on point D, corresponding to the composition of the effluent liquid in the still. If, on the diagram as constructed, this does not happen, it means that, from the point of view of material and heat balances, the column cannot operate to meet all the conditions set. Thus, to look at it in one way, the overflow chosen is incompatible with the separation assumed. The choice of a slightly different overflow, however, will change the slopes of the operating lines AC and DC, and a very slight shift in these will make the last step fall at D. It is not usual, however, to make such an adjustment, because, if one sees to it that the last step overlaps the point D, one is on the safe side. In other words, an ideal column with this number of steps would give the separation required with a trifle smaller overflow.

Inspection will show that the steeper the enriching line, *viz.*, the larger the ratio of reflux to vapor, the smaller the number of steps and therefore the less the necessary length of the column. Since reflux is obtained, however, particularly that in the upper part of the column, by generating vapor in the still and condensing it at the top, not to be taken off as distillate, but to be returned down the tower, it is obvious that steepness of the enriching line and resulting saving in column height are obtained by increased heat consumption. Heat can be saved by using less reflux, a flatter enriching line and a longer column.

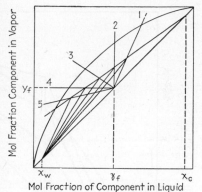

Fig. 177.—Effect of condition of feed upon intersection of enriching and stripping lines.
1. q is greater than 1 (cold feed).
2. q is equal to 1 (increase in overflow equals mols of feed).
3. q is between 0 and 1 (feed is partly vapor).
4. q equals 0 (no change in overflow; increase in vapor equals mols of feed).
5. q is less than 0 (decrease in overflow; feed is superheated vapor).

Intersection of Operating Lines.—The slopes of the operating lines AE and DF are not independent of each other but are related by the composition and condition of the feed. This relation is most easily shown by defining q as the difference in the mols of overflow below and above the feed plate divided by the mols of feed, *i.e.*, $q = (O_f - O_{f+1})/F$; and by material balance $(1-q)$ equals $(V_f - V_{f-1})/F$. The quantity q is most satisfactorily obtained by an enthalpy balance around the feed plate. At the intersection y_n must equal y_m and x_n must equal x_m; call these common coordinates y_i and x_i. By subtracting Eq. 6a from Eq. 5a and remembering that $Dx_c + Wx_w = Fz_f$, where z_f is the average mol fraction of the component in the feed, one obtains

$$y_i = \frac{qx_i}{q-1} - \frac{1}{(q-1)} z_f. \tag{6b}$$

Thus the intersection of the two operating lines must occur on a line of slope $q/(q-1)$ which intersects the $y=x$ line at z_f, as shown in Fig. 177.

Where the enthalpy is essentially the same for the liquid on the feed plate and on the plate above, and for the vapor from the feed plate and the plate below, then q may be approximated by the heat required to vaporize 1 mol of the feed divided by the molal latent heat of vaporization of the feed. Thus in such a case q would be 1 for an all-liquid feed at its boiling point, and

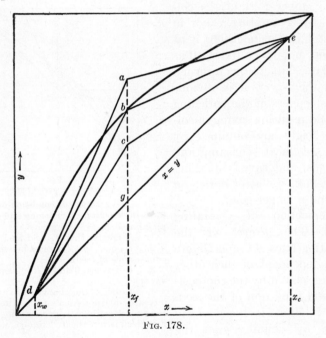

Fig. 178.

would be zero for an all-vapor feed at its dew point. Likewise a cold liquid feed would give values of q greater than 1 and a superheated vapor feed would give a negative value for q.

The operating conditions for various values of q are illustrated in Fig. 177, all based on the same value of O/V in the section above the feed.

Theoretically Minimum Reflux Ratio.—Since, however, operating concentrations cannot exist to the left of the equilibrium curve, inspection of Fig. 178 makes it clear that any such lines as da and ae are inoperable and that the flattest operable enrichment line is represented by *be*. For this case, however, it will be clear that in drawing in the steps corresponding to successive plate conditions, at the point *b* one will encounter an *infinite* number of differentially small steps on both the enriching and the exhausting lines. In other words, this would involve a column of infinite height. The reflux ratio corresponding to this line will be called the **minimum reflux ratio.** The minimum reflux ratio for the tower can be calculated by the equation:

$$\frac{O'_{n+1}}{V_n} = \frac{x_c - y_n}{x_c - x_n}. \qquad (7)$$

Also, since $V_n = O'_{n+1} + P$

$$\frac{O'_{n+1}}{P} = \frac{x_c - y_n}{y_n' - x_n} \qquad (7a)*$$

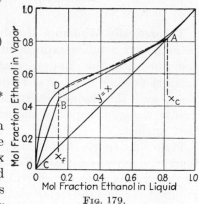

Fig. 179.

For mixtures having equilibrium curves of normal shapes (see page 528), the minimum reflux ratio is obtained where y_n and x_n correspond to the coordinates of the intersection of the *q*-line (see page 563) with the equilibrium curve. For abnormal cases, such as alcohol-water, one could plot the line *be*, and from its slope determine O'_{n+1}/V_n. Better precision, however, is obtained by calculating this value from Eq. 7.

Actual operation will always correspond to a greater reflux ratio and a steeper enriching line, *i.e.*, to some such combinations as *dc* and *ce*.

Illustration 4.—It is desired to estimate the minimum reflux ratio for the continuous rectification of an aqueous solution containing 30 per cent ethanol by weight when producing a 92 weight per cent product and leaving only 0.1 per cent ethanol in the residue, using the type of apparatus shown in Fig. 175.

The mol fractions corresponding to the above weight per cents are 0.141 for the feed, 0.818 for the overhead product and 0.00039 for the residue.

Figure 179 shows the equilibrium diagram for ethanol-water mixtures expressed in mol fraction of alcohol. Inspection of this diagram will show that, if one attempts to draw an enriching line from the point on the 45-deg. line corresponding to the composition of the product, 0.818, to intersect the equilibrium curve at the composition of the feed, 0.141, this line would cross the equilibrium curve in its upper end, slightly above $x = 0.75$, and is, therefore, inoperable. The lowest operable ratio of reflux to vapor corresponds

* The symbols P and D are used interchangeably.

to a line starting at this same upper right-hand point and drawn tangent to the equilibrium curve, *i.e.* line AB on the equilibrium diagram. This line corresponds to the minimum reflux ratio, which may be calculated by Eq. 7 or 7a.

$$\text{Minimum } \frac{O}{V} = \frac{0.818 - 0.448}{0.818 - 0.141} = 0.547$$

or

$$\text{Minimum } \frac{O}{P} = \frac{0.818 - 0.448}{0.448 - 0.141} = 1.21.$$

Theoretically Minimum Number of Plates.—It is interesting to note that a reflux ratio of unity makes the operating lines coincide with the 45-deg. diagonal *dge*. This requires the smallest possible number of steps which will, under any conditions, give the desired separation. Such a column has, however, a negligible capacity and an infinite heat consumption per unit product.

Plate Efficiency.—In practice, equilibrium between vapor and liquid is never reached. The number of theoretical plates necessary for a given enrichment, divided by the number actually required, is called the *overall plate efficiency* of the column. While this will obviously vary with operating conditions and character of construction, for all types of bubble plates the variation is remarkably small. Based on the overflow and vapor leaving a plate, overall plate efficiencies higher than 100 per cent have been found. This is due to the fact that there is a concentration gradient in the liquid across the plate, and the *average* concentration of the more volatile component in the liquid on the plate is higher than in the overflow leaving the plate. In such cases the efficiency of exchange for an individual bubble may be only 70 to 80 per cent, and the resulting high plate efficiency is obtained by the rectification occurring as the liquid flows across the plate. The efficiencies are also defined for the individual plates, and the most commonly used of these is the Murphree efficiency, which is defined as $(y_n - y_{n-1})/(y_n^* - y_{n-1})$, *i.e.*, the actual change in vapor composition divided by the change that would occur on a theoretical plate. Data[4a] on a well-designed laboratory column gave individual plate efficiencies from 60 to 100 per cent for six binary mixtures composed of water and the lower aliphatic alcohols. These efficiencies were obtained at superficial vapor velocities of 1 to 5 ft. per sec. Where operating conditions are unsatisfactory, however, efficiencies drop off sharply. Thus, if the bubble caps are so designed that the vapor bubbles are excessive in size, if the plates are not properly designed so that most of the vapor goes through some of the caps and little or none through others, or if the overflow short-circuits across the plate without properly mixing with the liquid on it, operating efficiencies as low as 20 to 25 per cent may be encountered. In

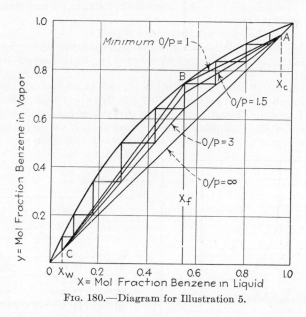

Fig. 180.—Diagram for Illustration 5.

the design and operation of the equipment, it is important to provide against such contingencies. Packed columns are discussed on pages 472 and 505.

Illustration 5.—A 55 mol per cent benzene–45 mol per cent toluene mixture is to be separated by continuous rectification into a distillate containing 95 mol per cent benzene and a residue containing 95 mol per cent toluene. It is desired to estimate the number of plates required for the separation as a function of the reflux ratio. An overall plate efficiency for the column of 70 per cent will be used, and the column will be provided with a total condenser and a still. The feed will enter as liquid at its boiling point and the usual simplifying assumption as to constancy of O/V will be made.

The y-x curve for benzene-toluene is given in Fig. 180. The minimum reflux ratio corresponding to an infinite number of plates would give an intersection of the operating lines at point B. This minimum reflux ratio can be calculated from Eq. 7a, using the coordinates of points A and B,

$$\frac{O}{P} = \frac{0.95 - 0.75}{0.75 - 0.55} = 1.0$$

The minimum number of theoretical plates, corresponding to total reflux, i.e., O/P equal to infinity, is obtained by determining the number of steps between the $y = x$ line and the equilibrium curve necessary to go from point A to C. This is found to be 5.5 theoretical plates, or for an overall plate efficiency of 70 per cent:

Minimum number of actual plates $= 5.5/0.7 = 7.9$.

These two simple calculations give the limits between which the actual column must operate. They are represented by the two asymptotic lines in Fig. 181.

For values of O/P between 1 and ∞ it is possible to construct the operating lines by drawing a line of slope $O/V = 1/[(P/O)+1]$ through point A, and then drawing a line through point C such that it intersects the line through A at $x = x_f = 0.55$. Operating lines for intermediate values of O/P are shown on Fig. 180. The number of theoretical plates for each O/P is obtained by the stepwise method. The results of such calculations are tabulated below.

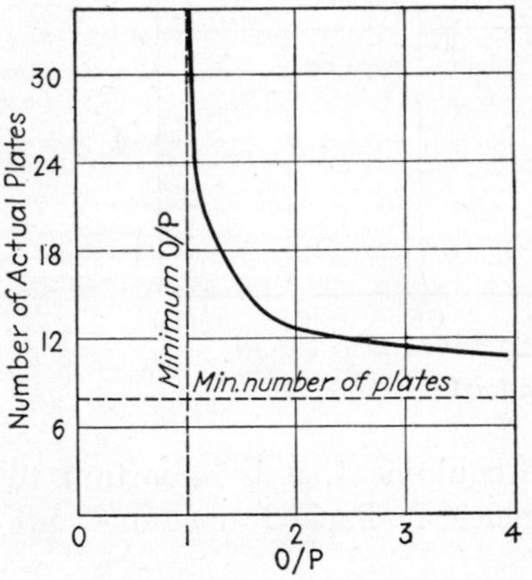

FIG. 181.—Effect of reflux ratio on number of plates required.

O/P	Theoretical Plates	Actual plates
1.0	∞	∞
1.05	19.6	28
1.10	16.2	23.2
1.20	13.8	19.8
1.40	11.9	17.0
1.80	9.3	13.2
3.0	7.9	11.3
∞	5.5	7.9

These values are plotted in Fig. 181 and form a hyperbolic curve that is asymptotic to the minimum O/P and the minimum number of plates. In general, the curve of the number of plates vs. reflux ratio is of this type. By determining the two asymptotes (minimum O/P and $O/P = \infty$) and the number of plates for two or three other reflux ratios, it is possible to sketch the whole curve accurately enough for most design purposes.

The choice of the proper reflux ratio is an economic problem of balancing the operating costs against the fixed charges on the equipment. The cost of the fractionating column itself is infinite both at the minimum reflux ratio and at the minimum number of plates. In the first case it would require an infinite number of plates and in the second case the tower would have to have an infinite cross section in order to produce a finite amount of product. The tower cost therefore passes through a minimum at some intermediate reflux ratio. The costs of both the condenser and the still increase as the reflux ratio is increased. The fixed charges on the equipment as a function of the reflux ratio therefore pass through a minimum. The operating costs, which are largely the cost of the heat required and the cost of cooling the reflux condenser, increase almost proportionally to the reflux ratio. These conditions are sketched in Fig. 182. The total cost, which is the sum of the operating costs and the fixed charges, also passes through a minimum as the reflux ratio is increased above the minimum. The minimum in the total costs moves toward the minimum O/P, the higher the operating costs are relative to the fixed charges.

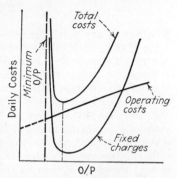

FIG. 182.—Determination of optimum O/P.

Equations for Unequal Molal Overflow.—As explained on page 558, the proof there given that the enriching and exhausting lines are linear depended upon certain simplifying assumptions which it is now desirable to eliminate. It must, however, be kept in mind that Eqs. 5, 5a, 6 and 6a depend only on continuity of operation and are valid irrespective of any of the other assumptions made. The first case to consider is that in which the molal heats of vaporization of the two components of the mixture are different. Calling the molal heats of vaporization of the two components r_1 and r_2, respectively, the total latent heat of the vapor rising from the nth plate is given by the expression

$$Q_n = V_n[y_n r_1 + (1 - y_n)r_2].\tag{8}$$

Neglecting change in temperature of liquid and vapor from plate to plate and heat losses through the walls of the column, this quantity Q_n is constant at every section through the column above the feed plate. Combining this with Eq. 3, page 555, one obtains

$$O_{n+1} = \frac{Q_n}{y_n r_1 + (1 - y_n)r_2} - D.\tag{9}$$

Inspection of this expression shows that in this case the overflow, instead of being constant, is a function of y_n. Insertion of any specific value of y_n in Eq. 9 gives the corresponding value of the overflow. Substitution of this value for O_{n+1}, along with the corresponding value of y_n in Eq. 5, gives the value of x_{n+1}, thereby determining a point on the enrichment curve. By assuming various values of y_n, one can thus determine any desired number of points on the enrichment curve. Plotting these determines the enrichment curve, which is then used in design in exactly the same manner as the enrichment line for constant molal overflow.* Below the feed plate, operating in an entirely analogous manner, one obtains the equation

$$O_{m+1} = \frac{Q_m}{y_m r_1 + (1 - y_m) r_2} + W. \tag{10}$$

Substituting any particular value of y_m in this equation, one obtains the value of O_{m+1} to be substituted in Eq. 6. The corresponding values of y_m and x_{m+1} determine a point on the exhausting or stripping curve.

Where the change in temperature through the column is not negligible, but the pressure drop is small, the temperature at any point is determined by the vapor composition (see the boiling-point curve such as shown in Fig. 166, page 525). If now, as in the preceding paragraph, one assumes a value of y_n, the temperature of the vapor at the point in question is immediately determined, but the value of Q_n is greater than the total latent heat content of the vapors leaving the top of the column by an amount sufficient to heat the overflow from its temperature at the top of the column to its temperature at the section in question. This temperature of the overflow is unfortunately not determined until one knows the value of x_{n+1}. One can get an approximate value of x_{n+1} by neglecting this temperature correction and using the method of the preceding paragraph; then determine the corresponding temperature by the boiling-point curve and repeat the process until the correct value of x_{n+1} is obtained by successive approximation. Thus, one can compute any required number of points on the enrichment curve and similarly below the feed plate.

Where pressure drop through the column and heat losses through the sides are appreciable, it is necessary to correct for these by similar methods. This requires a knowledge of the number of plates above the section in question. It is usually sufficient to estimate these particular corrections by making a preliminary determination of the number of plates by assuming constant molal overflow and then applying these corrections to the temperature of the vapor and the heat quantity Q_n as determined by the boiling-point curve, uncorrected for pressure drop.

It is entirely practicable to compute the concentration changes from plate to plate down the column, one plate at a time, by the use of these equations. Furthermore, where the total number of plates is small, *i.e.*, where the concentration changes per plate are large, this stepwise method is the shortest way of solving the problem except for the case of constant molal overflow. Where the number of plates is large, however, the graphical method is shorter because one needs to determine only a relatively small number of points on the operating lines as contrasted with the large number of computations necessary by the algebraic stepwise method. Furthermore, the graphical method possesses the decided advantage of offering an easy visualization of what is happening in the column, which it is difficult or impossible to obtain by the algebraic method alone.

* It should be noted that the values of y_n and x_n chosen need not correspond quantitatively to conditions at any specific plate; nonetheless they determine coordinates of the enrichment curve.

The above equations are derived on the assumption that the heat supplied to the bottom of the column is indirect. Particularly in those cases where water is the high-boiling component of the mixture, it is common practice to heat by blowing live steam into the still. It is obvious that in such cases the equations representing the material balances must be modified accordingly.

Multicomponent Mixtures

The estimation of the number of theoretical plates required for the separation of a complex mixture is more difficult than for a binary mixture. In a binary mixture, fixing the mol fraction of one component in either the liquid or the vapor and the total pressure definitely fixes the temperature and the composition of the other phase. However, in the case of a multicomponent mixture of n components, $(n-1)$ concentrations as well as the pressure must be fixed before the system is completely defined. Thus, in a multicomponent mixture the $y-x$ relationships of a given component are a function of both the physical characteristics of the other components and their relative amounts. In other words, no unique y vs. x equilibrium curve can be drawn, but instead at a given pressure there is an infinite number of such curves depending on the relative amounts of the other components present. This necessitates a large amount of equilibrium data for each component in the presence of varying proportions of the others, and, except in the special cases in which some generalized rule (such as Raoult's law) applies, these data are not usually available and it is very laborious to obtain them. However, the largest use of multicomponent rectification is in the petroleum industry, and, for a large number of the hydrocarbon mixtures usually encountered in these rectifications, generalized rules have been developed which give multicomponent vapor-liquid equilibria with precision sufficient for design calculations. Where the vapor-liquid equilibria are known, it is possible to start with the composition of the liquid in the still and predict the equilibrium vapor above it. Equation 6 applies to any given component regardless of the number of other components present. Thus, by applying this material balance to each component in the equilibrium vapor, it is possible to calculate the composition of the liquid on the plate above the still. From the vapor-liquid equilibria it is then possible to estimate the equilibrium vapor above the plate, but in general a "trial-and-error" calculation will be involved since the temperature on this plate is not known. The temperature must be such that the liquid on the plate will exert a pressure equal to the prevailing pressure in the column. The calculated equilibrium-vapor composition under such conditions is then utilized for each component together with Eq. 6 to determine the composition of the liquid on the plate above, and these operations may be repeated in order to proceed up the column. At the feed plate it is necessary to make heat and material balances to take account of the condition of the feed; thereafter Eq. 5 must be utilized instead of Eq. 6. The calculations are continued until a composition similar to the overhead product is obtained—a composition which, together with the composition of the residue, the mols of distillate and residue, must give an overall material balance for each component. While such a procedure is more laborious than for the corresponding calculations for a binary mixture, owing to the larger number of components and the "trial-and-error" estimations that are involved, it is fundamentally exactly the same. In the foregoing discussion it was assumed that the composition in the still was known as a starting point for the calculation. Often the determination of the complete composition at some position in the column as a starting point is the most difficult part of the whole calculation. This difficulty arises since, for a given feed composition, reflux ratio and total pressure, it is possible to fix only two additional factors before the system is completely defined.*

In general, the complete composition of neither the residue nor the distillate can be determined by fixing two terminal conditions, in which case it is necessary to estimate the complete composition of either the product or the residue and then proceed with the calculations as before until the desired degree of separation is obtained. If, then, the calculated product and residue compositions satisfy a material balance for each component, the estimated composition was correct. However, if a material balance is not satisfied, it is necessary to estimate a new composition and repeat the calculation. This estimation is often simplified owing to the fact that the degree of separation is so high that the heavier components will appear in the product in

* The discussion assumes constancy of O/V in each section, definite feed location, definite thermal condition of the feed and theoretical plates.

quantities so small as to be negligible, and the same will be true for the lightest components in the residue. For detailed design methods for multicomponent mixtures, the reader is referred to the following references: (4), (5), (7), (10), (11) and (16).

Vapor Velocity.—In designing columns the vapor velocities must be kept within reasonable limits to avoid undue friction and entrainment, *i.e.*, vapor passages must be adequate. There must, of course, be sufficient pressure to overcome the liquid head on the slots and the friction through the vapor passages into the liquid. This latter is largely due to the orifice action of the slots, and the equation for such flow is similar to the weir equation (page 70), *i.e.*, $q = \frac{2}{3}cb\sqrt{2g}x^{3/2}$, giving the average velocity $u_{av.} = \frac{2}{3}\sqrt{2g}cx^{1/2}$, where q is flow in cubic feet per second, b is width of slot, x is pressure drop across orifice in feet of vapor, g is acceleration due to gravity and c is a constant having a value of approximately 0.6. This excess pressure below the plate backs the liquid on the plate below up into the overflow pipe by a corresponding amount. The net distance between plates must be sufficient to provide for this pressure, as otherwise the liquid in the column will back up into the condenser.

There should be at least 6 in. between plates to allow for spattering and splashing, and even with this allowance entrainment of liquid into the plate above may be considerable. If the vapor velocity through the tower becomes too great, this splashing will reach a point where the liquid is carried almost bodily into the plate above and from the top plate into the condenser. This effect is what limits the capacity of a column. The inadequate data available indicate that this effect is determined by the superficial vapor velocity over the whole cross section of the column; the droplets of liquid thrown into the vapor space between the plates tend to be carried to the next plate by the drag due to superficial velocity of the vapor. The entrainment from one plate to another, which partially destroys the countercurrent action of the tower, is frequently the predominant factor in determining the tower capacity. For this reason the settling formula (page 300) has been applied to the allowable superficial velocity, as

$$u_{\text{allowable}} = C\sqrt{\frac{\rho_L - \rho_G}{\rho_G}}$$

where ρ_L and ρ_G are the densities of the liquid and vapor, respectively, and C is a factor that depends on the plate spacing and the physical properties of the system. In well-designed bubble cap columns, operating under atmospheric pressure, the allowable superficial vapor velocities without excessive entrainment are 1 to 5 ft. per sec. Although the allowable linear velocity as given by the above formula increases with decreasing pressures, the allowable mass velocity increases approximately as the square root of the pressure, and the capacity of a column of given diameter may be increased by operating under a pressure above atmospheric. As shown on pages 525 to 527, vapor composition does not change very rapidly with change in pressure. It follows that the operation of a rectifying column under pressure is advantageous because capacity is increased with little sacrifice of separation. This principle has for many years been successfully practiced in the separation of ammonia and water in absorption refrigeration machines.

It should be remembered that, if the amount of reflux for a given product is increased in order that the number of plates in the column may be decreased, as suggested on page 568, two disadvantages are at the same time introduced. First, the heat consumption of the operation is proportionally increased, and, second, the cross section of the column must be enlarged to accommodate the greater volume of vapor which must rise through it.

It is important to provide adequate overflow pipes for the reflux, especially in those cases where the vapor quantity is small compared with the overflow, as in alcohol columns below the feed plate and the like. The capacity of these pipes is limited by the amount of liquid that can enter them, since this flows in under low head. The upper edge of the pipe acts as a weir, and the flow can be calculated by the weir equation (page 71). Since perimeter is the essential thing, rectangular or oval shapes are preferred, the width being approximately three times the height of the liquid above the upper edge.

There is in practice a certain amount of variation in the depth of the liquid seal above the top of the slots in the bubble caps. A depth of several inches has been employed but it seems better to restrict this depth to a fraction of 1 in. to 1 in. When a bubble rises through the liquid, the outside of the bubble soon comes to equilibrium, but the interior is protected by this saturated vapor film on the surface, and further interaction is slow.   The bubble should therefore be broken up and reformed in order to mix the vapors, *i.e.*, the bubble should pass to the next plate.

Allowable velocities of vapor and liquid in packed columns are given on p. 492.

Free Energy of Separation of Liquid Mixtures.—The minimum work required to separate 1 mol of a mixture into its two volatile components under *reversible* isothermal conditions is

$$W = RT\left[x \ln_e \frac{P}{p} + (1-x) \ln_e \frac{P'}{p'} \right]$$

where R is the gas constant, T is the absolute temperature, x is the mol fraction of the first component and $1-x$ that of the second, p is the partial pressure of the first component in the mixture and P is that of the same component in the pure state, while p' and P' apply similarly to the second component.   This relation is not dependent upon Raoult's law but does assume that the vapors obey the gas laws.   For mixtures that follow Raoult's law it simplifies to

$$W = -RT[x \ln_e x + (1-x) \ln_e (1-x)].$$

At any definite temperature this expression is independent of the pressures of the pure components, *i.e.*, the energy theoretically required to separate such a mixture into its components is independent of their boiling points. On the other hand, this reversible work is seen to be proportional to the absolute temperature at which the separation is carried out.   The minimum work of separation at 70°F. of an equimolal mixture which follows Raoult's law is 730 B.t.u.   Since the heat of vaporization of one-half of a mol of the low-boiling component alone is approximately 4000 B.t.u., it follows that distillation as ordinarily carried out is an extremely inefficient process. To secure high energy efficiency the heat employed should be (so far as possible) re-utilized, as is done, for example, in multiple-effect evaporation. Furthermore, since separation by distillation is more difficult as the boiling points approach each other, one concludes that methods other than direct*

---

* Thus methyl alcohol and acetone not only have boiling points that differ by less than 9° but form a constant-boiling mixture.   Their separation may, however, be effected by addition of some material very soluble in one but not in the other.   Such a material will obviously lower the vapor pressure of the first but not the second.   Caustic soda or potassium carbonate may be employed but tends to polymerize the acetone.   Sodium thiosulfate is almost equally effective and does not have this disadvantage.   If this substance is admitted into the top of a rectifying column, the methyl alcohol is effectively washed down the column while the acetone distills over.   The thiosulfate is most conveniently added as a saturated aque-

distillation should, if possible, be employed for separating mixtures, the components of which boil close together, *i.e.*, distillation is not a reversible process.

References

1. BAKER, CHILTON and VERNON, *Trans. Amer. Inst. Chem. Eng.*, **31**, 296 (1935).

2. BROWN, SOUDERS and SMITH, *Ind. Eng. Chem.*, **24**, 514 (1932).

3. CUMMINGS, Sc.D. Thesis in Chemical Engineering, Massachusetts Institute of Technology, 1933.

4. GILLILAND, *Ind. Eng. Chem.*, **27**, 260 (1935).

4a. GADWA, Sc.D. Thesis in Chemical Engineering, Massachusetts Institute of Technology, 1936.

5. GUNNESS, Sc.D. Thesis in Chemical Engineering, Massachusetts Institute of Technology, 1936.

6. LEWIS and CAREY, *Ind. Eng. Chem.*, **24**, 882 (1932).

7. LEWIS and COPE, *Ind. Eng. Chem.*, **24**, 498 (1932).

8. LEWIS and KAY, *Oil Gas. J.*, **32**, no. 45, 40, 114 (1934).

9. LEWIS and LUKE, *Ind. Eng. Chem.*, **25**, 725 (1933).

10. LEWIS and MATHESON, *Ind. Eng. Chem.*, **24**, 494 (1932).

11. LEWIS and WILDE, *Trans. Amer. Inst. Chem. Eng.*, **21**, 99 (1928).

12. RAYLEIGH, *Phil. Mag.*, **8**, 534 (1904).

13. McCABE and THIELE, *Ind. Eng. Chem.*, **17**, 605 (1925).

14. OTHMER, *Ind. Eng. Chem.*, **20**, 743 (1928).

15. SOREL, "La Rectification de l'alcool," Paris (1893).

16. UNDERWOOD, *Trans. Inst. Chem. Eng. (London)*, **10**, 119 (1932).

ous solution and the methyl alcohol is later freed from it by distillation. In problems of distillation modifications of this sort may be employed advantageously.

CHAPTER XVII

HUMIDITY, AND WET- AND DRY-BULB THERMOMETRY

The amount of water vapor present in a gas is spoken of as the "humidity" of that gas. The design of apparatus of industrial importance for processes such as air conditioning, the drying of solids by gases, the drying of gases by liquids, the cooling of liquids by their evaporation into gases (cooling towers, spray ponds, etc.) depends upon a clear conception of this quantity and convenient units in which to express it.

DEFINITIONS

William Grosvenor[1] proposed a system of units which is admirable for the purpose of this work, and with some modifications it will be adopted. The basis of all calculations is one part by weight of dry air. While any unit may be employed, the pound will be used here. The following definitions will be adhered to in this book:

Humidity (H) is the number of pounds of water vapor carried by 1 lb. of dry air.* This is sometimes called **absolute humidity.**

Per cent absolute humidity is the number of pounds of water vapor carried by 1 lb. of dry air at a definite temperature, divided by the number of pounds of vapor that 1 lb. of dry air would carry if it were saturated at the same temperature. In other words, it is the humidity of air at any temperature expressed as per cent of the humidity of saturated air at the same temperature.

Per cent relative humidity is defined as $100p/P_s$, where p is the actual partial pressure of the water vapor and P_s is the vapor pressure of water at the same temperature.†

---

* In the discussion and calculations following, the total pressure is taken as normal barometric, unless otherwise stated.

† Since the per cent *relative* humidity is defined as $100(p/P_s)$ and the per cent *absolute* humidity equals $100[p/(760-p) \div P_s/(760-P_s)]$, the factor by which the former must be multiplied to convert it to the latter is $(760-P_s)/(760-p)$, where p and P_s are expressed in millimeters of mercury.

Dew point,* or saturation temperature, t_s, is the temperature at which a given mixture of air and water vapor is saturated with water vapor. In other words, it is the temperature at which water exerts a vapor pressure equal to the partial pressure of the water in the air.

Humid heat (s) is the number of B.t.u. necessary to raise the temperature of 1 lb. of dry air plus such water vapor as it contains 1°F. Humid heat obviously increases with increasing vapor content of the air, and is therefore a function of humidity. Since over the range of conditions involved the specific heats of dry air and water vapor are substantially constant, being 0.24 and 0.45, respectively, the following equation is used to calculate the humid heat: $s = 0.24 + 0.45H$.

Humid volume is the volume in cubic feet of 1 lb. of dry air together with the water vapor it contains. It is influenced by temperature, pressure and humidity.

Saturated volume is the volume in cubic feet of 1 lb. of dry air when it is saturated with water vapor; that is, it is the humid volume at saturation, and is determined by the temperature and pressure. It should be noted that the humid volume of air equals the product of its saturated volume at its dew point and the ratio of the absolute temperature of the air to the absolute temperature of its dew point.

CONSTRUCTION OF HUMIDITY CHART

In Fig. 183† the following four items are plotted as ordinates against temperature in degrees Fahrenheit as abscissas:

1. Humidity H, as pounds of water per pound of dry air, for air of various relative humidities.

2. Specific volume, as cubic feet of dry air per pound of dry air.

Obviously this factor is never greater than unity. For example, air of 50 per cent relative humidity at 100°F. has a per cent absolute humidity of 48.4.

* Called "dew point" because, on cooling, condensation begins at this temperature.

† This is similar to the Grosvenor[1] chart published by The Institute of Chemical Engineers, except that humid heat is plotted against humidity, instead of temperature, and curves for per cent relative humidity are shown. Figure 183 is based on more recent data for the physical properties of air and water.[2]

3. Saturated volume, as cubic feet of saturated mixture per pound of dry air.

4. Latent heat of vaporization, r, as B.t.u. per pound of water vaporized.

In addition, there are shown:

5. Humid heat s, plotted as abscissas against the humidity H as ordinates, and

6. Adiabatic humidification curves, humidity *vs.* temperature.

The construction of each of these curves will now be taken up in the order named. This chart represents mixtures of dry air and water vapor, the total pressure of the mixture being taken as normal barometric.

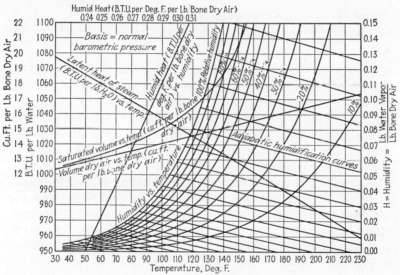

Fig. 183.—Humidity chart, ordinary range. (This chart is reproduced in larger scale on the folding chart facing page 720.)

1. Humidity, H.—Taking the actual pressure of water vapor in the mixture as p mm. of mercury, the pressure of the dry air is obviously equal to $760-p$. Since the molal ratio of water vapor to air is $p/(760-p)$, the mass ratio is

$$H = \frac{p(18.02)}{(760-p)(28.97)} \tag{1}$$

expressed as pounds of water vapor per pound of dry air.

The curve in Fig. 183 marked "100 per cent" is calculated by substituting in the preceding equation the saturation pressures of water vapor at various temperatures, data being taken from the latest steam tables.[2]   For example, the saturation pressure of water vapor at 100°F. is 49.1 mm. of mercury, and hence H at saturation at 100°F. is 49.1(18.02)/(710.9)(28.97) or 0.0428. If a mixture of air and water vapor at 100°F. has a relative humidity of 40 per cent, the partial pressure of water vapor is 0.4(49.1) or 19.64 mm. of mercury, and the absolute humidity is 19.64(18.02)/(740.4) (28.97) or 0.0165.

2. Specific Volume (Dry Air).—This quantity is calculated from the gas laws (see pages 5 to 7).   These state that 1 lb. mol of air (28.97 lb.) occupies 359 cu. ft. at standard conditions, namely, 492°F. abs. (32°F.) and normal barometer.   Hence

$$\text{Specific volume} = \frac{(359)(t+460)}{(28.97)(492)} = 11.57 + 0.0252t \qquad (2)$$

where t is in degrees Fahrenheit.   It is clear that the specific volume increases linearly with t, as shown in Fig. 183.   Thus at 100°F. the specific volume equals 14.09 cu. ft. per lb. of dry air.

3. Saturated Volume and Humid Volume.—As defined, the saturated volume is on a basis of 1 lb. of dry air, and equals the sum of the specific volume of the dry air plus the volume of the water vapor associated with the particular saturated mixture. The weight of the water vapor in saturated air at 100°F. is seen from the 100 per cent humidity line to be 0.0428 lb., and the corresponding volume equals (0.0428)(359)(460+100)/(18.02) (460+32), or 0.97 cu. ft.   The saturated volume at 100°F. is then $14.09 + 0.97 = 15.06$.   A curve of such values is shown in Fig. 183.

Since **humid volume** is defined as the volume of any mixture, expressed as cubic feet of mixture per pound of dry air, and since both the specific and saturated values are on the basis of 1 lb. of dry air, the humid volume for any humidity may be obtained directly by interpolation between the curves for specific and saturated volumes.   For example, air having a humidity of 0.0165 at 100°F. has a humid volume of 14.09 plus (15.06−14.09) (0.0165/0.0428), or 14.46.   An interpolation of the chart will check this figure.

4. Latent Heat of Vaporization.—This value, expressed as B.t.u. per pound of water evaporated, is taken from the steam tables[2] and is found to decrease as temperature rises as shown in Fig. 103.

5. Humid Heat *s.*—From the definition of humid heat,

$$s = 0.24 + 0.45H \tag{3}$$

and it is seen that it should be plotted *vs.* the actual humidity of the air; it is so shown in Fig. 183. For example, the value of *s* for air, having an absolute humidity of 0.0222, is 0.24 plus (0.45)(0.0222) or 0.250. In Fig. 183 the scale for *s* is shown at the top of the plot, and it should be noted that *s* is the only variable not plotted against temperature.

6. Adiabatic Humidification Curves.—A process is said to be "adiabatic" when there is no heat interchange with the surroundings. Since in many processes of drying and humidification substantially these conditions are found, equations for adiabatic evaporation are of value.

Consider the case of steady flow of a gas through an ideally insulated enclosure in which the gas is brought into contact with water, enough feed water being added at the temperature T' to replace that evaporated. As an overall result, the air is cooled from the original temperature t_1 to t_2 and the humidity increases from H_1 to H_2. The overall heat balance, per pound of air, is

$$(H_2 - H_1)(t_2 - T' + r_2) = s_1(t_1 - t_2). \tag{4*}$$

Now suppose that the surface of contact is infinite so that the air is cooled to saturation at the definite saturation temperature t_s. The heat balance for the adiabatic saturator is

$$(H_s - H_1)(t_s - T' + r_s) = s_1(t_1 - t_s). \tag{5}$$

If the temperature of the make-up water is fixed, since H_s and r_s are fixed by t_s, and s_1 depends only on H_1, it is seen that H_1 is a unique function of t_1. Since s_1 decreases with decrease in H_1, it is clear that a plot of H_1 as ordinates vs. t_1 as abscissas would give a curve concave upward. Such adiabatic saturation curves,† based on T' equal to t_s, are shown on the humidity

---

* The exact relation is $(H_2 - H_1)(i_{v2} - i_{LT'}) = s_1(t_1 - t_2)$, where i_{v2} is the enthalpy of the *vapor* at H_2 and t_2 and $i_{LT'}$ is the enthalpy of the *liquid* at T'. However, unless the final mixture is considerably superheated, Eq. 4 is sufficiently accurate.

† Sometimes called *curves of constant enthalpy.*

chart and are based on the relation

$$\frac{(H_s - H)}{(t_s - t)} = -\frac{s_1}{r_s},$$ (5a)

The curves end at H_s and t_s, and run downward to the right with a decreasing slope. For convenience, a number of curves are shown for a number of saturation temperatures arbitrarily chosen at 5° intervals.

With finite contact area, the air leaves the apparatus unsaturated, but, when one writes the appropriate heat balances, one finds that these adiabatic saturation curves may also be used as "path curves," even when the final air is not saturated. The values read from these curves give the correct final temperatures and humidities of the air, provided the make-up water enters, as assumed, at the adiabatic saturation temperature. If the make-up water enters at a somewhat higher or lower temperature, owing to the fact that in Eq. 4 the term $t_2 - T'$ is ordinarily small relative to the latent heat, the results shown on the curves are usually satisfactory approximations. For precise calculations, Eq. 4 should be used.

DETERMINATION OF HUMIDITY

Although the water content of air may be determined accurately by chemical methods, or by measurement of its dew point, in much engineering work the humidity is calculated from observations of the "wet" and "dry" bulb temperatures of the air. The mechanism of the process will be considered in detail, not only because of its intrinsic importance, but also on account of the light thrown on all the phenomena of evaporation of a liquid into a gas.

Mechanism of Evaporation of a Liquid into a Gas.—If in unsaturated air there is placed a drop of water at a temperature slightly above the dew point of the air, vaporization will occur. Inasmuch as the water vapor is carried away from the drop by diffusion, the rate of evaporation will be proportional to the area of the drop and to the difference between the vapor pressure of the drop and the partial pressure of water vapor in the surrounding air. Calling the surface area of the drop A, its temperature T, the corresponding vapor pressure P, the partial pressure of the aqueous vapor in the surrounding air p, the air being at t, the *instantaneous* rate of evaporation W is given by the equation $W = kA(P-p)$, where k is the diffusion coefficient through the gas film on the drop.

If the water is colder than the air heat will flow from the air to the drop in accordance with Newton's law: $q = hA(t-T)$, where h is the coefficient of heat transfer through the gas film on the surface of the drop and q is the *instantaneous* rate of heat transfer. This will raise the temperature of the drop, increasing the rate of evaporation but decreasing the rate of heat flow. This process will continue until ultimately a condition of dynamic equilibrium is reached in which the heat transferred from the surroundings will exactly supply the heat of vaporization r_w of the water evaporating at the temperature t_w. The corresponding heat balance is

$$q = r_w W = kAr_w(P_w - p) = hA(t - t_w). \qquad (6)$$

This dynamic equilibrium temperature t_w is called the **wet-bulb temperature.**

Although the above equation for evaporation of water into unsaturated air is based on the assumption that the water was initially colder than the air, the same condition of dynamic equilibrium described above will be obtained regardless of the initial water temperature. Thus, if the initial water temperature is higher than that of the air, the water will be cooled, not only by evaporation, but also by heat transfer from the drop to the air. If the air had been saturated, no evaporation would occur and the wet-bulb, dry-bulb and saturation temperatures would be the same.

Wet- and Dry-bulb Thermometers (Hygrometers).—If a drop of liquid is left in a gas, it rapidly assumes the equilibrium temperature represented by this equation, and use is made of this fact to determine the water content of the air. The temperature of the air, t, is measured with an ordinary mercurial thermometer, while the surface of the bulb of a second thermometer is kept wet by being enclosed in a cloth or wick thoroughly moistened with water. The unknown partial pressure of water vapor in the air is

$$p = P_w - \frac{h}{kr_w}(t - t_w). \qquad (6a)$$

Since t and t_w may be observed, and since the vapor pressure P_w can be read from the steam tables to correspond to the temperature of the wet bulb, t_w, a knowledge of the term h/kr_w, called J, enables one to determine the amount of water in the air for any condition of temperature and humidity. Allowing for these variations* in J, the above equation is the basis of all humidity tables and charts. It is found to be a function of both the total pressure and the temperature, but the change is sufficiently small to be negligible for many engineering calculations. Thus, if temperatures are given in degrees centigrade and pressures of water vapor in millimeters of mercury, J is practically 0.5 for water in air at normal barometric pressure. The difference of the "dry-bulb" and "wet-bulb" temperatures is sometimes called the wet-bulb "depression" or "psychrometric difference."

Effect of Radiation.—The heat transferred to the wet bulb by radiation from the surroundings is constant for definite temperature conditions, entirely independent of air velocity; by increasing the air velocity, the heat received by conduction and convection can be increased to such a degree as to render the radiation a quantity negligible in comparison. The coefficient of heat transfer h in Eq. 6 equals the sum of the coefficients h_c for conduction and convection and h_r for radiation. Designating the dimensionless ratio h/h_c or $(h_c+h_r)/h_c$ by the symbol α, Eq. 6 becomes

$$(P_w-p)=\frac{\alpha h_c(t-t_w)}{kr_w}=J(t-t_w). \qquad (6b)$$

The effect of air velocity upon the radiation correction factor α is shown in Fig. 184.†

Since the surroundings are usually at the dry-bulb temperature, radiation raises the temperature of the wet bulb. As motion of air over the wet bulb is increased, α decreases, as shown in Fig. 184, and J also decreases, asymptotically approaching a constant value. As would be expected, the value of J obtained upon calibrating hygrometers of the stationary type is always

---

* The quantities affecting J will be discussed later.

† The values of h_c are based on the data for flow at right angles to a single cylinder, shown in curve GH of Fig. 40, page 112, taking D as 0.0229 ft. (7 mm). The value of h_r is based on the radiation equation $h_r=4\sigma p_r T^3_{av.}$, where $T_{av.}$ is the arithmetic mean of the *absolute* temperatures of the surroundings and the wet bulb, the emissivity p_r being taken as 0.95.

higher than when high gas velocities are used. Since it is difficult to keep the air perfectly still, and since when the motion is slight a small change in the velocity produces a large variation in J, the velocity of air should be such as to produce a substantially constant value of J.

The humidity of air at a given point in a drier, or other apparatus in which the air velocity is high, may be obtained from the readings of stationary wet- and dry-bulb thermometers. The make-up water, necessary to compensate for that evaporated, should be at the wet-bulb temperature. For measuring the

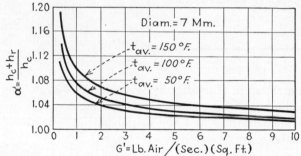

Fig. 184.—Effect of air velocity upon radiation correction factor.

humidity of stagnant air, the desired high velocity (15 to 25 ft. per sec.) is obtained with the sling psychrometer, which consists of thermometers mounted on a stick with a handle attached so that they may be swung by hand. In some cases, instead of swinging the thermometers, air is drawn past stationary thermometers by a fan (to avoid heating effect on the air passing through the fan).

Technique of Psychrometry.—The technique of the use of a sling psychrometer is important. Before the psychrometer is swung, the temperature of the wetted bulb should be adjusted to a point just above the true wet-bulb temperature of the air being tested. If the initial temperature of the water on the bulb is too high, it will take a long time to cool the bulb to the wet-bulb point and before this point is reached the water will have evaporated to such an extent that the thermometer never reaches the true wet-bulb temperature (see curve 1, Fig. 185). If the initial temperature of the wet bulb is but slightly above that corresponding to the true wet-bulb reading, the thermometer will

cool quickly to the wet-bulb temperature long before the water
has evaporated to any serious extent and a long flat minimum
in the temperature curve will be observed (see curve 2a, Fig. 185).
If, however, the initial temperature is considerably below that
of the true wet-bulb reading, the thermometer will rise in tem-

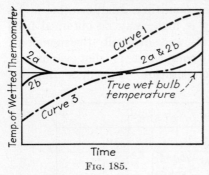

perature throughout the
period of slinging. It is true
that there will be a flat portion
in the temperature curve as
shown by curve 3 (Fig. 185),
but the estimation of this
point of inflection is inaccurate. For accurate work the
instrument should be calibrated under standardized
conditions.

FIG. 185.

**Determination of Humidity by Wet- and Dry-bulb Thermom-
eter Readings.**—A quantitative relation between the wet- and
dry-bulb temperatures and the actual partial pressure of water
in air has been previously derived (Eq. 6b).

In order to be able to plot this relation on the humidity chart,
the term $P_w - p$ will be converted into a term involving $H_w - H$.
In Chap. XIV, page 449, it is shown that the mass-transfer coefficient k is a function of the partial pressure of the noncondensing
gas, i.e., k equals k_1/p_{nf} where p_{nf} is the mean partial pressure of
the inert gas in the effective gas film. For the usual case there is
little fractional variation in the partial pressure p_n of the inert
gas through the film, and hence little error is introduced by
replacing the term $(P_w - p)/p_{nf}$ by the term $(H_w - H)(M_n/M_v)$,
where M_n and M_v are the molecular weights of the gas and vapor,
respectively. Making these substitutions in Eq. 6b gives

$$\frac{(H_w - H)}{(t - t_w)} = \frac{\alpha h_c}{r_w k'} \tag{6c}$$

where k' represents the term $k_1 M_n/M_v$.

Upon applying Eq. 6c to the recent data of Dropkin,[3]*
the values of the radiation correction being obtained from Fig.

* The experiments covered values of H ranging from 0.0043 to 0.0169,
dH_s/dt from 0.000276 to 0.00095 and h_c/k_{HS} from 0.933 to 0.975, but the
last term was independent of the air velocity.

184, the mean value of $h_c/k's$ was found to be 0.945 for mass velocities G' ranging from 0.94 to 2.5 lb. of air per sec. per sq. ft. of cross section, corresponding to linear velocities of 12.5 to 33.3 ft. per sec. reduced to 70°F. and normal barometer. At an air velocity of 16.7 ft. per sec. (G' of 1.25), Fig. 184 shows that α is 1.058 and the psychrometer equation (6c) becomes

$$\frac{(H_w - H)}{(t - t_w)} = \frac{s}{r_w},$$

which is identical in form with that of the adiabatic saturation curve (Eq. 5a). Hence, if the air velocity over the wet-bulb is 1.25 lb. per sec. per sq. ft., the humidity of the air can be read from the adiabatic saturation curves on the humidity chart, by locating the wet-bulb temperature on the saturation curve, drawing a line parallel to the nearest adiabatic curve and reading the ordinate corresponding to the dry-bulb temperature. In other words, at this *standard* air velocity the adiabatic saturation temperature and wet-bulb temperature are identical. At higher velocities, where the radiation correction factor is slightly less, the wet-bulb temperature is slightly less than the adiabatic saturation temperature, and at lower velocities the reverse is true.

This procedure is based on the best available data, which are unfortunately small in amount. The available data were obtained at low humidities where the specific and humid heats were practically the same. The humid heat, rather than the specific heat, was brought into the correlation merely for convenience, since it was desired to utilize the adiabatic cooling curves (which properly involve humid heat) in evaluating the humidity from the wet- and dry-bulb temperatures. For accurate work the humidity should be determined by chemical methods.

Although for mixtures of air and water ordinarily encountered, owing to the fortuitous circumstance that $h_c/k's$ is approximately one, there is little difference between the wet-bulb temperature and the adiabatic saturation temperature; for other mixtures, such as air and toluene vapor, where $h_c/k's$ is approximately 1.8 (see page 593), the wet-bulb temperature is much *higher* than the adiabatic saturation temperature, even when the radiation correction has been made. In other words, as shown in Fig.

186, the slope of the chord connecting the points H_{w_1}, t_{w_1} and H_1, t_1 is much greater than the slope of the chord connecting the points H_s, t_s and H_1, t_1. If dry air is partially saturated by

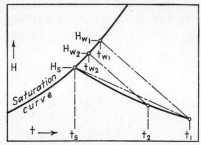

Fig. 186.—Humidity chart for air and toluene vapor.

exposure to toluene in an adiabatic chamber fed with make-up liquid toluene at t_s, the resulting mixture will have the toluene humidity H_2 and temperature t_2, as read from the adiabatic evaporation curve based on Eq. 5a. The corresponding toluene

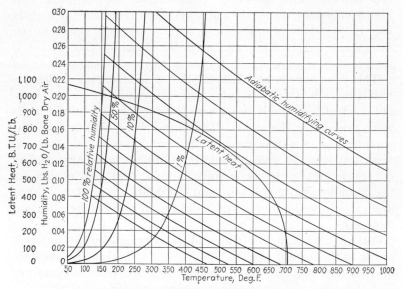

Fig. 187.—High range humidity chart.

wet-bulb temperature t_{w_2} is seen to be lower than t_{w_1}, and hence the wet-bulb temperature falls during the process, finally reaching t_s where the air is saturated with toluene. For mixtures of air and water vapor, owing to the fact that the wet-bulb lines and adiabatic curves are nearly identical, there is almost no change in t_w as the air approaches saturation.

Any change consisting only in a decrease of the temperature of the air must be represented by a horizontal line on Fig. 183 until the saturation point is reached.   Furthermore, the inclined curves represent adiabatic evaporation, and also make possible the immediate estimation of the condition of the air from its wet- and dry-bulb readings.   Also the absolute amount of moisture picked up or given up by a unit weight of air is determined immediately by the difference between the ordinates corresponding to its initial and final states.

Figure 187 is a humidity chart similar to the one previously described, except that here the ranges of humidity and temperature are far greater; it is useful in the solution of certain types of problem in drying (pages 662 to 666).

ILLUSTRATIONS SHOWING THE USE OF THE HUMIDITY CHART

Illustration 1.—Assume a drier in which 200 lb. of water is evaporated hourly from the material being dried; the available air has a humidity of 0.0100 and a temperature of 75°F., and is heated to 155°F. before entering the drier.   The air leaving the drier has a wet-bulb temperature of 100°F. and a dry-bulb temperature of 130°F.   No other assumptions are made as to the material being dried, nor as to the construction and operation of the drier.   Calculate the air consumption.

Solution.—The air enters this drier as stated with a humidity of 0.0100. Its humidity on leaving the drier is obtained by following the cooling line starting at 100°F., the wet-bulb temperature, down to the right to 130°F., indicating a final humidity of 0.0356.   The rise in humidity of the air going through the drier is therefore the difference, or 0.0256.   Hence this figure is lb. of water picked up/lb. of dry air.   Since the water evaporated per hr. is 200 lb., the air consumption per hr. is 200 divided by 0.0256 or 7810 lb. of bone-dry air.

Illustration 2.—Referring to the data in the preceding illustration, what was the volume of air before and after preheating?

Solution.—The air entering the preheater had a humidity of 0.0100 and a temperature of 75°F.   Reference to Fig. 183 indicates that its per cent humidity entering the preheater was 55; interpolation between the curves for saturated volume and specific volume at 75°F. indicates that the humid volume (of the mixture of water vapor and dry air) was 13.70 cu. ft./lb. of dry air at the entrance to the preheater.

The air leaving the preheater at a humidity of 0.0100 and a temperature of 155°F. had a per cent humidity of about 4; a similar interpolation at 155°F. indicates that the humid volume of the air leaving the preheater was

15.70 cu. ft./lb. of dry air. *Other things being equal*, the fan for forcing the air through the apparatus should be designed on the basis of the humid volume of the air *entering* the preheater, inasmuch as the fan should be placed where the air has the maximum density, because, with a given volumetric capacity to the fan, the weight capacity is at a maximum when the air handled is coldest. Note that these calculations require no knowledge of the theory of the drying process itself, or of the mechanism of the drier under consideration.

Illustration 3.—The water in the stock being dried in this apparatus entered the drier at 70°F. and the water vapor removed left the drier at 130°F. Calculate the B.t.u./hr. (*a*) supplied to the drier other than in the air entering at 155°F. and (*b*) that supplied by the preheater, neglecting* heat losses to the surroundings and that necessary to warm up the stock and the conveying mechanism.

Solution.—Per pound of water evaporated the heat consumption is that necessary to warm the water from 70 to 130°F., or 60 B.t.u., plus that necessary to evaporate it at 130°F., or, as read from the chart, 1020 B.t.u., a total of 1080 B.t.u. The heat utilized for evaporation, expressed per lb. of dry air, is therefore, 1080×0.0256 or 27.7 B.t.u. The heat given up per lb. of dry air during its passage through the apparatus is equal to the drop in temperature (155–130°) times its humid heat 0.244, or 6.1 B.t.u. This quantity is less than the heat consumption, thus demonstrating that this drier is furnished with some sort of heat supply other than that of the drying air itself, and the difference between these two quantities, 21.6 B.t.u., is the heat furnished by the heating surface within the drier, expressed per lb. of dry air. Since 7810 lb. of dry air was consumed, the B.t.u./hr. furnished by the heating surface within the drier was 169,000.

Since the entering air was preheated from 75 to 155°F., a rise in temperature of 80°, the humid heat of this air being 0.245, the heat furnished by the preheater was the product of these two quantities, 19.6 B.t.u., expressed per lb. of dry air; or the total was this times the amount of dry air per hr. = 153,000 B.t.u.

Other Illustrations.—Additional illustrations of the use of the chart will be found in the chapters on Air Conditioning and Drying.

DISCUSSION OF PSYCHROMETER EQUATIONS

Based on a heat balance in terms of the equations for the rates of heat transfer and mass transfer, it was shown on page 586 that the psychrometer equation could be written

$$k'(H_w - H)r_w = \alpha h_c(t - t_w). \tag{6c}$$

The derivation implicitly assumes that the cooling of the air is differential, so small that the actual changes in temperature and humidity of the air are

* These quantities sometimes are considerable.

negligible. The values of $(H_w-H)/(t-t_w)$ or $\alpha h_c/k'r_w$ are best determined by calibration under carefully standardized conditions. Since these ratios are found to be characteristic of the gas and liquid employed, it is desirable to inquire further into the factors influencing the rate coefficients h_c and k' for any liquid and gas.

As shown in Chap. II, the gas in the imme- diate neighborhood of the surface is flowing in streamline motion, whereas beyond this film, of thickness B_f, the gas is mixed by the eddies in the turbulent stream (Fig. 188).* Exclusive of the effect of radiation, which is allowed for separately, the overall thermal resistance $1/h_c$ by conduction and convection is the sum of the conduction resistance B_f/λ of the film and the convection or eddy resistance r_c.

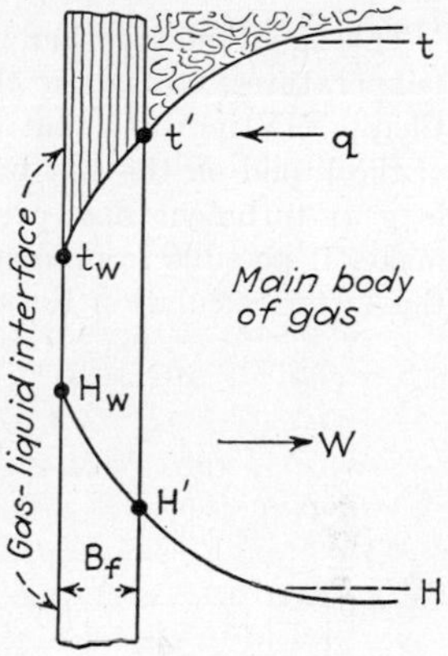

A similar application of the resistance con- cept to the mass transfer of vapor from the wet bulb to the gas stream (page 448) gives $1/k' = (B_f/\ D_mM_n)+(r_c')$ where r_c' is the resist- ance to mass transfer through the turbulent portion of the gas stream, D_m is the molal diffu-

Fig. 188.

sivity of the vapor through the true gas film and M_n is the molecular weight of the vapor-free gas.

Although the thermal conductivity λ and vapor diffusivity D_m appear in the film-resistance terms, B_f/λ and B_f/D_mM_n, there is no reason to sup- pose that these properties affect the convection resistances r_c and r_c'. By definition r_c and r_c' equal $A(t-t')/q$ and $A(H'-H)/W$, respectively. Con- sider the transfer of given mass of gas ω by the turbulent eddies from the region, where the conditions t' and H' exist, to the main body of the gas, identified by t and H; for such a convection transfer q is equal to $\omega s'(t-t')$ and W equals $\omega(H'-H)$ and the substitution of these quantities in the definitions of r_c and r_c' gives

$$\frac{r_c'}{r_c}=\frac{A(H'-H)/W}{A(t-t')/q}=\frac{A(H'-H)/\omega(H'-H)}{A(t-t')/\omega s'(t-t')}=s' \qquad (7)\dagger$$

where s' is the humid heat at the outer boundary of the gas film and the term r_c'/r_cs' should be independent of velocity and other factors affecting turbulence. As shown in earlier chapters, the film thickness B_f would be reduced upon increasing the velocity. Upon writing the ratio of h_c to k', eliminating r_c by Eq. 7 and rearranging, one obtains

* For exact shape of curves, see Fig. 137, p. 445.

$\dagger$ Since r_c equals $1/h_e$ and r_c' equals $1/k_e'$, this relation may also be written

$$\frac{h_e}{k_e'}=s',$$

i.e., the ratio of the heat-transfer and mass-transfer coefficients, h_e and k_3', for the eddy-diffusion zone equals[4] the humid heat s'.

$$\frac{r_c'}{B_f} = \frac{\dfrac{1}{D_m M_n} - \dfrac{h_c}{k'\lambda}}{\dfrac{h_c}{k's'} - 1}. \tag{8}$$

This equation, together with experimentally determined wet- and dry-bulb temperatures, will allow the calculation of r_c'/B_f. The considerations of Chap. XIV indicate that this ratio should be independent of the nature of the liquid on the wet bulb and only slightly affected by gas velocity as long as turbulent flow exists. One experimental determination therefore makes it possible to predict the wet-bulb conditions for other liquids. For this latter calculation Eq. 8 can be arranged

$$\frac{h_c}{k's'} = \frac{\dfrac{1}{D_m M_n} + \dfrac{r_c'}{B_f}}{\dfrac{s'}{\lambda} + \dfrac{r_c'}{B_f}} = \frac{\dfrac{B_f}{r_c' D_m M_n} + 1}{\dfrac{B_f s'}{r_c' \lambda} + 1}. \tag{8a}*$$

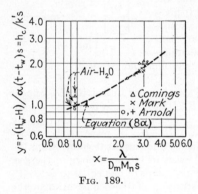

$$x = \frac{\lambda}{D_m M_n s}$$

Fig. 189.

Calculated values of $h_c/k's$ are given in column 5 of Table I together with the experimental values; in these calculations the value of r_c'/B_f for toluene was taken for the calculation of $h_c/k's$.

Figure 189 is a plot of the experimentally determined value of the psychrometric ratio $h_c/k's$ vs. the dimensionless ratio $x = \lambda/D_m M_n s$. The dotted curve is based on the theoretical relation (Eq. 8a), using the empirically determined value of r_c'/B_f based on the toluene run. It is seen that the predicted curve agrees satisfactorily with the experimental values.

Another method of attack would be to substitute predicted or experimental values for the heat-transfer and mass-transfer coefficients, h_c and k', in Eq. 6c.[5],[7],[9],[10]

Nomenclature

A = area of surface, sq. ft.
B_f = thickness of true film of gas, ft.
D = diameter of wet bulb, ft.
D_m = diffusivity in molal units, lb.-mols/(hr.)(ft.).
G' = mass velocity, lb./(sec.)(sq. ft.).
H = absolute humidity, lb. of vapor/lb. of noncondensable gas.

---

* It is interesting to note that, if, as is approximately true for air and water, the physical properties happen to be such that the dimensionless term $\lambda/D_m M_n s$ closely approaches 1, $h_c/k's'$ will be substantially 1.

TABLE I.—EXPERIMENTAL VALUES OF PSYCHROMETRIC RATIO $h_c/k's' = r_w(H_w-H)/\alpha s(t-t_w)$ FOR VARIOUS LIQUIDS AND AIR

Reference: Liquid on wet bulb	(5)	(6)	(7)	(8)*	Calculations from Eq. 8a
Water ($x=0.962$)................	1.16	1.03	0.95	....	0.985
Methanol ($x=1.51$)...............	....	....	1.22	....	1.22
Propanol ($x=2.26$)...............	....	....	1.54	....	1.55
Ethyl bromide ($x=2.40$)..........	....	....	....	2.21	1.60
Benzene ($x=2.52$)................	1.61	1.65	....	2.04	1.68
Ethyl acetate ($x=2.66$)...........	....	1.69	....	....	1.72
Brombenzene ($x=2.74$)...........	....	....	....	1.92	1.75
Toluene ($x=2.78$)................	2.00	1.79	1.77	1.92	
Chlorbenzene ($x=2.88$)...........	....	1.76	1.83	2.12	1.81
Carbon tetrachloride ($x=2.92$).....	2.00	1.76	....	2.08	1.83
n-Propyl acetate ($x=2.97$).........	2.07	....	....	....	1.85
Ethyl propionate ($x=2.97$)........	....	....	1.77	....	1.85
Xylene ($x=3.06$).................	....	....	1.91	....	1.90
Ethylene tetrachloride ($x=3.12$)...	....	2.00	....	....	1.92

* These values are not corrected for radiation, and are not plotted in Fig. 189.

TABLE II.—EXPERIMENTAL VALUES OF $r_w(H_w-H)/s(t-t_w)$ FOR WATER IN VARIOUS DRY GASES (APJOHN)[11]

Gas	s	$r(H_w-H)/(t-t_w)$	$r(H_w-H)/s(t-t_w)$
CO_2, with 10.8% air......	0.205	0.195	0.95
H_2O, with 16% air.......	0.206	0.203	0.99
H_2, with 4.3% air........	2.12	3.24	1.53

H_s, $H_w = H$ at saturation and wet-bulb temperatures, respectively; H_s corresponds to t_s, H_w to t_w.

h_c, h_r = coefficients of heat transfer by conduction and convection and by radiation, respectively, B.t.u./(hr.)(sq. ft.)(deg. F.); $h = h_c + h_r$; $h_e = q/(A)(t-t')$.

J = a ratio, equal to $(P_w-p)/(t-t_w) = \alpha h_c/kr_w$.

k, k_1, k', k'_e = coefficients of mass transfer of vapor, defined by the equations: $dW/dA = k(P_w-p) = k_1(P_w-p)/p_{nf} = k'(H_w-H) = k'_e(H'-H)$.

M_n, M_v = molecular weights of noncondensable gas and pure vapor, respectively.

P_s, P_w = vapor pressures of liquid, at saturation and wet-bulb temperatures, respectively.

p, p_n =partial pressure of vapor and noncondensable gas, respectively.

p_{nf} =logarithmic-mean partial pressure of noncondensable gas.

p_r =emissivity for radiant heat, dimensionless.

q =rate of transfer of sensible heat, B.t.u./hr.

r, r_s, r_w =latent heat of vaporization, B.t.u./lb., at t, t_s and t_w, respectively.

r_c, r_c' =thermal and mass-transfer resistances in turbulent portion of gas phase lying outside the true film, respectively, defined by the equations: $q = (t-t')/r_c$ and $W = (H' - H)/r_c'$.

s =humid heat, heat capacity of mixture, expressed in B.t.u./ (deg. F.) (lb. of dry air).

T, T' =temperature of water and of feed water, respectively, deg. F.

t, t_s, t_w =temperatures of dry bulb, at saturation temperature and of wet bulb, respectively, deg. F.

W =rate of evaporation, lb./hr.

x =dimensionless ratio, $\lambda/D_m M_n s$.

α(alpha) =radiation correction factor, equal to $(h_c + h_r)/h_c$, dimensionless.

θ(theta) =time, hr.

λ(lambda) =thermal conductivity of mixture of gas and vapor, B.t.u./ (hr.)(sq. ft.)(deg. F./ft.).

μ(mu) =viscosity of mixture of gas and vapor, lb./(hr.)(ft.).

σ(sigma) =Stefan-Boltzmann constant.

ω(omega) =mass of gas-vapor mixture transferred by convection.

Subscripts 1 and 2 refer to specific conditions.

References

1. GROSVENOR, W. M., *Trans. Amer. Inst. Chem. Eng.*, **1**, 184 (1909).

2. KEENAN, J. H., and F. G. KEYES, "Thermodynamic Properties of Steam," John Wiley & Sons, Inc., New York, 1936.

3. DROPKIN, D., *Eng. Expt. Sta. Bull.* 23, July, 1936, Cornell University, Ithaca.

4. MERKEL, Z. *Ver. deut. Ing.*, **67**, 81, 106 (1923).

5. SHERWOOD, T. K., and E. W. COMINGS, *Trans. Amer. Inst. Chem. Eng.*, **28**, 88–105 (1932).

6. MARK, J. G., *Trans. Amer. Inst. Chem. Eng.*, **28**, 107–115 (1932).

7. ARNOLD, J. H., *Physics*, **4**, 255–262 (July, 1933); **4**, 334–340 (September, 1933).

8. HILPERT, Z. *Ver. deut. Ing.*, Forschungsheft 355, 1–22 (1932).

9. CHILTON, T. H., and A. P. COLBURN, Personal Communication, 1934.

10. CARRIER, W. H., and C. O. MACKEY, *Trans. Amer. Soc. Mech. Eng.*, **59**, 33 (January, 1937).

11. APJOHN, J., *Trans. Roy. Irish Acad.*, **18**, pt. 1, 1 (1838).

CHAPTER XVIII

AIR CONDITIONING

The equilibrium relationship in a system comprised of water, water vapor and air, and the temperatures reigning in such a system, form the basis of certain types of apparatus much employed in industrial work. The more important are included under the descriptive terms *humidifiers, dehumidifiers* and *water coolers*.

GENERAL CONSIDERATIONS

When it is desired to increase the humidity of air or other gas, live steam may be blown into it. However, this increases the temperature and introduces any impurities present in the steam. Where considerable heat is being developed in a room owing to the operation of machinery, the humidity may be increased and the temperature decreased by spraying in finely divided water, but this does not provide for ventilation. It is generally more satisfactory to bring the air into direct contact with liquid water in an apparatus designed to give the desired humidity and temperature, distributing this conditioned air through ducts to the desired points, or to provide a portable "unit conditioner" which is installed directly in the room.

Visualize an enclosure such as a packed tower, spray chamber or other device in which unsaturated air is brought into direct contact with water. The surface of the liquid is separated from the main body of the gas by what amounts to a stagnant film of gas (page 591). All available data indicate that, at the interface between the liquid surface and gas film, equilibrium is closely approached; consequently the gas at the interface has the absolute humidity H_i read from the saturation curve of Fig. 183 at the interfacial temperature t_i.

If at a given cross section of the device t_i is such that H_i exceeds the humidity H of the main body of the air (*i.e.*, if t_i exceeds the dew point or condensation temperature of the water vapor in the air), water will evaporate and the humidity of the gas will increase, regardless of the air temperature, and hence *humidification* is occurring at this cross section of the apparatus.

The direction of flow of heat depends on the temperature difference existing between the air and water. Thus, if the surface of the water is warmer than the main body of the air $(t_i > t)$, heat will flow from water to air, increasing the temperature of the air, whereas, if the surface of the water is colder than the air, heat will flow in the reverse direction, cooling the air.

The direction of change of water temperature depends on the heat balance. Thus, if the surface of the water is warmer than the wet-bulb temperature of the air, the water is cooled, while, if it is colder, the reverse is true. If t_i is at the wet-bulb temperature, where the heat transferred from air to water is exactly balanced by that consumed in evaporation, the water temperature remains unchanged.

Humidifiers.—In a humidifier where surface is provided either by the use of a water spray or by allowing water to flow by gravity over suitable packing, a relatively large amount of water must be circulated in order to maintain the wet surface. At ordinary temperatures the rate of evaporation from such a surface is small and hence only a small percentage of the water circulated is evaporated. Consequently, the unevaporated water is recirculated by means of a pump, and make-up water is added to compensate for that evaporated.

In the winter, the recirculated water may be pumped through a steam-heated water heater. However, in the summer, when it is desired to cool the air, the recirculated water is not heated; hence the water attains the wet-bulb temperature of the air, and the air may be cooled to within a fraction of 1° of the wet-bulb temperature. Where the water temperature remains constant, the mean temperature difference between air and water is the same for parallel flow, cross flow and counterflow. With parallel flow the kinetic energy of the spray assists in causing the air to flow through the apparatus. Packed or plate towers (pages 548 and 551) may also be used, but, because of the expense of their construction and operation, plate towers are seldom employed, although three plates will give nearly saturated air. For pressure operation towers containing open packings are used.

Figure 190 shows a typical spray chamber as used for humidification. The air enters through the inlet dampers and passes through the preheating coils into the spray chamber. In order to eliminate droplets of liquid from the gas, the air leaving the spray chamber passes through the eliminators or baffles, which may be kept wet by flooding nozzles. The air then passes into subsequent apparatus, sometimes through reheating coils as shown. Usually such apparatus is automatic in action, the control depending on the readings of wet- and dry-bulb thermometers, or upon the "dew point" of the exit air (see page 637).

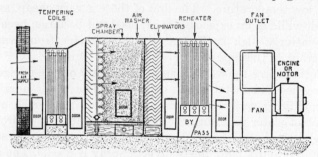

Fig. 190.—Sturtevant horizontal spray-type humidifier or air washer.

Humidifiers are used widely in air conditioning, especially to humidify air for "conditioning rooms" in which certain materials, such as textiles, foods or tobaccos, are allowed to regain moisture removed at some previous step in the process, or where the moisture in the stock must be kept at a predetermined figure.

Dehumidifiers.—It is sometimes necessary to remove moisture from air. Where complete removal is not required, it is usually most satisfactory to dehumidify by cooling and condensation rather than by adsorption or chemical absorption (page 436). When air is brought into contact with water (or a cooled surface) having a temperature *below* the dew point of the air, H_i is less than H and consequently water vapor diffuses from the main body of the gas through the gas film to liquefy at the interface, thus *dehumidifying* the air. Since the interface is colder than the air, heat is transferred from the main body of the air to the interface, and both the sensible and the latent heat are transferred through the condensate film and absorbed by the main body of the water or by the refrigerant. Since the temperatures of both air and water are changing, counterflow is desirable, an arrangement obtainable in a packed tower and approached with a number of spray chambers in series.* The cooling can be brought about by ordinary pipe coolers, but in such a case the heat-transfer coefficient is small, thus requiring a large amount of an expensive type of cooling surface. Instead of using a pipe cooler directly, sometimes the result can be accomplished more cheaply by the use of two pieces of apparatus: *first*, a spray chamber, or packed tower, in which cold water is brought into direct contact with the air; *second*, a tubular cooler in which the water is cooled by refrigerated brine or a suitable liquid evaporating at low temperature. The first of these is very cheap, and the second, while of an expensive type, need not be large, because of the relatively high coefficient of heat transfer from water to refrigerant in the pipe cooler.

In other cases the water is sprayed directly on the refrigerated surfaces located in the spray chamber. The water nozzles for dehumidifying spray chambers are designed to furnish a large volume of water to absorb the sensible and latent heat from the air, while in humidifying chambers a large evaporating surface is required and a more finely divided spray is used. The superficial air velocities employed in spray-type dehumidifiers are of the order of 400 to 550 ft. per min., compared with 500 to 700 ft. per min. in spray humidifiers.

Dehumidifiers are widely used in air conditioning of buildings and railway cars. They are also used in connection with driers in which air is dehumidified before recirculation. Dehumidifiers may also be used to salvage waste heat; thus hot moist air in a paper mill may be dehumidified to furnish warm water for process purposes.

Water Coolers.—When air comes in contact with water warmer than the wet-bulb temperature of the air, the water is cooled by evaporation. If this unsaturated air is cooler than the water, the latter is cooled not only by evaporation but also by the transfer of sensible heat to the air.

Water coolers are employed in engineering practice where cooling water is scarce. The forms ordinarily used are cooling towers and spray ponds. Figure 191 shows one type of water cooler.

---

* Where the refrigeration is obtained by a liquid evaporating at constant temperature, there is no advantage in employing counterflow.

To recapitulate, the humidity increases in a humidifier, decreases in a dehumidifier and increases in a water cooler; the water temperature is practically constant in an adiabatic humidifier, rises in a dehumidifier and falls in a water cooler; the air

Fig. 191.—Wheeler cooling tower.

temperature falls in the first and second and usually rises, but may fall, in the third.

METHOD OF CALCULATION

The humidity chart discussed in the preceding chapter is used for determining the relation between the initial and final temperatures and humidities of the air. Knowing these terminal conditions, by means of material and energy balances one can readily determine the stoichiometric relations between the amount of air handled, the change in humidity and the water evaporated or condensed.

The size of an apparatus for a given capacity and operating conditions may be calculated by applying judiciously three rate equations: one for the rate of transfer of *sensible* heat between the air and the water surface, another for the rate of diffusion of water vapor between the air and this same water surface, and the third for the rate of heat transfer between the interface and the main body of the water.

The heat effect due to evaporation or condensation is disre‚ garded in the first equation, except as it influences the interfacial temperature and hence the average temperature difference between water and air. Both of these processes, heat transfer and diffusion, take place simultaneously and the coefficients of the first two equations are tied together by a very simple relation. The necessary coefficients for these equations are determined experimentally for each type of apparatus.

Nomenclature

A = wetted transfer surface, sq. ft.

a = wetted transfer surface per unit volume of apparatus, sq. ft./cu. ft.

D_m = molal diffusivity, lb. mols/(hr.)(ft.).

D_t = tower diameter, ft.

ϵ = base of natural logarithms, 2.718.

G = mass velocity of air, lb./(hr.)(sq. ft. of cross section).

H = absolute humidity of air, lb. of water vapor/lb. of dry air.

H_i, H_T, H_w = humidity of saturated air; H_i corresponds to t_i, H_T to T, and H_w to t_w.

$h_G a$ = individual coefficient of sensible heat transfer through gas film, B.t.u./(hr.) (cu. ft.) (deg. F. temp. diff. across gas film).

$h_L a$ = individual coefficient of total heat transfer through liquid film, B.t.u./(hr.)(cu. ft.) (deg. F. temp. diff. across liquid film).

$k'a$ = individual coefficients of vapor diffusion, lb./(hr.) (cu. ft.) (unit humidity difference between main body of gas and interface).

$K'a$ = overall coefficient of vapor diffusion, lb./(hr.)(cu. ft.) (unit overall humidity difference, $H - H_T$).

M_m = mean molecular weight of gas-vapor mixture

r = latent heat of vaporization, B.t.u./lb.

S = cross-sectional area of apparatus, sq. ft.

s = humid heat = $0.24 + 0.45H$, B.t.u./(deg. F.)(lb. of dry air).

T = bulk temperature of main body of water, deg. F (not absolute).

$t =$ bulk temperature of main body of air, dry-bulb temperature, deg. F.

$t_d =$ temperature of dew point, deg. F.

$t_i =$ temperature at interface between water and air films, deg. F.

$t_w =$ wet-bulb temperature of the air, deg. F.

$U_Ga =$ overall coefficient of sensible heat transfer from air to water, B.t.u./(hr.)(cu. ft.)(deg. F. overall temp. diff.).

$V =$ tower volume, cu. ft., equals SZ.

$w =$ mass rate of flow of dry air through apparatus, lb./hr.

$x =$ lb. of water sprayed/(hr.)(sq. ft. of cross section of chamber).

$Z =$ length of spray chamber or height of tower, ft.

$\mu =$ absolute viscosity, lb./(hr.)(ft.).

Subscript 1 refers to conditions of *both* liquid and gas at the *gas* inlet, and subscript 2 refers to conditions at the outlet.

Basic Equations for Steady Flow.—Consider a tower in which the air to be treated enters at the bottom and leaves at the top, while the water enters at the top and leaves at the bottom. At any given cross section the main body of the air has a dry-bulb temperature t and absolute humidity H, and the mass rate of flow of air is w lb. per hr. At this same section the mass rate of flow of liquid water is L lb. per hr.; the main body of the water is at T and the interface between air and water is at the temperature t_i. Designate the conditions at the air entrance end by the subscript 1, and those at the other end by the subscript 2.

The overall water balance is

$$L_1 - L_2 = w(H_1 - H_2) \tag{1}$$

Neglecting heat exchange with the surroundings, the overall heat balance may be written in several alternate forms:*

$$L_2(T_1 - T_2) = ws_1(t_1 - T_1) + w(H_1 - H_2)r_{T_1} - ws_2(t_2 - T_1) \tag{2a}$$
$$L_1(T_1 - T_2) = ws_1(t_1 - T_2) + w(H_1 - H_2)r_{T_2} - ws_2(t_2 - T_2). \tag{2b}$$
$$L_1(T_1 - t_1) - L_2(T_2 - t_1) = ws_2(t_1 - t_2) + w(H_1 - H_2)r_{t_1} \tag{2c}$$
$$L_1(T_1 - t_2) - L_2(T_2 - t_2) = ws_1(t_1 - t_2) + w(H_1 - H_2)r_{t_2}. \tag{2d}$$

Now focus attention on what happens in a differential height dZ, corresponding to the differential volume dV, having cross section S; dV equals $S\,dZ$. The corresponding water and heat

---

* These four alternate forms are obtained by using T_1, T_2, t_1 and t_2 as datum temperatures, respectively. In all cases the specific heat of liquid water is taken as 1.

balances are:

$$-dL = -w\ dH \tag{1a}$$
$$-L\ dT = -ws\ dt - wr\ dH. \tag{2a'}$$

The differential interfacial area dA is equal to the product of the wetted surface a per unit volume of tower and the volume dV of the differential section, *i.e.*, dA equals $a\ dV$. The rate of transfer of sensible heat between the main body of the air at t and the water surface at t_i is then

$$-ws\ dt = (h_G)(a\ dV)(t-t_i). \tag{3}$$

The rate of diffusion of water vapor between the main body of the gas (having the absolute humidity H) and the interface (having the absolute humidity H_i) is then given by the mass-transfer equation (page 447)

$$-w\ dH = (k'a)(dV)(H-H_i). \tag{4}$$

The rate of heat transfer from the interface (at t_i) to the main body of the water (at T) is then

$$-L\ dT = (h_L)(a\ dV)(t_i-T). \tag{5}$$

These five differential equations, and data regarding the necessary coefficients in the rate equations, are the general solution to the problem of direct contact between air and water in a steadily operated apparatus. Upon dividing Eq. 4 by Eq. 3, one obtains the significant relation

$$\frac{dH}{dt} = \left(\frac{k's}{h_G}\right)\left(\frac{H-H_i}{t-t_i}\right) \tag{6}$$

Since it was shown on pages 590 to 593 that for air and water the physical properties were such that the dimensionless ratio $h_G/k's$ was substantially 1, Eq. 6 may be written as

$$\frac{dH}{dt} = \frac{(H-H_i)}{(t-t_i)}. \tag{6a}$$

Adiabatic Humidifiers.—In an adiabatic humidifier the heat transferred from air to water tends to heat the water but the evaporation tends to cool it. Where the unevaporated water is recirculated, it attains the wet-bulb temperature where these two effects balance and the water temperature remains unchanged, *i.e.*, dT is zero.   The heat balance then takes the form

$$L_2 - L_1 = \frac{ws_1(t_1 - t_2)}{(r_{t_2} + t_2 - T_2)}$$

which is the same as that given on page 581.   If the temperature T_2 of the make-up water is substantially the same as the adiabatic saturation temperature t_s, one may employ the curves for adiabatic evaporation plotted in Fig. 183, page 579.

Since no heat is transferred to the main body of the water, it is unnecessary to use Eq. 5, and, since the rate coefficients of Eqs. 3 and 4 are tied together, one may choose either equation. Selecting Eq. 3 and recalling that t_i is substantially constant at t_w, integration gives

$$\ln \frac{(t_1 - t_{w_1})}{(t_2 - t_{w_2})} = \frac{h_G a V}{ws}. \tag{3a}$$

A similar integration of Eq. 4 gives

$$\ln \frac{(H_{w_1} - H_1)}{(H_{w_2} - H_2)} = \frac{k' a V}{w} \tag{4a}$$

The rate coefficients are discussed on page 606.

It is interesting to note that the fractional humidification (actual humidification $H_2 - H_1$, divided by that obtainable with an infinite apparatus, $H_w - H_1$) takes the form*

$$\frac{(H_2 - H_1)}{(H_w - H_1)} = 1 - e^{-\frac{k' a V}{w}} \tag{4b}$$

which is analogous to the Murphree rectification efficiency (page 566) for a bubble plate, where gas-phase resistance is controlling. Equation 3a takes a similar form

$$\frac{(t_1 - t_2)}{(t_1 - t_w)} = 1 - e^{-\frac{h_G a V}{ws}}. \tag{3b}$$

* Equations 4b and 3b are obtained from Eqs. 4a and 3a, respectively, by assuming that the water remains at the wet-bulb temperature throughout the process.

The fractional cooling or humidification given by a bubble plate is of the order of 0.8.*

Adiabatic Dehumidification.—Consider a given cross section where the main body of the air is unsaturated, such as the point having coordinates H_1 and t_1 in Fig. 192. If the surface temperature of the water is less than that of the main body of the air, the conditions at the air-water interface will be represented by a point H_i, t_i on the saturation curve. Since H_i is less than H_1, water vapor will flow from the main body of the gas through the gas film, and will liquefy at the interface, thus dehumidifying

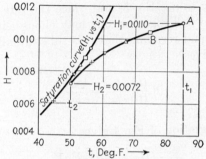

Fig. 192.—Dehumidification diagram.

the air. Since t_i is less than t, the air will be cooled and the sensible heat so transferred will flow through the same gas film. Since both the sensible and latent heats are transferred to the water, the temperature of the latter will rise.

In consequence, as the water flows through the apparatus the temperature t_i of the interface will rise, moving to higher positions on the saturation curve, or as the air flows through the apparatus it encounters water at lower temperatures. At each cross section Eq. 6a applies, *i.e.*, $dH/dt = (H - H_i)/(t - t_i)$, which means that the instantaneous slope of the path is dependent on the prevailing ratio of the vertical distance, $H - H_i$, to the horizontal distance,

* Occasionally the performance of a humidifier is rated in terms of the "height of a transfer unit" (H.t.u.), where Z is the effective length or height of the apparatus, and the number (n) of "transfer units" is arbitrarily defined as the ratio of the decrease in air temperature to the logarithmic-mean temperature difference from air to water: H.t.u. $= Z/n$. Inspection of Eq. 3a shows that H.t.u. also equals $ws/h_Ga S$ or Gs/h_Ga, where G is the mass velocity of the air based on the total cross section S.

$t - t_i$. The situation is indicated diagrammatically in Fig. 192, and it is seen that the path curve will be convex upward. Given data for the rate coefficients h_G and h_L, since for air and water k' may be taken equal to h_G/s, the necessary size of apparatus for given operating conditions can be calculated by graphical integration of the equations. An approximate solution may be obtained by substituting finite increments for the differential terms in the basic equations, thus making stepwise calculations, with intermediate calculations of t_i, assuming that dH/dt is constant over short finite intervals at a value equal to the value of $(H - H_i)/(t - t_i)$ (see Fig. 192).

If the gas temperatures are above that of the surroundings, the apparatus should not be insulated, unless it is being operated to preheat the water. However, for air conditioning in the summer, where the air is being cooled below outdoor temperatures, the apparatus should be insulated.

If the air entering is saturated, it tends to remain saturated as it cools, but with substantial temperature differences there is a marked tendency toward formation of fog in the gas film. Computations for the dehumidification of saturated air are often made by the approximate method given on page 606 for water coolers.

Water Coolers.—If at a given cross section the temperature of the water surface is above the wet-bulb temperature of the main body of the air, the water will be cooled even if the air is hotter. However, it is desirable to have the air colder than the water so that the water will be cooled both by its own evaporation and by transfer of heat to the colder air. Packed towers are often used for two reasons: first, because counterflow is desirable to give high average values of the driving forces $(T - t_i, t_i - t$ and $H_i - H)$, and, second, because high coefficients $h_L a$ for the liquid film are obtainable since the liquid film is being continually deformed as the water flows over the packing. The general problem is solved by applying the basic relations given on pages 601 to 602. However, for packed towers one sometimes employs an approximate method based on the assumption that $h_L a$ is so high that t_i equals T, thus eliminating the use of Eq. 5. In such cases the individual coefficient k' multiplied by $(H_i - H)$ is replaced by an *overall* coefficient K multiplied by the "overall driving force" $H_T - H$, and Eq. 4

becomes

$$w \, dH = Ka \, dV(H_T - H). \tag{7}$$

Similarly Eq. 3 is written

$$ws \, dt = U_G a \, dV(T - t) \tag{8}$$

where U_G is the overall coefficient of sensible heat transfer based on the "overall temperature difference," $T - t$. There is no reason why U_G/K_G should equal s; tests show that this ratio may substantially exceed the humid heat. The approximate equations (7 and 8) are then used over finite increments employing arithmetic-mean values of the driving forces. It should be noted that the water temperature, and hence H_T, varies throughout the apparatus. In designing a water cooler, the initial and final water temperatures T_2 and T_1 and the rate of input L_2 of the water are known, as is the initial temperature t_1 and humidity H_1 of the entering air. Furthermore, data for the coefficients $U_G a$ and $K'a$ are available for towers of certain types. Hence, with Eqs. 2, 7 and 8 and the humidity chart, it is possible to calculate the amount of air required, the volume of the apparatus and the temperature and humidity of the air leaving the water cooler. As a first approximation, the temperature of the air leaving the apparatus may be taken as 5 to 10°F. below that of the entering hot water. This trial value must later be checked against values required by the equations used.

Discussion of Capacity Coefficients.—The following points should be kept clearly in mind:

1. The coefficient $h_G a$ is obtained experimentally and is expressed as B.t.u. (*as sensible heat only*) per hour per °F. *average individual* temperature difference per cubic foot. Although $h_G a$ can be determined by experiment, it consists of two factors, neither of which can conveniently be determined separately. The exact values of $h_G a$ and $U_G a$ cannot, in general, be predicted for apparatus for humidification, dehumidification and the like, but the qualitative effect of changing certain variables, such as velocity of gas or liquid, may be predicted in certain cases.

2. Since the term a represents the square feet of wetted surface per cubic foot of apparatus, it will vary widely with the type or design of the apparatus. Even in a definite type of apparatus,

gas velocity or rate of liquor circulation or both nearly always affect the active surface per unit of volume.

3. In addition to this, as brought out repeatedly in the chapter on Flow of Heat, changes in velocity and viscosity have marked effects on certain film coefficients of heat transfer.

All these facts make the prediction of values of the coefficients extremely difficult, and hence for accurate design it is necessary to determine the coefficients for the particular conditions under consideration. However, by having a clear insight into the nature of the variables involved, the amount of experimental work required may be reduced to a minimum. While the designing of apparatus of these types in the absence of preliminary experimental work is undesirable, yet the problem sometimes arises, and here one must interpret the results of experiments in similar apparatus with care and employ suitable factors of safety.

RATE COEFFICIENTS

Horizontal Spray Chambers.—Tests on a number of spray-type humidifiers show that the heat-transfer coefficient h_Ga varies but slightly with gas velocity over the usual range of from 1200 to 3000 lb. per hr. per sq. ft. of cross section, but increases rapidly with increase in the rate at which water is recirculated through the nozzles. Tests[1] on a chamber 4 ft. long and 56 sq. ft. in cross section, with parallel flow of air and water, are correlated by the equation

$$h_Ga = 0.0078(x)^{1.5}$$

where x represents the pounds of water sprayed per hour per square foot of cross section. The number of nozzles per square foot of cross section ranged from 0.8 to 1.6, the water rate per nozzle from 180 to 510 lb. per hr., the water pressure on the nozzles from 3 to 15 lb. per sq. in., the air velocity G from 1200 to 2400 lb. per hr. per sq. ft. of cross section and h_Ga from 20 to 160.

Tests on a humidifying chamber 10 ft. long, with four nozzles per square foot and with water sprayed from both ends, gave h_Ga of 170 at G of 3000.

Packed Towers.—Tests[2] on a slat-packed cooling tower, interpreted by the approximate method, gave

$$Ka = 0.0525G \quad \text{and} \quad U_Ga = 0.0173G$$

where G varied from 1020 to 2280 lb. of air per hr. per sq. ft. of cross section, and the water rate was 3180 lb. per hr. per sq. ft. of cross section.

Wetted-wall Towers.—Data on the evaporation of water and a number of pure organic liquids, flowing by gravity down the inside wall of a vertical 1-in. pipe, into a turbulent air stream at the same temperature, are correlated[3] by the dimensionless equation

$$\frac{K'D_t}{D_mM_n} = 0.023\left(\frac{D_tG}{\mu}\right)^{0.83}\left(\frac{\mu}{D_mM_m}\right)^{0.44}.$$

Values of the diffusivity D_m are shown on page 460. For water this reduces to

$$K' = (0.025 + 0.000055t)G^{0.83}$$

where t is the temperature of the air, expressed in degrees Fahrenheit.

Analogy between Absorption and Mass Transfer.—By means of this analogy,[4] data on the evaporation of pure liquids into air and data on the dehumidification of air by contact with sulfuric acid were brought into fair agreement with heat-transfer data from gas to solid. By this procedure the ordinates of Fig. 40, page 112, are taken as $(k'M_m/M_nG)(\mu/D_mM_m)^{\frac{2}{3}}$ instead of $(h/C_pG)(C_p\mu/k)^{\frac{2}{3}}$.

ILLUSTRATIVE PROBLEMS

Illustration 1.   Humidifier.—It is desired to cool 22,000 cu. ft. of air/min. from 95 to 75°F., using a horizontal spray chamber which sprays the recirculated water against the air flow. The temperature of the make-up water is 80°F., the dew point of the initial air is 58°F. and the barometer is normal. Calculate (a) number of spray nozzles required, and dimensions of chamber to house the sprays; (b) gal. of water recirculated/min., and theoretical horsepower for spray nozzles; (c) gal. of make-up water/min.

Data and Notes.—For a humidifier, h_Ga may be taken as 90 provided there are 12 lb. of water per min. per spray, two sprays per sq. ft. of cross section and the banks about 8 ft. apart (in the direction of flow of air). The water pressure on nozzles may be taken as 20 lb. gauge for new sprays when the rate of flow is 12 lb. per min. per spray.

Solution.—From Fig. 183, page 579, it is seen that the humidity of air saturated at 58°F. is 0.0100, the wet-bulb temperature is 70°F., and the humidity attained during adiabatic cooling to 75°F. in contact with water is 0.0147.

The humid volume at 95°F. is seen (by interpolation between the value of 14.82 cu. ft. for saturated air and 13.96 cu. ft. for dry air) to be 14.20 cu. ft. mixture/lb. of dry air. Then w equals $22{,}000/14.20 = 1550$ lb. of dry air/min. The sensible heat removed by cooling the air, having initial humid heat of 0.2445, from 95 to 75 is $(1550)(95-75)(0.2445)$ or 7600 B.t.u. per min. Since the recirculated water attains the wet-bulb temperature (70°F.), the temperature difference between air and water is $95-70$ or 25°F. at the entrance and $75-70$ or 5°F. at the exit. From Eq. 3a it is seen that

$$\frac{h_G a V}{ws} = \ln \frac{(t-t_i)_1}{(t-t_i)_2}$$

or

$$V = [\ln (25/5)](1550)(0.2445)(60)/(90) = 409 \text{ cu. ft.}$$

Since the value of $h_G a$ used was determined for one nozzle per 4 cu. ft. and for two nozzles per square foot of cross section, the theoretical number of nozzles equals 102, the square feet of cross section is about 51 and the length of spray chamber is about 8 ft. For 102 of these nozzles in one bank, the water rate is $(102)(12)/8.33$ or 147 U. S. gal./min.

According to Eq. 1 the make-up water equals $(1550)(0.0147 - 0.0100)$ or 7.3 lb./min. It is obvious that the mixing of 7 lb. of water at 80°F. with 1224 lb. at 70°F. would not appreciably raise the temperature above 70°F.

The theoretical horsepower dissipated in the nozzles equals

$$\frac{(1224)(20)(144)}{(62.3)(33{,}000)} \text{ or } 1.72 \text{ hp.}$$

It can easily be shown that the dissipation of this power will not cause appreciable rise in water temperature.* The calculated values are:

a. 102 nozzles in one bank housed by a spray chamber 8 ft. long and about 7 by 7.5 ft. in section.

b. Water recirculated at rate of 147 gal./min., the pump theoretically requiring 1.72 hp. for the resistance caused by the nozzles alone.

c. About 1 gal. of make-up water required per min.

A safety factor should be included on the size of the spray chamber and number of nozzles to allow for decrease in effectiveness of sprays with time. The volume given above (409 cu. ft.) is that of the spray chamber alone; obviously, the actual apparatus must include air dampers at the entrance and water eliminators at the exit. Suitable strainers should be provided on the water line leading to the sprays. For use in winter heating, coils should be provided.

Illustration 2. Dehumidifier.—It is desired to design a coke-packed tower to dehumidify continuously 2000 cu. ft./minute of air saturated at

* In calculating the actual horsepower of the motor for the pump, one must allow for the friction losses and lift in the piping system as well as for the nozzle friction and the combined efficiency of motor and pump.

80°F. and 1 atmosphere to produce saturated air at 55°F. Cooling water is available at 50°F. What shall be the height and diameter of the tower?

Data and Notes.—A tower packed with 3-in. coke[5] has been found to give U_Ga of 250 when L/S is 1150 and G is 1200 lb./(hr.)(sq. ft.).

Solution.—Since U_Ga depends on both G and L/S, it is safe to employ the given U_Ga if G and L/S are equal to, or exceed, the values given. The humid volume of the entering air is 14.08 cu. ft./lb.; hence w will be $2000 \times 60/14.08 = 8530$ lb. dry air/hr. The cross section S will then be $8530/1200 = 7.11$ sq. ft., which calls for a tower diameter D_t of $\sqrt{7.11/0.785}$ or 3.01 ft.

The inlet water rate L_2 will be 1150(7.11) or 8180 lb./hr. The overall heat balance (Eq. 2a) is $8180(T_1-50)=8530(0.25)(80-T_1)-8530(0.244)(55-T_1)+8530(0.01305)(1051.5)$, whence the outlet water temperature T_1 is found to be 70.8°F.* The overall temperature differences $(t-T)$ from air to water are $(80-66.5)$ or 13.5°F. at the bottom and $(55-50)$ or 5°F. at the top. The arithmetic-mean temperature difference, 9.25°F., will be employed as an approximation. The equation for the transfer of sensible heat from air to water is $(8530)(0.247)(80-55)=250(7.11Z)(9.25)$, whence the height is found to be 3.2 ft.

Note.—If the entering air had been unsaturated, it would have been necessary to solve for the outlet humidity that would be obtained when cooling the air to 55°F. This would require the use of Eq. 7, together with the numerical value of $K'a$, which for this case is known[5] to be 1200.

Illustration 3. Water Cooler.—A slat-packed cooling tower is to be designed to cool 3000 gal./min. of condenser water from 110 to 85°F. by means of air flowing up through the tower. With forced draft, it is estimated that the velocity of the entering air will be 500 cu. ft./(min.) (sq. ft.). Under the worst conditions the available air will be saturated at 80°F.

Using the data given below, and neglecting heat losses to the surroundings, calculate: (a) cu. ft. of air/min. entering the tower; (b) height and ground area of tower; (c) temperature and humidity *of* exit air.

Data.—For similar towers handling 3180 lb. of water/(hr.) (sq. ft. of ground area), it is found that $K'a=0.0525G$, and $U_G/K'=0.33$.

Solution.—Since the coefficients were determined for 3180 lb. water/(sq. ft. of total cross section), the ground area of the tower equals $(60)(3000)(8.33)/3180=472$ sq. ft. The volumetric capacity of the fan equals $(472)(500)=236,000$ cu. ft./min. at 80°F. Since the humid volume of the entering air is 14.1 cu. ft./lb. of dry air, G equals

$$(472)(500)(60)/(14.1)=1,000,000 \text{ lb. dry air per hr.}$$

(It will be noted this corresponds to about $\frac{2}{3}$ lb. of dry air/lb. of water fed.)

On the basis of 1 lb. of water, an approximate heat balance is

$$(0.667)(s_{av.})(t_2-80)+(0.667)(H_2-0.0220)(1046)=(1)(110-85). \quad (A)$$

* If the use of the given air and water velocities had called for an outlet water temperature above that of the entering air, it would have been necessary to increase the water rate.

The equation for the transfer of sensible heat to the air (Eq. 8) is

$$(1,000,000)(s_{av.})(t_2 - 80) = U_G a V\left(\frac{110 - t_2 + 85 - 80}{2}\right).$$

Since the mass velocity G of dry air is $(60)\ 16{,}700/472 = 2120$ lb. dry air/ (hr.) (sq. ft. of total cross section), $K'a$ equals $(0.0525)(2120) = 111.6$, and $U_G a = (0.33)(111.6) = 36.8$.
Hence the preceding equation becomes

$$(1,000,000)(s_{av.})(t_2 - 80) = (36.8)(V)(115 - t_2)/2. \qquad (B)$$

The equation for the diffusion of water vapor into the air (Eq. 7) is

$$(1,000,000)(H_2 - 0.0220) = (112)(V)\left(\frac{0.0584 - H_2 + 0.0260 - 0.0220}{2}\right),$$
$$(1,000,000)(H_2 - 0.0220) = \frac{(112)(V)(0.0624 - H_2)}{2}. \qquad (C)$$

Since

$$s_{av.} = 0.24 + 0.45\left(\frac{0.022 + H_2}{2}\right)*,$$

there are three equations $(A, B,$ and $C)$ and three unknowns: V, H_2 and t_2. If Eq. B is divided by Eq. C, V is eliminated, and hence values of t_2 and H_2 must satisfy (A) and (B/C). As a first trial, t_2 is usually taken as 5°F. less than the temperature of the entering water. The values of t_2 and H_2 which satisfy the above conditions are

$$t_2 = 107°\text{F.}$$
$$H_2 = 0.0512 \text{ or } 95 \text{ per cent saturated.}$$

Substituting these values in Eq. C, and later in Eq. B as a check of the arithmetic, $V = 47{,}000$ cu. ft. Hence the height of the tower equals

$$(47{,}000)/(472) = 99.5 \text{ ft.}$$

Note.—This cooling tower was designed for the "worst conditions" of the air, namely, *saturated at* 80°F. When the air is not saturated, or cooler than 80°F. or both, the water will be cooled to a temperature lower than 85°F. Since the calculated height of 99.5 ft. is excessive, the designer would probably compromise by using a shorter tower, thereby sacrificing somewhat the cooling of the water.

References

1. ROBINSON, P., and C. S. ROLL, Chemical Engineering Thesis, Massachusetts Institute of Technology, 1922.

2. Recalculated by C. S. ROBINSON [*Mech. Eng.*, **45**, 99 (1923)] from data given by W. G. Stephan in *J. Ohio Soc. Mech. Elec. Civil Eng.*, **7**, 23 (1914).

* The use of this equation complicates the solution of the problem, and, since s varies only slightly, it is advisable to assume it as constant.

3. GILLILAND, E. R., and T. K. SHERWOOD, *Ind. Eng. Chem.*, **26**, 516–523 (May, 1934).

4. CHILTON, T. H., and A. P. COLBURN, *Ind. Eng. Chem.*, **26**, 1183–1187 (1934).

5. KEATS, J., Chemical Engineering Thesis, Massachusetts Institute of Technology, 1921.

CHAPTER XIX

DRYING

PART I. METHODS OF DRYING

Introduction.—Although the term "drying" may have a peculiar significance in a few specialized industries, in general engineering practice it may be taken to mean the removal of water from a system or structure, when the amount of water present is comparatively small. For purposes of study the subject matter may be classified from a number of different points of view.

The material to be dried may be either a gas, a liquid or a solid. If a gas, the water may be carried simply as vapor, or in addition it may be present in the form of a spray or fog. If a liquid, water is removed by *drying* only when present in small amounts; otherwise the process is described as evaporation or distillation. Thus fusel oil, alcohol or acetone may be "dried" by removing the water therefrom. In solids the amount of water may vary from a mere trace to the large amount present in fresh fruit or in a glue jelly.

As the moisture leaves a wet solid there is often a tendency for the structure to diminish in volume cr shrink. If great care is not taken, this shrinkage will not be uniform, and cracking or warping results, which deteriorates the product. Examples of this action are found in timber and unburned pottery. Or, if a material is dried under tension and lateral shrinkage is prevented, the structure loses its strength. Such is the case when paper is dried on certain machines as compared to that slowly dried in a loft. Many materials such as eggs, fruit or milk must be dried rapidly at as low a temperature as is practical, in order to preserve their characteristic flavor and the other valuable properties they possess. Some substances deteriorate when allowed to remain for a considerable length of time in a wet condition. Material such as glue, starch and sugar cannot be heated while wet owing to the solvent action of the water upon them. Many substances containing water of crystallization cannot be dried under ordinary conditions because of a loss of all or a portion of this water.   These widely varying conditions may be cared for in drier design by considering the rate of drying, condition of the drying medium and the nature of the exposed surface.   Each of these factors is complex and will be discussed in detail later.

Methods of Drying.— The available methods of drying are:

1. Deposition of the moisture as either water or ice.
2. Decomposition of the water.
3. Chemical precipitation.
4. Absorption.
5. Adsorption.
6. Mechanical separation.
7. Vaporization.

The completeness with which dryness can be effected by any process depends upon the factors controlling the equilibrium conditions then obtaining.   These will be considered as each method is discussed.

1. Deposition of the Moisture as Water or Ice.—When condensation takes place in a gas, it is obviously the reverse of vaporization and depends upon the same fundamental considerations. The clumsy term "dehumidification" has come into general use for operations of this character and the subject has been treated together with humidification processes.   The Gayley dry blast for smelting iron is an example of the large-scale application of this idea.

Water may be removed from liquids by converting it into ice and in this form separating it from the portion having a lower freezing point.   The alcoholic content of a liquid possessing a delicate flavor can in this way be readily increased.   Fruit juices are concentrated by cooling with agitation and subsequently separating the ice crystals by passing through a centrifugal machine.

The amount of moisture remaining in air dried by cooling depends upon the temperature to which it is cooled.   Also in the case of a liquid it depends upon the temperature reached, but is limited when a eutectic mixture is formed.

2. Decomposition of the Water.—When a small amount of water is held in either a gas or a liquid, it may be removed by decomposing it and separating the products formed.   Thus ether is dried by placing it in contact with metallic sodium.

The caustic soda formed clings to the surface of the metal and, if separated, will eventually settle out. Certain circumstances allow of using other water-decomposing agents such as the carbides and nitrides. Here the completeness of the process is largely a function of mechanical agitation of the liquid and the reacting substance. The vapor pressure of water with which the substances formed are in equilibrium is so small as to be negligible.

3. Chemical Precipitation.—Somewhat larger amounts of water may be advantageously withdrawn in the form of a chemically combined precipitate. Thus lime forms calcium hydroxide; anhydrous sulfate of copper or sodium takes on water of crystallization and separates from the liquid. The amount of water remaining in the liquid is controlled by the vapor pressure of the hydroxide or the crystalline substance formed. Phosphorus pentoxide and calcium chloride may be used for drying gases, and for drying liquids in which they are insoluble; again the completeness of drying is limited by the vapor pressure of the resulting hydrated substance.

4. Absorption.—In some technical processes water is removed from a material by the capillary action of porous bodies. Thus the cream of clay and water used for casting pottery is deprived of the greater part of its water by placing it in molds of plaster of Paris. The capillary character of this mold withdraws the water from the liquid clay mixture and deposits upon itself a layer of solid clay, the thickness of which is controlled by the time of standing. Certain types of candies, such as gumdrops, are dried mainly by contact with the starch molds in which they are cast. The drying effect of sponges, towels and materials of this kind is due to this same action.

5. Adsorption.—The wonderful ability of certain substances to adsorb moisture makes possible the application of this process to drying gases, and to some extent also liquids (see pages 424 to 513).

6. Mechanical Separation.—Some materials are of a spongy nature and hold by capillarity large quantities of moisture which may be expelled by pressure alone. When such is the case, it is evidently desirable to get rid of as large a percentage as possible by such means before passing to other more expensive methods. This may be readily accomplished in many cases (textiles, wool, grain and the like) by centrifugal force (see page 336). Or a positive pressure may be exerted by a screw as is shown in Fig. 193, or by passing the material between a pair of rolls.

7. Vaporization.—By far the most important processes for drying liquids and solids depend upon first vaporizing the water and in this form separating it from the structure of which it formed a part.   If air or some inert gas is used to carry away the water vapor formed, the process is called **air drying.**   If the

Fig. 193.—Screw press.

vapor is passed to a condenser, a pump being employed to withdraw the air from the apparatus, the process is spoken of as **vacuum drying.**   By far the greater proportion of this chapter is devoted to drying by means of vaporization.

PART II.   GENERAL PRINCIPLES OF DRYING BY VAPORIZATION INTO A GAS

General Considerations.—Every solid and liquid substance exerts at any definite temperature a perfectly definite vapor pressure.   If the substance is a mixture, each component exerts its own particular and definite vapor pressure.   These separate or partial pressures are additive and together make up the total vapor pressure of the substance.   If the component parts of a mixture are mutually soluble, the partial pressure of each component will be thereby somewhat decreased.   The vapor pressure of liquids increases as the temperature rises and obviously there will be some definite temperature at which this vapor pressure equals the pressure of the atmosphere.   At this point the vapor of the liquid will continue to form, and not only diffuse but actually push back the atmosphere into space, maintaining as total pressure the atmospheric pressure then existing.   The liquid is

then said to **boil** and this temperature is called its **boiling point.**
As the pressure of the atmosphere varies, clearly the boiling point
of a liquid will vary also.

These elementary conceptions are so essential to a ready
understanding of the discussion which follows that the reader is
referred to pages 365 to 372 for further exposition of them.

As the science of drying developed, there were adopted a
number of expressions which at times vary in their meaning from
that which normally attaches to them. A full discussion of these
definitions is given in the chapter entitled Humidity and Wet- and
Dry-bulb Thermometry (see pages 577 to 594).

MECHANISM OF AIR DRYING OF SOLID MATERIALS

The discussion of the mechanism of vaporization of liquids
suspended in air (pages 582 to 585) has shown the influence of the
temperature, humidity and air velocity upon the rate of vaporization. It will now be shown that, when water is admixed with
other materials, the composition and form of the mixture profoundly modify the evaporative rate. In order to determine the
effect of these new variables, they will first be studied under
constant drying conditions.

Most solid materials to be dried exist in either sheet or lump
form with the water* from which they are to be freed dis-
seminated throughout the mass. The mechanism of removal of
this water is somewhat complicated, but must be thoroughly
understood in order to appreciate the factors controlling the
drying of such materials.

For the sake of definiteness, consider the drying of a sheet
material freely and equally exposed to the drying air on both sides
of the sheet. The sheet will be assumed so large in comparison
with its thickness that the drying from the edge of the sheet
may be neglected, as compared with the drying from the faces of
the sheet. It will be assumed that, initially, the water is uniformly distributed throughout the thickness of the sheet. As
soon as the sheet comes into contact with the drying air, evaporation will start at the surface, and the concentration of water on
the surface will therefore diminish. This will cause a difference
in concentration between the interior of the sheet, which is still

---

* Although water is the liquid used in this discussion, it should be remembered that a similar treatment applies to other liquids.

wet, and the surface, which has been partially dried by evaporation.   In consequence of this concentration difference, there will be a flow of liquid water *by diffusion* from the interior of the sheet to the surface.*   These two processes, *i.e.*, evaporation from the surface and diffusion through the sheet from the interior to the surface, will go on simultaneously until the drying operation is suspended or the sheet has come into equilibrium with the drying air.   In some cases, resistance to surface evaporation is the controlling factor in drying, while in others the resistance to diffusion of the water from the interior to the surface limits the rate of drying.   In any case, it is essential to keep in mind the part played by each of these processes in order intelligently to control the drying operation.

Diffusion of Liquid Limiting Factor.—The importance of these two processes will be appreciated from the following illustrations.   Wet, green wood must be dried prior to use.   During the drying it shrinks.   If the surface evaporation is excessively rapid, the surface becomes very dry while the interior is still impregnated with moisture, *i.e.*, there is set up a large gradient in moisture concentration from the interior toward the surface. The surface shrinks owing to the evaporation of its moisture, and is put under high tension because of the incompressible character of the wet interior.   If the surface shrinkage is excessive, this results in rupture of the surface with the production of cracks or checks which ruin the lumber for finer uses.   In drying such lumber it is therefore essential to avoid setting up too large a concentration gradient between the surface and the interior, and this is done by raising the humidity of the air to make the rate of surface evaporation commensurate with the rate of diffusion of water.   Exactly the same applies to the drying of articles molded from wet clay in the ceramic industry.

Surface Evaporation as Limiting Factor.—In the drying of paper, chrome leather and similar materials, the sheets possess a finely fibrous structure which distributes the moisture through them by capillary action, thus securing very rapid diffusion of moisture from one point of the sheet to another.   This means that it is almost impossible to remove moisture from the surface

* With porous materials evaporation may occur within the solid.   In a porous material containing grains of diverse sizes, the movement of water may be controlled by capillarity[6, 7] and not by concentration gradients.

of the sheet without having it immediately replaced by capillary diffusion from the center. The drying of such sheets is, therefore, essentially a phenomenon of surface evaporation.

Mechanism of Surface Evaporation.—In any case, the phenomenon of surface evaporation is a diffusion of water vapor from the surface of the sheet through the air film to the surrounding air, into which further dissemination is affected by convection. This film (page 34) is relatively thick when the motion of the gas is slight, but with high velocity of the gas past the solid surface the thickness of this film rapidly decreases, the film never, however, disappearing. In the case of the evaporation of water from a wetted solid surface into air, the inner layer of the air film in contact with the solid is maintained saturated with moisture as long as the moisture concentration of the surface of the sheet is sufficient. According to the law of diffusion, the rate of vapor diffusion (weight per unit of time) varies directly as the cross-sectional area of path taken at right angles to the direction in which the gas is diffusing, directly as the difference of the partial pressure of the vapor at the two points in question, and inversely as the length of path. The thickness of the air film is not known; it is, however, a function of velocity, decreasing with increasing velocity; the diffusion therefore increases as the velocity goes up. The evaporation of water is accompanied by a definite and large absorption of heat. This heat supply must, in general, come from the surrounding air by conduction through the air film, and is proportional to the temperature difference. As pointed out elsewhere, so long as the sheet remains sufficiently wet, it assumes the wet-bulb temperature* of the air, so that, for given conditions of the drying air, the driving force causing diffusion remains constant. As the water content of the sheet decreases, the concentration of water on the surface eventually becomes so small that the rate of evaporation decreases, and hence the temperature on the surface of the sheet starts to rise.

Effect of Vapor-pressure Lowering.—Since the rate of drying is proportional to the difference between the vapor pressure of the liquid and its partial pressure in the surrounding space, it

---

* This is not the case where radiant heat is employed, or where the stock is in direct contact with the heating surface. However, the above discussion deals with air drying.

follows that material which is appreciably soluble in the liquid with a consequent vapor-pressure lowering in the liquid will dry more slowly than one which is insoluble. Thus sand carrying a definite weight of water will dry more rapidly than common salt of the same water content, other things being equal.

Effect of Adsorption.—It is well known that certain materials contain definite, and sometimes appreciable, percentages of moisture when exposed indefinitely to air of a given temperature

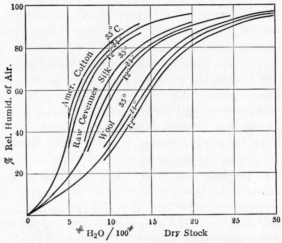

Fig. 194.—Humidity-moisture equilibrium curves for textiles.

and humidity. This water is probably adsorbed; in any event it represents a true dynamic equilibrium. Figure 194* shows the per cent equilibrium moisture of textiles plotted against the per cent *relative* humidity of air at various temperatures. For all hydroscopic materials investigated the shapes of the curves are similar to those shown in Fig. 194 and the per cent equilibrium moisture for a given per cent relative humidity always decreases as the temperature rises. At the per cent relative humidities ordinarily encountered the percentage of adsorbed water is appreciable in the case of certain amorphous organic substances, such as textiles, wood, leather, paper, flour and the like. Only the moisture in excess of that adsorbed, namely, the total minus the equilibrium moisture, is subject to removal. For more complete drying, high temperature or very dry air is necessary.

* Data from M. T. SCHLOESING, JR., *Bull. soc. encour. ind. nat.* (1893).

PART III. DRYING APPARATUS AND AUXILIARY EQUIPMENT

The two fundamental factors controlling the rate and completeness of drying, namely, the supply of heat and the removal of the vapor formed, have been presented* as a basis for drier design and operation, but without regard to the mechanical means for making these factors effective. Unless the source of heat is the sun and the removal agency is the natural air currents, it is clear that an enclosing structure must be provided and that the material to be dried must be moved into and out of this structure. A discussion of the driers now commercially available will therefore be presented from the point of view, first, of the method of moving the material and air in the drying enclosure, and, second,† of the method of supplying heat for the drying operation.

Intermittent vs. Continuous Driers.—In most forms of driers, the operation can be either intermittent or continuous; that is, the charge may be placed in the enclosure and allowed to remain there until dried, then removed and replaced by a fresh charge; or the charge may pass through the enclosure, entering one end wet and coming out the other end dry.

The advantages attaching to an intermittent drier are economy in construction, simplicity in operation and opportunity for variation of the drying conditions. It is easy to build and inexpensive to maintain, and for experimental work or small installations it has these points to recommend it. On the other hand, in almost every industry, continuity of operation offers marked advantages in routing material in process through the plant, and in lower labor costs in transporting and working the same. But in air drying, continuous operation has two additional advantages so great that intermittent drying is justified only when the amount to be handled is small or when the most exact control of the drying conditions is required.

In the first place, the heat economy of an intermittent drier is very poor. While the thermal efficiency at the beginning of the operation is high, the hot dry gases quickly taking up a large amount of water from the wet stock, the rate of evaporation rapidly decreases as the water content of the stock falls. The

* See pp. 371 to 372.
† See pp. 640 to 641.

result is that the heat content of the circulating air is utilized to a small and decreasing extent as the drying proceeds. Second, an intermittent drier is irregular in its action, producing as a rule nonuniform product. The material in immediate contact with the hot dry air as it enters loses its moisture more rapidly than that in contact with the cooler and more humid air leaving the apparatus. This results in either removing the product while a portion is but partly dry or in reducing the capacity of the drier by retaining a part of the material after it is completely dry. In any case continual attention on the part of the man in charge is demanded, necessitating an operator of the grade and with the wage scale of an inspector. Even then a continual error of judgment is introduced, which, with continuous operation and automatic control, is eliminated.

It is nonetheless possible by the use of an intermittent drier to secure more exact control of the drying conditions throughout the drying schedule than in any other way. On this account such a drier is recommended for those cases in which the drying rate must be continuously varied throughout the drying period, as in drying lumber, to prevent "casehardening" and the resulting evils of cracking, warping and the like (see pages 618 and 624).

DESCRIPTIVE CLASSIFICATION OF DRIERS

For the purpose of discussing the method of moving the material to be dried and the air for drying, the following classification of driers is made:

A. Intermittent driers
- Loft
- Compartment, Chamber, Cabinet

B. Continuous driers
- Tunnel
  - Parallel current
  - Countercurrent
- Drum
  - Atmospheric pressure
  - Vacuum
- Rotary
  - Parallel current
  - Countercurrent
  - Reversed current*
  - Vacuum
- Spray driers
  - Atmosphere press.
    - Hot air
    - Superheated steam
  - Vacuum

*A combination of parallel and counterflow.

A. *Intermittent Driers*

Since the rate of drying is proportional to the area exposed per unit of weight, it is advantageous so to dispose the material that all sides will be effective in evaporation. This is usually accomplished by hanging sheet material from hooks or bars and by supporting lump or granular material upon perforated trays or shelves. These trays may be either placed on supports in the drying chamber or held in a framework on a truck which can be run into the chamber. The latter method has the advantage of being easier to load and unload, the entire truck being mechanically turned on its side for the latter operation. Frequently transportation through the plant may be effected while the material is loaded for the drying operation.

Loft Driers.—The simplest form of drying chamber is a room or "loft" containing steam coils arranged in various ways within it. Such have been used in the past for drying writing paper, leather, fiber board and products of this type. These driers are bad from many standpoints. First, it is impossible to secure uniform distribution of heated air. There will always be air pockets and channels where the velocity will be either negligible or excessive. This makes uniformity of product impossible unless all the material is allowed to remain until the slowest drying is finished, greatly reducing the capacity of the drier. If that which is dry is removed and a fresh charge introduced, the drying of that nearly complete will be interfered with by the excessive moisture content of the air passing over the wet stock. The labor cost of constant inspection and the floor space required are factors not to be overlooked.

Cabinet, Compartment and Chamber Driers.—However, where a material must be dried very slowly to produce the best results, as in fine writing paper and heavy sole leather, a drier of this type produces a high grade of product. The above disadvantages may be overcome at a low cost by building the drier in small compartments or chambers arranged around a central exhaust, and causing the air to be circulated in accordance with the principle of the ring furnace (see page 209). This will secure practical continuity of operation, excellent distribution of the heat and drying air, and a lower labor cost.

When the material is lumpy or granular, or if it cannot be supported by hooks or bars, trays or racks are employed, and these are placed as a rule in a smaller space usually spoken of as a cabinet or compartment. For small self-contained installations, chamber driers as shown in Fig. 195 are very satisfactory and can be readily installed and operated. However, their overall efficiency is poor compared with that of a continuous drier.

Lumber must be dried in accordance with a definite time schedule, the temperature being the maximum and the humidity

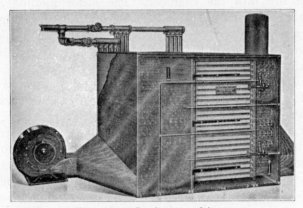

Fig. 195.—Gordon tray drier.

the minimum that the stock will bear without injury, to secure rapid diffusion with a limited concentration gradient through the stock. The drying conditions vary with the species and with the thickness of the stock, a characteristic schedule being given in Fig. 196.* The air temperature is marked T, the dew point D, and the per cent relative humidity H.

The maintenance of this schedule is most easily effected by intermittent operation of the chamber or kiln employed. One type of kiln is shown in Fig. 197. The kiln is enclosed and the drying air recirculated by natural convection, the lumber being slanted to utilize the increase in density of the air with evaporation to facilitate the movement. The air leaving the pile is partially dehumidified by the water spray F and then reheated by the steam pipes H. The drying conditions are con-

* H. D. Tiemann, "The Kiln Drying of Lumber," J. B. Lippincott Company, Philadelphia, 1917.

trolled by two thermometers inserted below and above the steam coils, the former showing the dew point and the latter the dry-bulb temperature of the drying air.

The two dotted curves in Fig. 196 show the moisture content of the wood at the points where the air enters the pile and leaves it. The horizontal distance between these two curves is the "lag" in drying caused by the increase in the moisture content

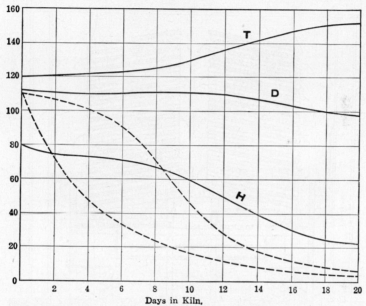

Drying Conditions Suitable for One Inch Red Gum, Black Gum and Black Walnut

Fig. 196.—Drying schedule for wood (*Tiemann*).

of the air as it passes through the pile. This emphasizes the inadequacy of natural circulation in such a case. Higher air velocity, or periodical reversal of its direction of flow, would dry the whole pile at the fastest rate allowable.

Attention is called to the care exercised in the design of this kiln to prevent air circulation other than through the pile and to secure uniform distribution of the air through the stock.

Drying in Vacuum.—In the driers so far described, air is used to carry away the water vapor from the drying material. When the nature of the product is such that it cannot be maintained hot in contact with air, or when drying at a low temperature is imperative, or when it is desired to condense and recover the liquid volatilized, vacuum driers are employed. These are either shelf or drum driers enclosed in an airtight vessel strong enough to sustain an external pressure of 15 lb. per sq. in., or a rotary drier in which may be maintained a diminished pressure. The vapor formed is led to a suitable condenser, and the air and any

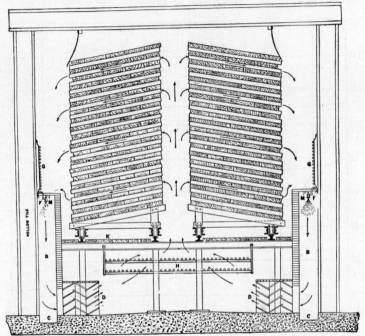

Fig. 197.—Diagram of the Tiemann water-spray humidity-regulated dry kiln (cross-sectional elevation).

fixed gases entering with the material to be dried are exhausted by a pump. Direct-heated shelf driers are of simple construction, the heat being introduced by means of steam coils and plates on which the trays are supported. They cannot easily be made continuous.

B. Continuous Driers

Tunnel Driers.—It is evident that, if the hooks, bars or trays on which the material is supported are moved through the drying space, the operation becomes continuous. The space will then be made long in relation to its cross section and the apparatus is spoken of as a tunnel drier (Fig. 198). Instead of moving the stock by supports placed on trucks, it may be propelled on an endless belt or moving platform, or other type of traveling conveyor (Fig. 199).

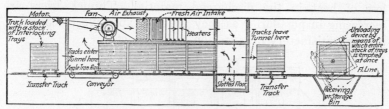

Fig. 198.—Tunnel drier.

In the case frequently encountered where the drying rate increases with increase in air velocity it is desirable to increase the air velocity without changing the ratio of the rates of supply of air and stock. This can be done in an apparatus of the type shown in Fig. 200, in which the air may be recirculated across the trucks and over the air reheaters by means of the fans within the drier. Such an apparatus can be operated as a constant-temperature drier if desired.

The heated drying air may be made to pass in the same direction as the stock, *parallel flow*, or it may pass in a direction

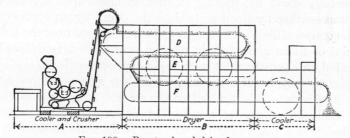

Fig. 199.—Proctor band drier for soap.

opposite to that of the stock, *countercurrent flow*. It is obvious that for efficient use of the heat and moisture-carrying capacity of the air the countercurrent method is in every way superior and should be used. When, however, it becomes necessary to have the stock leave the drier with a definite amount of moisture, or when so-called "casehardening" of the material is liable to occur, parallel flow gives a more satisfactory control of the temperature and humidity obtaining throughout the operation. Whenever allowable, heating elements (usually steam pipes) should be distributed through the space so as to keep the air at such a temperature that a satisfactory rate of evaporation may be obtained without overheating the product or causing undue loss of heat in the discharged material. Tunnel driers are increasing in popularity as they are not expensive to construct and are satisfactory in operation and product.

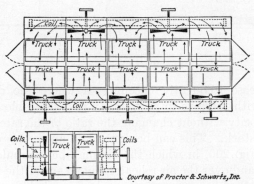

Courtesy of Proctor & Schwartz, Inc.

FIG. 200.—Tunnel drier with internal recirculation and reheating of air.

Drum Driers for Solids.—When the material to be dried is in the form of a continuous web, as, for example, paper or cloth, it is generally dried by passing it over steam-heated cylinders or drums—either by itself or held to the drum by an endless felt. The temperature of the sheet may be maintained near the boiling point of water and, since in passing over successive drums it is heated on alternate sides, very rapid evaporation is effected. In order to increase the capacity of such a system, sometimes a blast of warm air is directed on the stock. In a series of drums of the same diameter running at uniform speed, the linear velocity at a point near the wet end is the same as that at the dry end. If the material tends to shrink in drying, it must evidently suffer mechanical elongation of the sheet equal to the natural contraction of the material. Thus paper dried on a rapidly driven continuous machine has less tensile strength than the same stock dried slowly in a loft where it is free to shrink as the water leaves it. Apparently the difficulty could be met by rotating succeeding drums at a decreased rate of speed, or by making the drums with a successively smaller diameter.

Drum Driers for Liquids.—Many finely divided materials are of such character that, when supplied in the form of a thick cream or mush, they cling to the surface of a heated drum (Fig. 201) and are dried while the drum makes one revolution. Since the surface of the drum is the only source of heat, it is clear that it should be maintained at as high a temperature as the material being dried will tolerate. The thickness of the layer of material is regulated by a scraping knife or "doctor" on the feed side, and the dry

Fig. 201.—Atmospheric drum drier for liquids.

product is removed from the surface of the drum by a similar mechanism.

For a very large output of material the surface may be horizontal and the drier takes the form of a rotating disk or plate on which the material is fed through a slit from above. The discharge is effected by scraping the surface toward either the center or the periphery of the disk, or by a "doctor" which lifts the layer to a platform from which it is removed by a screw conveyor. These driers may be enclosed to prevent dusting or contamination of the air with poisonous materials.

When a low temperature is necessary, and yet rapid drying must be effected, drum driers are placed within heavy walls and a vacuum maintained.

Since the rate of evaporation is dependent upon the rate of heat flow through the drying layer, it is evident that, if a low temperature is to exist on the heating surface, the vapor pressure of the evaporated liquid in the surrounding space must be kept low. By maintaining a very low air pressure in the drier, an efficient condenser and a thin film of material on the drum, material such as whole milk may be dried at a very low temperature and yet with considerable rapidity. If the material will tolerate a high temperature, it is clear that exceedingly rapid drying can be effected by using high-pressure steam and maintaining a high vacuum.

The construction of a continuous drum or rotary *vacuum* drier is a complicated matter, as provision must be made for supplying the feed material and taking away the dry product without breaking the vacuum.

Rotary Driers.—The method of transporting material through a cylindrical reaction chamber by rotating the chamber on its horizontal axis with the discharge end slightly lower than the feed end is admirably adapted to the design of driers for handling all granular, crystalline or lumpy material which does not under this motion run together or roll itself into larger unit pieces. If the material is not injured by being in direct contact with the products of combustion of fuel, flue gases may be led directly through the cylinder and very rapid evaporation realized.

Lifting plates or shelves may be fastened to the inside of the cylinder, or shell, running through its entire length parallel to the axis and extending radially toward the center. The rotation of the cylinder continually elevates the material and throws it through the current of hot gas or air, the inclination of the shell moving the charge forward.

A simple form of such a rotary drier consists of a single shell made of heavy steel plate supported on steel tires riveted to it, which rest on rollers held in suitable bearings, very much as a cement kiln or a tube mill. It is driven by a gear fastened to the shell which engages a pinion keyed to a driving shaft. The discharge end of the drier is placed in direct contact with a furnace, and the flue gases are drawn through the drier either by a stack or by a fan. A fan is preferable to a stack because in the latter the gases must be so hot in order to maintain the draft that much heat is carried out of the apparatus, and, so far as drying is concerned, is unused. An exhaust fan permits excellent control of the supply of heated gases and therefore produces a more uniform product. The installation should be so arranged that, in case the drier for any reason stops, the flue gases may be by-passed to a stack and excessive heating avoided. If it is desired to calcine the product as well as dry it, the shell may be lined with fire brick and both operations may be carried on in the same apparatus.

Counterflow.—In an arrangement of this kind the hot dry gases from the furnace meet the charge as it leaves the drier, rapidly taking up any moisture that still remains in it. These gases leave the drier when in contact with the cold and wet charge, thus fully utilizing their heat and moisture-carrying capacity. This is as it should be. But there may be two disadvantages to this countercurrent arrangement. *First,* the charge may be heated excessively, and possibly ignited or otherwise injured (as, for example, coal); and, even if it does not suffer from the high temperature, heat is carried away with the hot charge and lost. *Second,* there is a minimum of heat at the feed end where the greatest amount is needed for preheating the entering cold charge and effecting prompt evaporation. Thus a material originally lumpy may carry so much moisture that a very slight increase in water content through condensation from the air will reduce it to a paste or make it ball together. In countercurrent flow the air can become so saturated with moisture in the middle or evaporating zone that it will deposit water when it strikes the cold incoming charge. It is in this case necessary to sacrifice the heat economy of the apparatus to make it operative, if at the same time it is to remain "foolproof." The difficulty may be met by feeding the drier at the furnace end, *i.e.,* by the use of parallel flow. The fresh charge now comes in contact with the hot dry gas and later condensation upon it through a fall in temperature is avoided. If in countercurrent flow the above condition is met, it may be remedied either by increasing the flow of air through the drier or by cutting down the rate of feed.

Parallel Flow.—It is sometimes desirable to reduce the moisture content of a material from a high to a low but definite content, and not to dry below this value. In this case parallel flow offers marked advantages, in that it is possible so to regulate the amount of entering flue gas that, on account of the resulting humidity and temperature of the exit gases, the moisture content of the charge cannot fall below the predetermined amount.

Reversed Current.—A combination of the good points of both systems of flow is obtained by passing the flue gases along the outside of the shell parallel to the charge, bringing them back in the inside countercurrent to and in contact with the charge. Although the coefficient of heat transfer from the gas to the shell and through this to the charge is smaller than that directly from gas to the charge, nevertheless, owing to the great temperature difference at the feed end of the shell, the gas is here materially cooled and the charge heated. The gases meeting the

FIG. 202.—Ruggles-Coles reversed-current drier.

finished charge at the discharge end are still dry, but so reduced in temperature that no ill effects are suffered. It should be noted that even in this type of drier the loss in heat through the discharge of product at a high temperature is frequently very large and should not be overlooked.

When the drier is placed in the flue from the furnace, the flue-gas velocities are, in ordinary practice, low, resulting in a low coefficient of heat transfer to the shell. This objection may be met by constructing the flue so as to be concentric with the shell, at such a distance from it that the velocity of the furnace gases along its surface is relatively high (see page 112). This will reduce the resistance to heat flow as far as possible, and furthermore reduce the area and hence the heat loss from the outside of the flue. Or, two concentric cylinders may be employed, feeding the charge into the space between the shells and passing the flue gases down through the center of the drier parallel to the charge, and back between the shells countercurrent to it (Fig. 202). Heat loss is reduced by placing the hottest gases on the inside, but obviously a greater heat transfer would be obtained from gases outside a single shell, owing to the much greater area exposed, provided the gas velocity be kept high by proper flue construction as above indicated. This also results in cheaper and more substantial shell construction.

Notes on Rotary Driers.—Rotary direct-fired driers, both single and double pass as above described, are suitable for drying all materials occurring in aggregates which are not injured by contact with flue gas or by the relatively high temperature of these gases coming direct from the furnace. Such materials are ores, coal, cement rock, phosphate pebbles and many products of this kind. Where contamination with dust must be avoided, hot air may be used instead of flue gases.

The capacity of such driers is limited by that velocity of the gas in contact with the charge which is allowable without blowing the stock from the drier. This allowable velocity must be determined for each specific material to be dried. Great advantage results from using entering gas at high temperature, since this enables each pound of gas to pick up a much larger amount of water vapor, thereby reducing the necessary gas consumption, and therefore greatly increasing the capacity without exceeding the allowable gas velocity. For materials uninjured by heat the temperature of the gas is limited by the danger of warping and corroding the shell. Entering gas at 1400°F. can be employed without danger in this regard, especially if the temperature of the shell at the point of gas entrance is kept down by contact with the wet charge as in parallel-current and reverse-current operation.

Such driers cannot be operated with sticky materials. Materials sticky while wet, but nonsticky and reasonably absorbent when dry, can be successfully handled in such rotary driers by shunting a portion of the dry discharged material back to the feed end of the drier and mixing it there with the wet material in such proportion as to absorb its moisture sufficiently to render it nonsticky. The mixture then passes through the drier without "balling up" or sticking to the sides. The amount of dry discharge that must be returned for admixture with the wet stock is determined experimentally for each individual case.

In drying certain other materials such as fuller's earth for decolorization purposes, kaolin, ocher and products used for pigments, it is not permissible to use direct firing. In this case a

single-pass indirect-fired drier is employed. But such a drier
may be fitted with flues or ducts on the outside shell through
which the flue gases return, and thus become a double-pass
drier. These ducts function as the shelves or lifting plates to
distribute the charge through the drying space. When a relatively low and well-regulated temperature must be maintained
as in drying brewers' grains, cottonseed, cattle foods and other
organic material, a bank of steam coils may replace the furnace,
the drying taking place solely at the expense of the heat in the air.
Or, steam pipes may be set in a header at the lower end of the
drier and may be carried its entire length parallel to the axis of
rotation. The condensed water is drained into the header and by
hollow trunnions is periodically expelled. For drying sand and
materials used in glass and pottery, or other products which
would be injured by the presence of rust, steam-heated rotary
driers may be lined with wood.

Spray Driers.—It is sometimes desirable to evaporate a large
amount of water and yet quickly produce a dry product. This
requires very rapid vaporization, necessitating the exposure of
the largest possible surface at the highest allowable temperature.
When the material is not injured thereby, the liquid, preferably
superheated, is sprayed under high pressure directly into a rotary
drier together with the flame itself from an oil burner or the other
source of heat employed in the drier. In place of radial shelves
the drier should be fitted with loose chains hanging horizontally.
These keep the surface of the drier clear of adhering material.
The product may be so fine as to necessitate an air separator for
its total recovery (see page 314). Strong solutions of inorganic
salts may be dried in this manner.

If the material is partly organic, as, for example, the concentrated liquor from the soda or sulfate process for making cellu-
lose pulp, the rotary drier may also function as a furnace, and the
material may not only be evaporated and dried but also calcined
in the one operation.

Driers have been proposed in which the material (solution or
emulsion) is sprayed into a chamber through which superheated
steam is recirculated, as in Fig. 203. The heat transfer does not
here take place under favorable conditions and therefore the use
of such an apparatus is limited to the drying of liquids sensitive
to air when hot.

Superheated Vapor.—Superheated vapor as a means of carrying heat adapts itself admirably to the drying of material which cannot come into contact with air and which is itself a poor heat conductor. Thus, where wool or leather has been degreased by treatment with naphtha, it is hard to dry because

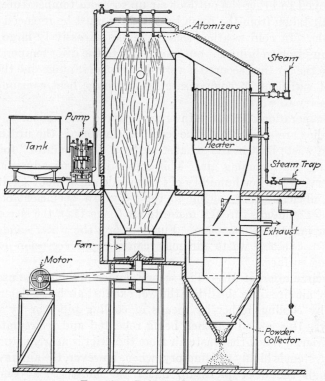

Fig. 203.—Buhl spray-type drier.

of the difficulty in getting the heat necessary for the vaporization of the solvent into the material by direct contact with steam pipes or other heating surface. By circulating a current of superheated naphtha vapor through the mass, the liquid naphtha is volatilized and carried out of the drier. An amount of vapor equal to the liquid vaporized is continuously drawn off to a condenser, and the material is left practically free from all naphtha vapor. This method of drying seems capable of wide application when the material is not so difficult to handle as the above, but where the liquid is to be recovered.

AUXILIARY OPERATIONS AND EQUIPMENT

Most driers utilize air drawn from the room, which is usually warmer than the outdoor temperature. However, the drier in reality utilizes outdoor air, because artificial heat must be employed to bring the outdoor air up to room temperature, and any air taken from the room by the drier must be replaced from outside. In cold weather this means an excessively large heat consumption to bring the outdoor air up to the drier temperature. While the air thus secured is very dry, the advantage due thereto is not sufficient to compensate for the large heat consumption necessary to warm it.

Recuperation of Heat.—In order to avoid this difficulty, three remedies are available. The least satisfactory is the utilization of the waste heat in the exhaust air by a "recuperator" for pre-heating the incoming air. This method has the advantage of conserving the low humidity of the outside air without sacrificing heat efficiency, but, owing to the very low coefficient of heat transfer from gas through metal to air (page 112), the size of the "recuperator" is excessive. Furthermore, the water condensed from the moist waste air may cause rapid corrosion of the cooling surface.

Recirculation of Air.—The second device involves the use of a closed air circuit in the drier, the wet exhaust air being dehumidified by cooling, either by means of cooling pipes or by water sprays, this cooled air then being reheated and recirculated to the drier. When the waste air from the drier is nearly saturated, this system is highly satisfactory; when, however, the air traveling through the drier picks up but little moisture—a condition encountered toward the end of intermittent drying operations—the quantity of air which must be cooled and reheated is so large that the heat efficiency is very low. Under such conditions resort is best made to a third method, namely, the removal from the waste air of a portion which is thoroughly cooled and dehumidified. This dry fraction is then mixed with the remainder of the wet air, reducing its humidity to the desired point by dilution. By this device it is possible to realize good heat economy.

Automatic Control of Air Temperature.—The maintenance of automatic control of temperature and humidity is of great importance in drying operations. This is done by the utilization of thermostatic regulators, devices which consist of a sensitive element exposed to the temperature it is desired to control, and which produce some sort of physical effect that can be utilized to regulate the heat supply. Some regulators employ as the sensitive element a metal, the expansion of which operates the mechanism; others use the expansion of a liquid; others use the change in resistivity of an electrical conductor, and so on. Some operate through direct mechanical devices while others function electrically. Regulators can be obtained on the market which are simple in construction and maintenance and which will easily control the temperature within 5°F. Indeed, control within 1° is realized in commercial practice, though generally the closer the control, the more complicated the mechanism and the more attention it will require. To avoid localized variations in the conditions of the air, it is important to insure perfect mixing of the air before it reaches the sensitive element of the regulator.

Automatic Control of Humidity.—Thermostatic regulators operate solely to maintain a definite temperature. They can, however, be employed to maintain any desired humidity by utilizing them as wet- and dry-bulb thermometers. If the sensitive element of a regulator is covered with a wick, kept moist, and exposed to air at a sufficiently high velocity, the element assumes the wet-bulb temperature. Any variation in the wet-bulb temperature will cause the regulating mechanism to function.

If, for example, it is desired to supply a drier with air of 30 per cent humidity at 100°F., it can be automatically done as follows: The outdoor air employed is passed through a bank of steam coils, and in addition a steam jet blowing live steam into the air, preferably just as it enters the heating coils, is provided. The valve controlling the steam supply to the heating coils is operated by a thermostatic regulator, the element of which is placed at the entrance to the drier and set to function at 100°F. The live-steam supply to the jet is controlled by a second valve operated by a second sensitive element placed beside the first, but this second element is surrounded by a wick kept wet and its regulator is set to function at 75°F. If the air entering the drier is too cold, the first thermostatic regulator will increase the steam supply in the heating coils, thereby raising the tempera-

ture of the air.   If the wet-bulb temperature of the air entering
the drier is too high, the second thermal regulator will reduce the
steam supply to the jet, thereby reducing the moisture content
of the air and, in consequence, its wet-bulb temperature.

A still more satisfactory method of controlling the humidity
of the air entering this drier is to mix the relatively dry outdoor
air with the humid waste air from the drier itself.   In such a case,
the wet-bulb regulator controls the damper in the duct leading the
recirculated air to the air entrance of the drier; the dry-bulb
regulator controls, as before, the steam coils in the air-feed duct.
If the dry-bulb temperature of the air entering the drier is too
low, the regulator turns on more steam.   If the wet-bulb temperature is too high, the regulator closes the damper in the wet-
air return pipe, thus giving a larger proportion of dry outside air.

A device frequently employed for humidity control in driers
operating with a closed air circuit is to control the temperature
to which the recirculated air is cooled.   Where the recirculated
air is at its dew point after passing through the dehumidifying
apparatus, the temperature of the air determines its moisture
content.   Thus, in the Tiemann drier (see page 624, humidity
control is obtained by two regulators: the first controlling the
dry-bulb temperature (dew point, in this case) of the recirculated
air as it leaves the spray coolers; and the second the dry-bulb
temperature of this same air after being heated by its passage
through the steam pipes just previous to coming in contact with
the wood.   While giving excellent humidity control, it must be
borne in mind, as shown above, that this method involves low
heat efficiency unless the air discarded from the drier is nearly
saturated.

Air Circulation.—One of the most important points in the
design of drying apparatus and the control of drying operations
is the provision for adequate and uniform air velocity past the
material.   Especially in the drying of thin sheets and fine grains
or lumps, a reasonably high velocity is desirable to secure most
rapid evaporation.   In the case of thicker sheets and larger
lumps, high velocity does not help so much because, as will be
shown on page 653, the major resistance to evaporation in such
cases is in the diffusion of the moisture from the interior of the
material to the surface.   Even in these cases, however, *uniformity*
of air distribution past the surface is essential to secure uniform

drying. This requires the avoidance in design of sharp bends, especially at those points where the air enters the drying apparatus, of inequalities in cross section and the like.

Where the total amount of air required for drying is small, but the velocity past the material must be relatively large, it is highly desirable to use *transverse* circulation of the air over the material, so that the air flows through the apparatus in a spiral path, as illustrated on page 677. Such circulation involves additional fans, but secures both rapidity and uniformity of evaporation.

In the drying of sheet materials the air must of necessity flow parallel to the sheets. The air impinging against the edges of the sheets dries those edges far more rapidly than the middle, resulting in warping of the sheets due to unequal shrinkage. This can be avoided by protecting these edges from the air. For example, the sheets may be supported on wire gauze fastened to a frame made of wood or angle iron, the sides of which serve as protection for the edges of the sheet.

For the circulation of air through a drier, the pressure drop is usually substantial while the volume of air required is small. It is consequently advisable to utilize centrifugal fans designed for these conditions. For the *transverse* circulation of air within the drier itself, in order to secure high air velocity past the material being dried, a very large volumetric capacity is desirable. In order to limit the power consumption and the initial cost of the fan, the recirculation should be carried out in such a way as to introduce a negligible resistance to the air flow, thus making it possible to employ the so-called "volumetric" type of fan, *i.e.*, a fan with propeller blades which drive the air in a direction parallel to the axis of the fan. Such fans can be used only against very small pressure heads but under these conditions handle large volumes at good efficiency and with low initial cost.

PART IV. DESIGN OF DRIERS

Steps to Be Taken in the Design of Air Driers.—The steps taken in the design of apparatus in which a solid is dried *by means of air* are eight in number and may be taken in the following order:

1. Choose the type of drying apparatus and the drying conditions to be employed, *using the highest safe temperature.*

2. Sketch diagrammatically the apparatus chosen, indicating amounts, moisture contents and temperatures of the material entering and leaving the apparatus, and the temperatures and humidities of the air entering and leaving and, where possible, at other points in the drier.

3. From a knowledge of the capacity desired, calculate the air required to carry away the water vapor. Complete details of this step are given on pages 589 to 590.

4. Calculate the necessary heat supply, making suitable allowance for heat necessary to vaporize the water, heat carried out in stock and conveyors and heat losses to the surroundings (pages 589 to 590).

5. Choose suitable methods and devices for controlling the temperatures and humidities of the air at the various points in the equipment (pages 636 to 638), and indicate these in the sketch.

6. Calculate the time necessary for the escape of the moisture, and the cross section and length of the drier.

7. Calculate the necessary heating surface, and arrange it so as to maintain the desired drying conditions.

8. Calculate the pressure drop and fan horsepower necessary to maintain the circulation of air.

Characteristics of Drying Apparatus.—The following classification of driers is based upon the methods used in supplying the heat to the charge, these methods depending mainly upon the sensitiveness to heat of the material being dried. This classification is useful in choosing the type of apparatus and the drying conditions to be employed (Step 1) and will be used later as a basis for the design of various types of driers.

1. *Steam Heated Drum and Tray Driers.—The charge is in direct contact with the surface of a solid heating element, and all heat is received directly therefrom; the temperature of the heating surface is insufficient to injure the charge.* This type is suitable for thick liquids or pastes which become dusty when dry (pigments), or for similar material requiring very rapid evaporation (milk). Low temperature can be secured by the use of vacuum.

2. *Direct-fired Rotary* Driers.—The drier is heated directly by hot furnace flue gases.* This is suitable for granular, lumpy, nondusting materials insensitive to heat.

* Tunnel driers could be employed.

    A. Direct contact of flue gas with charge.
      a. Flow countercurrent.
      b. Flow parallel current.
      c. Flow reverse current.
    B. Indirect contact of flue gas with charge.
      a. Flow countercurrent.
      b. Flow reverse current.
3. *Air Driers for Sensitive Materials.*
    A. Adiabatic driers giving maximum allowable wet-bulb temperature—suitable for materials sensitive to heat when wet but not when dry (glue, sugar, etc.).
    B. Constant-temperature driers, operated at maximum allowable air temperature—suitable for materials sensitive to heat when dry but not when wet (textiles, rubber, etc.).
    C. Controlled humidity driers—suitable for materials sensitive to humidity conditions.
      a. Decomposition results if humidity falls outside definite upper and lower limits: hydrated crystals and materials from which adsorbed water must not be completely removed, *e.g.,* soda lime. Controlled humidity drier with highest evaporation rate consistent with the humidity limits.
      b. Material injured by excessive rate of drying *i.e.,* by excessive humidity difference: lumber, heavy leather, fine paper, ceramics, plastic films, etc. Controlled humidity drier operated to limit properly the evaporation rate. Intermittent driers sometimes are preferable because of more exact control and because the temperature and humidity conditions necessary for maximum safe drying capacity are incompatible with continuous operation.

Definitions.—Referring to the list of steps to be taken in designing driers, it will be seen that some of the steps cannot be taken intelligently without a thorough knowledge of the mechanism of drying, and hence the problem of determining the proper drying time (Step 6) will be discussed first.

Before taking this up, it is advisable to define the units in which percentage moisture is to be expressed in order to facilitate calculations in drier design, and to define "drying conditions."

Dry vs. Wet Basis.—The analytical laboratory usually reports percentage total moisture on the *wet* basis, *i.e.*, material containing 10 per cent moisture contains 90 units of weight of bone-dry stock and 10 units of weight of moisture. However, in the calculations which follow, it is preferable to calculate percentage water on the *dry* basis. Thus the material referred to above would contain 11.1 per cent of water on the dry basis, namely, 11.1 lb. of moisture per 100 lb. of bone-dry stock. The latter method reduces all moisture data to a common basis and hence has an advantage over the former method. For example, the water to be evaporated per ton of product to reduce the moisture content from 60 to 20 per cent of water (wet basis) is 2000 (0.80) ($^{60}/_{40}$ — $^{20}/_{80}$) or 2000 lb. *Throughout the following pages it will be assumed that all moisture data are expressed on the dry basis; the pounds of total water per pound of bone-dry stock will be designated by the symbol T.*

Equilibrium Water or "Regain."—As shown on page 620, certain materials hold definite and appreciable percentages of moisture when kept exposed to air of a given relative humidity. This adsorbed water is called the "equilibrium" moisture, and in industry, the "regain." The pounds of equilibrium moisture per pound of bone-dry stock will be called the *equilibrium moisture* and designated by the symbol E.

Free Moisture.—The total moisture T less the equilibrium moisture E is defined as the *free* moisture or *free* water W, and it will be seen that this difference, $T - E$, is one of the important factors controlling the rate of drying.

Drying Conditions.—The rate of evaporation of moisture from a material is determined by the temperature and humidity of the air with which it is in contact, by the character of its exposure to that air, by the velocity of the air passing it and by any radiant heat it may receive, *i.e.*, by the *condition of its surroundings*. These external conditions are called the *drying conditions* to which the material is exposed.

RATE OF AIR DRYING OF SOLIDS UNDER CONSTANT DRYING CONDITIONS

First, differential equations will be derived for the air drying of solids *under constant drying conditions*. In some cases the equations so derived may be used for commercial driers without introducing serious error. In other cases, it will be shown how these equations must be modified for *variable drying conditions.*

Assume that initial moisture concentration is uniform and sufficiently high so that the surface of the slab is thoroughly wet at the start. As soon as the sheet is brought into contact with the warmer air, the water on the surface begins to evaporate and the vapor flows through the air film into the surrounding air and is carried out of the drier by the air stream. This decrease in water concentration at the surface causes liquid water to flow from the interior of the sheet toward the surface, depleting the

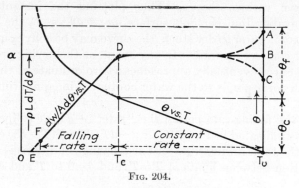

Fig. 204.

total water content of the sheet. So long as the surface remains sufficiently wet, evaporation proceeds at constant rate, since during this period the surface behaves as a wet-bulb psychrometer and the heat transferred from the warmer air and surroundings to the surface is quantitatively consumed in evaporating water at the temperature of the surface of the sheet. This period corresponds to the curve *BD* of Fig. 204.

If the drying operation is continued, the surface concentration of liquid eventually becomes so low that the surface no longer behaves as thoroughly wet, and hence the evaporative rate decreases and the so-called "falling-rate" period has begun. Since the rate of evaporation is now less than before, the rate of heat consumption likewise decreases, but the rate of heat input is momentarily unchanged. The surplus heat must therefore be absorbed by the sheet, raising the temperature of the surface. Although this increase in temperature increases the difference in partial pressure of water vapor across the air film, the surface concentration of water is still decreasing, and the rate of drying continues to decrease. The moisture content at which the rate of drying starts to decrease is called the **critical water content** T_c, and is usually expressed as weight of total water per unit weight of bone-dry stock.

During the falling-rate period water may continue to evaporate only at the surface, or may evaporate in the interior of a sufficiently porous material. Depending upon the thickness of the slab, and upon other factors such as the rate of evaporation during the constant-rate period and the ease with which liquid water flows through the interior, the rate curve in the falling-rate period may have various shapes. Thus plotting the instantaneous rate of evaporation per unit surface $dw/A \, d\theta$ vs. T, the weight ratio of total water to dry stock, the curve may be convex upward, linear or concave upward. In any event, as the drying proceeds, the rate curve eventually approaches a zero ordinate at the point E, which corresponds to the water content E in equilibrium with the air.

If in the falling-rate period the "rate" $-dT/d\theta$ is linear[1] in $T - E$, as indicated in Fig. 204, *i.e.*, $-dT/d\theta = K(T - E)$, calculation of the total drying time for fixed drying conditions is simple. Integration between limits of $T = T_c$ and $\theta = 0$ to T and θ_F gives

$$\theta_F = \frac{1}{K} \ln \frac{T_c - E}{T - E} = \frac{1}{K} \ln \frac{W_c}{W} \qquad (1)$$

where W is the free water and is equal to $T - E$. This equation shows that the time in the falling-rate period is proportional to the fractional reduction in free water, *i.e.*, a given time is required to halve the existing value of W, regardless of its magnitude.

For example, upon drying a certain material under constant drying conditions, it is found that 2 hr. are required to reduce the free-moisture concentration from 20 to 10 per cent, no constant-rate period being encountered. How much longer would be required to reduce the free water to 4 per cent? Upon applying Eq. 1 to each portion of the run, K is eliminated by dividing one equation by the other, giving $\theta/2 = \log{(10/4)}/\log{(20/10)} = 1.32$, *i.e.*, an additional time θ of 2.64 hr. is required.

Since the rate at the beginning of the falling-rate period equals that in the constant-rate period, one may write $KW_c = (W_0 - W_c)/\theta_c$, or

$$\theta_c = \frac{W_0 - W_c}{KW_c}. \tag{2}$$

Hence the total time $\Sigma\theta$ to dry from T_0 to T is

$$\Sigma\theta = \frac{1}{K}\left[\frac{W_0 - W_c}{W_c} + \ln\frac{W_c}{W}\right]. \tag{3}$$

Also, the ratio of the drying time in the two periods is independent of K:

$$\frac{\theta_F}{\theta_c} = \frac{\ln\dfrac{W_c}{W}}{\dfrac{W_0 - W_c}{W_c}} \tag{4}$$

and depends only on the numerical values of the W-terms. For example, if W_0 is 2, W_c is 1 and W is 0.1,

$$\frac{\theta_F}{\theta_c} = \frac{2.3 \log (1/0.1)}{(2-1)/(1)} = 2.3.$$

Thus, although the falling-rate period removed only 0.9 times as much water as the constant-rate period, it was 2.3 times as long. If the final water content had been 0.01, θ_F/θ_c would have been 4.6.

The Constant-rate Period.—The rate of evaporation in this period is fixed by the drying conditions chosen. Thus in terms of the nomenclature of page 682 the magnitude of the air velocity and the angle of incidence of the air stream upon the surface fix both the coefficient of heat transfer h_c by conduction and convection from the air to the surface of the sheet, and the rate coefficient k' for the transfer of the water vapor from the surface of the sheet to the main body of the air. The humidity of the air is also fixed arbitrarily. Assuming that the sheet initially has the uniform temperature t_s, these terms are related by the heat balance

$$(A/A_w)[h_c(t-t_s)+h_r(t'-t_s)]/\lambda_s = k'(H_s - H) = \alpha \tag{5}$$

where α is the constant rate of evaporation per unit wetted surface.

Assuming equilibrium at the interface, H_s is the humidity of saturated air at the temperature t_s of the surface of the sheet.

Where all the surface is wetted, A equals A_w, and, if the temperatures t of the air and t' of the surroundings are the same, t_s is the wet-bulb temperature; if the air velocity is high, h_c is large compared with h_r, and t_s approaches the true wet-bulb temperature t_w of the air. In any event the heat balance requires that t_s be constant during the constant-rate period.

When small samples are dried in the laboratory, it is sometimes the practice to waterproof the edges. If the dry surface $A - A_w$ is a substantial fraction of the total surface, a heat balance shows that the sheet will attain a temperature above that of the wet-bulb of the air, and, as shown in Fig. 205,[2] a higher rate of evaporation will be obtained than when drying large thin sheets of the same material. When material supported in trays is dried, heat conduction through the bottom and sides of the tray will increase the heat supply and raise the temperature of the wetted surface, thus increasing the rate of drying.

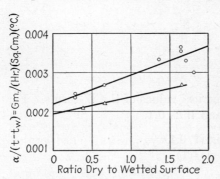

Fig. 205.—Effect of waterproofing edges of blocks on rate of drying during constant-rate period.

The following table[5] shows the evaporative rates in the constant-rate period when drying various materials in a pan over

TABLE I.—RATES OF EVAPORATION FROM VARIOUS MATERIALS[5]

Material	Gm./(Hr.)(Sq. Cm. Wet Face)
Water	0.27
Whiting pigment	0.21
Brass filings	0.24
Brass turnings	0.24
Sand (five sizes)	0.20–0.24
Clays	0.23–0.27

which air at 130°F. and of low humidity was blown at a velocity of approximately 11 ft. per sec. Since the ratio of dry to wetted surfaces was 1.65, the rates were higher than would have been obtained with A_w equal to A, but the various materials, including water, gave nearly the same evaporation rates, α.

In a laboratory drier containing only one sample, the effect of radiation may be much more marked than in a commercial drier where only a few samples are exposed to the radiation from the surroundings.

Clearly the rate of drying per unit surface in the constant-rate period may be increased (1) by using warmer and less humid air, thus increasing $t-t_s$ (Fig. 206),[13] (2) by using radiation and metallic conduction in addition to heat transfer from the air itself, and (3) by increasing the air velocity, thus increasing h_c and k' (Fig. 207).

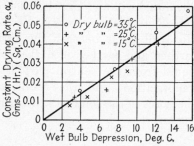

FIG. 206.—Effect of increasing wet-bulb depression in increasing rate of drying in constant-rate period.

For fixed drying conditions it is seen that the rate of drying per unit surface is independent of the thickness of the sheet and is not affected by shrinkage. Let Q be the weight of bone-dry stock in the sheet. Assuming the stock initially has the uniform temperature t_s, the constant-rate time θ_c may be calculated from heat-transfer considerations:

$$\theta_c = \frac{Q(T_0-T_c)\lambda_s}{A[h_c(t-t_s)+h_r(t'-t_s)]}.$$

(6)

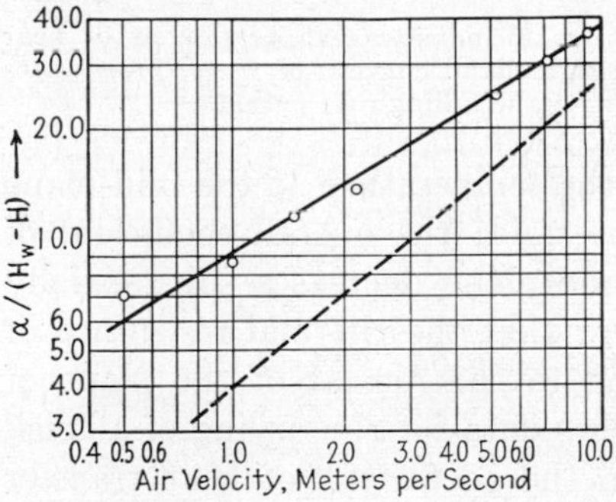

FIG. 207.—Effect of increasing air velocity upon rate of drying per unit humidity difference, in constant-rate period. The solid line is based on data[13] for drying slabs of clay 3 cm. thick, $A_w/A = 0.6$, with air at 40°C. having a relative humidity of 60 per cent. The dotted line is based on evaporation of water in a wetted-wall tower (see reference 3, p. 612).

The Falling-rate Period.— Visualize a run under fixed drying conditions with a material having but little porosity. If the drying conditions are such that in the constant-rate period the rate of evaporation per unit surface is small, when the surface concentration falls below the critical value, the falling-rate period begins but the liquid will be able to flow from the interior to the surface (or to a plane near the surface) and will evaporate at that plane throughout the falling-rate period. If the rate in the constant-rate period is made sufficiently high by using more drastic drying conditions, when the falling-rate period ensues, the liquid will no longer be able to flow to the surface at the high rate demanded by the drying conditions. In this event evaporation will occur beneath the surface at a plane which retreats farther and farther into the solid as the run proceeds. The liquid from the central part of the slab flows to the plane of vaporization, and the resulting vapor diffuses out through the pores in the solid and through the gas film into the surrounding air.[3]

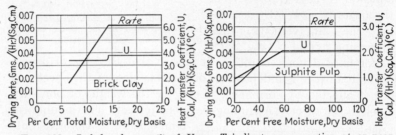

Fig. 208.—Left-hand curve[5] of U vs. T indicates evaporation at or near surface during the falling-rate period; right-hand curve[4] of U vs. T indicates retreat of the plane of vaporization during the falling-rate period.

It is instructive to measure the temperature at the mid-plane of the slab as the run progresses. If the overall coefficient of heat transfer U from air to mid-plane decreases substantially as the run progresses, it is clear that the thermal resistance of the interior is increasing owing to the retreat of the plane of vaporization.* Figure 208 shows data for the drying of a brick clay[5] under conditions where the coefficient of heat transfer showed no substantial decrease in the falling-rate period, while the data for the sulfite-pulp block[4] show subsurface evaporation.

Figure 209 shows data[3] for the drying of slabs of paper pulp with air of the same temperature, humidity and velocity. In the falling-rate period subsurface evaporation occurred in the more porous sample, which was similar to blotting paper, but evaporation occurred at the surface of the less porous pulp, which was similar to writing paper.

* Ordinarily one may neglect the sensible heat picked up by the slab compared with the heat consumed in vaporizing water.

With quite porous solids capillarity plays an important part,[6] and with a nonhygroscopic material containing grains of non-uniform size the movement of water is controlled by capillarity and not by concentration gradients. With porous materials where drastic drying conditions are used, subsurface evaporation

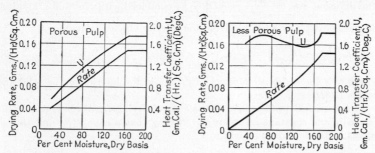

FIG. 209.—In the falling-rate periods, the curves of U vs. T indicate retreat of the plane of vaporization for the porous sample and vaporization at or near the surface for the less porous sample.

will be encountered and it is desirable to ventilate the solids.[7] In some cases it is practical to blow the air through a bed of the solid, or rotary driers (page 630) may be used.

Evaporation at the Surface during Falling-rate Period.—When the drying conditions are such that the water diffuses to the surface before evaporating, drying equations may be developed from the diffusion laws and certain assumptions.

If the falling-rate period has been preceded by a constant-rate period such that the moisture-distribution curve will have approached the parabolic form,

$$\frac{c_m - c}{c_m - c_s} = \frac{(x-L)^2}{L^2} \qquad (7)$$

wherein c is the concentration at the distance x from one face, c_m is the concentration at the mid-plane and L is the half-thickness of the sheet (see Fig. 210). Differentiation of this equation and substitutions of x equal to zero and

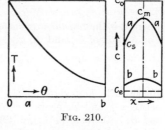

FIG. 210.

$2L$, respectively, give the concentration gradients at the surfaces:

$$-\left(\frac{dc}{dx}\right)_s = \mp \frac{2(c_m - c_s)}{L}. \qquad (7a)$$

The average concentration $c_{av.}$ at any time equals $(1/L)\int_0^L c\,dx$. Eliminating

c by means of Eq. 7, this integration gives $c_{\text{av.}} = c_m - \dfrac{(c_m - c_s)}{3}$; hence one may write

$$c_{\text{av.}} - c_s = \frac{2(c_m - c_s)}{3}. \tag{7b}$$

The diffusion law, $-\dfrac{L\rho\,dT}{d\theta} = -D\left(\dfrac{dc}{dx}\right)_s$, combined with (7a) and (7b), gives the rate of diffusion of liquid from the interior of the surface:

$$-L\rho\frac{dT}{d\theta} = -D\left(\frac{dc}{dx}\right)_s = \frac{2D}{L}(c_m - c_s) = D\frac{2}{L}\frac{3}{2}(c_{\text{av.}} - c_s) = \frac{c_{\text{av.}} - c_s}{(L/3D)} = \frac{c_{\text{av.}} - c_s}{r_i} \tag{8}$$

where r_i is the *resistance to liquid diffusion* in the interior of the solid and equals $L/3D$.

At the critical water content, the rate of drying $(c_{\text{av.}} - c_s)/r_i$ equals the rate α in the constant-rate period. Noting that c equals $T\rho$ and that r_i equals $L/3D$, this gives

$$\frac{(T_c - T_{sc})\rho D}{\alpha L} = \frac{1}{3}. \tag{8a}$$

It should be remembered that Eqs. 8 and 8a for the falling-rate period depend on the assumptions that the constant-rate period was long enough for the parabolic concentration gradient to be established in the slab, and that the concentration gradient remains parabolic during the falling-rate period. However, they may be used as approximations even where there is no constant-rate period and the error will not be serious in the usual case where a large fraction of the original water is removed.

Assume that in the falling-rate period the instantaneous rate of evaporation per unit surface is proportional to the difference between the surface concentration c_s and the concentration c_e corresponding to equilibrium with the main body of the air flowing past the surface:

$$-L\rho\frac{dT}{d\theta} = \frac{c_s - c_e}{r_s} \tag{9}$$

where r_s is the *resistance to surface evaporation*.

Comparison of (8) and (9) gives the relation

$$\frac{T - T_s}{T_s - E} = \frac{r_i}{r_s}. \tag{9a}$$

Hence, with any given value of the resistance ratio r_i/r_s, the difference between T and T_s bears a constant relation to the difference between T_s and E; both these potential differences decrease as the run proceeds, their ratio remaining constant.

Since the rate of evaporation at the beginning of the falling-rate period equals that in the constant-rate period, one may write $(T_{sc} - E)\rho/r_s = \alpha = k'(H_{sc} - H)$, which gives

$$r_s = \frac{(T_{sc} - E)\rho}{\alpha} = \frac{(T_{sc} - E)\rho}{k'(H_{sc} - H)}. \tag{9b}$$

Solving Eqs. 8 and 9 for the driving forces and adding to eliminate c_s give

$$-\frac{dT}{T-E}=\frac{d\theta}{L(r_i+r_s)}=K\,d\theta \qquad (10)$$

where K is called the *drying coefficient* and represents the term $1/(L)(r_i+r_s)$. Equation 10 shows that a plot of $-dT/d\theta$ vs. $T-E$ should be linear, as illustrated by curve DF of Fig. 204.

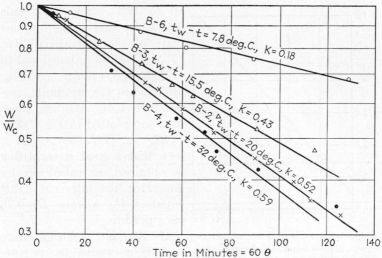

FIG. 211.—Semilogarithmic plot of data for drying of slabs of clay[5] during the falling-rate period.

Upon neglecting shrinkage and assuming r_i and r_s constant, integration between limits of $\theta=0$ and $T=T_1$, and θ and T, gives

$$\ln\frac{T_1-E}{T-E}=\frac{\theta}{L(r_i+r_s)}=K\theta. \qquad (11)$$

It is to be noted that K is the slope of the line obtained when plotting $T-E$ on a logarithmic scale *vs.* the falling-rate time plotted to a uniform scale, as in Fig. 211. The values of K are based on θ expressed in hours.

Case 1. *Both Resistances Important.*—Equation 11 applies, but it is instructive to eliminate r_i and r_s, giving

$$\frac{1}{K}=\frac{\theta}{\ln\dfrac{T_1-E}{T-E}}=L\left[\frac{L}{3D}+\frac{\rho(T_{sc}-E)}{\alpha}\right]. \qquad (11a)$$

Where runs have been made with various constant drying conditions, α, L and E are the only variables. As can be seen from Eq. 11a, a plot of $1/KL^2$ vs. $(T_{sc}-E)/\alpha L$ should give a straight line having a slope of ρ and at zero abscissa the intercept on the $1/KL^2$-scale should equal $1/3D$.

Figure 212 shows falling-rate data for slabs of whiting[2] dried with air at constant velocity. The half-thickness varied from 0.315 to 1.91 cm., and the wet-bulb depression $t-t_w$ ranged from 10 to 16°C. Since α equals

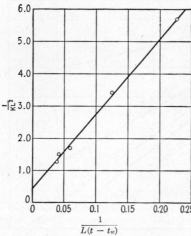

$h(t-t_s)/\lambda$, and since for this material E is negligible, $(T_{sc}-E)/\alpha L$ is proportional to $(1/L)(t-t_{sc})$. Since t_{sc} closely approaches the wet-bulb temperature t_w of the air, these data are plotted in Fig. 212 as $1/KL^2$ vs. $(1/L)(t-t_w)$. It is seen that a good straight line is obtained, as called for by Eq. 11a; the intercept $1/3D$ equals 0.44, whence $D=0.76$ cm.^{2} per hr.

FIG. 212.—Graphical determination of D for slabs of whiting; values of K were determined from slopes of the lines obtained upon plotting the data[2] for the falling-rate periods as $\ln W$ vs. θ.

If the air velocity were varied, α would be proportional to the nth power of the mass velocity G of the air, and Fig. 212 could be modified by plotting $1/KL^2$ vs. $(T_{sc}-E)\rho/L(t-t_{sc})G^n$.

Alternatively one can calculate α from existing data on k' (page 608), estimate T_{sc} by extrapolating the equilibrium curve of E to 100 per cent relative humidity and calculate D from Eq. 11a.*

Case 2. Resistance to Surface-evaporation Controlling.—In this case Eq. 11 reduces to

$$\ln \frac{T_1-E}{T-E} = \frac{\theta}{r_s L}.$$

* Values of D may also be obtained from constant-rate data by the use of Fig. 216, as explained on p. 656.

Eliminating r_s by means of (9b), one obtains

$$\ln \frac{T_1 - E}{T - E} = \left[\frac{k'(H_{sc} - H)}{L(\rho)(T_{sc} - E)} \right] \theta = \frac{\beta \theta}{L} = K\theta \qquad (11b)*$$

where K is the drying coefficient. For a given fractional decrease in $T - E$, it is seen that the time increases directly with the *first power* of the thickness and is inversely proportional to k' and $H_{sc} - H$. Hence the drying time would be reduced by increasing the air velocity or by increasing the wet-bulb depression, *i.e.*, by increasing the air temperature or by lowering the absolute humidity. When the internal resistance to diffusion of liquid is negligible, Eq. 11b applies even where there is no constant-rate period.

Case 3. Resistance to Liquid-diffusion Controlling.—If the resistance r_s to surface evaporation is negligible compared with the resistance r_i to liquid diffusion, where $r_i = L/3D$, Eq. 11 reduces to

$$\ln \frac{T_1 - E}{T - E} = \frac{3D\theta}{L^2} = K\theta. \qquad (11c)$$

In this case factors affecting the surface resistance, such as air velocity and humidity difference, should have no effect on the drying coefficient K, except insofar as affecting the temperature of the stock and the corresponding diffusivity D. In general, D increases with increase in temperature, because of decrease in viscosity of the liquid. One encounters this case in drying very thick materials, or materials having low diffusivities.† It is seen that the time required for a given fractional decrease in $T - E$ is proportional to the *square* of the thickness. This equation gives a fairly satisfactory correlation of data on the drying of clay,[10] soap[8],[11] and wood.[9],[11]

In deriving Eq. 11c it was assumed that the parabolic moisture gradient had been established in the constant-rate period. For the case where the constant-rate period is negligible, an equation has been derived[8],[9],[11],[12] from the diffusion equation:

---

* By definition. the coefficient of surface evaporation β equals k' $(H_{sc} - H)/(\rho)(T_{sc} - E)$.

† See also p. 618.

$-\dfrac{L\rho}{d\theta}\dfrac{dT}{} = -\dfrac{D}{\partial x^2}\dfrac{\partial^2 c}{}.$ The boundary conditions are c equals c_e at both $x = 0$ and at $x = 2L$; at $\theta = 0$, c equals c_0. Assuming D constant and neglecting shrinkage, a solution is

$$\frac{W}{W_0} = \frac{8}{\pi^2}\left[e^{-\frac{\pi^2 X}{4}} + \frac{e}{9}^{-\frac{9\pi^2 X}{4}} + \frac{e}{25}^{-\frac{25\pi^2 X}{4}} \right] \qquad (11d)*$$

where X equals $D\theta/L^2$. A plot of $\ln (W/W_0)$ as ordinates vs. X shows a curve concave upward until W/W_0 falls to 0.6, and is linear below this point. The corresponding rate curve $-dW/dX$ plotted against W is concave upward until W falls to $0.6W_0$ and thereafter is linear. So long as the final W lies between 0.4 and 0.01, the time calculated from Eq. 11c differs less than 10 per cent from that calculated from Eq. 11d.

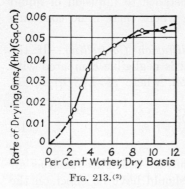

FIG. 213.[2]

Other Cases.—For some materials, particularly when dried at high rates, the plane of vaporization gradually retreats within the solid during the falling-rate period, and the rate curves are not necessarily linear in W; hence K (in Eq. 10) varies with W. The problem can be handled by fitting straight lines to approximate the several sections of the rate curve (Fig. 213), giving $-dW/d\theta = \alpha/\rho L$ for the constant-rate period (if any), $-dW/d\theta = C_1 + K_1 W$ for the first section of the falling-rate period, $-dW/d\theta = C_2 + K_2 W$ for the second section, etc. The effect of humidity and air velocity, upon the factors K and C may be determined, and the resulting relations may then be integrated to allow for changes in the humidity of the air as it flows through the continuous drier. It is generally found that air velocity affects K_1 and C_1 more than K_2 and C_2.

The Critical Moisture T_c.—As previously indicated, the falling-rate period begins as soon as the surface concentration c_s falls below a critical value c_{sc}. It has been suggested[3] that c_{sc}

---

* It is interesting to note that this is the same equation derived on page 165 for the cooling of a slab when the thermal resistance at the surface is negligible.

may be estimated by extrapolating the plot of equilibrium water E to 100 per cent relative humidity and multiplying the value of E_{sc} so obtained by ρ, the weight of dry stock per unit total volume: $c_{sc} = E_c\rho$. Since the value of E at high humidity varies widely with the material, this procedure would predict considerable variation in c_{sc} from one material to another. While directly measured values of c_{sc} are meager, the indications are that they are greater for the more hygroscopic materials.

The critical moisture content is not, as is generally supposed, merely a property of the material being dried. Consider what happens during the constant-rate period of the drying of a slab of homogeneous material having initially a uniform moisture concentration c_0. If the drying conditions require a small value of α, and if the liquid will flow to the surface owing to a small concentration gradient, T_c will be but little greater than c_{sc}/ρ, making T_c relatively small. However, if the air velocity and wet-bulb depression are increased sufficiently, a very high value of α

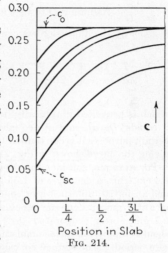

Position in Slab
FIG. 214.

will be obtained, and now such a steep gradient at the surface is required that virtually no water will have been removed from the surface before c_{sc} is reached; hence T_c will be but little less than the original water T_0; the constant-rate period will be over before the second weighing is taken. While neither of these extremes is usually encountered, both can be approached— the first by slowly drying a thin sheet and the second by rapidly drying a thick sheet. An intermediate case is illustrated in Fig. 214. It can be seen that the value of T_c is proportional to the average ordinate of the curve of c vs. x at the end of the constant-rate period where c_s equals c_{sc}. Since in the constant-rate period the concentration gradient at the surface is proportional to α, it is clear that T_c will increase with increase in thickness. If the initial concentration is less than c_{sc}, no constant-rate period will be obtained.

For those materials in which the movement of liquid follows the diffusion law $dc/d\theta = D\, d^2c/dx^2$, and for which evaporation occurs at the surface, one may derive a quantitative relation between T and the factors that control it.[15]   Consider a large slab of total thickness $2L$ dried from both sides at a constant rate α, expressed as weight of water evaporated per unit time per unit surface.   The sheet originally has a uniform moisture concentration and is at the temperature t_{sc} at the start.   Take the origin of x at one face. At the mid-plane, across which no water diffuses, dc/dx is zero.   At the surface $x=0$. dc/dx equals α/D; similarly, at the other surface, $x=2L$ and $-\dfrac{dc}{dx}=\dfrac{\alpha}{D}$.   Assuming D to be constant and neglecting shrinkage, a solution is given by the dimensionless converging series:[15]

$$\frac{(T_0 - T_x)\,D\rho}{\alpha L} = \left[\frac{(x-L)^2}{2L^2} - \frac{1}{6} + X - \frac{2}{\pi^2}\sum_{1}^{\infty}\frac{(-1)^n}{n^2}e^{-\pi^2 n^2 X}\cos\frac{n\pi(x-L)}{L} \right] \quad (12)$$

which is presented graphically in Fig. 215, where Y_x is equal to $(T_0 - T_x)z$, z equals $D\rho/\alpha L$ and X equals $(T_0 - T)z = D\theta/L^2 = (T_0 - T)\rho D/\alpha L$.   For certain purposes it is convenient to replot curve 1 of Fig. 215 as X/Y_s vs. Y_s, giving the curve shown in Fig. 216, which applies only at the surface.

For example, consider the drying of clay slabs having a diffusivity D of 0.4 cm.²/hr., a density ρ of 1.55 gm. of bone-dry stock/c.c. of total volume and an initial uniform water concentration corresponding to T_0 of 0.27 gm. of water/gm. of bone-dry stock.   The drying conditions are such that α is 0.2 gm. water evaporated/(hr.) (sq. cm.).   In order to predict T_c, one should employ the surface moisture T_{sc} prevailing at the end of the constant-rate period.   The surface concentration, corresponding to equilibrium with substantially saturated air at the wet-bulb temperature, is 0.05.   Let the original half-thickness L be 0.4 cm.   The abscissa in Fig. 216, $(T_0 - T_{sc})$ $(D)(\rho)/\alpha(L)$, equals $(0.27 - 0.05)(0.4)(1.55)/(0.2)(0.4)$ or 1.71, and the corresponding ordinate $(T_0 - T_c)/(T_0 - T_{sc}) = (T_0 - T_c)/(0.22)$ equals 0.8, whence $T_0 - T_c$ equals 0.176 and T_c is 0.094.   The drying time in the constant-rate period would be $(0.176)(0.4)(1.55)/(0.2)$ or 0.545 hr.

If the sheet had been five times as thick, the critical moisture would have been 0.215 and the corresponding constant-rate drying time would have been 0.86 hr.

A study of Fig. 216 shows that in the straight section ABC the following equation applies:

$$\frac{T}{T_0} = 1 - 0.74\left(\frac{\rho D}{\alpha L}\right)\left(\frac{T_0 - T_s}{T_0}\right)^2. \quad (12a)$$

Hence for given values of T_0, T_s, ρ and D the critical water will be only a small fraction of the original value when αL is small, corresponding to either a slow drying rate or a thin sheet, whereas with rapid drying or thick sheets T_c will be nearly as large as T_0.

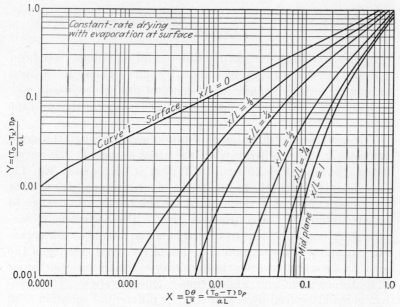

Fig. 215.[15]—Theoretical distribution of moisture during constant-rate period, based on Eq. 12.

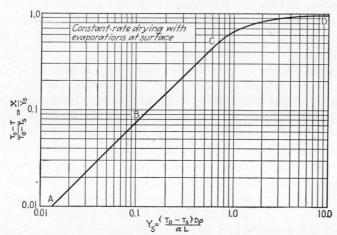

Fig. 216.—Moisture concentration at surface during constant-rate period, based on curve 1 of Fig. 215. In the range *ABC* Eq. 12a applies.

DRYING OF SOLIDS BY AIR UNDER VARIABLE DRYING CONDITIONS

In the preceding paragraphs differential equations have been derived for the drying of solids by air. These have been integrated for *any definite set of constant drying conditions, i.e.*, by assuming the drying coefficients to be constant for the constant drying conditions.

The coefficient of diffusion D of liquid water through the stock increases as the temperature of the stock is raised. However, where the resistance to liquid diffusion is controlling, Eq. 11c may be applied directly to the design of a continuous drier, using an average value of K determined for the temperature range to be encountered in the continuous drier. The coefficient of surface evaporation $\beta*$ varies directly as the humidity difference $H_s - H$, and directly as some function of the mass velocity of the air. In a continuous drier the humidity of the air varies as the air flows through the drier, and in consequence β varies. The problem is readily solved by combining the differential equation with a water balance, giving new integrals for variable drying conditions.

Design of Driers.—Referring to the list of steps to be taken in the designing of a drier (see page 639), it is seen that the only one presenting any major difficulties is the sixth one, that of determining the drying time.

Having considered the factors upon which drying depends, and the mechanical methods in use for handling material to be dried, it is now desirable to indicate how the fundamental concepts of drying may be applied to the design of suitable apparatus for any given purpose.

Although a knowledge of the physical constants and other properties of a material is essential to an intelligent attack of the subject, it is seldom that these alone are sufficient to enable one to determine the dimensions and conditions for the most efficient operation. It is necessary, therefore, for an intelligent design, to obtain by experimentation upon the material in question the characteristic data on the rates of drying and critical moisture contents for various sets of constant drying conditions. It is entirely possible to obtain these data by experimentation on a

* It will be recalled that β represents the term $k'(H_{sc} - H)/(\rho)(T_{sc} - E)$.

laboratory scale, although the larger the scale on which the work is done, the less liable the result will be to error from the omission of factors, present in commercial operation but not in the laboratory. In these experiments, it is necessary to have operating conditions duplicated as nearly as possible. For example, if the exposure is to be in a rotary drier, the experimental apparatus should be of this type. The size of lump material, thickness of sheet and its physical condition as to percentage of water and temperature should be the same as that which will form the feed of the drier to be designed.

The equations given in the following discussion are to be used, therefore, for but two purposes: either the design of commercial apparatus for the drying of a specific material on the basis of coefficients determined from experiments upon the material itself, or to enable one to predict quantitatively the results of changes in either operation or construction of a given drying apparatus handling a definite material. The coefficients in the latter case are determined by studying the actual performance of the apparatus, or the problem is solved by a ratio calculation, in which case the coefficients cancel.

The subsequent treatment of drier design follows the apparatus classification based on the method of supplying the heat (see pages 640 to 641).

1. *Design of Steam-heated Drum and Tray Driers*

The design of driers of this type may be considered conveniently as a problem in heat transfer. As emphasized in the chapter on Flow of Heat, one must consider the various resistances met by the heat in flowing from one medium to another. In this case there are three resistances: from condensing vapor to metal wall, that of the wall itself, and from the metal wall to the air in the room. This last resistance really includes three resistances: contact resistance from metal to stock, resistance of stock itself and resistance from stock to air. Where it is desired to measure the individual resistances, skin temperatures must be taken.

The surface temperature of a material may be obtained by placing a thermocouple upon the surface, the element having previously been heated to approximately the temperature of the material. By noting whether the element rises or falls in temperature, it is possible to determine whether the material is hotter or colder than the couple; a few trials will enable one to have the couple at substantially the same temperature as the sheet.[16]   To prevent radiation the element should be mounted flush with the inner surface of an insulating pad, and the whole pressed upon the surface to be measured.   It must not be kept in contact with this surface for any great length of time because the pad will prevent evaporation and will therefore cause a local rise in the surface temperature of the sheet.

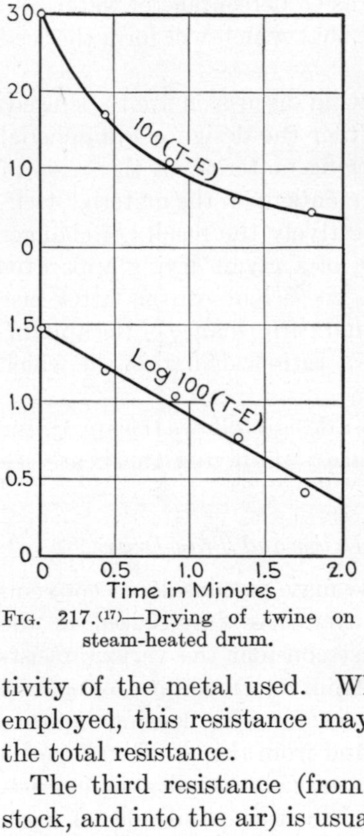

FIG. 217.[17]—Drying of twine on steam-heated drum.

a. Drum Driers for Solids.— Textiles are frequently dried by passing them over a series of hollow metal drums provided with means for supplying steam and removing condensate and air.

The first resistance (from steam to metal) depends on the percentage of noncondensable gas in the steam (this should be small in good practice), the velocity of the steam, the fraction of the total internal heat-transfer surface that is submerged in condensate, etc.

The second resistance (that of the wall itself) depends on the thickness and thermal conductivity of the metal used.   Where very thick cast-iron rolls are employed, this resistance may be an appreciable percentage of the total resistance.

The third resistance (from drum to the stock, through the stock, and into the air) is usually the greatest of the three resistances.   Hence it is clear that design should be based on results of experiments for the type of drier and material in question, conditions in the experiments being as similar as possible to those to be used in production.   In a certain drier of this type handling wood pulp, the third resistance was about 76 per cent of the total resistance to heat flow.   The *overall* coefficient was about 24 B.t.u./(hr.) (deg. F.) (sq. ft. of outer surface).

As the thickness of the stock is doubled, the water to be evaporated is doubled and the heat has to travel twice as far. It would therefore be anticipated that the drying time would vary with the square of the thickness of the stock. The drying time would also increase with increase in the fraction of water removed. Figures 217 and 218 show data[17] for the drying of twine in contact with a steam-heated drum, correlated by use of Eq. 11c, page 653.

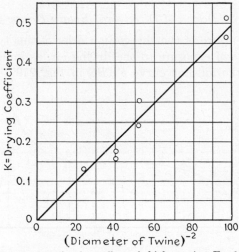

FIG. 218.[17]—Drying of twine; effect of thickness (see Eq. 11c, p. 653).

b. Drum Driers for Liquids.—When solutions or suspensions are concentrated or reduced to a solid on a steam-heated drum, the film of material in immediate contact with the drum becomes dry in a very short time, and this dry inner layer serves as an insulation to separate the more moist layers from the heating surface. The process then reduces to a conduction of heat through the dry layer into that portion which still remains wet. When the rate of heat flow is great, the temperature of the sheet will approach the boiling temperature of the liquid at the pressure used. Hence it follows that the use of vacuum in the chamber housing the drum will lower the surface temperature and thus increase the rate of heat flow and consequently the evaporative rate.

c. Tray Driers.—Where the material to be dried is placed on trays, the heat may be supplied solely from the air, and in this case special drying equations are available (see Rate of Air Drying, pp. 642 to 657). Where the trays are supplied with heat other than as described above, as when the trays are placed on hollow shelves or pipes supplied with steam, the problem is conveniently treated from the heat-transfer point of view. The resistances here met are similar to those discussed under Drum Driers for Solids. It should be noted that a very important factor is the thickness of the material on the trays.

2. *Design of Direct-fired Rotary Driers*

The temperature of the charge in a drier of this type changes with the time of exposure to the drying air, as indicated qualitatively by the full-line curve *FABC* in Fig. 219. During the

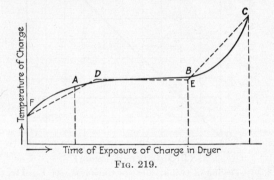

Fig. 219.

preliminary period, *FA*, the charge is heating up but evaporation is negligible. Evaporation then takes place in the zone *AB*, accompanied by a slight temperature rise. Finally the charge is superheated and the last trace of moisture expelled in the period *BC*. If a completely dried product is not desired, the operation is stopped before the point *C* is reached.

The exact determination of this curve would be difficult, but it is a satisfactory approximation to assume constancy of temperature during the evaporative period, *i.e.*, to assume that the temperature of the charge follows the dotted straight lines *FDEC* rather than the full curve in the plot. The important point is, therefore, the estimation of the temperature of evaporation, *DE*.

Direct-fired driers always employ high-temperature gases and in consequence develop a high rate of evaporation. The temperature of the charge therefore approaches the boiling point, and changes but slightly during the period of evaporation (see humidity chart, page 588). From inspection of the chart it is obvious that, for material so wet that the surface is saturated, the temperature of the charge during the evaporative period when exposed to gases 300°F. and above will be from 110 to 160°F. For lower moisture content, however, the charge temperature increases asymptotically to the boiling point, *i.e.*, to approximately 180 to 210°F. The difference in temperature between the charge and hot gases is so great that any reasonable error in estimating the temperature of evaporation will not invalidate the calculations.

The design of such driers resolves itself therefore into a simple calculation of heat transfer, the process being assumed to take place in three separate stages: the preheating, the drying and the superheating of the charge. In the equation for heat transfer, $q = hA \Delta t$, it is not convenient to determine the surface exposure A, and hence the term hA is treated as a single coefficient. The value of hA is proportional to the volume V of the drier for apparatus of the same type. Obviously the coefficient hA must be determined for each material and type of apparatus, from the performance of actual driers, preferably on the full scale.

Illustration 1.—A rotary drier is constructed of a steel shell 4 ft. 6 in. inside diameter and 20 ft. long, and rotates at 4 r.p.m. It is drying 12,000 lb. hourly of a wet ore carrying 16 per cent moisture. The dry ore has a specific heat of 0.18 and is discharged at 240°F. The ore occupies roughly 20 per cent of the volume of the drier. The flue gas flows countercurrent to the ore, enters at 1065°F. and leaves at 160°F. Its Orsat analysis is 3.2 per cent CO_2, 17.3 per cent O_2 and negligible CO. Its dew point at entrance to the drier is 76°F. ($p_{H_2O} = 22.8$ mm.). The temperature of the surroundings may be assumed 70°F. as a base, and the barometer is normal. Assume the drier to be thoroughly lagged.

Calculate the dry gas in lb. mols passing/hr., the linear gas velocity at the cold end, the heat consumed in evaporation and the heat lost in the dry ore. Design an ore cooler of a type similar to the drier to recover 85 per cent of the heat now lost in the product by preheating the air for the furnace.

Solution.—The heat utilized by the drier is that involved in heating the ore from 70 to 240°F. and in converting water at 70°F. into water vapor at 160°F. The first is obviously $(12,000) (0.84) (0.18) (240 - 70)$ or 309,000 B.t.u./hr. and the second 1092 B.t.u./lb. of water; for 1920 lb. of water, it is 2,098,000 B.t.u./hr., making 2,407,000 B.t.u./hr. in all. This heat is furnished by the cooling of the flue gases from 1065 to 160°F.

Basis: 100 mols of dry flue gas:

This contains $[22.8/(760 - 22.8)]100 = 3.09$ mols of water vapor.

Gas	Mols	$(1065-60)$ $(MC_p)_{av.}$	$(160-60)$ $(MC_p)_{av.}$	Difference	B.t.u.
CO_2	3.2	11,050	910	10,140	32,500
O_2	17.3	7,620	704	6,916	120,000
N_2	79.5	7,240	696	6,544	520,000
H_2O	3.09	8,640	811	7,829	24,200
Total..	103.09	......	...	......	696,700

Neglecting radiation loss, this therefore requires 2,407,000 (100)/697,000 = 346 lb. mols of dry flue gas/hr. or 357 lb. mols of wet flue gas. The evaporation is 106.6 mols of water/hr., making a total of 464 mols of gas/hr. leaving the drier at 160°F., or 210,000 cu. ft./hr. giving a velocity of 3.66 ft./sec.

In order to use these data in the design of similar apparatus, the heat transfer must be estimated. Base this figure on the unknown but relatively constant surface area A of charge exposed in the present drier. Evaporation may be assumed to take place at 200°F. On this assumption, the heat transfer takes place in three stages. *First,* (130) (1) (1920)+(130) (0.18) (10,080) =486,000 B.t.u. is needed to raise the 12,000 lb. of wet ore from 70 to 200°; *second* (1920) (974) =1,870,000 B.t.u. disappear in the evaporation of 1920 lb. of water at 200°F.; finally (10,080) (40) (0.18) =72,600 B.t.u. is used to superheat the ore from 200 to 240°F. Neglecting the changes of specific heats of the components of the flue gases with temperature, the gases used (346 lb. mols gas) lose (3.46) (697,000)/905 =2660 B.t.u./deg. fall in temperature. In the last stage therefore, they drop only 72,600/2660 = 27.3° to 1038°F. The drop in the second stage is not so directly estimated because the gases are cooled not only by the evaporation of the water, but also by the dilution with the water vapor produced. Call the gas temperature at the end of the second stage t°F. Then from a heat balance in the evaporating zone, 2660 (1,038−t) =1,870,000 +1920 (0.48) (t−200), whence t =300°F.

	Hot end	End of evaporation	Start of evaporation	Cold end
Temperature of gases....	1065	1038	300	160
Temperature of charge..	240	200	200	70
Temperature difference..	825	838	100	90
Average Δt for each stage of process............		832	347*	95

* This log mean, though not strictly applicable to this case on account of the dilution effect, is used as an approximation.

For each section of the drier corresponding to each of the three stages of the process one may write $q = hA(\Delta t)_{\text{av.}}$, where the subscripts 1, 2 and 3 correspond to the first, second and third stages of the drying operation. Obviously, the total exposed area in the drier,

$$A = A_1 + A_2 + A_3.$$

For each section q and $(\Delta t)_{\text{av.}}$ are given; hence,

For superheating zone, $hA_1 = \dfrac{q_1}{(\Delta t_{\text{av.}})_1} = \dfrac{72,600}{832} = 87$ B.t.u./(hr.) (deg. F.)

For evaporating zone, $hA_2 = \dfrac{q_2}{(\Delta t_{\text{av.}})_2} = \dfrac{1,870,000}{347} = 5390.$

For preheating zone, $hA_3 = \dfrac{q_3}{(\Delta t_{\text{av.}})_3} = \dfrac{486,000}{95} = 5120.$

The main resistance to the flow of heat in all three zones is that of the gas film. This coefficient (h) varies as the mass velocity of the gases, which velocity is approximately constant for this problem. Adding,

$$hA_1 + hA_2 + hA_3 = 10,600.$$

The mols of air to be used in the cooler are found by using the nitrogen content of the flue gas, since this came from the air, *i.e.*,

$$\text{mols of air} = 354(79.5/79.1) = 356.$$

The heat to be recovered in the cooler is 85 per cent of 309,000 B.t.u. or 738 B.t.u./mol of air heated. Since 1 mol of air at 70°F. has a heat content (above 32°F.) of 243 B.t.u., at its point of exit from the cooler it will have 738 more, or a total of 981 B.t.u., corresponding to 176°F. as read from Fig. 1, page 10.

	Deg. F.	Difference
Temperature of air entering cooler................	70	25.5
Temperature of ore leaving cooler*................	95.5	
Temperature of ore entering cooler................	240	64
Temperature of air leaving cooler................	176	
Hence logarithmic-mean temperature difference, °F..	.....	41.8

* Ore cooled 85 per cent of $(240-70)$.

The value of hA for the cooler is therefore determined by the equation

$$hA = \frac{q}{(\Delta t_{\text{av.}})} = \frac{(0.85)(309,000)}{(41.8)} = 6290.$$

Since the original drier gave a total value of hA of 10,600, and since the value of this quantity is obviously proportional to the volume of the drier, the cooler should be 6290/10,600 the size of the drier, or 60 per cent. To keep the air velocity practically the same, the diameter should be the same, but the cylinder six-tenths the length.

This drier gives trouble in operation, in that the temperature of the discharging material fluctuates widely. When the rate of feed decreases slightly, the discharge is exceedingly hot; with an increased rate of feed, the material is incompletely dried. The difficulty lies in the fact that the superheating zone, after evaporation is completed, is too short, and the gas temperature at that point too high. To secure a larger factor of safety in operation, the superheating zone should be longer and the gas temperature lower. This can be accomplished by resort to the "double-pass" principle (see page 632).

3. Design of Air Driers for Sensitive Materials

Introduction.—It should be recalled that under *constant* drying conditions the drying operation in general occurs in two stages: a constant-rate period, wherein

$$-\frac{dW}{d\theta} = B(H_s - H) \tag{13}$$

and a falling-rate period, wherein

$$-dW/d\theta = f(W). \tag{14}$$

At the critical point where W equals W_c, both equations apply, and hence $B(H_s - H) = f(W_c)$. In the constant-rate period the rate is independent of W, while in the falling-rate period the rate is a function of the free-water content. In any continuous drier, drying conditions may vary from point to point in the apparatus, but, since they remain constant at any given point, these differential equations apply at each such point. They must therefore be applied differentially and integrated for the drier as a whole.

Wherever there is a constant-rate period, Eq. 13 is combined with the water balance and integrated from the original water content W_0 to the critical value W_c. Let m be the weight ratio of bone-dry air to bone-dry stock employed in the continuous drier. The water balance is then given by the simple relation

$$-dW = \pm m \, dH, \tag{15}$$

the sign depending on the direction of flow of air and stock. If the desired final water content is equal to or greater than

W_c, the problem is solved by using the relation

$$\frac{B\theta}{m} = \mp \int \frac{dH}{H_s - H}.$$ (16)

In general, it is necessary to dry to a final value of W below W_c. The falling-rate period must therefore be treated separately.

For the general case, *i.e.*, where both surface evaporation and interior diffusion should be taken into account, integration of Eq. 14 is complicated. Usually satisfactory approximate equations may be developed.

Where the resistance to interior diffusion is controlling, it is usually allowable to neglect variation in K in a given drier, and Eq. (11c) may be employed directly to calculate the falling-rate time.

Where the resistance to surface evaporation is the controlling factor, the important variable is the humidity, and Eq. (10) can be integrated as shown below. Discussion is therefore limited to modifications of Eq. (10). For continuous apparatus where the resistance to surface evaporation is controlling, the *general* differential equations applicable to driers of adiabatic, constant temperature or controlled-humidity type will be derived. Two such equations will be established, one for countercurrent flow of air and the other for parallel flow. These equations will then be integrated for the special cases given. Finally, a discussion of intermittent driers will be added.

In any drier in which the stock is dried by means of air, and where surface evaporation is the controlling resistance, the differential equation, as shown on page 653, is

$$-\frac{dW}{d\theta} = \frac{\beta W}{L} = \frac{f(G)(H_s - H)W}{L}$$ (17)

where, at any time θ in the falling-rate period, W is the free water on the dry basis, L is half the thickness of the stock, β is the experimentally determined coefficient of surface evaporation for the definite drying conditions and particular material. As indicated by the equation, β equals $f(G)(H_s - H)$, where G is the mass velocity of the air past the stock and $H_s - H$ is the humidity difference, also called ΔH. It will be recalled that H_s is the humidity of saturated air at the temperature of the *surface* of the sheet and H is the humidity of the drying air.

Counterflow.—Since driers are usually designed to give constant mass velocity of the gases, the term $f(G)$ remains constant throughout the drier. In order to allow for the variation in the humidity H of the air passing through the drier, one may make a moisture balance between the water lost by the stock and that picked up by the air. The subscript 0 will be used to designate the condition of *both* air and stock at the end where the stock *enters*, and the pounds of free water per pound of bone-dry stock and the humidity of the air will be called W and H, respectively, at any section y ft. distant from the feed end and W_2 and H_2, respectively, at the discharge end. The moisture balance between the feed end and any section y ft. distant gives $W_0 - W = m(H_0 - H)$, or

$$H = H_0 - \frac{(W_0 - W)}{m} \qquad (18)$$

where m represents the pounds of bone-dry air per pound of bone-dry stock. It should be noted that this moisture balance is based on the assumption of constant equilibrium moisture of the stock passing through the drier, a restriction removed later. Elimination of H from the water balance and Eq. 17 gives

$$-\frac{dW}{d\theta} = \frac{f(G)}{Lm}[m(H_s - H_0) + W_0 - W](W). \qquad (19)$$

Parallel Flow.—Calling the pounds of free water per pound of dry stock at the feed end W_0 and the humidity of the air entering at the *same* end H_0, a moisture balance* gives $(W_0 - W) = m(H - H_0)$, which, when combined with (17), gives

$$-\frac{dW}{d\theta} = \frac{f(G)}{Lm}[m(H_s - H_0) - W_0 + W](W). \qquad (20)$$

The general equations (19 and 20) just derived apply to all countercurrent and parallel-flow driers, respectively, which operate at temperatures so low that the resistance to surface evaporation is the controlling factor, *however the heat may be applied to the driers.* To integrate them, however, the exact method of heat supply must be taken into account.

Adiabatic Counterflow Driers.—The salient characteristic of adiabatic driers is constancy of wet-bulb temperature, *i.e.*,

---

* This equation also assumes E to be constant.

$t_s = t_w$, and consequently $H_s = H_w$. These driers are therefore used for materials sensitive to heat while still wet, as the stock temperature is automatically controlled (*e.g.*, glue, sugar, heavy leather, vegetables, etc.)

Since in any given drier of this type H_w, H_0 and W_0 are constant, Eq. 19 may be written as

$$-\frac{dW}{(W)(M-W)} = \frac{f(G)\,d\theta}{Lm},$$

in which

$$M = m(H_w - H_0) + W_0. \tag{21}$$

Integrating from W_c to W_2 gives

$$\ln_e\left(\frac{(W_c)(M-W_2)}{(W_2)(M-W_c)}\right) = \frac{f(G)\,M(\theta_2 - \theta_c)}{Lm}. \tag{21a}$$

If the total weight of dry stock exposed in the drier is called Q, and the weight of dry stock fed per unit time is called F, it is obvious that

$$Q/F = \theta_2 \tag{22}$$

where θ_2 is the total drying time.

This type of drier, simple in construction and operation, can be used to control the humidity and temperature of the air with which the dried stock is in contact, and hence to control the moisture content of the product (*e.g.*, water of crystallization, textile products, etc.) and yet simultaneously secure rapid evaporation due to the high initial temperature of the drying air.

Adiabatic Parallel Flow.—Since in any given drier of this type m, H_w, H_0 and W_0 are constant, Eq. 20 may be written as

$$-\frac{dW}{(W)(N+W)} = \frac{f(G)d\theta}{Lm}$$

in which

$$N = m(H_w - H_0) - W_0. \tag{23}$$

Integration from W_c to W_2, and from θ_c to θ_2 gives

$$\ln_e\left(\frac{(W_c)(N+W_2)}{(W_2)(N+W_c)}\right) = \frac{f(G)N(\theta_2-\theta_c)}{Lm}. \tag{24}$$

Constant-temperature Driers.—Materials injured by heat after they have become dry are usually dried in constant-temperature driers. This is necessary in the case of materials existing in large lumps or thick sheets (for example, raw rubber), because, when the drying operation is even partially complete, the surface of the sheet or lump is relatively dry, the remaining moisture existing only in the interior. While the interior is therefore cold, the surface is practically at the temperature of the drying air and therefore is liable to injury. In present commercial practice, these driers are also frequently used for materials such as salts with water of crystallization, textiles and the like, which, as will be shown later, are more advantageously handled in other apparatus.

The drying capacity of any drier, in which the air temperature is kept at a constant level by supplying heat in the necessary quantity in the drying compartment itself, is found by the use of the integral of Eq. 17:

$$-\int_{W_c}^{W_2} \frac{dW}{(W)(\Delta H)} = \frac{f(G)(\theta_2 - \theta_c)}{L}. \tag{25}$$

This integral involves, however, not one but two variables, W and ΔH, and, unlike the case of adiabatic driers, it is impracticable to express ΔH algebraically in terms of W. Nonetheless ΔH can be found as follows: For various values of W, between W_c and W_2, calculate H from the water balance (Eq. 15). Knowing the operating temperature t and the humidity H, just calculated, H_w can be read directly from the humidity chart. ΔH is H_w minus H. Knowing ΔH for various values of W, it is possible to plot $1/(W)(\Delta H)$ against W, and the area under this curve is the integral required.

When the air temperature is high (above 200°F.), the value of ΔH usually changes but little during the drying operation. In such a case one may use an arithmetic mean $(\Delta H)_{\text{av.}}$ of the values of ΔH at the terminals of the zone in which W falls from W_c to W_2, giving

$$\ln_e \frac{W_c}{W_2} = \frac{f(G)(\theta_2 - \theta_c)(\Delta H)_{\text{av.}}}{L}. \tag{26}$$

Illustration 2.—A drier is to be designed to dry a lump material, producing 1400 lb. of product/hr. The wet feed will be loaded on trucks carrying trays made of large-mesh wire screen. The drier will hold two parallel lines of these trucks, and will contain propeller-type fans to recirculate air crosswise over the trays and over steam coils located within the drier. The trucks will be 5½ ft. long overall, and will carry seven trays, each 5 ft. long by 4 ft. wide and 10 in. deep. Each tray when loaded will contain 3 lb. of dried product/sq. ft. of tray surface, *i.e.*, each tray will hold 60 lb. of dried product. The wet stock contains 116 per cent water on the dry basis, and the final product is to contain 10 per cent water, dry basis. The dryer is to be designed to operate at 170°F. with air entering the preheater at 70°F. with a relative humidity of 80 per cent.

In order to obtain information on the drying characteristics of the material, a loaded tray of the wet stock was placed in a drier of the same type as that which it is planned to construct. The weight was obtained at frequent intervals, and the following data were tabulated:

Time, min.	% water, dry basis	Time, min.	% water, dry basis	Time, min.	% water, dry basis
0	116.0	211	57.4	415	28.6
17	111.7	226	53.6	438	26.4
36	106.0	242	49.6	465	24.8
58	100.0	255	46.6	506	22.8
80	93.5	277	42.8	541	22.2
97	88.9	287	41.0	601	15.4
125	81.0	302	38.6	615	14.6
144	75.5	313	37.1	635	13.5
160	71.2	345	33.3	785	11.4
176	66.6	362	31.4	822	10.2
194	61.8	390	29.2		

This test was run at 95°F. at a relative humidity of 7 per cent. The air velocity over the tray was the same as that to be used in the proposed dryer.

The following data are available on the equilibrium moisture E of the stock.

% relative humidity	10	20	30	40	50	60	70	80	90
E, % water, dry basis	3.0	3.2	4.1	4.8	5.4	6.1	7.2	8.8	10.7

It will be assumed that the critical moisture, expressed as $100(T_c - E)$, is independent of the air temperature and humidity, and that at any free moisture content the rate of drying is proportional to the humidity difference, $H_w - H$.

Calculate the required length of the drier, assuming that the air leaves at 170°F. with a relative humidity of 60 per cent, (*a*) for countercurrent movement of air and trucks, and (*b*) for parallel flow.

Solution.—From the test data the values of $-\dfrac{100 dT}{d\theta}$ were calculated and are shown plotted vs. T in Fig. 220.

100T, % water	$-\dfrac{100dT}{d\theta}$, %/min.
116–58	0.279
54	0.237
47	0.202
40	0.153
34.5	0.115
26	0.084
17.3	0.0515

The plots of air humidity and wet-bulb humidity *vs.* per cent water in the solid (dry basis) are also given in Fig. 220 for both cases. These plots together with one of equilibrium water (per cent water, dry basis) are sufficient to calculate the data given in the two tables below.

T	H	% RH at 170°F.	E	H_w-H	$T-E$	Rate at 95°F., at this $T-E$, %/min.	Rate at 170°F., %/min.	1/Rate
				Countercurrent Flow				
10	0.0125	5	1.1	0.0190	8.9	0.027	0.0625	16.0
25	0.0393	15	2.7	0.0159	22.3	0.073	0.142	7.05
40	0.0665	24	3.6	0.0133	36.4	0.139	0.226	4.42
55	0.0933	32	4.2	0.0118	50.8	0.234	0.335	2.98
70	0.120	40	4.8	0.0102	65.2	0.279	0.346	2.89
85	0.147	47	5.2	0.0089	79.8	0.279	0.302	3.31
100	0.174	53	5.6	0.0083	94.4	0.279	0.282	3.54
116	0.203	60	6.1	0.0071	109.9	0.279	0.241	4.15
				Parallel Flow				
10	0.203	60	6.1	0.0071	3.9	0.012	0.0104	96.1
25	0.175	53	5.6	0.0081	19.4	0.062	0.061	16.4
40	0.148	48	5.2	0.0090	34.8	0.131	0.144	6.95
55	0.121	40	4.8	0.0100	50.2	0.228	0.278	3.65
70	0.095	33	4.3	0.0118	65.7	0.279	0.400	2.5
85	0.068	24	3.6	0.0133	81.4	0.279	0.468	2.14
100	0.041	16	2.8	0.0159	97.2	0.279	0.529	1.89
116	0.0125	5	1.1	0.0190	114.9	0.279	0.645	1.55

The values in column 7 of the upper part of the table are read from the rate curve of Fig. 220, and are the rates of drying at 95°F., expressed in %/min., at the values of $T-E$ shown in column 6. Since in the laboratory run

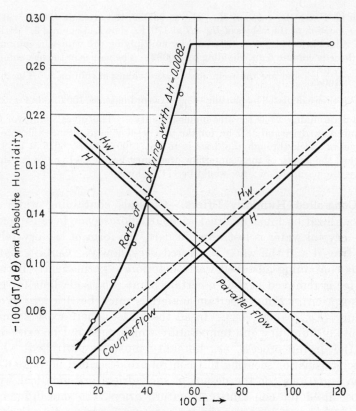

Fig. 220.—Diagram for Illustration 2.

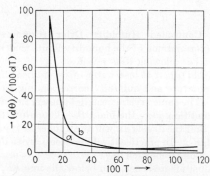

Fig. 221.—The areas under the curves determine the drying times for parts (a) and (b) of Illustration 2.

with 95°F. air the value of $H_w - H$ was 0.0082, the rates at 170°F. will be in proportion to the values of $H_w - H$ at 170°F., shown in column 5.   Hence the values in column 8 are obtained by multiplying the values in column 7 by those in column 5 and dividing by 0.0082.   The values in the last column are $-\dfrac{d\theta}{100dT}$, and are the reciprocals of the values in column 8.   The total time is then calculated by plotting $-\dfrac{d\theta}{100dT}$ as ordinates *vs.* $100T$, as in Fig. 221, and determining $\Sigma\theta$ as the area under the curve.   This gives 8.5 hr. for the counterflow drier and 18.7 hr. for the parallel-flow case.   Since the rate of travel of stock through the drier is to be $(1400)/(2\times7\times60/5.5)$ or 9.15 ft./hr., the length of the counterflow drier must be 8.5×9.15 or 78 ft.; similarly, the parallel-flow drier would be 171 ft. long.

Controlled Humidity Driers.—Crystals containing water of crystallization must be dried without efflorescence because, once the crystal water is lost, even in part, the form of the crystal is destroyed and the water recovered very slowly.   Certain materials containing adsorbed water deteriorate permanently if that water is removed beyond a certain point (*e.g.*, soda lime for gas absorption).   Finally certain materials must be dried to avoid injury (*e.g.*, paper, etc.).   In all these cases there exist definite limits of humidity and temperature which must not be exceeded in the drying process, *i.e.*, humidity must be controlled.   The mechanisms for securing this control are described on page 637. The equations for the design of such driers are identical with those used for constant-temperature driers, the one difference being that one must use the temperature corresponding to each value of the humidity limitations of the particular material being dried.

Illustration 3.   Controlled Humidity Drier (Counterflow Drying of Crystals).—The determination of the humidity limits that must be observed will be clear from the following illustration:

Crystals of $Na_2HPO_4\cdot12H_2O$ lose water of crystallization if subjected to conditions of temperature and humidity corresponding to any point *below* AB^* in Fig. 222.   The same crystals will deliquesce, *i.e.*, dissolve to form a solution, at any condition *above* the line CB.   Therefore, drying conditions must be so chosen that the drying air will at all times be represented by some point in the field ABC.   In practice it will be necessary to design the drier to operate above AB, along some such line as DE, chosen to secure a satisfactory *factor of safety* against efflorescence, and below the line EF, this latter being sufficiently low to maintain a reasonable evaporative rate.   Furthermore,

---

* For the construction of these curves see pp. 681 to 682.

the crystals must be cooled and stored prior to packing, in air the humidity of which lies in the same field. It is obvious from the plot that the temperature of the crystals leaving the drying zone theoretically must not exceed 97°F. and for safety should be below 86°F. This latter temperature gives, however, a humidity difference and hence a drying rate so low that it is agreed not to allow the air to rise above 85 per cent humidity. Therefore it must not rise above 79°F. If, for example, air at 70°F. and of 80 per cent humidity is to be used, design the drier to operate with a countercurrent stream of

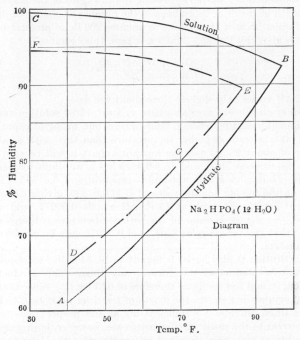

FIG. 222.—Diagram for Illustration 3.

air, entering at the point G, and rising in temperature as its humidity increases along the curve GE, the air being discharged at 79°F. with a humidity of 85 per cent. In this way one will at all times maintain the highest drying temperature and evaporative rate consistent with safety.

Assume that it is required to produce hourly 200 lb. of crystals of apparent specific gravity 0.9, containing not over 0.5 per cent moisture (wet basis) from wet crystals carrying 5 per cent of free water, wet basis. The critical water W_c exceeds 0.05, so there will be no constant-rate period. In the drier the crystals rest in a layer 1 in. deep in perforated trays set to give 1 in. clear space between the trays. Between these trays air passes at a rate of 25 lb./(sq. ft. of clear cross section) (min.). For the sake of illustration, assume that under these conditions experiments show that a drying coefficient, $f(G)/L$, equal to 3.0,* can be realized and that the material contains no "equilibrium moisture."

Solution.—Two hundred pounds of product containing 0.5 per cent moisture corresponds to an hourly evaporation of 9.48 lb. of water. F equals 3.32 lb. of dry stock/min.   The air enters the drier with a humidity of 0.0125 and leaves with a humidity of 0.0188; hence each 100 lb. of air picks up 0.63 lb. of water, requiring for the above amount 1505 lb. of air/hr., or 25.1 lb./min.   The net cross section of the drier is therefore 1 sq. ft., and the gross cross section is 2 sq. ft., neglecting the thickness of the trays.

The length of the drier depends upon the number of pounds of dry stock, Q, which must be in it at any time to produce 200 lb. of product/hr.   This quantity is given by Eq. 26.   Since θ_c is zero, this becomes

$$\ln \frac{W_0}{W_2} = \frac{f(G)(\Delta H)_{\text{av.}} . Q}{LF},$$

provided ΔH varies only slightly throughout the drier.

The water on the wet crystals exists as a saturated solution and during drying will not be at the wet-bulb temperature, but, owing to vapor pressure lowering, at a somewhat higher temperature than this with a percentage humidity of about 98.   From the humidity chart it will be seen that air entering the drier at 70°F. and $H_s = 0.0125$ has a wet-bulb temperature of 66°F. and a humidity at the wet-bulb temperature of 0.01345.   By interpolation on the cooling line the value of H is 0.01336, giving ΔH or $H_s - H$ equal to 0.00086.   Similarly at 75°F. ΔH equals 0.00077, and at 80°F., 0.00062.   The change in value of ΔH with temperature is therefore not so great but that an average value $(\Delta H_{\text{av.}})$ of 0.00075 may be employed in the above equation.

By substitution Q (dry basis) is found† to be 3465 lb., corresponding to about 3480 lb. product in the drier at any time.   This product weighs 56.1 lb./cu. ft. and has a volume therefore of 62.1 cu. ft.   Since the net cross section of crystals is 1 sq. ft., the length of the drier must be 62.1 ft.

Such a drier provides for sufficient air at the proper velocity flowing countercurrent to the stock; its dimensions are, however, impractical.   The same conditions may be maintained by constructing the drier as shown in Fig. 223.   If trucks 5 ft. high, 3 ft. wide and 2 ft. 8 in. long are used, each truck will contain thirty shelves.   Each truck will then hold

$$(30)\ (3)\ (2.67)\ (1/12) = 20 \text{ cu. ft. of crystals;}$$

hence about three trucks are needed to hold 62 cu. ft. of crystals.   In order to provide a suitable factor of safety, six trucks should be used.

The enclosure AB is the tunnel with inside dimensions about 5 ft. high by 4 ft. wide by about 16 ft. long.   Through this space are propelled six trucks, each supporting thirty shelves.   The air has, in addition to its motion

---

* $f(G)/L = 3.0$, when using time in minutes and ΔH as in this illustration.

† $2.3 \log_{10} \left(\dfrac{(0.05/0.95)}{(0.005/0.995)} \right) = \dfrac{(3.0)\ (0.00075)\ (Q)}{3.32}$, whence $Q = 3465$.

counter to the trucks, a rapid transverse circulation across the trucks as indicated by arrows. This transverse movement is reversed in successive compartments to secure uniformity in drying. Short-circuiting of the air is prevented by the horizontal partitions *D*, leather flaps *E* being used as seals at the lines of contact. Heating elements must be provided in the

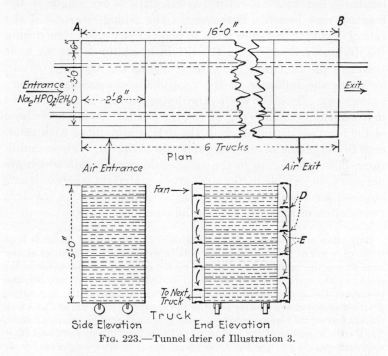

Fig. 223.—Tunnel drier of Illustration 3.

sides of the drier, so controlled as to maintain the required temperature-humidity relations at each point.

Intermittent Adiabatic Driers.—Occasion may arise for the use of an intermittent adiabatic drier, *i.e.*, the drier being filled with charge, and then run until the drying process is completed, when it is emptied to give way to a new charge. Such an arrangement is always to be avoided, if possible, as it involves, *first*, slow drying toward the end of the cycle, with consequent low drying efficiency, *i.e.*, poor utilization of the heat content of the air, and, *second*, unequal drying due to the rapid drying of the stock at the point where the fresh, dry, hot air enters and slow evaporation at the other end where the cooled moisture-laden air leaves.

This second disadvantage can in a large degree be eliminated by using either a short rotary drier with provision for mixing the charge from end to end during the drying or a shelf or tray drier, in either case periodically reversing the direction of the air current. For such an apparatus calculations are simple in the constant-rate period. However, in the falling-rate period the rate of drying varies from point to point at any given time during the drying cycle, owing to the rise in humidity of the air as it traverses the apparatus, and decreases as the drying proceeds, owing to the influence of the continually decreasing moisture in the stock. In other words, the drying rate is a function of two independent variables, *i.e.*, of the time in the drying cycle, and of the location of the stock in the drying apparatus with reference to the points of entrance and exit of the air. These conditions, however, obtain in the small-scale experiments which are necessary to establish, for any given materials, the constants required for the design of a drier. The consideration involves the solution of a partial differential equation.

Derivation of Equation.—For such a case, *i.e.*, where the charge is kept thoroughly mixed, let Z = the actual total water content in the drier at any time θ from the beginning of the run; c = the concentration of water in the stock; a = the surface area of the stock, available for evaporation, per unit volume of the drying equipment; S = the cross section of the apparatus; y = the distance of any specific point in the apparatus from the end at which the air leaves; ΔZ^* = the water content of the differential length of drier, Δy; H = the humidity of the drying air at the point y in the drier, and H_w = that corresponding to the wet-bulb temperature; w = the weight of dry air passing through the drier per unit time.

The differential equation expressing the drying mechanism is

$$-\frac{d(\Delta Z)}{d\theta} = \left[\frac{f(G)}{L}\right][(c)(a)(S)(\Delta y)(L)][(H_w - H)].$$

Since all water evaporated goes into the air, the right-hand side of this equation, representing as it does the water carried out of the section under consideration per unit time, must equal that picked up by the air:

$$w\Delta H = -f(G)c(H_w - H)aS\Delta y.$$

* The fact that H varies only with y is indicated by writing the differential coefficients of these variables as ΔH and Δy; since the moisture Z varies only with θ, the differential coefficients of these variables are written as dZ and $d\theta$. It should be noted this meaning of ΔH is different from that used elsewhere.

By integration,

$$\ln_e (H_w - H) = \frac{f(G)caSy}{w} + \text{constant};$$

or, if H_0 = the humidity of the air leaving the drier, at $y = 0$

$$\ln_e \frac{H_w - H}{H_w - H_0} = \frac{f(G)caSy}{w},$$

an equation which applies at any time θ in the falling-rate period.

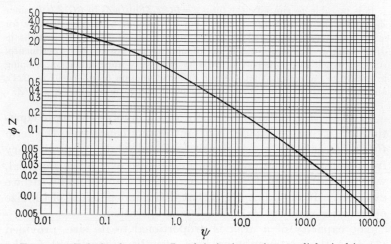

FIG. 224.—Relation between ϕZ and ψ, for intermittent adiabatic driers.

It is obvious from a water balance that throughout the drying period

$$-dZ = (w)(H_0 - H)d\theta.$$

However, from the preceding integral,

$$\frac{H_w - H_0}{H_w - H} = \frac{H_w - H + H - H_0}{H_w - H} = 1 - \frac{H_0 - H}{H_w - H} = e^{\frac{-f(G)caSy}{w}}.$$

Since $c/c_0 = Z/Z_0$, when the subscripts 0 apply to the condition of the stock entering the drier at the time, $\theta = 0$,

$$-dZ = w(H_w - H)\left[1 - e^{\frac{-f(G)c_0aSyZ}{wZ_0}} \right]d\theta,$$

or, if $f(G)c_0aSy/wZ_0$ is designated by φ,

$$-dZ = (w)(H_w - H)(1 - e^{-\varphi Z})d\theta,$$

or, by integration,

$$\frac{Z_0}{Z} - 1 - \frac{1}{\varphi Z}[\ln (1 - e^{-\varphi Z}) - \ln (1 - e^{-Z_0})] = \frac{w(H_w - H)\theta}{Z}. \qquad (27)$$

If ψ is used to designate the function,

$$\psi = -\frac{1}{\varphi Z}[\ln (1 - e^{-\varphi Z})], \quad \text{and} \quad \psi_0 = -\frac{1}{\varphi Z_0}[\ln (1 - e^{-\varphi Z_0})],$$

this equation may be written as,

$$\psi + \frac{Z_0}{Z}(1 - \psi_0) - 1 = (w)(H_w - H)\frac{\theta}{Z}. \tag{27a}$$

It is possible to simplify the term $\varphi = f(G)c_0 Z Say/wZ_0$ to $f(G)Z/wL$, since Z_0 equals the term $SayLc_0$. Equation 27a cannot be solved directly for w or Z, but can be solved for θ, the quantity most frequently sought in drier design. Its main use is in calculating the results of experimental runs, in which case it is solved for φ by successive approximation, keeping in mind the facts, first, that ψ is in a definite function of φZ (see Fig. 224), and, second, that ψ_0 and ψ must correspond to a ratio of $\varphi Z_0/\varphi Z = Z_0/Z$.

In all these equations for driers which involve the basic equation for drying rate under constant drying conditions, the term $f(G)$ represents the same quantity. Its absolute value will vary from material to material, and, in the case of a given material, will be less in any type of drier offering inadequate surface exposure. It should be noted that $f(G)$ is independent of the size of the drier or the scale of the drying operation.

The capacity of a drier is proportional to its size, provided (1) that the air supply be kept strictly proportional to the water to be evaporated, (2) that the mass velocity of the air past the material be unchanged, (3) that the wet material be dried from the same initial to the same final water content, (4) that the average thickness or dimension of the material be constant, (5) that the temperature and humidity of the initial air be kept the same, and finally (6) that the degree of exposure of the surface to the drying air be unchanged. If in experimentation these conditions are fixed at the values it is desired to realize in practice, then the size of a drier of exactly the same type can be calculated by simple proportionality. When, however, any one of these conditions is to be different from those obtaining in the experiment, or when another type of flow is to be used, proportionality no longer holds, and resort must be had to the equations.

As has already been emphasized, the constants for the design of drying apparatus must be determined by experimentation upon the material itself. In such experiments it is important to have the nature of exposure of the material to the drying air similar to that in the apparatus it is proposed to build.

CONSTRUCTION OF Na₂HPO₄·12H₂O CURVES

(Fig. 222, page 675)

The humidities determining curve AB are calculated from the decomposition pressures P^* of $Na_2HPO_4 \cdot 12H_2O$ at various temperatures† and from the pressures P_0 of water at the same temperatures‡ as shown by the relationship $H = 18(P)/29(760 - P)$. The results are given in Table I.

TABLE I

t	P	$Na_2HPO_4 \cdot 12H_2O$		H_0	Per Cent Humidity
		H	P_0		
42.2	4.61	0.00378	7.39	0.00610	62.0
51.5	6.38	0.00526	9.69	0.00800	65.7
59.0	8.84	0.00730	12.73	0.01056	69.1
63.1	10.53	0.00872	14.70	0.01228	71.0
68.3	13.09	0.01087	17.56	0.01470	73.9
73.4	16.19	0.01350	21.0	0.01764	76.5
80.6	21.58	0.01814	26.5	0.02243	80.8

For nomenclature, see page 682.

In determining curve CB, the humidity of air in equilibrium with the saturated solution H_s is calculated as before, and expressed in terms of that of air saturated at the same temperature.

The vapor pressures of the saturated solutions at the temperatures of saturation, however, have not been determined, and must be obtained indirectly. The solubilities J, *i.e.*, the composition of the saturated solution at any temperature,§ and the pressures P_{760} of solutions of varying strength at 212°F.¶ are available. Making use of the fact brought out in the discussion of Evaporation (page 412) that the relative vapor-pressure lowering of any solution not too concentrated is independent of the temperature, one can calculate the relative lowering from the data at 212°F. and then obtain the pressure at the saturation point p_s from the pressure P_0 of pure water at the saturation temperature. These steps are indicated in Table II.

* All values of pressures are given in millimeters of mercury.

† FROWEIN, *Z. physik. Chem.*, **1**, 1 (1887).

‡ SCHEEL and HEUSE, *Ann. Physik*, (4), **31**, 715–730 (1910).

§ MULDER, Bijdragen tot de geschiedenis van het scheikundig gebonden water, Rotterdam (1864).

¶ TAMMANN, *Mem. Acad. Petersburg*, **7**, 35 (1887).

TABLE II

t	J	$760 - P_{760}$	$\dfrac{100(760 - P_{760})}{760}$	P_0	$P_0 - P_s$	P_s	H_s	H_0	Per Cent Humidity
30.4	1.9	3.23	.425	4.29	.02	4.27	0.00351	0.00352	99.6
32	2.5	4.25	.559	4.58	.03	4.55	0.00374	0.00376	99.3
50	3.9	6.62	.871	9.18	.08	9.10	0.00752	0.00758	99.2
68	9.3	15.78	2.076	17.41	.36	17.05	0.01425	0.01454	98.0
86	24.1	38.2	5.03	31.56	1.59	29.97	0.02547	0.02690	94.7

t = deg. F.

J = gm. of anhydrous salt/100 gm. of water in saturated solution.

$760 - P_{760}$ = vapor-pressure lowering at 42°F., mm. of mercury.

$\dfrac{100(760 - P_{760})}{760}$ = per cent vapor-pressure lowering.

P_0 = pressure pure water, mm. of mercury

P = pressure of solid duodecahydrate, mm. of mercury.

H_0 = humidity of saturated air, lb. of water vapor/lb. of dry air.

H = humidity of air in equilibrium with duodecahydrate.

P_s = pressure of saturated solution, mm. of mercury.

H_s = humidity of air in equilibrium with saturated solution.

Nomenclature

A, A_w = surface area, total exposed and wetted, respectively.

a = surface per volume of drier.

B, C = constants.

b, b' = constants.

c, $c_{av.}$, c_m, c_s, c_{sc} = concentration of liquid, weight per unit total original volume; c corresponds to the position x, $c_{av.}$ to the integrated average in the stock, c_m to mid-plane, c_s to the surface and c_{sc} to the surface at the critical point.

D = diffusivity of liquid.

d = prefix, indicating differential.

E, E_{sc} = equilibrium water, weight per unit weight of bone-dry stock; E corresponds to the humidity and temperature of main body of air, and E_{sc} to equilibrium with substantially saturated air at the surface temperature at the critical point.

F = rate of feed to a continuous drier, expressed as weight of bone-dry stock per unit time.

$f(G)$, $f(v)$ = an empirically determined function of the mass velocity of the air.

G = mass velocity of air.

H, H_s, H_{sc}, H_w = absolute humidity, weight per unit weight of bone-dry air; H corresponds to the main body of the air. H_s or H_{sc} to saturation at the surface temperature in the constant-rate period and H_w to the wet-bulb temperature.

h_c, h_r = coefficients of heat transfer from air to surface, by conduction and convection and by radiation, respectively.

K = drying coefficient, in units of the reciprocal of time.

k' = evaporation coefficient, based on humidity difference, weight per unit time per unit wetted surface.

M, N = constants.

m = weight of bone-dry air per unit of bone-dry stock.

L = half-thickness before drying starts.

p = partial pressure of water vapor.

Q = total weight of bone-dry stock in drier.

q = heat-transfer rate.

r_i, r_s = resistances to diffusion of liquid from the interior to the surface and resistance to evaporation at the surface, respectively.

S = cross section of drier.

T, T_1, T_2, T_c, T_s, T_{sc} = total moisture content, weight per unit weight of bone-dry stock; T corresponds to θ, T_1 to any time in the falling-rate period, T_2 to a later time, T_c to the critical point, T_s to the surface and T_{sc} to the critical value at the surface.

t, t' = temperature of air and of surroundings, respectively.

U = overall coefficient of heat transfer based on the heat transferred to the stock and upon the temperature difference between air and mid-plane.

V = volume of drying of apparatus.

W = free water, $T - E$.

w = rate of flow of bone-dry air through drier, weight per unit time.

X = a dimensionless ratio, equal to $D\theta/L^2 = (T_0 - T)D\rho/\alpha L$.

x = distance from surface into solid.

Y_x = a dimensionless ratio, equal to $(T_0 - T_x)\rho D/\alpha L$.

y = distance from air exit.

Z = weight of water in stock in drier.

z = The term $D\rho/\alpha L$, having units of $1/T$.

Greek Letters

α = alpha, rate of evaporation, weight per unit time per unit wet surface, in constant-rate period.

β = beta, coefficient of surface evaporation.

Δt =temperature drop from air to stock.

λ =lambda, latent heat of vaporization, heat units per unit weight.

$\theta, \theta_c, \theta_F, \Sigma\theta$ =theta, drying time, length of constant-rate period, a time interval in the falling-rate period, and total, respectively.

ρ =rho, weight of bone-dry stock per unit original volume.

φ, ψ =phi, psi; terms defined on pages 679 and 680.

References

1. LEWIS, W. K., *Ind. Eng. Chem.*, **13**, 427–432 (1921).

2. SHERWOOD, T. K., *Ind. Eng. Chem.*, **21**, 976–980 (1929).

3. McCREADY, D. W., and W. L. McCABE, *Trans. Amer. Inst. Chem. Eng.*, **29**, 131–159 (1933).

4. SHERWOOD, T. K., *Ind. Eng. Chem.*, **22**, 132–136 (1930).

5. SHERWOOD, T. K., and E. W. COMINGS, *Trans. Amer. Inst. Chem. Eng.*, **27**, 118–133 (1932).

6. COMINGS, E. W., and T. K. SHERWOOD, *Ind. Eng. Chem.*, **26**, 1096–1098 (1934).

7. HOUGEN, O. A., and N. H. CEGELSKE, paper presented at Toronto meeting, *Amer. Inst. Chem. Eng.*, May, 1937.

8. LEDERER, E. L., *Z. angew. chem.*, **37**, 750–754 (1924).

9. TUTTLE, F., *J. Franklin Inst.*, **200**, 609–614 (1925).

10. TROOP and WHEELER, *J. Cer. Soc.*, **27**, 303 (1927).

11. SHERWOOD, T. K., *Ind. Eng. Chem.*, **21**, 12–16 (1929).

12. NEWMAN, A. B., *Trans. Amer. Inst. Chem. Eng.*, **27**, 203–220, 310–333 (1931).

13. KAMEI, S., S. MIZUNO, and S. SHIOMI, *J. Soc. Chem. Ind. (Japan)*, Supplemental Binding, **38**, 456B-473B, (September, 1935).

14. DREW, W. N., Thesis in Chemical Engineering, Massachusetts Institute of Technology, 1911.

15. GILLILAND, E. R., and T. K. SHERWOOD, *Ind. Eng. Chem.*, **25**, 1134–1136 (1933).

16. BOYER, M. W., and J. BUSS, *Ind. Eng. Chem.*, **18**, 728 (1926).

17. MAVERICK, G., and D. WEBSTER, S. B. Thesis in Chemical Engineering, Massachusetts Institute of Technology, 1916.

APPENDIX

Viscosity of Gases—The absolute viscosity of a gas may be determined by applying a definite pressure difference at the two ends of a capillary tube of known length and diameter and observing the rate of flow, μ being calculated from Eqs. 12c (page 81) and 3 (page 46). However, it is difficult to obtain a long capillary tube of uniform diameter. This difficulty can be avoided by measuring relative viscosity. Since the viscosity varies with temperature, the determination should be carried out at a constant temperature. Figure 225 shows the viscosity of certain gases at various temperatures. The viscosity of gases is approximately proportional to a positive power function of absolute temperature. In plotting such data on logarithmic paper, it is found to fall on very flat curves in most cases, the average slopes varying from 0.5 to 1. According to kinetic theory, the viscosity of gases should be independent of pressure and directly proportional to the square root of the absolute temperature. Experimental data* show that the viscosity of carbon dioxide gas is practically independent of pressures from $\frac{1}{60}$ to 1 atmosphere, and even at 40 atmospheres pressure it has increased by only about 18 per cent. However, the exponent of the absolute temperature is nearer unity than the value of 0.5 called for by the kinetic theory. Additional data may be found in suitable physical-chemical tables, and it is customary to tabulate the absolute viscosity in c.g.s. units. The method of converting these to other units is given on page 690.

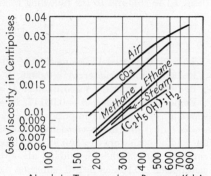

Fig. 225.—Viscosities of gases and vapors at atmospheric pressure.

Viscosity of Liquids.—The absolute viscosity of liquids may be determined by the use of a capillary tube, by the use of the MacMichael viscosimeter and in other ways.

In commercial work, the viscosity of a liquid is generally determined by measuring the time of efflux of a definite volume through a short tube in an apparatus called a **viscosimeter.** Thus a liquid with a viscosity of 80 Saybolt is one requiring 80 sec. to discharge a volume just sufficient to fill the chamber of the Saybolt viscosimeter through the nozzle of that instrument under the changing though definite head which that instrument gives.

* JEANS, "Dynamical Theory of Gases," Cambridge University Press, 1904.

687

The pressure drop through the tube itself is dependent upon the viscosity of the liquid, but the entrance and exit losses are practically independent of the absolute viscosity; hence the absolute viscosity is not directly proportional to the time of efflux.

The relation between the time of efflux θ in seconds and the viscosity varies for different makes of viscosimeters, and sometimes even for the various instruments supplied by a given manufacturer. Such instruments are calibrated against liquids of known viscosity. The instruments are designed to conform to the following relation:

$$\frac{\mu'}{\rho'} = A'\theta - \frac{B}{\theta},$$

Saybolt Universal Viscosimeter: $A' = 0.0022$, $B' = 1.8$
Redwood Viscosimeter: $A' = 0.0026$, $B' = 1.72$
Redwood Admiralty Viscosimeter: $A' = 0.027$, $B' = 20$
Engler Viscosimeter: $A' = 0.00147$, $B' = 3.74$,

where μ' is the viscosity in poises and ρ' is the density in gm./c.c. The ratio μ/ρ is called **kinematic viscosity.** An oil having viscosity of 100 Saybolt sec. and a specific gravity of 0.9 would have a kinematic viscosity of 0.202 sq. cm./sec. (or "Stokes"), and an absolute viscosity of 0.182 poise, or 18.2 centipoises. This empirical equation is satisfactory for streamline flow through the Saybolt nozzle. If liquids of low viscosity are used, turbulent flow ensues and the equation is inapplicable. For example, it would indicate a negative viscosity for a time of discharge less than 28.6 sec.

In the case of liquids, the viscosity always decreases as the temperature rises. Where data at a few temperatures only are available, it is often necessary to interpolate and sometimes to extrapolate on the curve of viscosity *vs.* temperature, but there is no satisfactory simple equation that can be used to predict the viscosity of all liquids. As shown in Fig. 226, the curvature is great at some temperatures and little at others. It is well known that interpolation and extrapolation are most reliable when the data can be made to approximate a straight-line relationship. Thus by plotting the reciprocal of the viscosity against the temperature, or the logarithm of viscosity *vs.* the reciprocal of the absolute temperature, or the logarithm of viscosity *vs.* the logarithm of the absolute temperature, or the logarithm of viscosity *vs.* the temperature, the curvature is greatly reduced, but none of these methods gives a straight-line relationship in all cases. If one is willing to employ three empirical constants, good results are often obtained with the relation log $\mu = \log n_1 + n_2 \log (t+n_3)$; based on this relation, special coordinate paper, μ vs. t, is available for plotting data for hydrocarbons. In some cases, n_3 is negligible with t in deg. F.; in such cases log μ is linear in log t. Although the method* illustrated by Fig. 227 has not yet been given a thorough test, it is believed that it possesses interesting possibilities. Here the ordinates are the temperature of the liquid in question, while the abscissas are the temperatures at which some standard liquid has the same viscosity, and it will be noted that straight lines are obtained for

---

* A. W. Porter, *Phil. Mag.*, **23**, 458 (1912).

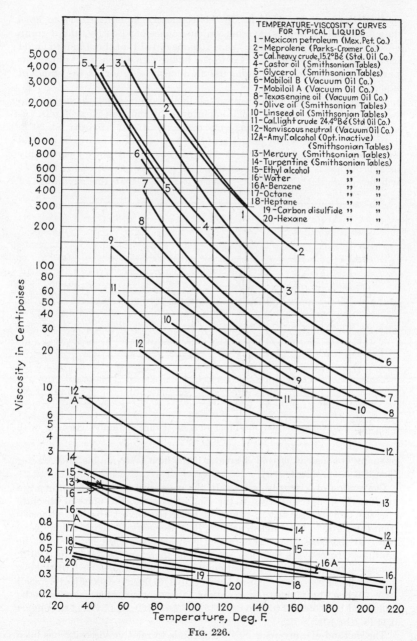

TEMPERATURE-VISCOSITY CURVES
FOR TYPICAL LIQUIDS

1 – Mexican petroleum (Mex. Pet. Co.)
2 – Meprolene (Parks-Cramer Co.)
3 – Cal. heavy crude, 15.2°Bé (Std. Oil Co.)
4 – Castor oil (Smithsonian Tables)
5 – Glycerol (Smithsonian Tables)
6 – Mobiloil B (Vacuum Oil Co.)
7 – Mobiloil A (Vacuum Oil Co.)
8 – Texas engine oil (Vacuum Oil Co.)
9 – Olive oil (Smithsonian Tables)
10 – Linseed oil (Smithsonian Tables)
11 – Cal. light crude 24.4°Bé (Std. Oil Co.)
12 – Nonviscous neutral (Vacuum Oil Co.)
12A – Amyl. alcohol (Opt. inactive)
        (Smithsonian Tables)
13 – Mercury (Smithsonian Tables)
14 – Turpentine (Smithsonian Tables)
15 – Ethyl alcohol " "
16 – Water " "
16A – Benzene " "
17 – Octane " "
18 – Heptane " "
19 – Carbon disulfide " "
20 – Hexane " "

FIG. 226.

most of the cases considered. In this connection it is necessary to have data for standard liquids covering various ranges of viscosity, and a group of such curves is shown by Fig. 226. It is suggested that the standard liquid chosen for a given case be similar to the liquid with which it is being compared, *e.g.*, for aqueous solutions use an aqueous solution as the standard liquid, etc.

As already stated, the viscosity of all liquids decreases with rise in temperature. This fact is of great importance in the pumping of oils. A certain crude oil at 120°F. has only one-sixteenth its viscosity at 60°F. If the flow is streamline, by pumping at 120°F. the friction loss will be reduced to one-sixteenth that at 60°F. If the flow is turbulent, since f varies only as approximately the fourth root of μ (see page 78), the friction at 120°F. will be one-half that at 60°F. Hence it is seen that the advantage of

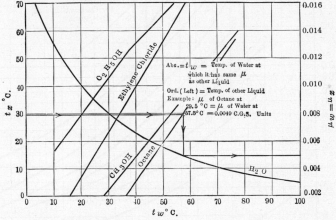

Fig. 227.—Porter's method for prediction of change of liquid viscosity with temperature.

pumping hot instead of cold is greater if the flow is streamline in character than if it is turbulent.

Conversion of Viscosity Units.—In the c.g.s. system, the units for μ are gm./(sec.)(cm.). Similarly, in the English system, the units of absolute viscosity are lb./(sec.)(ft.). Thus, in order to convert absolute viscosity from the c.g.s. to the English system, it is necessary to convert gm./(sec.) (cm.) to lb./(sec.)(ft.). The factor by which the c.g.s. value must be multiplied to convert it to lb./(sec.)(ft.) is, therefore, 30.5/454, or 0.0672. For example, the absolute viscosity of water at 68°F. (20°C.) is 0.0101 c.g.s. units (sometimes called "poises") or $(0.0101)(0.0672) = 0.000679$ lb./(sec.) (ft.). When the viscosity is expressed in centipoises, this value must be multiplied by 0.000672 to convert it to lb./(sec.)(ft.), and by 2.42 to convert it to lb./(hr.)(ft.).

The method of converting Saybolt seconds to relative viscosity has been given on page 688.

TABLE I.—VISCOSITY OF WATER AT VARIOUS TEMPERATURES*

(t = deg. F., and μ' = centipoises)

t	μ'	t	μ'	t	μ'	t	μ'	t	μ'
32	1.79	74	0.929	116	0.582	158	0.407	200	0.305
34	1.73	76	0.905	118	0.571	160	0.400	202	0.301
36	1.66	78	0.887	120	0.560	162	0.394	204	0.298
38	1.60	80	0.861	122	0.549	164	0.388	206	0.294
40	1.55	82	0.840	124	0.539	166	0.383	208	0.291
42	1.49	84	0.820	126	0.530	168	0.377	210	0.287
44	1.44	86	0.800	128	0.520	170	0.372	212	0.284
46	1.40	88	0.782	130	0.511	172	0.367	220	0.270
48	1.35	90	0.764	132	0.502	174	0.362	230	0.255
50	1.31	92	0.747	134	0.493	176	0.357	240	0.242
52	1.27	94	0.731	136	0.485	178	0.352	250	0.229
54	1.23	96	0.715	138	0.477	180	0.347	260	0.218
56	1.19	98	0.699	140	0.470	182	0.343	270	0.208
58	1.16	100	0.684	142	0.461	184	0.338	280	0.199
60	1.12	102	0.670	144	0.454	186	0.333	290	0.191
62	1.09	104	0.654	146	0.446	188	0.329	300	0.185
64	1.06	106	0.643	148	0.439	190	0.325	310	0.179
66	1.03	108	0.630	150	0.432	192	0.321	320	0.174
68	1.01	110	0.617	152	0.425	194	0.317	330	
70	0.978	112	0.605	154	0.419	196	0.313	340	
72	0.953	114	0.593	156	0.412	198	0.309	350	

* Condensed from "International Critical Tables," Vol. 5, p. 10, McGraw-Hill Book Company, Inc., 1929.

TABLE II.—STANDARD DIMENSIONS FOR STANDARD-WEIGHT
WROUGHT–IRON AND STEEL PIPE
(Crane Co.)

Nominal size, in.	Actual diameters		Trans-verse areas internal, sq. in.	Nominal thickness, in.	Length of pipe per sq. ft.	
	External, in.	Approximate internal, in.			External surface, ft.	Internal surface, ft.
⅛	0.405	0.269	0.057	0.068	9.431	14.199
¼	0.540	0.364	0.104	0.088	7.073	10.493
⅜	0.675	0.493	0.191	0.091	5.658	7.747
½	0.840	0.622	0.304	0.109	4.547	6.141
¾	1.050	0.824	0.533	0.113	3.637	4.635
1	1.315	1.049	0.864	0.133	2.904	3.641
1¼	1.660	1.380	1.495	0.140	2.301	2.767
1½	1.900	1.610	2.036	0.145	2.010	2.372
2	2.375	2.067	3.355	0.154	1.608	1.847
2½	2.875	2.469	4.788	0.203	1.328	1.547
3	3.500	3.068	7.393	0.216	1.091	1.245
3½	4.000	3.548	9.886	0.226	0.954	1.076
4	4.500	4.026	12.730	0.237	0.848	0.948
4½	5.000	4.506	15.947	0.247	0.763	0.847
5	5.563	5.047	20.006	0.258	0.686	0.756
6	6.625	6.065	28.891	0.280	0.576	0.629
7	7.625	7.023	38.738	0.301	0.500	0.543
8	8.625	8.071	51.161	0.277	0.442	0.473
8	8.625	7.981	50.027	0.322	0.442	0.478
9	9.625	8.941	62.786	0.342	0.396	0.427
10	10.750	10.192	81.585	0.279	0.355	0.374
10	10.750	10.136	80.691	0.307	0.355	0.376
10	10.750	10.020	78.855	0.365	0.355	0.381
11	11.750	11.000	95.033	0.375	0.325	0.347
12	12.750	12.090	114.800	0.330	0.299	0.315
12	12.750	12.000	113.097	0.375	0.299	0.318

TABLE III.—STANDARD CONDENSER-TUBE DATA*

Outside diameter, in.	Size number, B.-W.G.	Weight per ft., lb.†	Thickness, in.	Inside diameter, in.	Surface, sq. ft. per ft. of length		Inside sectional area, sq. in.	Velocity, (ft./sec.) for one (U. S. gal./min.)	Capacity at 1 ft./sec. velocity	
					Outside	Inside			U. S. gal./min.	Lb. water/hr.
½	12	0.493	0.109	0.282	0.1309	0.0748	0.0624	5.142	0.1945	97.25
	14	0.403	0.083	0.334	0.1309	0.0874	0.0876	3.662	0.2730	136.5
	16	0.329	0.065	0.370	0.1309	0.0969	0.1076	2.981	0.3352	167.5
	18	0.258	0.049	0.402	0.1309	0.1052	0.1269	2.530	0.3952	197.6
	20	0.190	0.035	0.430	0.1309	0.1125	0.1452	2.209	0.4528	226.4
⅝	12	0.656	0.109	0.407	0.1636	0.1066	0.1301	2.468	0.4053	202.7
	14	0.526	0.083	0.459	0.1636	0.1202	0.1655	1.939	0.5157	258.9
	16	0.424	0.065	0.495	0.1636	0.1296	0.1925	1.667	0.5999	300.0
	18	0.329	0.049	0.527	0.1636	0.1380	0.2181	1.472	0.6793	339.7
	20	0.241	0.035	0.555	0.1636	0.1453	0.2420	1.326	0.7542	377.1
¾	10	0.962	0.134	0.482	0.1963	0.1262	0.1825	1.758	0.5688	284.4
	12	0.812	0.109	0.532	0.1963	0.1393	0.2223	1.442	0.6935	346.8
	14	0.644	0.083	0.584	0.1963	0.1528	0.2678	1.198	0.8347	417.4
	16	0.518	0.065	0.620	0.1963	0.1613	0.3019	1.063	0.9407	470.4
	18	0.400	0.049	0.652	0.1963	0.1706	0.3339	0.9611	1.041	520.5
⅞	10	1.16	0.134	0.607	0.2291	0.1589	0.2893	1.108	0.9025	451.3
	12	0.992	0.109	0.657	0.2291	0.1720	0.3390	0.9465	1.057	528.5
	14	0.769	0.083	0.709	0.2291	0.1856	0.3949	0.8126	1.230	615.0
	16	0.613	0.065	0.745	0.2291	0.1951	0.4360	0.7360	1.358	679.0
	18	0.472	0.049	0.777	0.2291	0.2034	0.4740	0.6770	1.477	738.5
1	10	1.35	0.134	0.732	0.2618	0.1916	0.4208	0.7626	1.311	655.5
	12	1.14	0.109	0.782	0.2618	0.2048	0.4803	0.6681	1.497	748.5
	14	0.887	0.083	0.834	0.2618	0.2183	0.5463	0.5874	1.702	851.0
	16	0.708	0.065	0.870	0.2618	0.2277	0.5945	0.5398	1.852	926.0
	18	0.535	0.049	0.902	0.2618	0.2361	0.6390	0.5022	1.991	995.5
1¼	10	1.74	0.134	0.982	0.3271	0.2572	0.7575	0.4236	2.362	1181
	12	1.45	0.109	1.032	0.3271	0.2701	0.8369	0.3834	2.608	1304
	14	1.13	0.083	1.084	0.3271	0.2839	0.9229	0.3477	2.877	1439
	16	0.898	0.065	1.120	0.3271	0.2932	0.9852	0.3257	3.070	1535
	18	0.675	0.049	1.152	0.3271	0.3015	1.043	0.3075	3.253	1627
1½	10	2.12	0.134	1.232	0.3925	0.3227	1.193	0.2688	3.720	1860
	12	1.76	0.109	1.282	0.3925	0.3355	1.292	0.2482	4.030	2015
	14	1.36	0.083	1.334	0.3925	0.3491	1.398	0.2292	4.362	2181
	16	1.09	0.065	1.370	0.3925	0.3585	1.473	0.2180	4.587	2294
2	10	2.94	0.134	1.732	0.5233	0.4534	2.355	0.1362	7.342	3671
	12	2.40	0.109	1.782	0.5233	0.4665	2.494	0.1287	7.770	3885
	14	1.85	0.083	1.834	0.5233	0.4803	2.643	0.1213	8.244	4122
	16	1.47	0.065	1.870	0.5233	0.4896	2.747	0.1168	8.562	4281

* Prepared by T. B. Drew.
† In brass, specific gravity = 8.56.

TABLE IV.—AVERAGE VALUE OF k (RATIO OF SPECIFIC HEAT OF GASES
AND VAPORS AT CONSTANT PRESSURE TO SPECIFIC HEAT AT CONSTANT
VOLUME)

	k
Monatomic gases (A, He, Hg)	1.667
Permanent diatomic gases (Air, O_2, N_2, H_2, CO)	1.405
Hydrochloric acid vapor (HCl)	1.40
Chlorine vapor (Cl_2)	1.36
Carbon dioxide (CO_2)	1.30
Sulfur dioxide (SO_2)	1.26
Steam (H_2O vapor)	1.28
Ammonia vapor (NH_3)	1.30
Methane (CH_4)	1.31
Acetylene (C_2H_2)	1.26
Ethylene (C_2H_4)	1.24
Ethane (C_2H_6)	1.22
Carbon bisulfide (CS_2)	1.20
Benzol (C_6H_6)	1.10
Ethyl ether ($C_4H_{10}O$)	1.08

TABLE V.—THERMAL CONDUCTIVITIES
[Main body of table is k in B.t.u./(hr.)(sq. ft.)(deg. F./ft.)]
A. METALS

Temperature, deg. F.	32	212	392	572	752	Reference
Aluminum	117	119	124	133	144	1
Brass (70 Cu, 30 Zn)	56	60	63	66	67	1
Cast iron	29	28	...	...	...	1
Copper	224	218	215	212	210	1
Lead	20	20	19	18	...	1
Mercury	4.8	...	...	...	...	3
Nickel	36	34	33	32	...	1
Nickel alloy (70 Ni, 28 Cr, 2 Fe)	10.4*	...	...	...	...	3
Nickel alloy (62 Ni, 12 Cr, 26 Fe)	7.8*	...	...	...	...	3
Silver	242	238	...	...	...	1
Steel (mild), cold rolled	...	26	26	25	23	1
Tantalum	32*	...	...	...	...	1
Tin	36	34	33	...	...	1
Nickel-chromium steel (18 Ni, 8 Cr)	...	...	...	15†	...	2
Wrought iron (Swedish)	...	32	30	28	26	1
Zinc	65	64	62	59	54	3

* At 68°F.
† At 626°F.

TABLE V.—THERMAL CONDUCTIVITIES.—(*Continued*)

B. MISCELLANEOUS SOLIDS

Substance	Apparent density, lb./cu. ft.	Temperature, deg. F.	k	Reference
Asbestos..........................	36	32	0.087	3
	36	752	0.13	3
Asbestos board.....................	120	68	0.43	3
Aluminum foil (7 air spaces per 2.5 in.)..	0.2	100	0.025	3
Bricks:				
Building brick......................	......	68	0.4	3
Chrome (32 % Cr_2O_3 by weight).....	200	392	1.3	3
Diatomaceous, natural, across strata..	27.7	400	0.051	4
	27.7	1600	0.077	4
Fire clay (Missouri)................	......	392	0.58	6
	......	2552	1.02	6
Kaolin insulating brick.............	27	932	0.15	
	27	2100	0.26	
Magnesite (86.8 % MgO by weight)..	158	400	2.2	7
	158	2200	1.1	7
Silica (93 % SiO_2 by weight).........	105	932	0.76	3
	105	2012	0.93	3
Silicon carbide brick, recrystallized...	129	1112	10.7	5
	129	2552	6.3	5
Carbon, gas.........................	......	122	2.0	3
Cement, Portland....................	......	186	0.17	3
Coke, petroleum.....................	......	212	3.4	3
	......	932	2.9	3
Concrete, stone.....................	......	....	0.5	3
Cotton wool........................	5	86	0.024	3
Cork board.........................	7	86	0.023	8
	10.6	86	0.025	8
Diatomaceous powder, coarse..........	20	100	0.036	4
	20	1600	0.082	4
Moulded pipe covering..............	26	400	0.051	4
With cement, fired.................	61.8	400	0.16	4
Fiber, insulating board................	14.8	70	0.028	3
Glass, window.......................	......	....	0.3–0.6	3
Hair (cattle) felted....................	12	86	0.022	8
Ice................................	57.5	32	1.3	3
Kapok..............................	0.88	86	0.02	3
Lampblack..........................	10	104	0.038	3

TABLE V.—THERMAL CONDUCTIVITIES.—(*Continued*)
B. MISCELLANEOUS SOLIDS.—(*Continued*)

Substance	Apparent density, lb./cu. ft.	Temperature, deg. F.	k	Reference
Leather, sole	62.4	....	0.092	3
Magnesia	......	100	0.039	3
	......	400	0.046	3
Mineral wool	10	86	0.0225	8
	18	86	0.024	8
Paper	......	....	0.075	3
Porcelain	......	....	0.6	3
Rubber, hard	74.8	32	0.092	3
Para	......	70	0.11	3
Sand, dry	94.6	68	0.19	3
Sawdust	12	70	0.03	3
Slate	......	201	0.86	3
Snow	34.7	....	0.27	3
Wood (across grain):				
Balsa	7.5	86	0.025–0.03	3
Oak	51.5	....	0.12	3
Maple	44.7	122	0.11	3
Pine, white	34.0	59	0.10	3
White fir	28.1	140	0.062	3
Wood (parallel to grain):				
Pine	34.4	70	0.2	

C. GASES

Gas, at 1 atm.	k at 32°F.	k at 212°F.	Reference
Air	0.0129	0.0165	3
Carbon dioxide	0.0079	0.0110	3
Carbon monoxide	0.0124	0.0161	3
Hydrogen	0.0917	0.115	3
Methane	0.0170	0.0242	3
Nitrogen	0.0131	0.0166	3
Oxygen	0.0134	0.0172	3
Steam	......	0.0126	3

Table V.—Thermal Conductivities.—(*Continued*)
D. Liquids

Liquid	k at 86°F.	k at 167°F.	Reference
Ammonia, at 5 to 86°F...................	0.29	.....	11
Amyl alcohol (iso)........................	0.086	0.084	9
Butanol (*n*).............................	0.097	0.094	9
Ethanol, 100%...........................	0.104	0.100	9
Ethyl ether.............................	0.079	0.075	9
Kerosene................................	0.086	0.081	9
Mercury, at 32°F........................	4.83	.....	1
Methanol................................	0.122	0.119	9
Pentane (*n*)............................	0.078	0.074	9
Petroleum ether.........................	0.075	0.073	9
Petroleum oil...........................	0.08	.....	3
Propanol (iso)...........................	0.089	0.088	9
Water..................................	0.347	0.372	9

References for Table V

1. "International Critical Tables," McGraw-Hill Book Company, Inc., New York, 1929.
2. Martin, K. W., Massachusetts Institute of Technology Thesis, 1929.
3. Miscellaneous sources.
4. Townshend and Williams, *Chem. Met. Eng.*, **39**, 219 (1932).
5. Norton, F. H., "Refractories," McGraw-Hill Book Company, Inc., New York, 1931.
6. Norton, F. H., *J. Amer. Ceram. Soc.*, **10**, 30 (1927).
7. Wilkes, G. B., *J. Amer. Ceram. Soc.*, **16**, 125 (1933).
8. *U. S. Bur. Standards Letter Circ.* 227, Apr. 19, 1927.
9. Bridgman, P. W., *Proc. Amer. Acad. Arts Sci.*, **59**, 141 (1923).
10. Smith, J. F. D., *Ind. Eng. Chem.*, **22**, 1246 (1930).
11. Kardos, A. Z., *Ver. deut. Ing.*, **27**, 1158 (1933).
12. Kaye and Higgins, *Proc. Roy. Soc. (London)*, **A117**, 459 (1928).
13. Martin, L. H., and K. C. Lang, *Proc. Phys. Soc.*, **45**, 523 (1933).

Conversion Factors for Thermal Conductivities.—The values of k in Table V are expressed in B.t.u./(hr.)(sq. ft.)(deg. F./ft.). Conversion factors to other units are as follows:

Multiply by 12 to obtain B.t.u./(hr.)(sq. ft.)(deg. F./in.).
Multiply by 12 to obtain p.c.u./(hr.)(sq. ft.)(deg. C./in.).
Multiply by 0.00413 to obtain gm.-cal./(sec.)(sq. cm.)(deg. C./cm).
Multiply by 173 to obtain kilo-ergs/(sec.)(sq. cm.)(deg. C./cm.).
Multiply by 0.0173 to obtain watts/(sq. cm.)(deg. C./cm.).
Multiply by 1.49 to obtain kg.-cal./(hr.)(sq. m.)(deg. C./m.).

TABLE VI.—VALUES OF $C_p\mu/k$ FOR GASES AT 60 TO 80°F.
AND 1 ATMOSPHERE ABSOLUTE
(Expressed in Consistent Units)

Helium	0.695
Argon	0.668
Hydrogen	0.735
Oxygen	0.736
Nitrogen	0.733
Air	0.733
Nitric oxide	0.755
Carbon monoxide	0.775
Carbon dioxide	0.840
Ethylene	0.800
Methane	0.781
Steam, at 300°F. and 1 atmosphere	1.20

PROBLEMS

STOICHIOMETRY

1. In an electrolytic plant the moist chlorine gas in the pipe line at Section A is at a total absolute pressure of 750 mm. of mercury, and at a temperature of 80°F., the partial pressure of the water in the gas being 10 mm. of mercury. In order to measure the steady rate of flow of the gas, 20 lb.-mols of moist air/hr. are fed into the main at Section B. This air is at an absolute pressure of 750 mm. of mercury and at a temperature of 70°F., the partial pressure of water being 19 mm. of mercury. After these two streams are thoroughly mixed at Section C, the absolute pressure is 740 mm. of mercury and the temperature is 70°F. Orsat analysis shows 11.11 mol per cent air (on the dry basis) in the gas at A, and 32.9 mol per cent air (on the dry basis) in the mixed gas at C.

Calculate the pounds of chlorine flowing per hour.

2. A 31 per cent solution of Na_2CO_3 weighing 5000 lb. is cooled slowly to 20°C. The crystals formed during the cooling are sal soda $(Na_2CO_3.10H_2O)$. The solubility at 20°C. is 21.5 parts anhydrous salt per 100 parts of water. During the cooling period the amount of water evaporated is 5 per cent of the weight of the original solution. What is the weight of sal soda crystallized out?

3. A dry gaseous mixture containing 87 mol per cent CH_4 and 13 per cent C_2H_6 is burned with air. Orsat analysis of the combustion gas shows 5.3 per cent CO_2 and no CO. The air enters at 32°F. and normal barometer, and the partial pressure of water vapor in the air is 2 mm. of mercury.

   a. Calculate the per cent excess air.

   b. Calculate the cubic feet of flue gas, at 600°F. and normal barometer, per cubic foot of fuel gas measured at standard conditions.

4. In the operation of a dirigible, the exhaust gases from the gasoline engines pass through pipes exposed to cold atmospheric air at 45°F. and are cooled to a temperature t such that the weight of water condensed is equal to the weight of gasoline burned. The motor fuel is a volatile gasoline consisting only of hydrocarbons, and is burned to form exhaust gases having the following Orsat analysis: 12.6 per cent CO_2, 4.2 per cent CO and 83.2 per cent N_2. The air enters the carbureting system at a total absolute pressure of 460 mm. of mercury, and the pressure of water vapor in this air 6.4 mm. of mercury.

   a. Calculate the temperature t to which the exhaust gases are cooled, if at this temperature the residual exhaust gases are saturated with water vapor and the total absolute pressure is 460 mm. of mercury.

   b. Calculate the pounds of dry air used per pound of fuel burned.

5. Pyrites fines are burnt in a Herreschoff burner to form SO_2, the latter to be used for conversion to SO_3 in a sulfuric acid plant. The pyrites contain 89.7 per cent FeS_2 by weight and 10.3 per cent of gangue. The average analysis of the burner gas shows 9.32 per cent SO_2, 6.93 per cent O_2 and 83.75 per cent N_2, the results being on a volumetric basis.

a. Of the sulfur in the pyrites, what percentage was oxidized to SO_3?

b. Analysis of the cinder shows 5.38 per cent SO_3 by weight. Of the sulfur fired, what percentage leaves the burner as SO_3 in the burner gas?

6. In a test on an externally fired shaft type of lime kiln, the following averaged analyses are obtained:

Coal fired (by weight,) %	Limestone feed (by weight), %	Stack gases (by volume), %
72.0 C	90 $CaCO_3$	32 CO_2
5.5 H	6 $MgCO_3$	4 O_2
8.5 ash	4 inerts	64 N_2
2.0 N		
12.0 O		

Per ton of limestone fed, calculate:

a. Pounds of coal consumed.

b. Cubic feet of stack gases, at 740 mm. of mercury and 700°F.

7. A boiler is fired with a low-grade coal containing 52 per cent C, 8 per cent S, 6 per cent N and 19 per cent ash, under such conditions that the dry refuse contains 32 per cent combustible matter. This combustible matter is composed of 97 per cent C and 3 per cent H. The air enters at 68°F. and has a partial pressure of H_2O of 12 mm. of mercury. The barometer is 753 mm. Orsat analysis of stack gas gives 8.7 per cent CO_2, 0.9 per cent CO and 10.2 per cent O_2. Assume that all the sulfur goes to SO_2 and is analyzed as CO_2. The stack gases leave at 700°F. and 725 mm. absolute pressure. Calculate:

a. Per cent excess air on basis of fuel burnt.

b. Per cent excess air on basis of fuel fired.

c. Complete analysis of fuel.

d. Cubic feet of air per pound of fuel fired.

e. Cubic feet of stack gases per pound of fuel fired.

f. Sensible heat in stack gases above 300°F. per pound of fuel fired.

8. A power company operates one group of its boilers on natural gas and another group on oil. The analyses of the fuels show 96 per cent CH_4, 2 per cent C_2H_6 and 2 per cent CO_2 for the natural gas, and $C_nH_{1.8n}$ for the oil. The flue gases from both groups enter the same stack and an Orsat analysis of this combined flue gas, the sample being taken after mixing is certainly complete, shows 10.0 per cent CO_2, 0.63 per cent CO and 4.55 per cent O_2. The barometer is 749 mm. of mercury and the air enters at 40°F., saturated with water vapor. The stack gases at the point of sampling are at 450°F. and under a draft of 2.8 in. of water.

Assuming no loss of fuel to smoke, soot, cinders, etc., calculate:

a. Per cent excess air based on total fuel burned.

b. Cubic feet of stack gases leaving furnace per pound atom of total carbon burned.

c. Cubic feet of air entering per pound atom of total carbon burned.

d. What percentage of the total carbon burned comes from the oil?

9. The gases from a producer average 10 per cent CO_2, 18 per cent CO, 4 per cent CH_4, 21 per cent H_2 and 47 per cent N_2. The coal contains 65 per cent C, 6 per cent moisture, 10 per cent ash, 2 per cent N_2 and 1 per cent S. The tar produced amounts to 130 lb. per ton of fuel fired, and consists of 88 per cent C and 12 per cent H. The coal has a higher heating value of 12,500 B.t.u./lb. The air enters at 68°F. with a humidity of 0.008 lb. of water/lb. of bone-dry air. The producer gas leaves at 575°C., with a partial pressure of water of 125 mm. of mercury. The barometer is 745 mm. All S is analyzed as CO_2 in the producer gas. Calculate:

a. Cubic feet of gas produced (dry, S.C.) per pound of coal fired.

b. Pounds of H_2O decomposed per pound of total H_2O input.

c. Per cent of the heating value of the fuel that appears as sensible heat in the producer gas.

d. Per cent of the heating value of the fuel that is lost in the tar, assuming the heating value of tar to be equal to that of its components.

FLOW OF FLUIDS

1. Air is flowing at a steady rate of 0.0232 lb./sec. through a straight tube having an inside diameter of 0.902 in. At the first section the air has a temperature of 70°F. and is under an absolute pressure of 0.2 atmosphere. The tube is electrically heated, and the net input of power, between the first and second sections, is 174 watts. The air at the second section is under an absolute pressure of 0.1 atmosphere. The average specific heat of the air is 0.24 B.t.u./(lb.)(deg. F.).

Calculate the temperature of the air leaving the second section.

2. In a certain chemical plant the carbonate solution used in the absorption tower is pumped continuously from the bottom of the lye storage tank through a standard 4-in. steel pipe and thence through the spray head at the top of the scrubber. The depth of solution in the storage tank is 5 ft. and the vertical distance from the bottom of this tank to the spray head is 105 ft.

In a test on this equipment the following data were obtained: rate of flow, 200 U. S. gal./min.; specific gravity of the solution, 1.10; friction drop from tank to spray head, 15 ft.-lb./lb.; gauge pressure on spray head, 5 lb./sq. in.; power input to the pump, 14.0 hp.

Calculate the efficiency of the pump.

3. A sharp-edged circular orifice is to be made to measure water flowing at a rate not to exceed 1200 cu. ft./hr., with a differential head of 10 ft. What orifice diameter is required if D_1/D_0 is made 5/1?

4. The water output of a purification plant is measured by the use of a standard Venturi meter having a throat 12 in. in diameter. The differential head from the upstream section to the throat, measured on a vertical U-tube containing mercury and water, is found to be 3.0 in.

Calculate the rate of water flow expressed as U. S. gal./24-hr. day.

5. Petroleum oil is flowing isothermally through a horizontal pipe line having an actual inside diameter of 4.03 in. A properly made Pitot tube is inserted at the center line of the pipe, and its leads are filled with oil and attached to a vertical glass U-tube containing both water and oil. The difference in water levels is found to be 3 ft.

Based on the data given below, calculate the rate of oil flow expressed as cubic feet per minute.

Data.—The oil has a specific gravity of 0.900 and a viscosity of 200 Saybolt sec.

6. A steel pipe having an inside diameter of 13.25 in. is to be designed to carry 48,000 bbl. of oil/24-hr. day from a mid-continent field to a refinery located 578 miles from the source. The difference in elevation of the two ends of the line is negligible.

a. Calculate the horsepower theoretically required to overcome friction in the pipe line.

b. Since the maximum allowable pressure in any section of the line is 650 lb/sq. in., it will be necessary to insert additional pumping stations at suitable intervals along the pipe line. What is the smallest number of pumping stations required?

Data and notes.—At the average temperature involved, the oil has an absolute viscosity of 50 centipoises and a specific gravity of 0.87.

7. A natural gas at 60°F. is flowing at steady mass rate through a steel main having an inside diameter of 12 in. The absolute pressure drops from 40 to 20 atmospheres in a length of 500 miles of substantially horizontal pipe. The gas has an average molecular weight of 17.3 and a viscosity of 0.011 centipoise.

Calculate the hourly rate of flow expressed as cu. ft. measured at 60°F. and normal barometric pressure.

FLOW OF HEAT

1. A horizontal standard 4-in. steel pipe, carrying steam under pressure, is insulated with a 2-in. layer of magnesia pipe covering. The average temperatures on the inner and outer surfaces of the insulation are 350 and 100°F., respectively.

Estimate the B.t.u. per hour conducted through the covering per 100 ft. of pipe.

2. 45,000 lb. of air/hr. at 60°F. and normal barometer is to be heated to 180°F. in a tubular heater by means of saturated steam condensing at 220°F. around the tubes. The air is to be blown through a number of horizontal cold-drawn steel tubes having an actual inside diameter of 2.00 in., arranged in parallel, the tubes being expanded into suitable tube sheets at the two ends of the apparatus.

Assuming that the mass velocity of the air in the tubes is 7000 lb./(hr.) (sq. ft.), calculate (a) the number of tubes in parallel and (b) the length of each tube.

3. A properly designed steam-heated tubular preheater is heating 45,000 lb./hr. of air from 70 to 170°F., when using saturated steam at 5 lb. gauge pressure. It is proposed to double the rate of air flow and, in order to warm the air from 70 to 170°F., to increase the steam pressure.

a. What steam pressure would be required to meet the new conditions?

b. Would the present heater, operating under the new conditions, represent a balanced design? Give reasons for your answer.

VAPOR-PRESSURE DATA FOR WATER

Absolute pressure, lb./sq. in............	19.7	25	30	50
Saturation temperature, °F.............	227	240	250	281

4. It is desired to heat 200 lb./hr. of a mixture of gases of unknown specific heat C_p and thermal conductivity k from 100 to 280°F. while flowing through a pipe having an inside diameter of 2.07 in., whose inner wall is maintained at 300°F. by steam condensing in a jacket having an inside diameter of 3.07 in.

Calculate the tube length required.

Notes.—The viscosity μ of the mixture of gases is estimated as 0.03 lb./(hr.) (ft.), and the Prandtl group $C_p\mu/k$ is estimated as 1.0.

5. Consider an adiabatically operated counterflow liquid-to-liquid heat exchanger in which the specific heats of the hot and cold liquids are substantially constant and the overall coefficient of heat transfer is constant.

a. Plot the temperatures of each liquid versus the length of the exchanger, for each of the three runs described below. In run 1, the overall temperature difference at the hot end is roughly five times that at the cold end. In run 2, the overall temperature difference at the cold end is approximately five times that at the hot end. In run 3 the overall temperature differences are the same at both ends.

b. Give algebraic relations to justify the shapes of the curves for run 2.

6. A large surface condenser in a power plant was tested at three water velocities, both when new (with clean tubes) and after considerable service. The results are tabulated below, as overall coefficients of heat transfer, expressed as B.t.u./(hr.) (sq. ft. of outside surface) (deg. F. mean difference in temperature from steam to water).

Using a suitable graphical method (based on the resistance concept), plot the data, and determine the following individual coefficients of heat transfer, expressed as B.t.u./(hr.) (sq. ft.) (deg. F. difference):

a. Value of h on the steam side of the clean condenser, expressed per sq. ft. of *outside* surface.

b. Value of $h = k/L$ for the scale and slime deposited in the dirty tube, expressed per sq. ft. of *inside* surface.

c. Value of h on water side at a water velocity at 4 ft./sec.

DATA AND NOTES

Condition of tubes	Clean			Dirty		
Water velocity, ft./sec........	2.0	4.0	8.0	2.0	4.0	8.0
Overall coefficient............	357	550	795	293	410	534

The water flows inside the tubes, which are made of a metal having a thermal conductivity of 63 B.t.u./(hr.) (sq. ft.) (deg. F./ft.), and the tube has outside and inside diameters of 1.00 and 0.902 in., respectively.

7. In a liquid-to-liquid heat exchanger the hot oil enters at 400°F. and leaves at 200°F.; the cold oil enters at 100°F. and leaves at 200°F. Heat loss is negligible. Assuming that U is independent of temperature, what will be the true mean overall temperature difference from hot to cold oil (*a*) in a counterflow apparatus and (*b*) in the reversed-current apparatus of Fig. 44, page 123? What advantage does the latter apparatus have over the former?

8. Air is flowing steadily through a duct whose inner walls are at 600°F. A thermocouple, housed in a rusted steel well having an outside diameter of 1 in., indicates a temperature of 400°F. The mass velocity past the pyrometer well is 3600 lb./(hr.) (sq. ft.)

Estimate the true temperature of the air.

9. A flat slab of rubber, 1 in. thick, initially at 70°F., is to be placed between two heated steel plates maintained at 280°F. The heating is to be discontinued when the temperature at the mid-plane of the slab reaches 270°F. The rubber has a thermal conductivity of 0.092 and a thermal diffusivity of 0.0029 ft.²/hr. The thermal resistance from metal to rubber may be neglected.

Calculate (*a*) the length of the heating period; (*b*) the temperature of the rubber $\frac{1}{4}$ in. from the metal, at the end of the run; (*c*) the time required for the rubber to reach 270°F. at the plane specified in (*b*).

10. An experimental air cooler consists of a horizontal standard $\frac{1}{2}$-in. steel pipe, surrounded by a standard 2-in. steel pipe. Water flows through the $\frac{1}{2}$-in. pipe in one direction and hot air flows through the annular space in the opposite direction. The outside of the 2-in. pipe is so well insulated that heat loss to the room may be neglected. For the gas velocity used, the coefficient of heat transfer between gas and metal may be taken as 3 B.t.u./(hr.) (sq. ft.) (deg. F temperature difference).

At a point where the true temperature of the air is 400°F., and the temperature of the outside of the $\frac{1}{2}$-in. pipe is 100°F., calculate the instantaneous rate of heat flow expressed as B.t.u./(hr.) (sq. ft. of outside surface of the $\frac{1}{2}$-in. pipe).

FILTRATION AND SEDIMENTATION

1. A slurry has been filtered in a leaf-filter press and gave the following representative results:

	Minutes $= \theta_T$	Cu. ft. filtrate $= V_T$
Constant-rate period....	0 to 10	0 to 35.4
Constant-pressure period	10 to 35	35.4 to 86.7

A plot of V_T^2 vs. θ_T gave a straight line over the range 10 to 35 min. After each filtration operation, the necessary period for dumping, cleaning and reassembling is 15 min. In the above test the pump was running at maximum capacity.

In order to obtain maximum daily capacity without changing the maximum capacity of the pump, how many minutes should be devoted to actual filtration in each cycle? How many complete cycles should be run per 24 hr., and what would be the total filtrate obtained per 24-hr. day? Assume that press resistance is negligible.

2. At present a leaf filter is run according to the following schedule:

	θ, min.	Cumulative volume of filtrate, cu. ft.
Constant-rate period..........	0 to 53.3	0 to 80
Constant-pressure period.......	53.3 to 68.3	80 to 100

During the constant-pressure portion of the run the square of the cumulative volume of the filtrate is linear in time.

It is proposed to increase the pump capacity to permit doubling the rate of filtration in the constant-rate period. It is desired to obtain *maximum* daily capacity with the large pump, but it is agreed that at no time during the run shall the pressure exceed the maximum value now used. Time required for dumping, cleaning and reassembling will be 15 min. in both cases.

Fill in a table similar to the above so that the operator will know exactly what to do in order to obtain maximum daily capacity with the larger pump. Calculate (*a*) the expected daily capacity expressed as cubic feet of filtrate per 24 hr. and (*b*) the percentage increase in capacity obtained with the larger pump.

3. A filtration department is being designed for an output of 50,000 cu. ft. of filtrate/24-hr. day, 300 days per year. For the present it is decided to confine the investigation to plate-and-frame type presses, with the understanding that other types will be investigated before final decision is reached.

For the frame thickness specified, calculate the optimum number of presses, the maximum capacity of the pump to be used with each press and the square feet of filtering surface per press.

Data and Notes.—An empty 36-in. by 36-in. press, without plates or frames, costs $370 and the additional cost of the plates and frames is at the rate of $1.70 per sq. ft. of filtering area, regardless of the width of the distance frames. The maximum number of plates and frames accommodated by one empty press or holder depends on the frame thickness as shown in the table on page 706.

Annual fixed charges will be taken as 30 per cent of the combined first cost of the holders, plates and frames, and pumps. It is estimated that 2 hr. will be needed to dismantle, clean and reassemble one press filled with plates and 1-in. frames. This work will be done by two men who receive an hourly wage of 60 cents each. Of this 2 hr., $\frac{1}{2}$ hr. will be required for dismantling and reassembling and $1\frac{1}{2}$ hr. will be required for cleaning the

Frame thickness, in.	Maximum number of plates per press	Maximum number of frames per press	Maximum filtering area per press, sq. ft.
2	33	32	512
1½	40	39	624
1	50	49	784
⅔	60	59	945
½	66	65	1040

49 frames.   In general, it will be assumed that the time for dismantling and reassembling a press will be independent of the number of frames therein, and that the time for cleaning will be proportional to the number of frames. Supervision costs will be assumed independent of the number and size of presses.   It is proposed that each run be conducted in three stages: *first*, a constant-rate period in which the filtration rate remains constant until the gauge pressure reaches 50 lb./per sq. in., but to avoid the possibility of cloudy filtrate the rate should not exceed 1.5 cu. ft. of filtrate/(hr.) (sq. ft. of filtering area); *second*, a constant-pressure period in which the pressure remains constant at 50 lb./sq. in., until the frames are full of cake; *third*, a washing period during which the cake is given a "back-wash" with a volume of wash water one-fourth that of the total filtrate collected during the filtration operation just described.   The gauge pressure during washing is also to be 50 lb./sq. in.   During the constant-pressure portion of the run the centrifugal pump is still running at constant speed, excess feed being by-pressed back to the suction side of the pump.   A number of runs have been made on the material to be handled and it is found that the data are satisfactorily correlated in the constant-pressure portion of the run by the equation $du/d\theta = k/2u$, where u represents cumulative volume of filtrate, in cubic feet per square foot of filtering area, θ represents total hours elapsed since the beginning of the constant-rate period and k is 3.12.   Upon filling 1-in. frames with cake, 4.5 cu. ft. of filtrate are obtained per square foot of filtering area.   The coefficient of compressibility s may be taken as 0.1.   Filtration and washing are to be carried out at room temperature, which may be assumed constant.   Filter cloth costs 10 cents/sq. ft. of filtering area and the average life of a cloth is 60 runs.   Electric power costs 1.5 cents/hp.-hr. at the switchboard and the overall efficiency of motor and pump will be assumed constant at 45 per cent.   The first cost (in dollars) of each pump is roughly given by $35 + 0.27G$, where G represents the maximum capacity of the pump expressed in gallons per minute.   It will be assumed that motors cost $50/hp. of electrical input.

4. A laboratory test on a suspension of a solid in a liquid gave the following information:

Original height of sludge before settling = 10 in.
Free-settling rate = 0.10 in. per min.
Height of sludge at end of free-settling period = 6.5 in.

Height of sludge at end of 120 min. =4.0 in.
Height of sludge when settled completely =1.5 in.

One thousand cubic feet of similar sludge is to be settled in a vertical cylindrical tank, the diameter of which is to equal the depth of the liquid suspension in it. Calculate the time that it would take the solid to settle to a height of 20 per cent of the original height of the sludge.

5. The following data were obtained on the settling of lime sludge.

Weight of lime =225 gm.
Total volume of 2.6-normal sodium carbonate solution =2000 c.c.
Settling tank is 7¼ in. deep and 5¼ in. in diameter.

Amount of settling in inches	0	0.75	1.55	2.37	2.90	3.15	3.35	3.40	3.45	3.49	3.50
Time in minutes	0	2	4	6	8	10	12	14	16	18	20

If the sludge were to be settled in a continuous thickener, having an effective depth of 12 in., calculate the necessary diameter for the following conditions. The thickener is to be constructed with its diameter just sufficient to allow the smallest of the sludge particles to settle to the bottom, when flowing from the center of the tank at the surface to the circumference with a water rate of 1000 cu. ft./min. The water velocity may be assumed to be the same at all depths at any given distance from the center of the tank.

EVAPORATION

1. State the advantages of:

a. Film-type evaporators over the submerged-tube type.

b. Submerged-tube evaporators over film type.

2. What are the methods used, in both design and operation of evaporators, to offset evils of:

a. Entrainment?

b. Frothing?

3. *a.* Define boiling-point raising and state its disadvantages in evaporation.

b. Name causes of boiling-point raising.

4. State (*a*) the advantages of jet condensers over surface condensers, and (*b*) the advantages of surface condensers over jet condensers.

5. Plot the data given below as suggested by Dühring's rule and determine the boiling point of the solution at an absolute pressure of 739 mm. of mercury.

The following table shows data for an aqueous solution containing 50.3 per cent by weight of $CaCl_2$.*

Boiling temp., °C	82.10	90.28	95.45	100.85	106.10	110.61
Pressure, mm. mercury	112.9	162.4	202.6	253.0	311.6	371.3

* BAKER and WAITE, *Met. Chem. Eng.*, **25,** No. 26 (Dec. 28, 1921).

6. An aqueous solution is being continuously concentrated in a multiple-effect system of four evaporators connected in series, with parallel flow of steam and liquor. The following conditions are normal: steam pressure in the coils of the first effect, concentration and temperature of the feed, vacuum in the vapor space of the last effect, and concentration of the product from the last effect. The condensate from each effect is withdrawn from the system.

a. Assume that the capacity is normal but that the steam consumption is abnormally high. State the nature of the trouble and list, in the proper order, the steps to be taken to remedy the trouble.

b. Now assume that the steam consumed per lb. of total evaporation is normal, but that the capacity is abnormally low. List, in the proper order, what steps should be taken to locate and remedy the trouble.

7. An aqueous solution of sodium salts of organic acids is to be concentrated in a multiple-effect system of evaporators. The liquor is to enter the last effect at 170°F. containing 30 per cent solids by weight and the steam available for the heating surface in the last effect condenses at 165°F. The average production desired is 10,000 gal./24-hr. day of liquor containing 40 per cent solids by weight.

Calculate the necessary square feet of heating surface in this effect.

Per cent solids	Sp. gr.	Sp. ht.	Boiling temperature,°F.	Overall coefficient, U
30	1.32	0.720	110	50
40	1.45	0.615	130	30

8. A two-effect multiple system of evaporators, with parallel flow of liquor and vapor, is to be designed to concentrate continuously 20,000 lb./hr. of 5 per cent solution of a colloidal substance to a 25 per cent solution, the temperature of the feed being 170°F. It is planned to use saturated steam condensing at 220°F. in the coils of the first effect and a vacuum over the boiling solution in the second effect such that the solution will boil at 120°F. The condensate from the coils of each effect is withdrawn from the system. Making use of the data and assumptions listed below, calculate the following.

a. Pounds of steam fed per hour to first effect.

b. Degrees F. boiling temperature in the first effect.

c. Square feet of heating surface in each effect.

d. Pounds of water evaporated per hour in the first effect.

Notes.—Area of heating surface is the same in each effect and heat losses to surroundings are negligible. Specific heat of feed liquor is 0.95. Neglect boiling-point raising in each effect and assume overall coefficients of heat transfer in the first and second effects of 400 and 200 B.t.u./(hr.) (sq. ft.)/(deg. F.), respectively.

9. It is desired to design a two-effect evaporator for the service and conditions given below. (*a*) Assuming equal areas are used in each effect, determine the total area required with (1) backward feed and (2) forward feed.

(*b*) Repeat part (*a*) assuming that in each case the distribution of areas is such that the total area is a minimum. Tabulate the corresponding area ratios. What is the disadvantage of using unequal areas?

Data and Notes.—Saturated steam at 250°F. is supplied to the coils of the high-pressure effect, and the vacuum in the other effect is such that the liquor boils at 100°F. Boiling-point raising is negligible. To simplify the problem it is agreed to neglect changes in sensible heat relative to latent heat requirements and to neglect heat losses. The overall coefficients of heat transfer are directly proportional to the 0.9 power of the overall temperature differences, and are inversely proportional to the viscosities: $U = 55\Delta^{0.9}/\mu$. After passing through one effect, the solution has a viscosity five times that of water at the same temperature, and the viscosity of the product is 100 times the viscosity of water at the temperature of the product.

ABSORPTION AND EXTRACTION

1. HCl gas diffuses across a film of air 0.1 in. thick at 20°C. The partial pressures of HCl on one side of the film is 0.08 atmosphere and zero on the other. Estimate the rate of diffusion, as gm, mols of HCl/(sec.) (sq. cm.), if the total pressure is (*a*) 10 atmospheres, (*b*) 1 atmosphere, (*c*) 0.1 atmosphere. The diffusivity of HCl in air at 20°C. and 1 atmosphere is 0.145 cm.^{2}/sec.

2. A gas containing 8 mol per cent HCl is being scrubbed with water at 20°C. under such conditions that the effective gas-film thickness is 0.1 cm.

a. If the concentration in the water is such that the partial pressure of the HCl is negligible at the interface, estimate the rate of absorption of HCl, as gm. mols/(sec.) (sq. cm.) (1) at 10 atmospheres and (2) at 0.1 atmosphere.

b. Repeat (*a*) for a partial pressure of HCl at the interface equal to 0.06 atmosphere.

3. Water was evaporated in a wetted-wall tower 2.67 cm. in diameter and 117 cm. long. The water entered at the top with a temperature of 55.2°C., and left the bottom at a temperature of 48.5°C. The air entered at a rate of 120 gm./min. and its temperature was substantially constant at 50°C.; the total pressure was 520 mm. Hg. absolute. The rate of evaporation was 13.1 c.c./min. and the inlet humidity was 0.001 lb./lb. of bone-dry air. The diffusivity of water vapor through air is 0.263 cm.^{2}/sec. at 1 atmosphere and 30°C.

a. Estimate the effective gas-film thickness under the above flow conditions.

b. Compare this effective film thickness with that calculated from heat-transfer Eq. 11, page 111, under the same conditions of temperature, pressure and rate of air flow, but with no liquid flow.

c. Estimate the effective film thickness from the equation for wetted-wall towers, page 504.

4. A wetted-wall column operating at 820 mm. of mercury absolute was supplied with air at a rate of 100 gm./min. The liquid vaporized was *n*-butyl alcohol, which was supplied at such a temperature that the mean driving force is 24.4 mm. of mercury and the mean inert pressure was 799 mm. The specific gravity of the liquid was 0.807. Under these conditions the rate of evaporation of *n*-butyl alcohol was 6.9 c.c./min.

The same apparatus was used to evaporate water with an air rate of 120 gm./min. at a total pressure of 518 mm. of mercury absolute. The mean driving force was 62.5 mm., and the calculated mean inert pressure was 449 mm. Estimate the rate of evaporation of water under these conditions.

Note.—The diffusivity of water vapor through air may be taken as equal to three times the diffusivity of *n*-butyl alcohol vapor through air at the same temperature and total pressure.

5. Air containing 20 mol per cent ammonia is being treated with water in a packed tower, and under plant conditions gives the following data: rate of water flow is 20 lb./(min.) (sq. ft. of tower cross section) and of the inflowing gas is 4 lb./(min.) (sq. ft. of tower cross section); the total pressure is 3 atmospheres and the temperature is maintained at 35°C. throughout the tower by means of cooling coils; under these conditions 96 per cent of the ammonia in the incoming gas is absorbed. Assuming that the average effective film thickness is unchanged and that the temperature, pressure and rates of water and incoming gas, and wetted area per unit volume of tower are all constant, how much taller should the tower be made if it is desired to absorb 99 per cent of the ammonia in the incoming gas? Henry's law may be assumed to apply to the solutions involved.

6. A mixture of benzene vapor and flue gas contains 12.7 mol per cent benzene, and is to be scrubbed continuously in a packed tower operated at atmospheric pressure and at 43°C. The tower is to be designed to treat 36,000 cu. ft./hr. of entering gas, and the outlet gas is to contain 1.5 mol per cent benzene. The mineral oil entering at the top will contain 1.0 mol per cent benzene and will be supplied at the rate of 28 lb. mols per hour. The solution of benzene in oil may be assumed to follow Raoult's law, and the vapor pressure of pure benzene at 43°C. is 0.263 atm. It is agreed that the maximum allowable superficial velocity of the gas-vapor mixture is 1 ft./sec.

Calculate the height of tower required, assuming that the height of one transfer unit is 2 ft.

7. The purge gases from a synthetic ammonia plant contain 4 per cent ammonia by volume and 96 per cent hydrogen, nitrogen, argon and other inerts. This gas is to be scrubbed at 5 atmospheres pressure with water in a bubble-plate tower maintained at 68°F. by cooling coils. With water and inert gas rates of 0.88 and 4.0 lb./(min.) (sq. ft. of tower cross section), respectively, how many theoretical plates will be required to produce a solution containing 13 per cent ammonia by weight? The average molecular weight of the inert gas is 21.

Data.—The following table gives the equilibrium partial pressures of ammonia solutions at 68°F.

Partial pressure NH₃, mm. mercury	12.0	18.2	31.7	50.0	69.6	166
Grams of NH₃ per 100 gm. of water	2.0	3.0	5.0	7.5	10	20

8. It is desired to estimate the height of a packed tower necessary to carry out the same absorption as in Problem 7. All operating conditions will be the same and the tower packing is to be 1½-in. broken quartz. (*a*)

Using the data of Table I, page 501, what is the necessary height of tower? (*b*) Under these conditions what is the average H.E.T.P. for this packing? (*c*) What is the average H.T.U.?

9. The gas from a Mannheim furnace contains 25 per cent HCl and 75 per cent O_2, N_2, CO_2, CO and other inerts. This gas is scrubbed at atmospheric pressure and the temperature maintained at 20°C. The tower is producing an acid containing 36 per cent HCl by weight, with an HCl recovery of 99 per cent. Estimate the number of theoretical plates to which the tower is equivalent.

Data.—At 20°C.:

Partial pressure HCl, mm. Hg	5	13	22	46	72	100	200	390
Per cent HCl by weight.......	26	30	32	34	35	36	38.2	40

10. Fifty parts of copperas and lime per million parts of dye-house effluent removes 50 per cent of the color. How much will be required to reduce the color to 5 per cent, if $n = 8.5$?

11. Cotton is piled loosely in a steel chamber which is gradually evacuated to 20 mm. of mercury absolute pressure. The cotton charged at 24°C. contains 4.77 per cent of moisture (wet basis) and as piled contains 0.8 lb. of water-free cotton/cu. ft. The barometer is 760 mm., the specific gravity of the dry cotton is 1.48 and the heat capacity of the cotton is sufficient to prevent appreciable change in temperature during evacuation.

Calculate the ultimate moisture content of the cotton (wet basis) after evacuation.

Data.—At 24°C. cotton containing 5.00 per cent of moisture (dry basis) is in equilibrium with air containing 8.3 mm. of water vapor, and cotton containing 2.00 per cent of water (dry basis) is in equilibrium with air containing 1.65 mm. of water vapor.

DISTILLATION

1. For mixtures of heptane and octane, construct the following plots, all on one sheet. Assume that the laws of Raoult and Dalton apply.

a. Equilibrium diagram, for constant pressure of 1 atmosphere, plotted with $y^{\star}$, mol fraction of heptane in the vapor, as ordinates versus x, mol fraction of heptane in the liquid, as abscissas.

b. The boiling point as ordinates versus x.

c. Relative volatility α versus x.

d. Curve of $y^{\star}$ versus x computed from the equation on page 526, using the average value of α.

e. Plot weight fraction of heptane in the vapor $C^{\star}$ as ordinates versus the weight fraction of heptane in the liquid c, assuming the molecular weight of each component is the same in both the liquid and vapor.

Data:

VAPOR PRESSURES IN MILLIMETERS OF MERCURY

Temp., °C..................	80	90	100	110	120	130
n-C_7H_{16}.....................	427	589	795	1047	1367	
n-C_8H_{18}....................	175	254	354	482	646	859

2. An equimolal mixture of benzene and toluene is subjected to a simple batch distillation at atmospheric pressure. For the purpose of this problem assume $\alpha = 2.55$.

a. If the distillation is discontinued when the mols of distillate amount to 60 per cent of the mols charged, calculate:

    1. The concentration of the distillate.

    2. The concentration of the liquid left in the still.

    3. The amount of benzene in the distillate, expressed as a percentage of the amount of benzene in the charge.

b. If the distillation be discontinued when 60 per cent of the original benzene is in the distillate, calculate:

    1. Repeat (*a*-1).

    2. Repeat (*a*-2).

    3. The mols of distillate, expressed as a percentage of the mols of the charge.

3. A liquid under pressure containing 50 mol per cent benzene and 50 mol per cent toluene is continuously throttled to a pressure of 1 atmosphere. The temperature after throttling is found to be 96.5°C.

a. What per cent of the mixture is vapor after the throttle valve?

b. If the pressure before throttling was sufficiently high so that no vapor was present, what was the temperature of this liquid before throttling?

Data:

VAPOR PRESSURES IN MILLIMETERS OF MERCURY

Temperature, °C	90	94.6	96.5	99.2	104.6
Vapor pressure of benzene	1008	1148	1211	1308	1503
Vapor pressure of toluene	404	469	499	543	637

The average molal heat capacity of the liquid is 36 gm. cal./(gm. mol) (deg. C.) and the latent heat of vaporization of the liquid at 96.5°C. may be taken as 7100 gm. cal./gm. mol. Assume adiabatic operation of the throttling valve, and that no heat is conducted across the valve. Neglect kinetic energy changes.

4. Stearic acid is to be steam distilled at 200°C. in a direct-fired still, heat-jacketed to prevent condensation. Steam is introduced into the molten acid in small bubbles and the vapor leaving the still has a partial pressure of acid equal to 70 per cent of the vapor pressure of pure stearic acid at 200°C.

Plot the pounds of acid distilled per pound of steam added as a function of the total pressure for pressures ranging from 760 down to 25 mm. of mercury absolute.

Notes.—At 200°C. the vapor pressure of stearic acid is 3 mm. of mercury.

5. It is proposed to distill continuously a solution containing 10 mol per cent ammonia and 90 mol per cent water to produce a distillate containing 28 mol per cent ammonia. Per 100 mols of feed, calculate the mols of distillate obtainable by each of the two processes described below.

a. Continuous simple distillation without reflux.

b. Continuous distillation in a stripping column containing one perfect bubble-cap plate and a still.

Data and Notes.—In each case the feed enters as liquid at the boiling point, the still is heated by steam condensing in a closed steam coil, and residue is continuously withdrawn from the still. At equilibrium the mol fraction of ammonia in the vapor is 6.3 times that in the liquid; $y^\star = 6.3x$.

6. A liquid mixture containing equal mols of benzene and water is heated to 110°C. Calculate the total pressure and composition of the equilibrium vapor.

Data:

VAPOR PRESSURES IN MILLIMETERS OF MERCURY

Temperature, °C......	60	70	80	90	100	110	120
Benzene..............	...	540	756	1008	1338	1740	2215
Toluene..............	139	206	287	404	557	741	990
Water................	149	234	355	526	760	1075	1490

7. A vapor containing 80 mol per cent benzene and 20 mol per cent water at 120°C. is cooled slowly at a total pressure of 1 atmosphere.

a. What is the composition of the first condensate?

b. Plot the temperature and the compositions of the uncondensed vapor and condensate as a function of the per cent of the original mixture that is condensed.

Note.—See Problem 6 for data.

8. Repeat Problem 7 for a vapor containing 20 mol per cent toluene, 60 mol per cent benzene and 20 mol per cent water. See Problem 6 for data.

9. A continuous rectifying column is operating with a total condenser and a still heated by indirect steam (no live steam is blown into the column); the feed enters as liquid properly preheated. Make the usual simplifying assumptions leading to the constancy of molal overflow except as affected by the introduction of the feed itself.

a. Derive the equation of the enriching line.

b. Derive the equation of the stripping line.

c. Prove that these two operating lines intersect at $x = x_f$.

d. Prove that the enriching line intersects the diagonal at x_c.

e. Prove that the stripping line intersects the diagonal at x_w.

f. Prove that the minimum ratio of reflux to vapor in the enriching section, O_{n+1}/V_n equals $(x_c - y_f)/(x_c - x_f)$.

g. Explain why an infinite number of plates is required when using this minimum ratio of reflux to vapor.

h. When, in the enriching section, the ratio of reflux to vapor is unity, show that the operating line coincides with the diagonal.

10. It is desired to design a plate type of rectifying column to produce continuously a distillate containing 95 mol per cent benzene and a residue containing 5 mol per cent of benzene. The feed contains 50 mol per cent benzene and 50 mol per cent toluene, and will be introduced, as liquid at the boiling point, on the proper plate. The feed rate is to be 1750 lb. mols/24 hr. Vapors will be generated in a steam-heated still attached to the base of the column, and residue is to be withdrawn continuously from the still. The column is to be operated at normal atmospheric pressure with a total condenser, hot reflux returning to the top plate.

Referring to the data and notes given below, calculate:

a. Minimum reflux ratio in the enriching section.

b. Minimum number of theoretical plates corresponding to infinite reflux ratio, O/P.

c. For a reflux ratio (O/P) 1.25 times the minimum, estimate:

1. Inside diameter of the rectifying column, expressed in feet.
2. Number of actual plates required.
3. Location of the feed plate.

Data and Notes.—It is agreed that the superficial velocity of the vapor at the top of the column should not exceed 2 ft./sec. The overall plate efficiency may be taken as 60 per cent. Raoult's and Dalton's laws may be assumed to apply to all mixtures under consideration. See Problem 6 for vapor-pressure data.

11. Repeat Problem 10 for the case where the feed enters as an equilibrium mixture containing 50 mol per cent vapor and 50 mol per cent liquid.

12. *Oxygen Column.*—Liquid air is fed to the top of a bubble-plate stripping column operated at substantially atmospheric pressure. Sixty per cent of the oxygen in the feed is to be drawn off in the vapor from the still, and this vapor is to contain 0.2 mol per cent of nitrogen. Based on the assumption and data given below, calculate:

a. The mol per cent of nitrogen in the crude nitrogen vapor leaving the top plate.

b. The mols of vapor generated in the still per 100 mols of feed.

c. The number of theoretical plates required.

Notes.—To simplify the problem, assume that the molal overflow is constant throughout the column, and is equal to the mols of feed. Liquid air contains 20.9 mol per cent of oxygen and 79.1 mol per cent of nitrogen. The equilibrium data* for atmospheric pressure are shown below.

Temperature, °Kelvin	Mol per cent N_2 in liquid	Mol per cent N_2 in vapor
77.35	100.00	100.00
77.98	90.00	97.17
78.73	79.00	93.62
79.44	70.00	90.31
80.33	60.00	85.91
81.35	50.00	80.46
82.54	40.00	73.50
83.94	30.00	64.05
85.62	20.00	50.81
87.67	10.00	31.00
90.17	0.00	0.00

* Dodge, *Chem. Met. Eng.*, **35,** 622 (1928).

13. *Nitrogen Column.*—Liquid air is fed at an intermediate point between the top and bottom plates of a bubble-plate column operated at substantially atmospheric pressure. The vapor leaving the top of the enriching section is to contain 99.8 mol per cent of nitrogen. In this case no vapor is drawn off from the still, but liquid is drawn off from the still attached to the bottom of the stripping section. This liquid is evaporated in the jacket of a reflux condenser just above the top of the enriching section.

With an infinite number of perfect plates available, what would be the concentration of oxygen in the liquid drawn off from the still? Under these conditions, what is the corresponding percentage recovery of nitrogen?

14. A rectifying column containing the equivalent of two perfect bubble plates is to be supplied continuously with a feed containing 0.1 mol per cent of ammonia and 99.9 mol per cent of steam. Before entering the column the feed is converted wholly into vapor and enters between the two perfect plates. The vapors from the top plate (2) enter the top of a total condenser. Part of the hot condensate is fed to the top plate as reflux, and the rest is continuously withdrawn as overhead distillate. The liquid from the bottom plate (1) overflows to a direct-fired still, the vapor so generated rising to the base of the column and the liquid residue being withdrawn continuously from the still. Per mol of external feed, 0.60 mol of vapor is generated in the still and 1.3 mols of reflux return to the top plate. Over the entire range of concentrations involved, the equilibrium mol fraction of ammonia in the vapor is 12.6 times the mol fraction of ammonia in the liquid, $y^\star = 12.6x$. Calculate the mol fraction of ammonia in:

a. The residue, or bottoms from the still.

b. The overhead distillate, or product.

c. The liquid overflowing from plate 1.

d. The liquid overflowing from plate 2.

15. A plant has a batch of 100 mols of a mixture containing 20 mol per cent of benzene and 80 mol per cent of chlorbenzene, and it is desired to rectify this mixture at atmospheric pressure to obtain bottoms containing only 0.1 mol per cent of benzene. It is agreed to assume that the relative volatility is constant at 4.13. There is available a suitable still and column, the latter containing the equivalent of four perfect plates. The run is to be made at total reflux. While the steady state is being approached, a finite amount of distillate is held in the reflux trap. When the steady state is reached and the bottoms contain 0.1 mol per cent of benzene, the contents of the trap are drawn off and the desired fraction is removed from the still.

What yield of bottoms of the specified purity can be obtained by the above procedure with the available equipment? For these preliminary calculations it is agreed to neglect the hold-up of the column compared to that of the still and reflux trap.

16. An extraction plant for the solvent treating of lubricating oil is operating with anhydrous phenol as a solvent. The phenol is recovered from the extract and raffinate by steam stripping, and the phenol-water distillate is cooled to 20°C. and separates into two layers. It is desired to recover the phenol from the two layers in an essentially anhydrous condition. It is proposed to carry out the separation in a two-tower stripping system.   The water layer from the separator is preheated and fed to the top plate of tower 1 and this tower strips phenol from the water.   The phenol layer from the separator is preheated and fed to the top plate of tower 2 and this tower strips water from phenol.   The top vapors from both towers are sent to a common condenser and cooled at 20°C.; the aqueous layer of the condensed distillate is preheated and added to the feed of tower 1 and the phenol layer of the condensed distillate is preheated and added to the feed of the second column.   Column 1 is to be operated so that not over 0.5 per cent of the phenol entering this tower* is lost in the residue, and the phenol residue from column 2 is to be 99.9 weight per cent phenol.   Both columns will be operated at atmospheric pressure, and the usual simplifying assumptions will be made.   The stills will be heated by closed steam coils.

a. Estimate the number of theoretical plates that should be used in column 1 if 25 per cent more vapor than the minimum vapor for infinite plates is used.

b. If 25 per cent more vapor than the minimum vapor for infinite plates is used in column 2, estimate the number of theoretical plates that should be employed.

Data.—At 20°C. water saturated with phenol contains 1.68 mol per cent phenol and the phenol layer contains 33.1 mol per cent phenol.   The critical solution temperature for the mixture is 66.5°C.

PHENOL-WATER EQUILIBRIUM DATA*
Mol fraction of phenol at atmospheric pressure

x in liquid	$y^\star$ in vapor	x in liquid	$y^\star$ in vapor
0	0	0.10	0.029
0.001	0.002	0.20	0.032
0.002	0.004	0.30	0.038
0.004	0.0072	0.40	0.048
0.006	0.0098	0.50	0.065
0.008	0.012	0.60	0.090
0.010	0.0138	0.70	0.15
0.015	0.0172	0.80	0.27
0.017	0.0182	0.85	0.37
0.018	0.0186	0.90	0.55
0.019	0.0191	0.95	0.77
0.020	0.0195	1.00	1.0

* Data from H. D. Sims, Sc. D. Thesis, Massachusetts Institute of Technology, 1933.

17. A mixture of benzene, toluene and xylene is being continuously rectified at normal atmospheric pressure in a bubble-plate column, attached to a direct-fired still.   In the lower part of the stripping section there are 1.092 mols of overflow per mol of vapor.   The analysis of the bottoms shows

* With the exception of its own reflux.

1.76 mol per cent of benzene, 62.14 mol per cent of toluene and 36.10 mol per cent of xylene.   Vapor pressures are given below.   Calculate:

a. Temperature of the liquid in the still.

b. Analysis of the liquid on the first plate above the still.

Data:

VAPOR PRESSURE IN MILLIMETERS OF MERCURY

Temperature, °C	120	118	117	115	113
Benzene	2215	2138	2090	1993	1895
Toluene	990	920	895	850	805
Xylene	450	420	405	390	365

AIR CONDITIONING AND DRYING

1. Using vapor-pressure data from steam tables and assuming normal barometer, calculate

a. "Humidity" of air saturated at 130°F.

b. "Saturated volume" of air saturated at 130°F., assuming the perfect gas law.

c. Factor necessary to convert (by multiplication) "per cent relative humidity" to "per cent absolute humidity," for air having 50 per cent "relative humidity" at 130°F.

d. The adiabatic saturation temperature and the wet-bulb temperature for air having a dew point of 56°F. and a dry-bulb temperature of 130°F.

Tabulate with the figures just calculated, the values read from Fig. 183.

2. Air of 50 per cent relative humidity at 70°F. is preheated in a hot-blast heater to 160°F.   Tabulate the wet-bulb temperature and per cent relative humidity before and after preheating.

3. A drier is to be designed to reduce the water content of a certain material from 180 to 10 per cent (dry basis).   The available air is at 70°F. and has an absolute humidity of 0.010.   In order to produce the desired drying conditions, the air entering the drier is to have a temperature of 120°F. and a humidity of 0.010 lb. of water/lb. of dry air, and the exit air will leave at 110°F. with 70 per cent relative humidity.   On the basis of 1000 lb. of product/hr., and neglecting the heat capacity of the bone-dry stock, calculate:

a. Air entering preheater, as cu. ft./min.

b. Air entering the drier, as cu. ft./min.

c. B.t.u. per hour to be supplied by the preheater.

d. B.t.u. per hour to be supplied by the heating surface within the drier.

e. Total B.t.u. consumed per pound of evaporation.

f. Tabulate temperature of the "dry bulb," "wet bulb" and "dew point" for the air entering the preheater, the air entering the drier and the air leaving the drier.

4. Twenty thousand cubic feet of air per minute are to be cooled from 90 to 72°F. by the use of a horizontal-spray-type humidifier, employing counterflow of air and water.   The air has an initial humidity of 0.011 lb.

of water vapor/lb. of dry air. The unevaporated water collects inside the apparatus, to be recirculated to the spray nozzles, and "make-up" water at 70°F. is fed to the pump.

Based on data given below, calculate:

a. Cross section of spray chamber, in sq. ft.

b. Pounds of water sprayed per hour.

c. Pounds of make-up water required per hour.

d. Length of spray chamber, in ft.

e. Humidity of air leaving the chamber, as lb. of water vapor/lb. of dry air.

Data and Notes.—The spray chamber will operate substantially adiabatically, and normal barometric pressure prevails within the apparatus. When spraying 1200 lb. of water/(hr.) (sq. ft. of cross section of the spray chamber), and employing an air rate of 2400 lb. of dry air/(hr.) (sq. ft. of cross section), test data show that the overall coefficient of heat transfer, Ua, is 90 B.t.u./(hr.) (deg. F. mean difference)(cu. ft. of spray chamber).

5. It is desired to design a coke-packed dehumidifier to cool 2000 cu. ft. of saturated air/min. from 130 to 65°F. The operation is to be conducted at normal barometric pressure. Cooling water is available at 55°F., and will be permitted to rise to 110°F. It is agreed to use a gas velocity of 1200 lb. of dry air/(hr.) (sq. ft. of total cross section). Since it is desired to use the data of page 610, the water velocity must be at least 1150 lb./(hr.) (sq. ft. of total cross section).

Calculate the height and diameter of tower required, and the weight of cooling water per hour.

6. A cooling tower 2200 cu. ft. in volume gave on test the following data:

Temperature of water entering the top = 105°F.

Temperature of water leaving the bottom = 84.7°F.

Temperature of air entering the bottom = 71°F.

Temperature of air leaving the top = 90°F.

Humidity of the air entering the bottom = 0.0062.

Humidity of the air leaving the top = 0.0295.

Volume of air entering the tower = 55,900 cu. ft./min.

Volume of water entering = 707 gal./min.

If the temperature of the entering air were to rise to 100°F. with its absolute humidity remaining unchanged, which might happen between morning and noon of a summer day, the weight of air and water remaining the same as before, to what temperature would the water be cooled?

7. A wet solid is dried from 36 to 8 per cent moisture in 5 hr., under constant drying conditions. The critical moisture is 14 per cent and the equilibrium moisture is 4 per cent. All moisture contents are reported as per cent on the dry basis, *i.e.*, parts by weight of water per 100 parts by weight of "bone-dry" solid.

Calculate how much longer would be required, under the same drying conditions, to dry from 8 to 5.5 per cent water on a dry basis.

8. A continuous, countercurrent, adiabatic rotary drier is being designed for the production of 500 lb./hr. of a product containing 2 per cent moisture from wet crystals containing 30 per cent moisture, wet basis. The air entering the drier will have a dry-bulb temperature of 230°F. and a wet-bulb temperature of 102°F., and the air leaving the drier will be at a temperature of 115°F. Because of the small size of the crystals, the highest allowable air velocity is 10 lb./(min. of bone-dry air)(sq. ft. of cross section).

a. Calculate the pounds of bone-dry air required per minute.

b. Calculate the cross-sectional area of the drier, in sq. ft.

9. In order to dry continuously a sheet material from 100 to 50 per cent water on the "dry basis," it is proposed to employ an adiabatic drier of the tunnel type. The critical moisture is 40 per cent on the dry basis while the equilibrium moisture is 5 per cent on the dry basis. The sheets average 6 ft. by 2 ft. by $\frac{1}{4}$ in. thick, and are to be dried from both sides. The wet sheets weigh 15 lb. each. The air, with a wet-bulb temperature of 80°F., is to enter at 133°F. and leave at 90°F. The air is to flow parallel to the faces of the sheets, at an average velocity of 3600 lb./(hr.) (sq. ft. of free area between sheets), giving a coefficient of heat transfer of 4 B.t.u./(hr.) (sq. ft.) (deg. F.).

a. Calculate the required drying time, expressed in hours.

b. Assuming that the free area for air flow between each pair of parallel sheets is 6 ft. by $\frac{1}{12}$ ft., calculate the pounds per hour of dry air required, and the number of sheets over which the air flows in series.

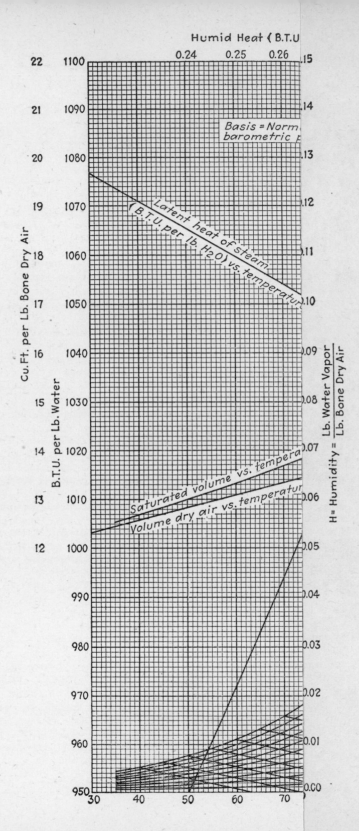

INDEX

A

Absolute pressure, 6

Absolute temperature, centigrade, 9
Fahrenheit, 5

Absorption, allowable velocity in, 492

  apparatus for, 462–463
  (*See also* Towers)

  bibliography, 513

  both films controlling, 452, 484–487

  capacity coefficients, correlation of, with heat transfer, 608

    diameter of tower, effect on, 504

    gas velocity, effect on, 499–505

    individual, 454–456, 499–505

    liquor velocity, effect on, 499–505

    mass velocity, effect on, 500–505

    molecular weight as affecting, 446, 460, 504–505

    overall, 451–454, 499–505

    temperature, effect on, 430, 455

    viscosity, effect on, 499–505

  diagrams, 452–454, 475–490

  diffusivity, 444–460

  drying by, 615

  effect of solubility, 451, 454

  equations, for point conditions, 442–454

    for variable conditions, 472–509

  equilibria, 428, 431–442

    approach from both sides, 432

    classification of, 432

  Fick's law in, 432

  film theory of, 449–456

  gas film controlling, 452, 482–484

  graphical solution of problems in, 474–491

Absorption, heat effects in, 491

  Henry's law in, 433, 451, 485–487

  liquid film controlling, 452, 481

  logarithmic mean, in, 486

  mass velocity in, 500–505

  mechanism of, 449–451

  multicomponent, 495

  nomenclature, for point conditions, 458–459

    for variable conditions, 512–513

  of air by water, 433

  of ammonia by water, 452, 486, 493, 501, 504

  of benzene by oil, 435, 496, 501, 508

  of carbon dioxide, 433, 440, 441, 502

  of complex mixtures, 446, 495–499

  of gases by solids (*see* Adsorption)

  of hydrocarbons in oil, 495–499

  of hydrochloric acid by water, 39, 454

  of moderately soluble gases, 452, 484

  of oxygen by water, 433, 453, 455

  of slightly soluble gases, 455, 481

  of sulfur dioxide by water, 428

  of sulfur trioxide, 39, 375

  of very soluble gases, 452, 482

  of water vapor by sulfuric acid, 441, 475, 480–484

  pressure in, 478

  problems in, 482–499

  process, 425, 462

  Raoult's law in, 434, 496, 508

  rate, of fluids and solids, 456–458, 506–512

    of gases by liquids, 429, 442–456, 472–505

  ratio of liquid to gas in, 474

  recovery of treating agent, 431

721